McGraw-Hill Electrical and Electronic Engineering Series

FREDERICK EMMONS TERMAN, *Consulting Editor*

RADIO ELECTRONICS

McGraw-Hill Electrical and Electronic Engineering Series

FREDERICK EMMONS TERMAN, *Consulting Editor*

BAILEY AND GAULT · Alternating-current Machinery
BERANEK · Acoustics
BRUNS AND SAUNDERS · Analysis of Feedback Control Systems
CAGE · Theory and Application of Industrial Electronics
CUCCIA · Harmonics, Sidebands, and Transients in Communication
    Engineering
EASTMAN · Fundamentals of Vacuum Tubes
EVANS · Control-system Dynamics
FITZGERALD AND KINGSLEY · Electric Machinery
GEPPERT · Basic Electron Tubes
GLASFORD · Fundamentals of Television Engineering
HAPPELL AND HESSELBERTH · Engineering Electronics
HARMAN · Fundamentals of Electronic Motion
HESSLER AND CAREY · Fundamentals of Electrical Engineering
HILL · Electronics in Engineering
JOHNSON · Transmission Lines and Networks
KRAUS · Antennas
KRAUS · Electromagnetics
LePAGE · Analysis of Alternating-current Circuits
LePAGE AND SEELY · General Network Analysis
MILLMAN AND SEELY · Electronics
ROGERS · Introduction to Electric Fields
RÜDENBERG · Transient Performance of Electric Power Systems
SEELY · Electronic Engineering
SEELY · Electron-tube Circuits
SEELY · Radio Electronics
SISKIND · Direct-current Machinery
SKILLING · Electric Transmission Lines
SKILLING · Transient Electric Currents
SPANGENBURG · Vacuum Tubes
STEVENSON · Elements of Power System Analysis
TERMAN · Electronic and Radio Engineering
TERMAN AND PETTIT · Electronic Measurements
THALER · Elements of Servomechanism Theory
THALER AND BROWN · Servomechanism Analysis
THOMPSON · Alternating-current and Transient Circuit Analysis
TRUXAL · Automatic Feedback Control System Synthesis

Radio Electronics

SAMUEL SEELY, Ph.D.

Professor and Head
Department of Electrical Engineering
Case Institute of Technology

McGRAW-HILL BOOK COMPANY, INC.

New York   Toronto   London

1956

RADIO ELECTRONICS

TK
6550
S45

THE MAPLE PRESS COMPANY, YORK, PA.

PREFACE

"Radio Electronics" and "Electronic Engineering" have been written as companion volumes, though written as independent textbooks. Together they represent a revision and extension of the author's "Electron-tube Circuits." It has been necessary to include a certain amount of material that is common to both books in order to ensure completeness and continuity of text material. Moreover, the common material is the same in each book, in the interests of economy of production. However, the amount of duplicated material has been kept to a minimum, consistent with the desire to have these books independent, and also to provide a complete and continuous development.

While one of the main objectives of this book, as its title would indicate, is a study of the important electronic aspects of radio, a much broader scope is contemplated. That is, more than just an analysis of the elements of radio systems is undertaken. For this reason general system block diagrams are discussed before any analysis is undertaken. Many of the important aspects of communication-systems engineering are also discussed in order to bring into focus some of the major factors that must be considered in system synthesis. This accounts for the inclusion of such topics as noise, signal/noise ratios, gain-bandwidth products, and an introduction to information theory, with consideration of the rate of transmission of information. Some of the systems discussed superficially require specialized techniques in their operation, and a discussion of these is deemed to be outside of the scope of this book. Therefore only very limited discussion will be found of pulse-modulation systems.

Wherever possible, the analysis proceeds in two stages. An effort is made first to present an explanation of the operation of the circuits from a physical point of view. This is followed by fairly rigorous mathematical analyses. Such mathematical analyses have a threefold objective: (1) To illustrate the techniques of analysis. Often, in fact, alternative developments have been included to demonstrate different methods of analysis. (2) To deduce a solution which yields a description of the operation of the circuit. (3) To examine the effects of the various parameters on the operation of the circuit.

In all analyses considerable care has been taken to include the requisite reference conditions for potential polarities, current directions, and

v

transformer-winding sense. These are an essential part of any circuit diagram, and without them the ultimate choice of a positive or negative sign would require a major decision.

Much of the material in this book has been used in two courses in radio at Syracuse University. The introductory chapters are essential in the first course, as this provides the students with their first introduction to electronic devices and their circuit applications. A more theoretical course in physical electronics follows rather than precedes this course.

The author wishes to acknowledge the helpful discussions with many of his former colleagues at Syracuse University. He is particularly indebted to Dr. Herbert Hellerman for his many helpful suggestions and for his assistance in proofreading the entire text.

SAMUEL SEELY

CONTENTS

CHAPTER 1

INTRODUCTION TO COMMUNICATION SYSTEMS

1-1. Elements of Communication Systems. Communication systems are concerned with the transmission and reception of intelligence. The form and features of the systems depend upon the type of intelligence being communicated. For example, telegraph transmission requires a frequency band of only several cycles per second, whereas the frequency band required for transmitting television intelligence is several megacycles per second; consequently, the details of the systems will differ markedly. However, despite the different waveforms and frequencies that the intelligence may demand for its transmission, all communication

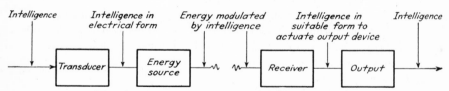

FIG. 1-1. The elements required of a complete communication system.

systems may be crudely represented by essentially the same blocks in their schematic representations. These are illustrated graphically in Fig. 1-1.

In such a system, it is the function of the transducer to convert the intelligence, whether it is voice or music as in radio, whether it is a message for a telegraph system, whether it is voice for a telephone system, or whether it is both aural and visual as in television, into such a form as to be suitable for modulating an energy source. The modulated energy source is in a form which will allow the energy to pass through the transmitting medium. The modulated energy reaches a second transducer—the receiver—which extracts the intelligence therefrom and provides this intelligence in a suitable form for actuating the output device.

In the specific case of radiobroadcast transmission, the transducer is the microphone, which converts the sound energy impinging on it into an appropriate electrical form at low power level. The energy source is a complicated device which includes amplifiers for raising the power level of the audio signal at the microphone to a sufficient value to modulate a

1

high-power high-frequency signal, which is generated in an oscillator. This modulated h-f "carrier" is fed to an antenna, from which radiation of the energy into free space occurs.

At the receiver some of the radiated energy is absorbed by an antenna. This energy is at very low power level, which is then amplified, and the intelligence is extracted from the modulated signal. The extracted signal is then applied to a loud-speaker, which is to reproduce the original signal.

From the foregoing discussion, the essentials of a communication system are the following:

1. A means or medium for transferring energy from a transmitter to a receiver.

2. A means for modulating the energy which will carry the intelligence from the transmitter to the receiver.

3. A means for preparing the intelligence in a form suitable for performing the function under (2).

4. A means for extracting the intelligence from the transmitted energy.

5. A means for presenting the intelligence in proper form.

Certain aspects under these topics will be considered in this chapter. This book will be concerned with details of many of the circuits required in a number of communication systems.

1-2. Systems for Communication. In the example given above of a communication system, it is stated that an h-f carrier is used. Actually, however, three basic systems of communication exist. These are:

1. Noncarrier systems.

2. Carrier systems.

3. Suppressed-carrier systems.

A noncarrier system is one in which energy appears only with the signal. In a carrier system, energy flows between the transmitter and the receiver even when no signal appears. The carrier current is modified by the signal in a way which will permit the ultimate extraction of the signal information. In the suppressed-carrier systems, no carrier energy flows between the transmitter and the receiver. However, the carrier originally existed in the system and was suppressed prior to transmission. The carrier must be reintroduced at the receiver in order to extract the signal information.

An example of a noncarrier system is found in simple telegraphy, in which a dot is a short-duration square pulse, first with one polarity, followed by the same duration square pulse, with reversed polarity. That is, a dot is a single-cycle square wave of relatively short duration. The dash is a single-cycle square wave of relatively long duration. A space is a region of no current. In this type of telegraph system, the complete signal consists of a series of square a-c waveform elements, the average current being zero.

1-3. Carrier Systems.   A second method of telegraph communication is one in which a dot is a current pulse of short duration, a dash is a current pulse of long duration, and a region of no current is a space. In this method, the average current is not zero, and the dot and the dash may be considered to modulate the current.   The essential aspects of the noncarrier and carrier methods are illustrated graphically in Fig. 1-2.

A modulated a-c carrier system is used also, as well as the amplitude-modulated d-c carrier system, for telegraphy.   If the amplitude of the a-c carrier is altered by the signal, the system is known as an amplitude-modulated (a-m) system.   If the frequency of the a-c carrier is altered by the signal, the system is known as a frequency-modulated (f-m) system.   If the phase of the a-c carrier is altered by the signal, the system is known as a phase-modulated (p-m) system.

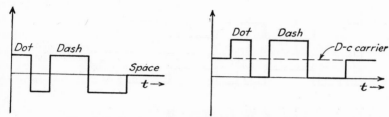

Fig. 1-2. A noncarrier and carrier telegraph signal.

The need for a relatively h-f carrier, and this may be as low as 15 kc (kilocycles per second) for telegraph communication, as high as 200 Mc (megacycles per second) for voice communication and 1,000 Mc for television signals, is to be found in the frequency band which is necessary for the amount of information that is being transmitted per second, and also in the fact that an h-f carrier is essential for the transmission by radiation of electromagnetic waves.   A number of practical considerations are also involved, an important one being the fact that the antenna problem for both transmitter and receiver is simplified at the higher frequencies.

Consider a waveform which may be represented analytically by the expression

$$e = A \cos (\omega t + \theta) \tag{1-1}$$

where t is the time.   In amplitude modulation, the amplitude A is varied in accordance with the modulating or signal information, while ω and θ remain constant.   In frequency modulation, the frequency ω is varied, while both A and θ remain constant.   In phase modulation, the phase θ is varied relative to some arbitrary datum, while A and ω remain constant.

The essential character of a modulated carrier may be illustrated graphically. This is done in Fig. 1-3, which shows an l-f square-wave signal and the form of the a-m, f-m, and p-m waves.

1-4. Comparison of Modulation Systems. Amplitude modulation is the oldest method of carrier transmission and is used almost exclusively in radiotelephony and -telegraphy. Commercial radiobroadcast transmission is predominately amplitude-modulated, although considerable f-m broadcast activity exists. The sound channel of TV transmission is of the f-m type. Also, frequency-shift keying is important for telegraphic work. This is an f-m system, with dots being pulses of equal

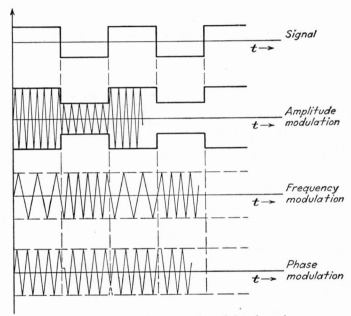

FIG. 1-3. The essential character of modulated carrier waves.

amplitude and duration which have been shifted in frequency by one amount, and dashes being pulses of the same amplitude and duration but which have been shifted in frequency by a different amount.

An important feature of a-m transmission is that the total frequency spread around the carrier frequency, which arises because of the modulation which is applied to the carrier, is twice the highest frequency in the modulating signal, the spread extending from $\omega_{m,max}$, the maximum modulating frequency, above the carrier to an equal spread below the carrier frequency. The frequency band above the carrier is called the *upper sidebands*, and the frequency band below the carrier is called the *lower sidebands*. For most commercial broadcasting, a total band spread of 10 kc is allowed. Inherently, therefore, a-m transmission might be called narrow-band transmission. Because of this, a-m transmission is possible over a very wide range of carrier frequencies, and such transmission is carried out commercially from several hundred kilocycles to 30 Mc.

In so far as the receiver is concerned, a consideration of fundamental importance is the ratio of signal to noise at the output. The nature and sources of noise will receive detailed consideration later in the text. It will suffice here to note that random noise is of two classes. One class is continuous and may be resolved into an infinite number of small sinusoidal components at all frequencies. The other class consists of occasional pulses of relatively short duration but of large amplitude. These, too, can be resolved into sinusoidal components covering a range of frequencies. Those components of noise from both sources which lie within the pass band of the reciever contribute to noise output.

In an a-m receiver, the noise output results from the interaction of the noise components with the desired carrier, thereby producing an l-f variation of amplitude. The noise has the same character as the a-m signal. It cannot be separated from the signal and remains as an undesired signal. While it is possible to limit the effect of large pulse bursts of noise, the random noise serves to limit the total allowable gain or sensitivity of the receiver, and so the minimum desired signal that might be received.

Frequency-modulated transmission has found considerable application, both for radiobroadcasting and as the sound channel of TV receivers. Phase modulation has found very little application, except as an intermediate step in certain systems for producing f-m waves.

Frequency modulation differs from amplitude modulation, in addition to the fundamental differences of character of modulation as illustrated in Fig. 1-3, in the fact that, in order to include all the sideband energy due to a complicated signal spectrum, such as that, for example, from an orchestra, a frequency band of approximately 100 kc on each side of the carrier is required. Because of this fact, frequency modulation is usually confined to the high frequencies, from perhaps 50 Mc and higher, in order to provide room for a number of f-m channels. Such frequencies are also dictated by the receiver problem, since it would be extremely difficult to design band-pass circuits of 200 kc bandwidth except at the higher frequencies.

It is instructive to examine certain of the features of an f-m transmitter. Since the amplitude of the carrier remains constant during modulation, the transmitter can be adjusted to give its rated output power, at which point the transmitter is operating at its optimum efficiency. In an a-m transmitter, the peak power with full modulation (100 per cent modulation) is four times the average value. Because of the essential differences in operation, a given transmitter will produce twice the modulation power at the receiver when it is operated as an f-m system.

In the f-m receiver, since the intelligence is carried in the frequency deviation and not in amplitude variations, a limiter is used to remove amplitude variations. Noise, which is amplitude-modulated, will similarly be limited when the noise is near its peak. It will be shown later, in fact, that those components of noise nearer to the carrier frequency will produce less frequency modulation, and so less noise in the output. When all factors are taken into account, the signal/noise ratio is about 30 db higher than with an a-m transmitter of the same peak power, when the deviation frequency is about 75 kc and the input signal/noise ratio is fairly good.

If the signal/noise ratio at the receiver is fairly poor, then, because of the wide receiver bandwidth of the f-m receiver, the extra noise potentials will contribute to noise in the output. In such cases, a relatively narrow-band f-m system is desirable and will yield a better signal/noise ratio than an a-m receiver in the same situation.

Another fact which will be discussed later is that two f-m signals of differing amplitude at the same carrier frequency will interfere less with each other than will comparable a-m signals. In fact, if the desired signal is about twice the amplitude of the interfering signal, the interference at the receiver output is very small.

1-5. Carrier Suppression. In an a-m system, even though most of the radiated power is contained in the carrier, the intelligence is contained only in the upper- and lower-frequency sidebands. In fact, the intelligence is contained in each sideband. Clearly, therefore, if the carrier were suppressed before amplification, the efficiency of the system could be improved materially.

The problem of the receiver design becomes more complex for suppressed-carrier reception than for ordinary amplitude modulation, because, as will later be seen, it is necessary to reintroduce the carrier before the intelligence can be extracted. While it is not difficult to generate locally an h-f signal, the reintroduced carrier must maintain the proper phase relation with respect to the sidebands if distortion is to be avoided. While it would be possible to transmit a pilot carrier to serve as a reference for controlling the locally produced carrier, this would introduce considerable complications. Also, since the phase of the locally generated carrier could not be controlled accurately enough for such operation, suppressed-carrier transmission is not very practical.

1-6. Single-sideband Systems. A satisfactory method in which the carrier is suppressed is possible if, at the same time, one of the sidebands is also suppressed. Such a system is theoretically feasible, since, as mentioned in Sec. 1-5, the signal information is contained in each of the sidebands, and, by later reintroducing the carrier, the signal information may be extracted. Such single-sideband operation is very desirable, since the total required band spread is half that when both sidebands are transmitted.

The phase of the reintroduced carrier in the single-sideband suppressed-carrier system must be fixed with respect to the transmitter datum; otherwise, phase distortion of the output results. However, for telephony work, no difficulty arises, as the ear is not sensitive to phase changes but does respond to frequency changes. As a result, if the frequency of the reintroduced carrier is different from that of the suppressed carrier, serious distortion may arise. However, it is possible to set the carrier properly, and satisfactory operation is feasible. Such single-sideband suppressed-carrier telephony is employed for long-distance (transoceanic) transmission by commercial organizations, the added complexity of the receiver being justified in view of the efficiency of the system.

1-7. Pulse Modulation. A number of p-m methods of transmission have been developed during recent years. Such methods depend on the fact that it is possible to reconstruct a given signal by sampling the wave at periodic intervals, provided that the frequency of sampling is made sufficiently high.

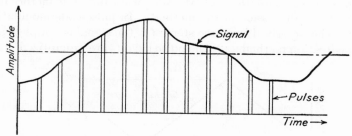

FIG. 1-4. Pulse-amplitude modulation.

In the pulse-amplitude-modulation (PAM) method, short pulses of r-f power are transmitted at regular intervals. The amplitude of each pulse is proportional to the instantaneous amplitude of the signal. The situation is illustrated graphically in Fig. 1-4. For speech confined to a frequency spread of 5 kc, the sampling frequency must be not less than 10 kc. If the pulse duration at each sampling point is, say, 5 μsec, this means that the duty cycle is only 5 per cent, permitting a theoretical 20 simultaneous messages at a given carrier frequency without overlap or interference. An adequate commutating means must be provided for switching both transmitter and receiver to the different channels. If the number of messages is small, then, for a given average power, the peak power during transmission may be quite high.

In pulse-duration, or pulse-width, modulation, the amplitude of each pulse is constant, but the width, or duration, of the pulse is made proportional to the instantaneous amplitude of the signal. This scheme is illustrated in Fig. 1-5. In such a method, the pulse duration might have a mean value of 5 μsec, the widths varying from 1 to 9 μsec.

If the deviation of the pulse from its datum (no signal) position is made proportional to the instantaneous amplitude of the signal, the system

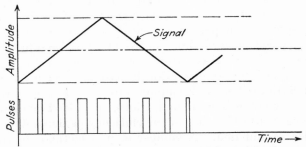

FIG. 1-5. Pulse-duration, or pulse-width, modulation.

is the pulse-time, pulse-phase, or pulse-position modulation. This situation is illustrated in Fig. 1-6.

In pulse-code modulation (PCM), somewhat different factors must be considered in a discussion of the method. In pulse-code modulation the process is characterized by three steps: (1) the signal is sampled, as in all pulse-modulation methods; (2) the pulse heights are "quantized"; and (3)

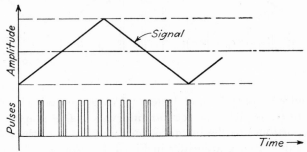

FIG. 1-6. Pulse-position modulation.

the quantized signal is converted into a sequence of coded pulses. The term quantization as here used implies the selection of a particular amplitude level to represent a range of amplitude variations. The quantizing process thus selects the nearest amplitude level, instead of the continuity of amplitudes that actually exists.

Suppose, for example, that a four-pulse group is available for coding the amplitude level. The signal value at a given single point will be

TABLE 1-1

BINARY CODE FOR FOUR-PULSE GROUPS IN PULSE-CODE
MODULATION (PCM)

Code	Amplitude represented	Code	Amplitude represented
0000	0	1000	8
0001	1	1001	9
0010	2	1010	10
0011	3	1011	11
0100	4	1100	12
0101	5	1101	13
0110	6	1110	14
0111	7	1111	15

coded as in Table 1-1. In this table the presence of a pulse is indicated by a 1, and its absence is indicated by a 0. Clearly the four-pulse groups can express all integral values from 0 to 15. Owing to this limitation in amplitude levels available, when the pulse groups are reconverted into a signal there will be a discrepancy between it and the original. This discrepancy is called "quantizing noise." Evidently, the larger the number of quantization levels available, the smaller will be the relative distortion produced by the system.

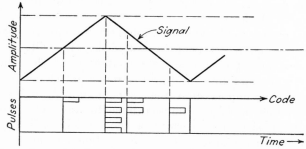

Fig. 1-7. Pulse-code modulation (a typical code for several signal amplitudes only is illustrated, and these do not have a realizable code pattern for the amplitudes shown).

As indicated above, the essential advantage of pulse-modulation systems is that time-division multiplexing is made possible, owing to the fact that the duty cycle is relatively small. However, not all pulse methods are equally favorable. The various systems will be examined in the light of receiver signal/noise ratio.

For the pulse-amplitude system, the signal/noise ratio is worse than with ordinary amplitude modulation, owing to the fact that the receiver bandwidth must be considerably wider in the pulse-amplitude-modulation receiver than for ordinary amplitude modulation. This broader bandwidth is necessary in order to permit a reproduction of the pulses.

In the pulse-duration and pulse-position methods, since the amplitudes of the pulses are to remain constant, limiters can be used. Although this may result in some loss of energy, the noise, which is amplitude-modulated, will be removed. However, noise which appears on the leading and trailing edges of the pulses will produce an effect on the over-all signal/noise ratio. Consequently, by increasing the bandwidth of the receiver, thereby permitting steeper sides to the pulses, the noise in the output is reduced. This is offset to some extent by the fact that, with a broader bandwidth, the input noise is increased. The net effect is that the signal/noise ratio decreases with increasing bandwidths, although an optimum bandwidth is dictated in such applications. If impulse noise occurs, this might increase the effective duration, in pulse-duration modulation, or it might alter the position in pulse-position modulation, with a resultant production of noise.

An important feature of pulse-code modulation is that distortion and noise must be very large before the presence or absence of a pulse cannot be recognized. In fact, if it is possible to establish the existence of a pulse combined with noise, it is theoretically possible to regenerate the original pulse. This characteristic of pulse-code-modulation systems makes their use in radio relay links particularly desirable. It is possible for the regeneration process to be carried out at each relay station, thus permitting a new signal to be available for retransmission.

1-8. System Block Diagram. As has probably been surmised, many of the fundamental circuits and techniques are common to all communication systems, although certain of the system elements will be special to the particular system. To serve as an introduction to the analytical discussion of circuits to follow, and also to indicate the general features of certain of the more important systems of communication, block diagrams of the essential elements incorporated in such systems will be given. It should be emphasized that certain of the blocks which are illustrated as separate entities might, in fact, be combined in achieving a given operation.

a. A-M Systems. The essential elements of a simple broadcast transmitter and of appropriate receivers are given below. The block diagram of an a-m transmitting system is given in Fig. 1-8. Nothing is here said concerning the power capacities of the various elements or stages. These will vary according to the particular circuits or systems of operation used and will be considered at the appropriate points in the text. The frequencies which appear at various points in the circuit are indicated on the diagram.

It will be observed that the a-m transmitter is a relatively simple device, consisting essentially of an audio amplifier for raising the level of the intelligence signal, a stable oscillator which establishes the carrier frequency of the transmitter, a modulator in which the signal and the carrier are combined to produce a modulated carrier, and power amplifiers for raising the power level of the modulated carrier before transmission. Observe that the modulator serves to translate the signal information at frequency ω_m as measured from the zero level to the information given with reference to the carrier level, ω_c.

The receiver for an a-m wave is shown in its simplest block form in Fig. 1-9. In the receiver, the r-f potential induced in the antenna is amplified from its usual low level of 5 μvolts to 1 mv to perhaps 1 to 30

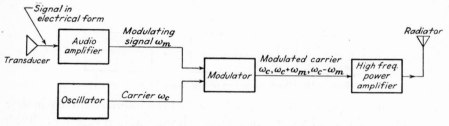

FIG. 1-8. The elements of an a-m transmitting system.

volts. This amplification may all occur at the center frequency ω_c of the transmitter, or it may be changed to some intermediate value ω_i within the receiver. The amplified modulated r-f signal is then passed through the demodulator, which extracts the signal from the modulated wave. In essence, therefore, the demodulator, or detector, serves in the inverse manner of the modulator. The demodulator may be considered to translate the frequency level from the carrier level ω_c to the zero level, so that the signal frequencies ω_m are specified with respect to the zero-frequency level. The audio signal is then amplified sufficiently to operate the loud-speaker and usually provides about 3 to 30 watts output.

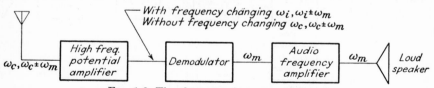

FIG. 1-9. The elements of an a-m receiver.

Two important different types of receivers are in widespread use, the tuned radio-frequency (trf) and the superheterodyne types. The tuned r-f receiver is illustrated in block form in Fig. 1-10, and the superheterodyne receiver is illustrated in block form in Fig. 1-11.

The tuned r-f receiver shown in Fig. 1-10 performs in precisely the manner of the general block diagram of Fig. 1-9. Tuning is accomplished by changing the resonant frequency of the parallel LC circuits of each stage, either by changing the capacitance or by changing the inductance.

The superheterodyne receiver illustrated in Fig. 1-11 is more common for normal broadcast reception. It comprises a single stage of tuned r-f amplification, although this is often omitted in many receivers, the output of which feeds into a mixer (and this is often referred to as the "first detector"). Also feeding into the mixer is the output from a local oscillator. The frequencies which are centered about the carrier ω_c combine with the local oscillator frequency ω_0, to produce a modulated carrier which is now centered either around the frequency $\omega_c + \omega_0$ or around

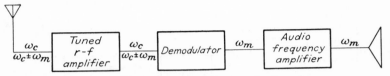

FIG. 1-10. Block diagram of the tuned r-f receiver.

$\omega_c - \omega_0$, depending on choice, which is called the intermediate frequency ω_i. The modulated i-f signal then passes through a fixed tuned amplifier, the output from which feeds a detector, or demodulator, as before.

The essential differences between the tuned r-f and the superheterodyne receivers are important. In the tuned r-f receiver, tuning and amplification are effected at the incoming carrier-frequency level ω_c. Because of this requirement, the circuits used are best from tuning considerations but are not optimum from selectivity considerations. In the superheterodyne receiver, tuning is accomplished by adjusting the frequency of the local oscillator. Each incoming signal is converted to the

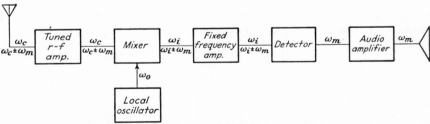

FIG. 1-11. The elements of a superheterodyne receiver.

same intermediate frequency ω_i, and the i-f signal is amplified in high-gain fixed tuned stages which have been chosen for optimum selectivity. This is possible since the requirement of tunability has been removed as a requirement of the amplifiers. The detector and audio amplifiers are substantially the same in both receivers.

 b. F-M Systems. An f-m transmitter in its most elementary form is given in Fig. 1-12. The audio-frequency (a-f) amplifier and the h-f power amplifiers are quite conventional. However, the high frequency used in f-m systems, as already noted, is usually considerably higher than that for the a-m system.   This requirement is made necessary by the broad band of frequencies which is required to transmit all the intelligence contained in the audio signal.   Specifically, to cover the normal audio spectrum to, say, 7,500 cps, the bandwidth required in the f-m system is approximately 150 kc.   To achieve a bandwidth of 150 kc without excessive loading, the standard broadcast carrier level for f-m transmission ranges from 88 to 108 Mc.

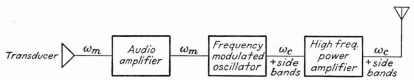

FIG. 1-12. The elements of an f-m transmitting system.

The f-m oscillator may take any one of a number of different forms. A common form incorporates a "reactance" tube as part of the oscillator circuit.   With such a device, the effective capacitance or the effective inductance of the oscillator tank can be changed in a manner dictated by the audio signal.   In this way, the audio signal is converted into changes in frequency.   The f-m oscillator output is usually at a considerably lower frequency than the ultimate station carrier, and the frequency is multiplied to the necessary levels by means of frequency-multiplying stages, before it is amplified to the high power level required for transmission.   Several of the other systems of producing f-m waves are too

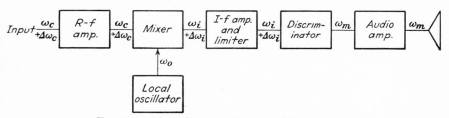

FIG. 1-13. Block diagram of a typical f-m receiver.

complicated for simple discussion, and will be deferred until Chap. 14, where they will be discussed in detail.

The basic circuit of an f-m receiver is somewhat similar to that of an a-m receiver of the superheterodyne type.   A block diagram is given in Fig. 1-13.   The r-f amplifier, mixer, and beat-frequency oscillator are common with those in an a-m superheterodyne receiver, except that the over-all bandwidth is greater, as already discussed.   The i-f amplifier is like that in the a-m superheterodyne, although the last stage is operated at low potential to produce limiting action. This serves to eliminate any fluctuations in the amplitude of the i-f carrier, no matter how produced. The other outstanding difference is the circuit used to demodulate the f-m carrier. The f-m discriminator serves to convert from frequency modulation to amplitude modulation. The resulting amplitude modulation is demodulated in a circuit that is peculiar to the f-m system.

CHAPTER 2

CHARACTERISTICS OF ELECTRON TUBES

2-1. Introduction. Before one undertakes a study of many of the details of the communication systems that have been discussed rather superficially in the previous chapter, it is desirable to examine the fundamental physical principles which govern the operation of the electron tubes that are used in such systems.

There are two important questions that relate to such devices. One relates to the actual source of the electrons and their liberation. The second relates to the control of the electron beam. A brief discussion of these matters will be included here.

EMISSION OF ELECTRONS

2-2. Source and Control of Electrons. According to modern theory, all matter is electrical in nature. The atom, which is one of the fundamental building blocks of all matter, consists of a central core or nucleus which is positively charged and which carries nearly all the mass of the atom. Enough negatively charged electrons surround the nucleus so that the atom is electrically neutral in its normal state. Since all chemical substances consist of groups of these atoms which are bound to each other, then all matter, whether it is in the solid, the liquid, or the gaseous state, is a potential source of electrons. All three states of matter do, in fact, serve as sources of electrons. A number of different processes serve to effect the release of electrons, those which are of importance in electron tubes being (1) thermionic emission, (2) secondary emission, (3) photoelectric emission, (4) high field emission, and (5) ionization. These processes will be considered in some detail in what follows.

With the release of the electrons, a means for their control must be provided. Such control is effected by means of externally controlled electric fields or magnetic fields, or both. These fields perform one or both of the following functions: (1) control of the number of electrons that leave the region near the emitter; (2) control of the paths of the electrons after they leave the emitter. Control method 1 is the more common, and such a control method is incorporated in almost all electron tubes, except those of the field-deflected variety. The cathode-ray tube is a very important example of a field-deflected tube. However, even in this latter case, a control of type 1 is incorporated to control the electron-tube current, even though the subsequent motion is controlled by means of electric or magnetic fields, or both.

2-3. Thermionic Emission. Consider matter in the metallic state. Metals are most generally employed in the form of a wire or ribbon filament. If such a filament contains electrons and if these are relatively free to move about in the metal (and this is the case since the application of a small potential difference between the ends of the wire will result in a current flow), it might be expected that some electrons might "leak" out of the metal of their own accord. This does not occur, however.

Consider what happens to an electron as it seeks to escape from a metal. The escaping, negatively charged electron will induce a positive charge on the metal. There will then be a force of attraction between the induced charge and the electron. Unless the escaping electron possesses sufficient energy to carry it out of the region of influence of this image force of attraction, it will be returned to the metal. The minimum amount of energy that is required to release the electron against this attractive force is known as the *work function* of the metal. This requisite minimum amount of energy may be supplied by any one of a number of different methods. One of the most important methods is to heat the metal to a high temperature. In this way, some of the thermal energy supplied to the metal is transferred from the lattice of the heated metal crystals into kinetic energy of the electrons.

An explicit expression relating the thermionic-emission current density and the temperature of the metal can be derived.[1]* The expression so derived has the form

$$J_{th} = A_0 T^2 e^{-b_0/T} \tag{2-1}$$

where A_0 is a constant for all metals and has the value of 120×10^4 amp/(m²)(°K²) and b_0 is a constant that is characteristic of the metal. The quantity b_0 is related to the work function E_W of the metal by

$$b_0 = 11{,}600 E_W \qquad °K \tag{2-2}$$

It has been found experimentally that Eq. (2-1) does represent the form of the variation of current with temperature for most metals, although the value obtained for A_0 may differ materially from the theoretical value of 120×10^4 amp/(m²)(°K²).

It follows from Eq. (2-1) that metals that have a low work function will provide copious emission at moderately low temperatures. Unfortunately, however, the low-work-function metals melt in some cases and boil in others, at the temperatures necessary for appreciable thermionic emission. The important emitters in present-day use are pure-tungsten,

* Superior numbers refer to citations at the end of some chapters.

thoriated-tungsten, and oxide-coated cathodes.   The thermionic-emission constants of these emitters are contained in Table 2-1.

TABLE 2-1

THE IMPORTANT THERMIONIC EMITTERS AND THE
THERMIONIC-EMISSION CONSTANTS

Emitter	A_0, amp/$(m^2)(°K^2)$	E_W, e-v
Tungsten....................	60×10^4	4.52
Thiorated-tungsten...........	3×10^4	2.63
Oxide-coated.................	0.01×10^4	1

Tungsten is used extensively for thermionic filaments despite its relatively high work function.   In fact, this material is particularly important because it is virtually the only material that can be used successfully as the filament in high-potential tubes.   It is used in high-potential X-ray tubes, in high-potential rectifier tubes, and in the large power-amplifier tubes that are used in radio and communication applications. It has the disadvantage that the *cathode emission efficiency,* defined as the ratio of the emission current in milliamperes to the heating power in watts, is small.   Despite this, it can be operated at a sufficiently high temperature, between 2600 and 2800°K, to provide an adequate emission.

It has been found that the application of a very thin layer of low-work-function material on filaments of tungsten will materially reduce the work function of the resulting surface.   A thoriated-tungsten filament is obtained by adding a small amount of thorium oxide to the tungsten before it is drawn.   Such filaments, when properly activated, will yield an efficient emitter at about 1800°K.   It is found desirable to *carbonize* such an emitter, since the rate of evaporation of the thorium layer from the filament is thus reduced by about a factor of 6.   Thoriated-tungsten filaments are limited in application to tubes that operate at intermediate potentials, say 10,000 volts or less.   Higher-potential tubes use pure-tungsten filaments.

The oxide-coated cathode is very efficient (about twenty times as efficient as tungsten) and provides a high emission current at the relatively low temperature of 1000°K.   It consists of a metal sleeve of konal (an alloy of nickel, cobalt, iron, and titanium) or some other metal, which is coated with the oxides of barium and strontium.   These cathodes are limited for a number of reasons to use in the lower potential tubes, say about 1,000 volts or less, although they do operate satisfactorily at higher potentials under pulsed conditions at relatively low-duty cycle.   They are used almost exclusively in receiving-type tubes and provide efficient operation with long life.

Curves showing the relative cathode efficiencies of tungsten, thoriated-tungsten, and oxide-coated cathodes are illustrated in Fig. 2-1. It will be seen that tungsten has a considerably lower efficiency than either of the other two emitters.

The thermionic emitters in their practical form in electron tubes may be of the directly heated, or filamentary, type or of the indirectly heated type, and in the case of gas and vapor tubes the cathode may be of the heat-shielded type. Typical filamentary cathodes are illustrated in Fig. 2-2. These filamentary cathodes may be of the pure-tungsten, thoriated-tungsten, or oxide-coated type.

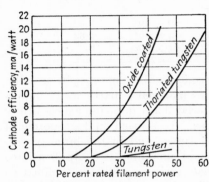

FIG. 2-1. Cathode efficiency curves of an oxide-coated, a thoriated-tungsten, and a pure-tungsten filament.

The indirectly heated cathode for use in vacuum tubes is illustrated in Fig. 2-3. The heater wire is contained in a ceramic insulator which is enclosed by the metal sleeve on which the oxide coating is placed. A cathode assembly of this type has such a high heat capacity that its temperature does not change with instantaneous variation in heater current when alternating current is used.

Heat-shielded cathodes, which can be used only in gas-filled electron tubes for reasons to be discussed in Sec. 2-24, are designed in such a way as to reduce the radiation of heat energy from the cathode. This materially increases the efficiency of the cathode. Several different types of heat-shielded cathodes are illustrated in Fig. 2-4.

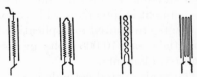

FIG. 2-2. Typical directly heated cathodes.

FIG. 2-3. Typical indirectly heated cathodes.

2-4. Photoelectric Emission. The energy that is required to release an electron from a metal surface may be supplied by illuminating the surface with light. There are certain restrictions on the nature of the surface and the frequency of the impinging light for such electron emission to take place. That is, electron emission is possible only if the frequency of the impinging light exceeds a certain *threshold* value that depends on the work function E_W of the surface according to the equation

$$f_c = \frac{eE_W}{h} \tag{2-3}$$

where e is the charge of the electron and h is Planck's constant. The

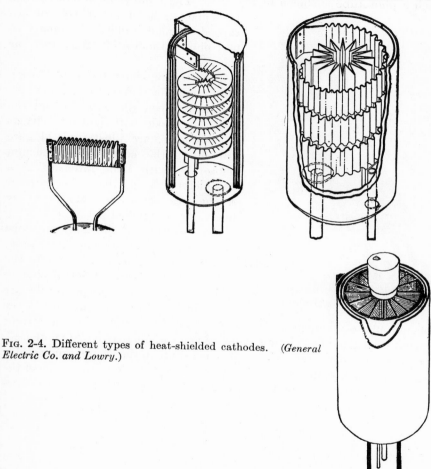

Fig. 2-4. Different types of heat-shielded cathodes. (*General Electric Co. and Lowry.*)

corresponding *threshold wavelength* beyond which photoelectric emission cannot take place is given by

$$\lambda_c = \frac{ch}{eE_W} = \frac{12{,}400 \text{ A}}{E_W} \tag{2-4}$$

where A is the angstrom unit (10^{-8} cm) and c is the velocity of light ($\doteq 3 \times 10^{10}$ cm/sec). For response over the entire visible region, 4000 to 8000 A, the work function of the photosensitive surface must be less than 1.54 volts.

The essential elements of a phototube are the photosensitive cathode surface and a collecting electrode, contained in a glass envelope that either is evacuated or contains an inert gas at low pressure. A photograph of such a phototube is shown in Fig. 2-5. The number of photoelectrons per square millimeter of area of a photocathode is small, and it is customary to use photocathodes of large area, as shown.

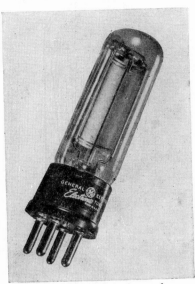

The current characteristics of such phototubes for different collecting potentials between the cathode and the collecting anode, with light intensity as a parameter, are illustrated. Figure 2-6 shows the curves of a vacuum phototube with light intensity as a parameter. Note that the current reaches near saturation values for very low values of applied potential.

The presence in the glass envelope of an inert gas, such as neon or argon, at low pressure materially alters the volt-ampere curves. A set of characteristic curves for a gas phototube are given in Fig. 2-7. The presence of the

FIG. 2-5. A typical phototube.

gas in a phototube increases the sensitivity of the phototube, the current output for a given light intensity increasing with increased plate potential, whereas the output remains sensibly constant in the vacuum phototube.

A significant comparison of the output from two phototubes, one of the vacuum type and the other of the gas-filled type, other characteristics

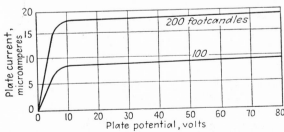

FIG. 2-6. The volt-ampere characteristics of a type PJ-22 vacuum phototube, with light intensity as a parameter.

of the tubes being the same, is contained in Fig. 2-8. Note that the photocurrent for the vacuum phototube is a linear function of the illumination, whereas that for the gas-filled cell shows deviations from the linear at the higher illuminations. However, the greater sensitivity of the gas-filled cell is clearly evident.

2-5. Secondary Emission. It is possible for a particle, either an electron or a positive ion, to strike a metallic surface and transfer all or a part of its kinetic energy in this collision to one or more of the internal electrons. If the energy of the incident particle is sufficiently high, some of the internal electrons may be emitted. Several tubes have been

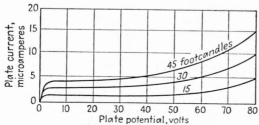

Fig. 2-7. The volt-ampere characteristics of a type PJ-23 gas-filled phototube, with light intensity as a parameter.

designed which incorporate secondary-emission surfaces as part of the device, and highly sensitive phototubes have such auxiliary elements in them. Frequently the secondary emission that exists is of a deleterious nature. This matter will be discussed in explaining certain features of the characteristics of tetrodes.

2-6. High Field Emission. The presence of a very strong electric field at the surface of a metal will cause electron emission. Ordinarily the

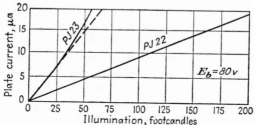

Fig. 2-8. Photocurrent as a function of illumination for a PJ-22 vacuum phototube and a PJ-23 gas-filled cell.

field in the average electron tube is too small to induce such electron emission. This process has been suggested to account for the electron emission from a mercury-pool cathode in a mercury rectifier.

2-7. Ionization. The process in which an atom loses an electron is known as *ionization*. The atom that has lost the electron is called a *positive ion*. The process of ionization may occur in several ways.

Electron Bombardment. Consider a free electron, which might have been released from the envelope or from any of the electrodes within the tube by any of the processes discussed above. Suppose that this free electron has acquired enough energy from an applied field so that, upon collision with a neutral atom, it removes an electron. Following this action, two electrons and a positive ion exist. Since there are now two electrons available, both may collide with gas particles and thus induce further ionization. Such a process as this may become cumulative, with consequent large electron release. This process is very important and accounts for the successful operation of gas- and vapor-filled rectifier tubes. It is also the basis of the gas amplification in gas-filled phototubes.

Photoelectric Emission. If the gas is exposed to light of the proper frequency, then this radiant energy may be absorbed by the atom, with resulting electron emission. This process is important in initiating certain discharges.

Positive-ion Bombardment. The collision between a positive ion and a neutral gas particle may result in electron release, in much the same manner as by electron bombardment. This process is very inefficient and is usually insignificant in normal gas tubes.

Thermal Emission. If the temperature of the gas is high enough, some electrons may become dislodged from the gas particles. However, the gas temperature in electron tubes is generally low, and this process is normally unimportant.

THE HIGH-VACUUM DIODE

2-8. The Potential Distribution between the Electrodes. Consider a thermionic source situated in a vacuum. This cathode will emit electrons, most of which have very little energy when they emerge. Those electrons which first escape will diffuse throughout the space within the envelope. An equilibrium condition will soon be reached when, because of the mutual repulsion between electrons, the free electrons in the space will prevent any additional electrons from leaving the cathode. The equilibrium state will be reached when the space charge of the electron cloud produces a strong enough electric field to prevent any subsequent emission.

The inclusion of a collecting plate near the thermionic cathode will allow the collection of electrons from the space charge when this plate is maintained at a positive potential with respect to the cathode; the higher the potential, the higher the current. Of course, if the thermionic emission is limited, then the maximum current possible is the temperature-saturated value.

In addition to such a simple two-element device, which is the diode, grids may be interposed between the cathode and plate. If a single grid is interposed, the tube is a triode. If two grids are present, the tube is a tetrode; three grids yield a pentode, etc.   Details of the characteristics and operation of such devices will be considered in some detail in the following pages.

Consider a simple diode consisting of a plane cathode and a collecting plate, or anode, which is parallel to it.   It is supposed that the cathode can be heated to any desired temperature and that the potential between the cathode and anode may be set at any desired value.   It is desired to examine the potential distribution between the tube elements for various cathode temperatures and fixed anode-cathode applied potential.

Suppose that the temperature of the cathode is high enough to allow some electrons to be emitted.   An electron space-charge cloud will be formed in the envelope.   The density of the electrons and the potential at any point in the interelectrode space are related by Poisson's equation

$$\frac{d^2V}{dx^2} = \frac{\rho}{\epsilon_0} \qquad (2\text{-}5)$$

where V is the potential in volts, ρ is the magnitude of the electronic-charge density in coulombs per cubic meter, and $\epsilon_0 = 10^{-9}/36\pi$ is the permittivity of space.   A study of this expression will yield significant information.

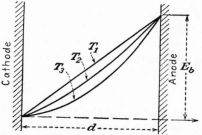

FIG. 2-9. The potential distribution between plane-parallel electrodes, for several values of cathode temperature.

It is supposed that the electrons that are emitted from the cathode have zero initial velocities.   Under these conditions, the general character of the results will have the forms illustrated in Fig. 2-9.   At the temperature T_1, which is too low for any emission, the potential distribution is a linear function of the distance from the cathode to the anode. This follows from Eq. (2-5), since, for zero-charge density,

$$\frac{d^2V}{dx^2} = 0 \qquad \text{or} \qquad \frac{dV}{dx} = \text{const}$$

This is the equation of a straight line.

At the higher temperature T_2, the charge density ρ is not zero.   Clearly, the anode-cathode potential, which is externally controlled, will be independent of the temperature, and all curves must pass through the fixed end points.   Suppose that the potential distribution is somewhat as illustrated by the curve marked T_2.   All curves must be concave upward, since Eq. (2-5), which may be interpreted as a measure of the curvature, is positive.   A positive curvature means that the change in slope dV/dx between two adjacent points must be positive.   Moreover, the curvature is greater for larger values of ρ, corresponding to the higher temperatures. It is possible to justify that the maximum current that can be drawn from the diode for a fixed plate potential and any temperature is obtained under the condition of zero electric field at the surface of the cathode. Under these optimum conditions,

$$\frac{dV}{dx} = 0 \qquad \text{at } x = 0 \tag{2-6}$$

This condition is valid under the assumption of zero initial velocities of emission of the electrons.

2-9. Equations of Space Charge. An explicit relation between the current collected and the potential that is applied between the anode and cathode is possible. In general, the current density is a measure of the rate at which the electrons pass through unit area per unit time in the direction of the field. If v denotes the drift velocity in meters per second, N is the electron density in electrons per cubic meter, and e is the electronic charge in coulombs, then the current density in amperes per square meter is

$$J = Nev = \rho v \tag{2-7}$$

Also, neglecting the initial velocity, the velocity of the electron at any point in the interelectrode space is related to the potential through which it has fallen by the following expression, which is based on the conservation of energy:

$$\tfrac{1}{2}mv^2 = eV \tag{2-8}$$

By combining the foregoing expressions, there results

$$\frac{d^2V}{dx^2} = \frac{JV^{-\frac{1}{2}}}{\epsilon_0(2e/m)^{\frac{1}{2}}} \tag{2-9}$$

This is a differential equation in V as a function of x. The solution of it is given by

$$J = \frac{\epsilon_0}{2.25}\sqrt{2\frac{e}{m}}\frac{V^{\frac{3}{2}}}{x^2} \qquad \text{amp/m}^2 \tag{2-10}$$

For electrons, and in terms of the boundary conditions $V = E_b$ at the anode, there results

$$J = 2.33 \times 10^{-6}\frac{E_b^{\frac{3}{2}}}{d^2} \qquad \text{amp/m}^2 \tag{2-11}$$

This equation is known as the *Langmuir-Childs*, or *three-halves-power*, *law*. It relates the current density, and so the current, with the applied potential and the geometry of the tube. It shows that the space-charge current is independent of the temperature and the work function of the cathode. Thus, no matter how many electrons a cathode may be able to supply, the geometry of the tube and the applied potential will determine the maximum current that can be collected by the anode. If the electron supply from the cathode is restricted, the current may be less than the value predicted by Eq. (2-11). The conditions are somewhat as represented graphically in Fig. 2-10.

For the case of a tube that possesses cylindrical symmetry, a similar analysis is possible. The results of such a calculation lead to the following expression for the current:

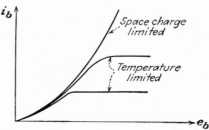

$$I_b = 14.6 \times 10^{-6} \frac{l}{r_a} \frac{E_b^{3/2}}{\beta^2} \quad \text{amp}$$

$$(2\text{-}12)$$

where l is the active length of the tube and β^2 is a quantity that is determined from the ratio r_a/r_k, the ratio of anode to cathode radius.

Fig. 2-10. The volt-ampere characteristics of a typical diode.

For ratios r_a/r_k of 8 or more, β^2 may be taken as unity.

Attention is called to the fact that the plate current depends upon the three-halves power of the plate potential both for the plane parallel and also for a diode possessing cylindrical symmetry. This is a general relationship, and it is possible to demonstrate that an expression of the form $I_b = kE_b^{3/2}$ applies for any geometry, provided only that the same

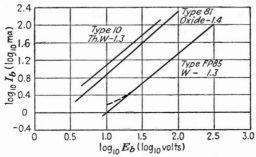

Fig. 2-11. Experimental results to verify the three-halves-power law for tubes with oxide-coated, thoriated-tungsten, and pure-tungsten filaments.

restrictions as imposed in the above developments are true. The specific value of the constant k that exists in this expression cannot be analytically determined unless the geometry of the system is specified.

The dependence of the current on the potential for any tube may be determined by plotting the results obtained experimentally on a logarithmic scale. Theoretically one should find, if the expression $I_b = kE_b^{3/2}$

is valid, that

$$\log_{10} I_b = \log_{10} k + \tfrac{3}{2} \log_{10} E_b \tag{2-13}$$

The logarithmic plots for three commercial tubes are shown in Fig. 2-11. The type 10 tube is a triode and was converted into a diode by connecting grid and plate together. The other tubes are diodes. It will be observed that the logarithmic plots are straight lines, although the slopes of these lines are all slightly less than the theoretical 1.5.

2-10. Rating of Vacuum Diodes. The current and potential ratings of a diode, i.e., the maximum current that the tube may carry and the maximum potential difference that may be applied between anode and cathode, are influenced by a number of factors.

1. A limit is set to the tube current by the cathode efficiency of the emitter. Thus, for a given input power to the filament, a maximum current is specified.

2. There is a maximum temperature limit to which the glass envelope of the tube may be safely allowed to rise. This is the temperature to which the tube was raised during the outgassing process. This is about 400°C for soft glass and about 600°C for pyrex. For higher temperatures, the gases adsorbed by the glass walls may be liberated. Owing to this limitation, glass bulbs are seldom used for vacuum tubes of more than about 1 kw capacity.

3. A very important limitation is set by the temperature to which the anode may rise. In addition to the fraction of the heat radiated by the cathode that is intercepted by the anode, the anode is also heated by the energy carried by the anode current. The instantaneous power carried by the anode current and supplied to the anode is given by $e_b i_b$, where e_b is the anode-cathode potential and i_b is the anode current. The temperature to which the anode rises will depend upon the area of the anode and the material of its construction.

The most common metals used for anodes are nickel and iron for receiving tubes and tantalum, molybdenum, and graphite for transmitting tubes. The surfaces are often roughened or blackened in order to increase the thermal emissivity. The anodes of many transmitting tubes may be operated at a cherry-red heat without excessive gas emission. To allow for forced cooling of the anode, cooling coils may be provided, or the tube may be immersed in oil. The newer type of transmitting tubes are frequently provided with radiator fins for forced-air cooling. Two different types of transmitting tubes are illustrated in Fig. 2-12.

4. The potential limitation of a high-vacuum diode is also dependent on the type of its construction. If the filament and anode leads are brought out side by side through the same glass press, some conduction may take place between these leads through the glass. This effect is

particularly marked if the glass is hot, and the resulting electrolysis will cause the glass to deteriorate and eventually to leak. The highest potential permissible between adjacent leads in glass depends upon the spacing and upon the type of glass but is generally kept below 1,000 volts. Higher-potential tubes are usually provided with filament leads at one end of the glass envelope, with the anode at the other end.

The glass envelope must be long enough so that flashover on the outside of the tube will not occur. In a diode as a rectifier, no current will

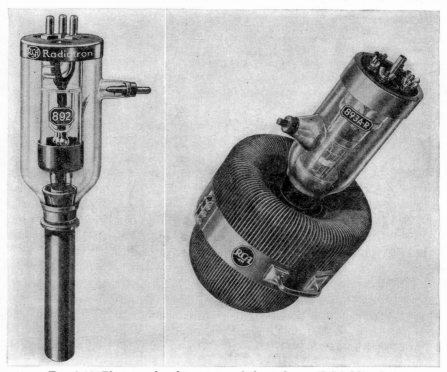

FIG. 2-12. Photographs of two transmitting tubes. (*RCA Mfg. Co.*)

flow during the time that the anode is negative with respect to the cathode. The maximum safe rating of a rectifying diode is known as the *peak-inverse-potential rating.*

Commercial vacuum diodes are made which will rectify current at high potential, up to 200,000 volts. Such units are used with X-ray equipment, with high-potential cable-testing equipment, and with the high-potential equipment for nuclear-physics research. The dimensions and shape of the glass envelope will depend upon the current capacity of the tube and the type of cooling to be used, oil-cooled tubes being generally smaller than air-cooled types.

THE TRIODE

2-11. The Grid. The introduction of a third element between the cathode and plate of the diode by DeForest in 1907 was the start of the extensive developments involving vacuum tubes. This new electrode, called the *control grid*, consists of a wire mesh, or screen, which surrounds the cathode and is situated close to it. The potential applied to the grid in such a tube is usually several volts negative relative to the cathode, whereas the plate is usually maintained several hundred volts positive with respect to the cathode. Clearly, the electric field resulting from the potential of the grid tends to maintain a large space-charge cloud, whereas the field of the plate tends to reduce the space charge. However, owing to its proximity to the cathode, a given potential on the grid will exercise a greater effect on the space charge than the same potential on the plate. This would seem to imply that a proportionality should exist between the relative effectiveness of the grid and plate potentials on the space charge and that the plate current might be represented approximately by the equation

$$i_b = k \left(e_c + \frac{e_b}{\mu} \right)^{3/2} \tag{2-14}$$

where e_b is the plate-cathode potential, e_c is the grid-cathode potential, and the factor μ is a measure of the relative grid-plate potential effectiveness on the tube current. The factor μ is known as the *amplification factor* of the grid.

The validity of Eq. (2-14), which is simply a natural extension of the three-halves-power space-charge equation of the diode, has been verified experimentally for many triodes. No simple, rigorous theoretical derivation of this equation is possible, even for a triode of relatively simple geometry. However, the value of the amplification factor μ can be calculated with a fair degree of accuracy from equations that are based on electrostatic considerations.

By maintaining the grid at some negative potential with respect to the cathode, it will repel electrons and will, in part, neutralize the attractive field of the anode, thus reducing the anode current. If the grid potential is made positive, the electron stream will increase because of the combined action of both the grid and the plate potentials. But, with a positive potential on the grid, some of the space charge will be attracted to it, and a current in the grid will result. The grid structure must be designed to dissipate the grid power if the grid potential is to be maintained positive; otherwise the grid structure may be seriously damaged. Generally the grid is maintained negative, although positive-grid triodes for power-amplifier applications are available.

The variations of the plate and grid currents with variances of grid potential are illustrated in Fig. 2-13. In this diagram, the plate potential is maintained constant. For sufficiently negative grid potential, cutoff of the plate current occurs. As the grid potential is made less negative, the plate current follows a smooth curve, the variation being expressed analytically by Eq. (2-14). As the grid potential is made positive, grid current flows, the magnitude of this current increasing rapidly with increasing grid potential.

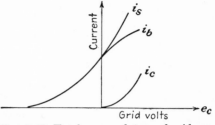

For positive grid potentials, and with the consequent grid current, Eq. (2-14) no longer represents the plate current, although it does give a good representation of the total space current. With increasing grid potentials, the grid current increases, and the plate current decreases.

FIG. 2-13. Total space, plate, and grid current in a triode, as a function of grid potential, with fixed plate potential.

2-12. Triode Parameters. In view of Eq. (2-14), the dependence of the plate current on the plate and the grid potentials may be represented functionally by the expression

$$i_b = f(e_b, e_c) \qquad (2-15)$$

Of course the plate current also depends upon the heater temperature, but as the heater current is usually maintained at rated value (this is

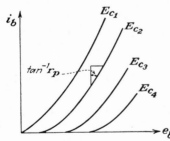

FIG. 2-14. The plate characteristics of a triode.

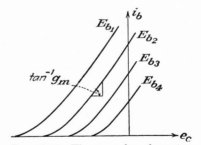

FIG. 2-15. The transfer characteristics of a triode.

such as to provide perhaps five to ten times the normal required current), this term usually does not enter into the functional relationship. If Eq. (2-15) is plotted on a three-dimensional system of axes, a space diagram representing the function $f(i_b, e_b, e_c) = 0$ is obtained. The projections of these surfaces on the three coordinate planes give three families of characteristic curves. These curves are given in Figs. 2-14 to 2-16.

The curves of Fig. 2-14 are known as the *plate characteristics* since they show the variation of the plate current with plate potential for various values of grid bias. The main effect of making the grid more negative is to shift the curves to the right, without changing the slopes appreciably. This is in accord with what would be expected from consideration of Eq. (2-14).

If the grid potential is made the independent variable, the *mutual*, or *transfer*, characteristics of Fig. 2-15 result. The effect of making the plate potential less positive is to shift the curves to the right, the slopes again remaining substantially unchanged.

The simultaneous variation of both the plate and the grid potentials so that the plate current remains constant gives rise to a third group of characteristics illustrated in Fig. 2-16. These show the relative effects of the plate and grid potentials on the plate current of the tube. But from the discussion of Sec. 2-11 it is the amplification factor that relates these two effects. Consequently, the amplification factor is defined as the ratio of the change in plate potential to the change in grid potential for a constant plate current. Mathematically, μ is given by the relation

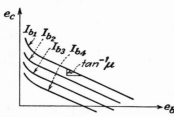

FIG. 2-16. The constant-current characteristics of a triode.

$$\mu = -\left(\frac{\partial e_b}{\partial e_c}\right)_{I_b} \tag{2-16}$$

The negative sign takes account of the fact that a decreasing grid potential must accompany an increasing plate potential if the plate current is to remain unchanged.

Consider the variation in the plate current. This is obtained by expanding Eq. (2-15) in a Taylor's expansion. But it is here assumed that the variation is small and that it is adequately represented by the first two terms of the expansion. Subject to this limitation, the expression has the form

$$\Delta i_b = \left(\frac{\partial i_b}{\partial e_b}\right)_{E_c} \Delta e_b + \left(\frac{\partial i_b}{\partial e_c}\right)_{E_b} \Delta e_c \tag{2-17}$$

This expression indicates simply that changes both in the plate potential Δe_b and in the grid potential Δe_c will cause changes in the plate current.

The quantity $(\partial e_b/\partial i_b)_{E_c}$ expresses the ratio of an increment of plate potential to the corresponding increment of plate current, for constant E_c. This ratio has the units of resistance, is known as the *plate resistance* of the tube, and is designated by the symbol r_p. Clearly, r_p is the inverse slope of the plate characteristics of Fig. 2-14 and has been so indicated there.

The quantity $(\partial i_b/\partial e_c)_{E_b}$, which gives the ratio of an increment of plate current to the corresponding increment of grid potential for constant plate potential E_b, has units of conductance. It is known as the *plate-grid transconductance*, or *mutual conductance*, and is designated by the symbol g_m. The mutual conductance g_m is the slope of the mutual-, or transfer-, characteristic curves of Fig. 2-15.

To summarize, the triode coefficients have the forms

$$\left(\frac{\partial e_b}{\partial i_b}\right)_{E_c} \equiv r_p \qquad \text{plate resistance}$$

$$\left(\frac{\partial i_b}{\partial e_c}\right)_{E_b} \equiv g_m \qquad \text{mutual conductance} \qquad (2\text{-}18)$$

$$-\left(\frac{\partial e_b}{\partial e_c}\right)_{I_b} \equiv \mu \qquad \text{amplification factor}$$

It is easy to show that μ is related to r_p and g_m by the expression

$$\mu = r_p g_m \qquad (2\text{-}19)$$

This is obtained by setting $\Delta i_b = 0$ in Eq. (2-17) and then using the definitions of Eq. (2-18).

The variations of these parameters for a fixed value of plate potential for the 6C5 tube are shown in Fig. 2-17. It is noticed that the plate resistance varies over rather wide limits, being very high at zero plate current, and approaches a constant value at the higher plate currents. The transconductance varies from a very small value at zero plate current and tends toward a constant value at the higher plate currents. The amplification factor remains reasonably constant over a wide range of currents, although it falls off rapidly at the low currents. The corresponding values for other

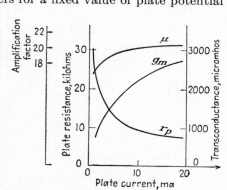

Fig. 2-17. The parameters μ, r_p, and g_m of a 6C5 triode as a function of plate current.

values of E_b may differ numerically, but the general variations will be similar.

High-power triodes are used extensively in transmitters. The grid of such a tube is driven positive with respect to the cathode during part of the cycle, and the current is cut off during part of the cycle. The characteristics of importance of such tubes are the plate curves and the

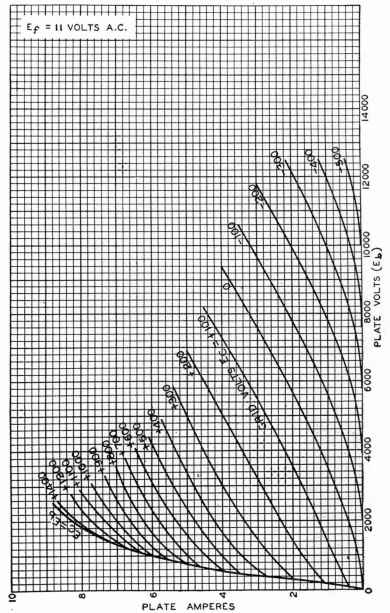

Fig. 2-18. The plate characteristics of a type 889A power triode.

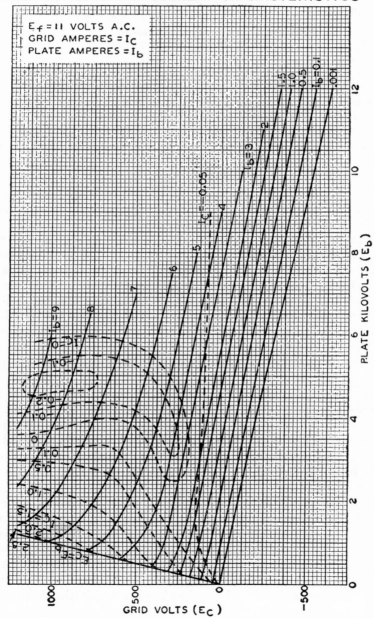

FIG. 2-19. The constant-current characteristics of the power triode of Fig. 2-18.

constant-current curves. The variations over normal operating limits are as illustrated in Figs. 2-18 and 2-19 for a type 889A tube.

MULTIELECTRODE TUBES

2-13. Tetrodes. In the tetrode a fourth electrode is interposed between the grid and the plate. This new electrode is known as the *screen grid*, or *grid 2*, in order to distinguish it from the "control" grid of the triode. Physically, it almost entirely encloses the plate. Because of its design and disposition, the screen grid affords very complete electrostatic shielding between the plate and the control grid. This shielding is such that the grid-plate capacitance is reduced by a factor of about 1,000 or more. However, the screen mesh does not interfere appreciably with the electron flow. The reduction of the grid-plate capacitance is a very important improvement over the triode, and this matter will be considered in some detail in Chap. 5.

Because of the electrostatic shielding of the plate by the screen, the potential of the plate has almost no effect in producing an electric field at the cathode. Since the total space current is determined almost wholly by the field near the cathode surface, the plate exerts little or no effect on the total space charge drawn from the cathode. There is, therefore, a significant difference between the triode and the tetrode. In a triode, the plate performs two distinct functions, that of controlling the total space current, and that of collecting the plate current. In a tetrode, the plate serves only to collect those electrons which have passed through the screen.

The passive character of the plate makes the tetrode a much better potential amplifier than the triode. This follows from the fact that in the triode with a resistance load an increase in load current is accompanied by a decreased plate-cathode potential, which results in a decreased space current. In the tetrode, the decreased plate-cathode potential still exists, but owing to the secondary role of the plate the space current is not materially affected.

The disposition of the cathode and the control grid is nearly the same in both the tetrode and the triode, and therefore the grid-plate transconductance is nearly the same in both tubes. Also, the plate resistance of the tetrode is considerably higher than that of the triode. This follows from the fact that the plate potential has very little effect on the plate current. Thus, with the high plate resistance and with a g_m that is about the same as for the triode, the tetrode amplification factor is very high.

2-14. Tetrode Characteristics. In the tetrode with fixed control-grid and screen-grid potentials, the total space current is practically constant.

Hence, that portion of the space current which is not collected by the plate must be collected by the screen; where the plate current is large, the screen current must be small, and vice versa.   The general character of the results is illustrated in Fig. 2-20.

Although the plate potential does not affect the total space current to a very great extent (although a slight effect is noted in the curve at the lower plate potentials), it does determine the division of the space current between plate and screen.   At zero plate potential, few of the electrons have sufficient energy, to reach the anode, and the plate current should be small.   As the plate potential is increased, a rapid rise occurs in the plate current, with a corresponding reduction of the screen current. When the plate potential is larger than the screen potential, the plate collects almost the entire space current and the screen current approaches zero or a very small value.

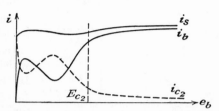

FIG. 2-20. Curves of total space current, plate current, and screen current in a tetrode.

An inspection of the curves of Fig. 2-20 shows that the plate current rises very rapidly with increasing plate potential, but this increase is followed by a region of plate-potential variation in which the plate current decreases with increasing plate potential.   This region is one of negative plate resistance, since an increasing plate potential is accompanied by a decreasing plate current.   The kinks, or folds, in the curves are caused by the emission of electrons from the plate by the process of secondary emission.   This results from the impact of the primary electrons with the plate.   That is, secondary electrons will be released from the anode, and if this is the electrode with the highest positive potential, the electrons will be collected by the anode, without any noticeable effect.   If, however, secondary electrons are liberated from the anode, and if these electrons are collected by some other electrode, then the anode current will decrease, whereas the current to the collecting electrode will increase. It is this latter situation which exists in the tetrode when the plate potential is low and the screen is at a high potential.

When the plate potential is higher than the screen potential, the secondary electrons from the plate are drawn back, without appreciable effect.   If under these potential conditions secondary electrons are liberated from the screen, these will be collected by the anode.   The corresponding plate current will be greater than that in the absence of secondary emission from the screen.

2-15. Transfer Characteristics.   Since the plate of a tetrode has no appreciable influence on the space current, it is expected that the cathode, the control grid, and the screen grid should possess characteristics not unlike those of a triode. This is actually the case, as illustrated in Fig. 2-21. These curves show the effect of variations of plate potential on plate current, for fixed E_{c2}. Because of the slight influence of the plate, the transfer curves are bunched together. These curves should

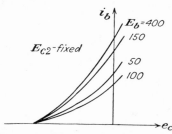

FIG. 2-21. The transfer characteristics of a tetrode, for a fixed screen potential, and with the plate potential as a parameter.

be compared with those of the triode in Fig. 2-15, where the transfer curves are widely separated.

The transfer curves become separated for plate potentials below the screen potential, and this is the region of operation which is generally avoided in practice. In fact, the transfer characteristic for $E_b = 100$ volts actually falls below that for $E_b = 50$ volts. This anomalous behavior is directly the result of the secondary-emission effects discussed above.

2-16. Tube Parameters. It is expected, on the basis of the foregoing discussion, that the plate current may be expressed as a function of the potential of the various electrodes by an expression of the form

$$i_b = f(e_b, e_{c1}, e_{c2}) \tag{2-20}$$

where e_{c1} is the potential of the first, or control, grid, e_{c2} is the potential of the second, or screen, grid, and e_b is the potential of the plate, all with respect to the cathode. This functional relationship is just a natural extension of that which applies for triodes. In fact, an approximate explicit form of the dependence is possible. This form, which is an extension of Eq. (2-14), may be written as

$$i_b = k\left(e_{c1} + \frac{e_b}{\mu_1} + \frac{e_{c2}}{\mu_2}\right)^{3/2} \tag{2-21}$$

where μ_1 and μ_2 are the control-grid and screen-grid amplification factors, respectively.

The variation in the plate current, second- and higher-order terms in the Taylor expansion being neglected, is given by

$$\Delta i_b = \left(\frac{\partial i_b}{\partial e_b}\right)_{E_{c1}, E_{c2}} \Delta e_b + \left(\frac{\partial i_b}{\partial e_{c1}}\right)_{E_b, E_{c2}} \Delta e_{c1} + \left(\frac{\partial i_b}{\partial e_{c2}}\right)_{E_b, E_{c1}} \Delta e_{c2} \tag{2-22}$$

Generally, the screen potential is maintained constant at some appropriate value, and hence $\Delta e_{c2} = 0$. The third term in the expansion may be omitted under these conditions. The partial-differential coefficients appearing in this expression furnish the basis for the definitions of the tube parameters.   These are

$$\left(\frac{\partial e_b}{\partial i_b}\right)_{E_{c1}, E_{c2}} \equiv r_p \qquad \text{plate resistance}$$

$$\left(\frac{\partial i_b}{\partial e_{c1}}\right)_{E_b, E_{c2}} \equiv g_m \qquad \text{mutual conductance} \qquad (2\text{-}23)$$

$$-\left(\frac{\partial e_b}{\partial e_{c1}}\right)_{I_b, E_{c2}} \equiv \mu \qquad \text{amplification factor}$$

The two subscripts associated with each term indicate the parameters that are maintained constant during the partial differentiation.   It can be shown that here too the relation $\mu = r_p g_m$ is valid.   Nominal values for the various parameters that appear in this relationship are $r_p = 10^5$ to 2×10^6 ohms, $g_m = 500$ to $3,000$ μmhos, and $\mu = 100$ to $1,200$.

2-17. Pentodes.   Although the insertion of the screen grid between the control grid and the anode in a triode serves to isolate the plate circuit from the grid circuit, the range of operation of the tube is limited owing to the effects of secondary emission. This limitation results from the fact that, if the plate-potential swing is made too large, the instantaneous plate potential may extend into the region of rapidly falling plate current, with a resulting marked distortion in the output.

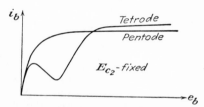

FIG. 2-22. The characteristics of a tube when connected as a tetrode and as a pentode.

The kinks, or folds, that appear in the plate-characteristic curves and that limit the range of operation of the tetrode may be removed by inserting a coarse *suppressor*-grid structure between the screen grid and the plate of the tetrode.   Tubes that are provided with this extra grid are known as *pentodes*.   The suppressor grid must be maintained at a lower potential than the instantaneous potential reached by the plate at any time in its potential excursions.   Usually the suppressor is connected to the cathode, either externally or internally.   Now since both the screen and the anode are positive with respect to the suppressor grid, secondary electrons from either electrode will be returned to the emitting electrode. The main electron stream will not be materially affected by the presence of the suppressor grid.   The effects of the insertion of the suppressor grid are shown graphically in Fig. 2-22.

The pentode has displaced the tetrode in radio-frequency (r-f) potential amplifiers, because it permits a somewhat higher potential amplification at moderate values of plate potential.   Likewise it permits a greater plate-potential excursion without distortion.   Power tetrodes are used extensively in high-power tuned amplifiers for reasons to be discussed in Chap. 10.

The transfer curves of a pentode are shown in Fig. 2-23. It is noted that the curves are almost independent of the plate potential.

2-18. Remote-cutoff Tubes. If in a pentode the grid-cathode spacing, the spacing between grid wires, or the diameter of the grid wires is not uniform along the entire length of the control-grid structure, the various portions of the grid will possess different degrees of electrostatic control over the plate current. That is, one portion of the grid may cause electron-flow cutoff, whereas an appreciable current might pass through a more widely spaced section of the grid. As a result, the plate-current control by the grid is considerably less effective than in a conventional pentode. The general character of the results is illustrated in Fig. 2-24.

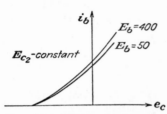
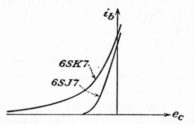

Fig. 2-23. The transfer curves of a pentode for fixed screen potential and with the plate potential as a parameter.

Fig. 2-24. The transfer curves of a 6SJ7 sharp-cutoff pentode and a 6SK7 remote-cutoff pentode.

Owing to its construction, a given grid-potential increment results in a plate-current change that is a function of the bias. This means that the mutual conductance is a function of the bias. For this reason, these tubes are called *variable-mu* tubes. They are also known as *remote-cutoff* and *supercontrol* tubes. They have applications in radio receivers and may be used in frequency-modulation (f-m) transmitters. Some applications will be considered in later chapters.

2-19. Hexodes, Heptodes. A number of special-purpose tubes containing more grid elements than the pentode are used extensively. These tubes possess a wide variety of characteristics, depending upon the grids to which fixed potentials are applied and those to which signals might be applied. These tubes are used extensively as converters in superheterodyne receivers and find f-m transmitter and other applications. More will be said about these applications at a later point in the text.

2-20. Beam Power Tubes. The suppressor grid is introduced into the pentode in order to extend the range of operation of these tubes beyond that of the tetrode. These tubes are quite satisfactory over wide limits, and the range of operation is limited when the instantaneous plate potential falls to the rapidly falling plate-current region at low potentials. This rapid change in plate current for small changes in plate potential in the region of low plate voltage results from the overeffectiveness of the suppressor grid at these low plate potentials.

Because of this, the shape of the suppressor grid in some modern pentodes has been so dimensioned that the effects of secondary emission are just suppressed or only admitted slightly at the low anode potentials. This results in an improved plate characteristic and is manifested by a sharper break in the plate characteristic.

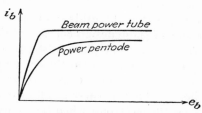

Fig. 2-25. The plate characteristics of a beam power tube and a power pentode.

The pentode and tetrode beam power tubes were designed with these considerations specifically in mind, and a plate characteristic is illustrated in Fig. 2-25. It will be noted that the plate current remains inde-

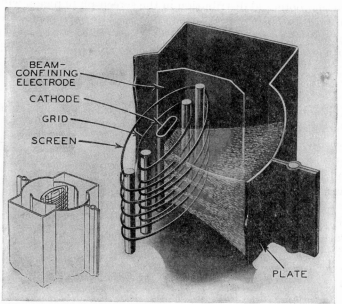

Fig. 2-26. Schematic view of the shapes and arrangements of the electrodes in a beam power tube. (*RCA Mfg. Co.*)

pendent of plate potential to a lower relative value in the beam power tube than in the power pentode. The essential features of the beam power tube are illustrated in the schematic view of Fig. 2-26. One feature of the design of this tube is that each spiral turn of the screen is aligned with a spiral turn of the control grid. This serves to keep the screen current small and hence leaves the plate current virtually unchanged. Other features are the flattened cathode, the beam-forming side plates (maintained at zero potential), the shape of the plate, the curvature of the grids, and the spacing of the various elements. As a result of these design characteristics, the electrons flow between the grid wires toward the plate in sheets, or beams.

The region between the screen and the plate possesses features which are somewhat analogous to those which exist in the space-charge-limited diode. That is, there is a flow of charge between two electrodes. However, the electrons, when they enter this region do so with an appreciable velocity. For such a case as this, the considerations of Sec. 2-9 would have to be modified to take account of the initial velocity. If this is done, it is found that a potential minimum will exist in the region between the two electrodes. This potential minimum acts as a virtual suppressor grid, and any secondary electrons that are emitted from either the plate or the screen are returned to the emitting electrode.

The actual potential distribution in the screen-plate region will depend on the instantaneous plate potential and the plate current, for a constant screen potential. The resulting variable suppressor action proves to be superior to that possible with a mechanical grid structure, as illustrated.

GAS TUBES

2-21. Electrical Discharge in Gases. There are two important classes of discharge in gases that play roles in electron tubes. One of these is the *glow* discharge, and the second is the *arc* discharge. The glow discharge utilizes a cold cathode and is characterized by a fairly high tube drop and a low current-carrying capacity. The potential drop across the tube over the operating range is fairly constant and independent of the current. The arc discharge is characterized by a low potential drop and a high current capacity. For an arc tube with a thermionic cathode, the temperature-limited cathode emission may be drawn with a tube drop approximately equal to the ionization potential of the gas. For a mercury-pool cathode, extremely high current densities exist (of the order of 5×10^8 amp/m^2), with high total currents possible and a tube drop approximately equal to the ionization potential of the mercury atom.

Consider a gas tube which consists of a cold cathode and a collecting anode, between which is connected a source of potential through a current-limiting resistance, and an indicating ammeter. The volt-ampere characteristic of such a tube has the form illustrated in Fig. 2-27. This curve shows that breakdown occurs at a potential which is somewhat higher than the maintaining potential but that there is a region where the tube drop remains substantially constant over an appreciable range of currents.   Visually, the discharge is characterized by a colored luminous region, the color being a function of the gas present in the tube.

It is desired to explain the mechanism of operation of these tubes. Consider, therefore, that a free electron exists within the tube; such an electron might have been released by ionization due to collision between a gas molecule and a cosmic ray or by photoelectric emission.   With the application of the potential between the electrodes, the electron will drift toward the anode.   If the field is large enough, the electron may acquire enough energy to ionize a molecule when it collides with it.   Now two electrons will be present, the original one and also the electron that has been liberated by the process of ionization, and a positive ion.   The two electrons and the positive ion will move in the applied field, the electrons moving toward the anode, and the positive ion toward the cathode.   If the field is large enough, the resulting cumulative ionization may continue until *breakdown* occurs.   Once breakdown occurs, the potential distribution within the tube is markedly modified, and most of the region of the discharge becomes virtually equipotential or force-free, containing as many positive as negative charges.   This is the plasma of the discharge.   Almost the entire potential change occurs in the very narrow region near the cathode.   Normal values for cathode-fall potential range between

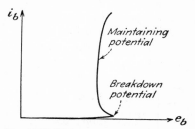

Fig. 2-27. Volt-ampere characteristic of a glow discharge.

about 59 volts (a potassium surface and helium gas) and 350 volts.   The presence of a low-work-function coating on the cathode will result in a low cathode fall with any gas.   Also, the use of one of the inert gases (helium, neon, argon, etc.) results in a low cathode fall with any cathode material.   The cathode fall adjusts itself to such a value that each positive ion, when it falls through this field, will release an electron from the cathode by secondary emission.   The positive ion combines with this electron and thus becomes neutralized.

Another feature of a normal glow discharge is that the current density at the cathode remains sensibly constant.   For higher currents, a greater portion of the cathode is covered with glow, the area of the glow on the cathode increasing directly with the magnitude of the current.   Once the cathode is completely covered with glow, any further current through the tube depends on an excess of secondary emission from the cathode over that required to neutralize the positive ions.   This is accompanied by a rising cathode fall.   This is the "abnormal" glow and is generally of small practical importance.

The dividing line between an arc and a glow discharge is rather indistinct. The arc discharge allows for the passage of large currents at low potential, the current density at the cathode being high. Nevertheless each discharge has associated with it the cathode fall, the plasma, and the anode fall (which is of minor significance in both types of discharge). The discharges differ in respect to the mechanism by which the electrons are supplied from the cathode. In the glow discharge, as discussed, the electrons are emitted from the cathode by the process of secondary emission resulting from positive-ion bombardment of the cathode. In the arc discharge, the emission of the electrons from the cathode occurs through the operation of a supplementary mechanism other than by positive-ion bombardment. In the thermionic arc, the electrons are supplied by a cathode that is heated to a high temperature, either by the discharge or externally by means of an auxiliary heating circuit. The mechanism for electron release is not fully understood in the arcs that employ a mercury-pool cathode or an arc between metal surfaces. However, in these discharges the primary function of the gas is to supply a sufficient positive-ion density to neutralize the electron space charge. Because of this, the normal potential drop across an arc tube will be of the order of the ionization potential of the gas.

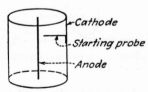

FIG. 2-28. Electrode structure in a VR tube.

2-22. Glow Tube. A glow tube is a cold-cathode gas-discharge tube which operates in the normal glow-discharge region. The potential drop across the tube over the operating range is fairly constant and independent of the current. When the tube is connected in a circuit, a current-limiting resistance must be used if serious damage to the tube is to be avoided.

One commercial type of tube consists of a central anode wire which is coaxial with a cylindrical cathode, as illustrated in Fig. 2-28. The electrodes are of nickel, the inner surface of the cathode being oxide-coated. The cathode fall is sometimes lowered by sputtering some misch metal (an alloy of cerium, lanthanum, and didymium) on the cathode. The gases that are commonly used are neon, argon, and helium. The tubes containing neon or helium usually contain a small amount of argon. The presence of the argon lowers the starting potential. These tubes are available with normal output potentials of 75, 90, 105, and 150 volts and bear the designations OA3/VR-75, OB3/VR-90, etc. The normal maximum current is 30 ma. The starting probe that is attached to the cathode, as illustrated in Fig. 2-28, serves to lower the breakdown potential of the tube.

Glow lamps are also available for pilot, marker, and test-lamp service.

Such tubes are available in several sizes from $\frac{1}{25}$ to 3 watts capacity. Photographs of a number of these are given in Fig. 2-29.

2-23. Cold-cathode Triodes.   A cold-cathode triode, or *grid-glow tube*, contains three elements, the cathode, the anode, and a starter, or control, anode.   The control electrode is placed close to the cathode.   The spac-

Fig. 2-29. Photographs of several low-capacity glow tubes.   (*General Electric Co.*)

ing of the electrodes is such that a discharge takes place from the cathode to the control electrode at a lower potential than is required for a discharge from the cathode to the anode.   Once the control gap has been broken down, however, it is possible for the discharge to transfer to the main anode.   The cathode-anode potential that is required for this trans-fer to occur is a function of the transfer current, the current in the control-electrode-cathode circuit.   Such a "trans-fer," or "transition," characteristic is given in Fig. 2-30.

For zero transfer current, which means that the control electrode is not connected in the circuit, the anode potential is equal to the breakdown potential between cathode and anode. It is observed from the curve that the required anode-cathode potential falls rapidly as the transfer current is

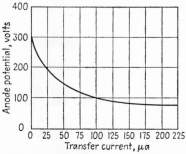

Fig. 2-30. Transfer characteristic of an RCA OA4G cold-cathode triode.

increased.   An increased transfer current indicates the presence of greater ionization.   Regardless of the magnitude of the transfer current, however, the anode-cathode potential can never fall below the maintaining potential for this gap.   The transfer characteristic approaches this sustaining potential asymptotically.

2-24. Hot-cathode Gas-filled Diodes.   These tubes are thermionic cathode diodes in which there is an inert gas at low pressure or in which

mercury vapor is added.   In the latter case a few drops of mercury are
added to the tube after evacuation.   The pressure in the tube is then a
function of the mercury-vapor con-
densation temperature.   The relationship between the pressure and
the temperature is shown in Fig.
2-31.   Under   normal   operating
conditions, the temperature of the
tube will be 15 to 20°C above
that of the surroundings (ambient
temperature).

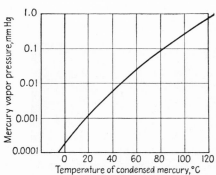

Fig. 2-31.   Mercury-vapor pressure as a
function of condensation temperature.

As already discussed, the sole
function of the gas in these tubes is
to provide ions for the neutralization
of space charge, thus permitting the
current to be obtained at much lower
potentials   than   are   necessary   in
vacuum tubes.   If more than saturation current is demanded by the
circuit, then gas amplification, resulting from positive-ion bombardment

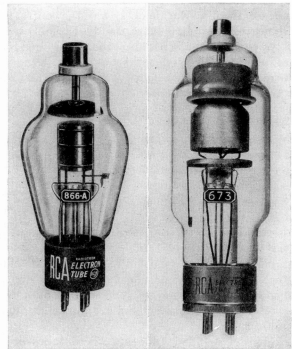

Fig. 2-32. Commercial mercury-vapor diodes of different capacity.   (*RCA Mfg. Co.*)

of the cathode, will occur.   Under these circumstances the cathode fall increases.   The tube drop should not be permitted to exceed the disintegration potential of the cathode (about 22 volts for a mercury diode with either oxide-coated or thoriated-tungsten cathodes); otherwise the cathode may be seriously damaged by the positive-ion bombardment.

Two typical commercial mercury-vapor-filled diodes are illustrated in Fig. 2-32.

2-25. High-pressure Gas Diodes.   Diodes are available which contain argon or a mixture of argon and mercury at a pressure of about 5 cm. The cathodes in such tubes consist of a short, heavy thoriated-tungsten or oxide-coated filament and are located close to heavy graphite anodes. These tubes, which are known as *tungar* or *rectigon* tubes, are used extensively in chargers for storage batteries.

The presence of the fairly high-pressure gas serves a twofold purpose. One is to provide the positive ions for reducing the space charge.   The second is to prevent the evaporation of the thorium or the coating from the filament.   This second factor is extremely important since the filament is operated at higher than normal temperature in order to provide the large currents from such a simple cathode structure.   The high-pressure gas in such a tube imposes a limitation on these tubes, and they are limited to low-potential operation.

2-26. The Thyratron.   The thyratron is a three-electrode tube which comprises the cathode, the anode, and a massive grid structure between them. The grid structure is so designed as to provide almost complete electrostatic shielding between the cathode and the anode.   In such a tube as this, the initiation of the arc is controlled by controlling the potential of the grid.   The grid usually consists of a cylindrical structure which surrounds both the anode and the cathode, a baffle or a series of baffles containing small holes being inserted between the anode and the cathode.   The electrode structure of such a tube is illustrated in Fig. 2-33.   The shielding by the grid is so complete that the application of a

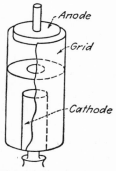

Fig. 2-33. The electrode structure of a negative-control thyratron.

small grid potential before conduction is started is adequate to overcome the field at the cathode resulting from the application of a large anode potential.

Once the arc has been initiated, the grid loses complete control over the arc.   Grid control is reestablished only when the anode potential is reduced to a value less than that necessary to maintain the arc.   Once the arc has been extinguished by lowering the plate potential, the grid once more becomes the controlling factor which determines when conduction will again be initiated. That is, if the grid potential is more positive than that necessary for the controlling action to prevail, conduction will take place; if more negative, no conduction will occur. The curve that relates the grid ignition potential with the potential of the anode for conduction just to begin is known as the *critical grid curve*. In fact, a knowledge of this static curve is all that is required to determine completely the behavior of a thyratron in a circuit.

Typical starting-characteristic curves of mercury-vapor thyratrons are given in Fig. 2-34. Two distinct types of characteristics are illustrated, viz., those in which the grid potential must always be positive, and those

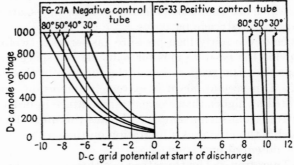

FIG. 2-34. Critical grid characteristics of a positive- and a negative-control thyratron for different temperatures.

in which the grid is generally negative, except for very low plate potentials. The physical distinction between these positive- and negative-control tubes lies essentially in the more complete shielding by the grid in positive control tubes.

In the negative-control tube, where the shielding is far less complete than in the positive-control type, the effect of the plate potential is clearly seen; the higher the plate potential, the more negative must the grid potential be in order to prevent conduction from taking place. For low plate potentials, positive grid potentials must be applied before ionization, and hence conduction, can begin. If the plate potential is reduced still more, even below the potential necessary for ionization, breakdown can still be obtained by making the grid sufficiently positive. Now, however, the function of the tube may be destroyed, since the arc may take place between the cathode and the grid, with very little current to the plate. The thyratron will be converted into a gas diode under these conditions, the plate acting as a dummy electrode, the cylindrical grid now serving as the anode. It is because of this that a high current-limiting resistance is connected in the grid circuit, as it is unwise to draw a large grid current.

In addition to the mercury-vapor- and gas-filled thyratrons of moderate current capacity, small argon-filled low-current-capacity tubes are available. The shielding between the cathode and the anode is not so complete in these tubes as in the higher-current units. Also, the critical grid curve is independent of temperature, since the number of gas molecules in the glass envelope remains constant. A typical critical grid curve for an 884 is given in Fig. 2-35.

2-27. Shield-grid Thyratrons. Before breakdown of the tube occurs, the current to the grid of a thyratron such as the FG-27A is a few tenths of a microampere. Although this current is entirely negligible for many applications, it will cause trouble in circuits that require very high grid impedances. This is especially true in circuits that employ phototubes. For

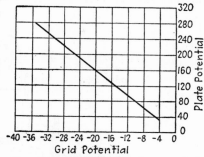

Fig. 2-35. Critical grid characteristic of an 884 argon-filled thyratron.

this reason, a fourth electrode, or shield grid, has been added to the thyratron. Such a shield-grid thyratron structure is illustrated in Fig. 2-36. The massive cylindrical shield-grid structure encloses the cathode, control grid, and anode. Owing to the shielding, the grid current is reduced to a small fraction of its original value, the preignition current being of the order of 10^{-3} μa.

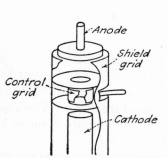

Fig. 2-36. Electrode structure of the FG-98 shield-grid thyratron.

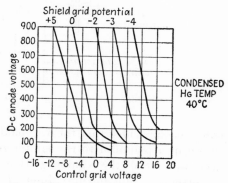

Fig. 2-37. Control characteristics of an FG-98 shield-grid thyratron.

The critical grid starting characteristics of such a tube are shown in Fig. 2-37. It will be observed that these characteristics are functions of the shield-grid potential.

2-28. The Ignitron. The ignitron is a mercury-pool-cathode diode which is provided with a third electrode for initiating the discharge between the cathode and anode. The third electrode, or igniter rod, is made of a suitable refractory material (such as silicon carbide, boron carbide, and carborundum) which projects into the mercury-pool cathode. Such a tube is illustrated in Fig. 2-38.

With an a-c potential applied between the cathode and the anode of the pool-cathode diode, the arc would be extinguished once each alternate

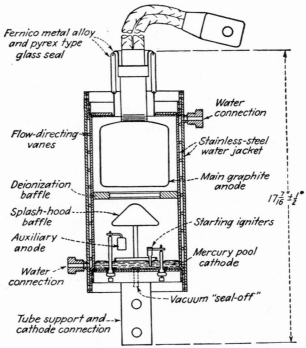

Fernico metal alloy
and pyrex type
glass seal

Water connection

Flow-directing vanes

Stainless-steel water jacket

Deionization baffle

Main graphite anode

Splash-hood baffle

Starting igniters

Auxiliary anode

Water connection

Mercury pool cathode

Vacuum "seal-off"

Tube support and cathode connection

$17\frac{7}{16}" \pm \frac{1}{2}"$

Fig. 2-38. Section view of a water-cooled metal ignitron. (*General Electric Co.*)

half cycle, provided that the arc could be initiated regularly. The application of a potential to the igniter rod at the appropriate point in the cycle will permit the regular ignition of the arc.

There is a fundamental difference between the control action in a thyratron and that of the igniter rod in an ignitron. In thyratrons, the grid prevents the formation of an arc, whereas the igniter initiates the arc. In the former case the electrons already exist in the tube, owing to the presence of an externally heated cathode, but the grid electrostatically prevents the electrons from flowing to the anode until a critical potential is reached. In the ignitron, the tube is in a nonconducting state until the igniter circuit is energized, when conduction is forced.

2-29. Tube Ratings—Current, Voltage, Temperature. Gas- and vapor-filled tubes are given average rather than rms current ratings. This rating specifies the maximum current that the tube may carry continuously without excessive heating of any of the parts. The time over which the average is to be taken is also specified by the manufacturer. That the average current is important in such a tube follows from the fact that the instantaneous power to the plate of the tube is given by the product of the instantaneous anode current and the instantaneous tube potential. Since the potential is substantially constant and independent of the tube current, the average power is the product of the tube drop and the average tube current. The tubes are also given peak-current

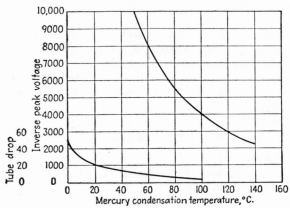

Fig. 2-39. Peak inverse potential and tube drop of an 866 diode as a function of temperature.

ratings, these ratings specifying the maximum current that the tubes should be permitted to reach in each conducting cycle.

Such tubes are also given peak-inverse-potential ratings. This is the largest safe instantaneous negative potential that may be applied to the tube without the possibility of conduction in the inverse direction arising because of breakdown of the gas in the tube. This potential is also referred to as the *flash-back* potential. The variation of the inverse peak potential with temperature for an 866 diode is shown in Fig. 2-39.

The maximum peak forward potential is a quantity that is significant only for thyratrons. It specifies the largest positive potential that may be applied to the anode before the grid loses its arc-initiating ability. That is, for potentials higher than this, a glow discharge may occur between anode and grid, which will immediately initiate the cathode-anode arc.

The condensed-mercury temperature limits are specified for the safe and efficient operation of mercury-vapor tubes. The range usually extends from about 30 to 80°C. The upper temperature limit is determined by the allowable peak inverse potential. The lower limit is set by the allowable tube drop, which increases with decreasing temperature and which may cause serious cathode disintegration, as well as a decreased efficiency.

2-30. Deionization and Ionization Times. The ionization time of a tube specifies the time required for conduction to be established once the potentials have been applied. It seldom exceeds 10 μsec and is approximately 0.01 μsec for the 884 thyratron.

The deionization time is a measure of the minimum time that is required after removal of the anode potential before the grid of a thyratron again regains control. It represents the time that is required for the positive ions to diffuse away from the grid and recombine with electrons to form neutral molecules. The deionization time depends on many factors, such as gas pressure, electrode spacing, and exposed areas. For commercial tubes that are operated under rated conditions, it varies between 100 and 1,000 μsec. This is considerably longer than the ionization time and may offer a serious limitation to the use of such tubes in many applications.

REFERENCE

1. For more details, see:
   Millman, J., and S. Seely, "Electronics," 2d ed., McGraw-Hill Book Company, Inc., New York, 1951.

PROBLEMS

2-1. A tungsten filament, 0.0085 in. diameter, $3^{11}\!/_{16}$ in. long, is operated at 2650°K. What is the temperature-limited current? If the temperature is increased by 50°K, by what percentage does the emission current increase?

2-2. The filament of an FP-400 tungsten-filament tube is 1.25 in. long and 0.005 in. in diameter. If the total emission current is 30 ma, at what temperature is the filament operating?

2-3. A simple inverted-V oxide-coated cathode is made of tungsten ribbon 0.125 by 0.020 in. and is 1.4 in. long. It is maintained at a temperature of 1100°K. What is the thermionic-emission current?

2-4. An oxide-coated emitter is operating at 1100°K. Calculate the relative thermionic-emission current if b_0 has the value 12,000; the value 11,000.

2-5. At what temperature will a thoriated-tungsten filament give as much current as a tungsten filament of the same dimensions which is maintained at 2650°K?

2-6. At what temperature will an oxide-coated cathode give the same emission as a thoriated-tungsten filament of the same physical dimensions which is maintained at 1750°K?

2-7. Monochromatic light of wavelength 5893 A falls on the following surfaces:
a. Cesium, with a work function 1.8 volts.

b. Platinum, with a work function 5.3 volts.

Is photoelectric emission possible in both cases? Explain.

2-8. A PJ-22 vacuum photocell is to be used to sound an alarm when the light at a given region of a room falls below 40 ft-c or increases above 120 ft-c. What are the corresponding photocurrents? A collecting potential of 45 volts is used.

2-9. Plot i_b vs. e_b of the 6H6 diode (see Appendix B) on log paper. From this plot, determine the quantities k and n in the expression $i_b = ke_b^n$.

2-10. The anode current in a type 5U4G diode with 54 volts applied between the plate and cathode is 200 ma. What is the required potential for a current of 100 ma? The tube operates under space-charge conditions.

2-11. Suppose that the FP-400 tube is operating under rated filament power input (see Prob. 2-2). The operating temperature is 2700°K, and the anode diameter is 0.50 in.

a. Calculate the saturation current.

b. At what potential will the current become temperature-saturated?

2-12. Plot i_b vs. $e_b + \mu e_c$ on log paper of the 6J5 triode (see Appendix B). From this curve, find the quantities k and n in the expression $i_b = k(e_b + \mu e_c)^n$.

2-13. The 6J5 triode is operated with $E_b = 135$ volts. Determine and plot curves of μ, g_m, and r_p as a function of e_c.

2-14. The rating of a certain triode is given by the expression

$$i_b = 130 \times 10^{-6}(e_c + 0.125e_b)^{1.58}$$

With $E_c = -20$ volts, $E_b = 350$ volts, find I_b, r_p, g_m, μ.

2-15. The plate and grid characteristics of a type 851 power triode are given in Appendix B. Plot $i_s = i_b + i_c$ vs. $e_b + \mu e_c$ on log paper, and find the quantities k and n in the expression $i_s = k(e_b + \mu e_c)^n$.

2-16. The current in a 6J5 triode for which $\mu = 20$ and which is operating with $E_c = -8$ volts, $E_b = 250$ volts is 8.7 ma. Estimate the current when $E_b = 200$ volts and $E_c = -6$ volts.

2-17. A 6J5 triode for which $\mu = 20$ is operating with $E_b = 250$ volts. What grid potential is required to reduce the current to zero?

2-18. Evaluate the value of μ, g_m, and r_p of the 6SJ7 pentode for $E_c = -3$ volts, $E_{cc2} = 100$ volts, $E_b = 150$ volts.

2-19. Evaluate the values of μ, g_m, r_p, of the 6SK7 supercontrol pentode for $E_{cc2} = 100$ volts, $E_b = 250$ volts, with $E_c = -1$ volts; with $E_c = -10$ volts.

2-20. Plot a curve of g_m vs. E_{c1} of a 6SK7 with $E_{cc2} = 100$ volts, $E_b = 250$ volts.

2-21. Use the plate characteristics of the 6SJ7 and the 6SK7 pentodes to construct mutual characteristics on the same sheet, with $E_b = 200$ volts for each tube. Determine the maximum and minimum values of g_m for each tube in the range of your sketch.

2-22. Plot a curve of g_m vs. E_{c3} of a 6L7 with $E_{cc1} = -6$ volts, $E_{cc2} = 150$ volts.

2-23. Refer to Sec. 2-15 for a discussion of secondary emission caused by electron impact. What happens to the secondary electrons that are produced by the impact of the primary current on the anode in a diode? In a triode?

2-24. The mercury-condensation temperature in a General Electric type FG-57A thyratron is 40°C. If the volume of the tube is 300 cm³, calculate the mass of the mercury vapor in the tube.

2-25. *a.* An OA4G cold-cathode triode is used in the circuit shown, with $E_{bb1} = 80$ volts, $E_{bb2} = 120$ volts. Determine the largest value of R for which the current will transfer to the main anode, for no input pulse.

b. Determine the value of the load resistance to limit the load current to the rated maximum of 25 ma.

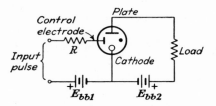

2-26. A VR-105 regulator tube is incorporated in the circuit shown to maintain a constant output potential. The supply potential remains constant at 250 volts, but the load fluctuates between 40 and 60 ma. Find the value of R so that the load potential is steady at 105 volts. Assume that the normal operating range of the tube is 5 to 40 ma.

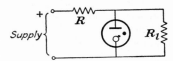

2-27. Suppose that the plate supply potential to a circuit containing a thyratron is sinusoidal. If the rms value of the potential is 220 volts, draw a sketch showing the supply potential and the corresponding critical grid curve for (*a*) a negative-control tube; (*b*) a positive-control tube.

CHAPTER 3

RECTIFIERS AND FILTERS

RECTIFIERS

3-1. Volt-ampere Relation; Plate Resistance. Some of the important basic characteristics of the vacuum diode were discussed in Secs. 2-8 to 2-10. As noted, space charge limits the flow of current in a vacuum diode, at least to the point where temperature saturation occurs. Ordinarily, however, the vacuum diode is operated under space-charge conditions, and the volt-ampere curve over the range of operation follows an approximate three-halves-power law. That is, over the range of operation when the plate is positive with respect to the cathode, the three-halves-power law specifies the approximate relation between the plate current and the plate potential. Of course, when the plate is negative with respect to the cathode, electrons are repelled by the plate and no plate current exists. Clearly, the relation between the potential across the tube and the current through it is nonlinear, whence the vacuum diode is fundamentally a nonlinear element.

The volt-ampere curve is a static curve and gives the relationship between the instantaneous potential across the device and the instantaneous current through it. The slope at any point of the curve is an important quantity, although the reciprocal of the slope, which is known as the plate resistance, is generally preferred. By definition, the plate resistance is given by the relationship

$$r_p = \frac{\partial e_b}{\partial i_b} \tag{3-1}$$

Note that the plate resistance is not a constant and is, in fact, different for every point on the curve. The plate resistance is infinite in the backward direction when the plate potential is negative with respect to the cathode; it possesses the varying value r_p in the forward direction. In practice r_p has meaning only for alternating or varying currents.

The gas diode has been discussed in Secs. 2-24 and 2-25. The influence of the gas is there shown to cause the volt-ampere characteristic of the gas diode to be materially different from that of the vacuum diode. The gas diode also possesses an effective infinite resistance in the backward direction.   In the forward direction there is a substantially constant potential drop across the tube, independent of the tube current.

Both the vacuum diode and the gas diode, by virtue of their nonlinear volt-ampere characteristics, possess the ability to convert an a-c current into a current which contains a d-c component in addition to a-c components.   In fact, any electrical device which has a high resistance to current in one direction and a low resistance to current in the opposite direction will effect rectification.   An ideal rectifier would be one with zero resistance in the forward direction and an infinite resistance in the backward direction.   No known device meets the conditions of the ideal rectifying element.   A number of devices do possess nonlinear characteristics, and many have been adapted as rectifying elements.   The important ones in widespread use are the high-vacuum thermionic diodes, gas-filled and vapor-filled thermionic diodes, pool-cathode mercury arcs, certain crystals which have been incorporated into diodes, and a number of metallic semiconducting contact rectifiers.

The discussion in this chapter will be limited to circuits which employ the vacuum diode and the gas diode as rectifiers.   Attention is called to the fact that the resulting operation in a circuit of these elements is slightly different, owing to the different volt-ampere characteristics.

3-2. Single-phase Half-wave Vacuum Rectifier.   The basic circuit for half-wave rectification is shown in Fig. 3-1.   It is assumed that the

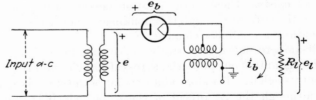

Fig. 3-1. A simple half-wave rectifier circuit.

load is a pure resistance.   Also, it is supposed that the power transformer is ideal, with negligible resistance and leakage reactance.

An application of Kirchhoff's potential law to the load circuit yields

$$e = e_b + i_b R_l \qquad (3\text{-}2)$$

where e is the instantaneous value of the applied potential, e_b is the instantaneous potential across the diode when the instantaneous current is i_b and R_l is the load resistance.   This one equation is not sufficient for the determination of the two unknown quantities i_b and e_b that appear in the expression.   Here, as for triodes and multielectrode tubes, a second relation is contained in the static plate characteristic of the tube.   Consequently a solution is effected by drawing the load line on the plate characteristic.

There is one significant difference between the solution of the diode as a rectifier and that for the other tubes as amplifiers. With the rectifier, an a-c source supplies the power to the circuit. A vacuum tube as an amplifier converts direct current from the plate supply into alternating current.

The dynamic characteristic of the rectifier circuit is obtained in a somewhat different manner from the corresponding curve for an amplifier. The procedure is illustrated in Fig. 3-2. For an applied potential e, the current is the intersection of the load line with the static characteristic, say point A. That is, for the particular circuit, the application of the potential e results in a current i_A. This is one point on the dynamic curve and is drawn vertically above e in the diagram. The slope of the load

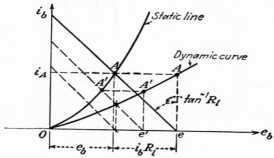

Fig. 3-2. The static and dynamic characteristics of a rectifier.

line does not vary, although the intersection with the e_b axis varies with e. Thus, when the applied potential has the value e', the corresponding current is $i_{A'}$. The resulting curve so generated is the dynamic characteristic.

If the static characteristic of the tube were linear, the dynamic characteristic would also be linear. Note from the construction, however, that there is considerably less curvature in the dynamic curve than there is in the static characteristic. It will be assumed in what follows that the dynamic curve is linear.

To find the waveshape of the current in the output circuit, the procedure followed is that illustrated in Fig. 3-3. This procedure is very much like that used to find the waveshape in a general amplifier circuit; in fact, the situation here is quite like that of a class B amplifier (see Sec. 8-6), except that cutoff of the tube exists at zero input.

If it is assumed that the relation

$$e_b = i_b r_p \tag{3-3}$$

is valid during conduction, and this supposes that the static characteristic is linear, then from Eq. (3-2) it follows that

$$e = e_b + i_b R_l = i_b(r_p + R_l) = E_m \sin \omega t \tag{3-4}$$

or

$$i_b = \frac{E_m}{R_l + r_p} \sin \omega t = I_m \sin \omega t \qquad \text{when } 0 \leq \omega t \leq \pi$$

$$i_b = 0 \qquad \text{when } \pi \leq \omega t \leq 2\pi \qquad (3\text{-}5)$$

where

$$I_m = \frac{E_m}{R_l + r_p}$$

The d-c power supplied to the load is defined as the product of the reading of a d-c ammeter in the load circuit and a d-c voltmeter across the

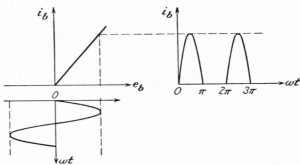

Fig. 3-3. The method of obtaining the output-current waveform from the dynamic characteristic.

load. Thus

$$P_{\text{d-c}} \equiv E_{\text{d-c}} I_{\text{d-c}} \qquad (3\text{-}6)$$

Clearly, the reading of the d-c ammeter is represented by

$$I_{\text{d-c}} = \frac{1}{2\pi} \int_0^{2\pi} i_b \, d\alpha = \frac{1}{2\pi} \int_0^\pi I_m \sin \alpha \, d\alpha = \frac{I_m}{\pi} \qquad (3\text{-}7)$$

and so

$$P_{\text{d-c}} = I_{\text{d-c}}^2 R_l = \left(\frac{1}{\pi}\right)^2 \frac{E_m^2 R_l}{(r_p + R_l)^2} \qquad (3\text{-}8)$$

The power supplied to the circuit from the a-c source, and this is the power that would be read by a wattmeter with its current coil in the line and with the potential coil across the source, is given by the integral

$$P_i = \frac{1}{2\pi} \int_0^{2\pi} e i_b \, d\alpha \qquad (3\text{-}9)$$

This becomes, by Eqs. (3-3) and (3-4),

$$P_i = \frac{1}{2\pi} \int_0^{2\pi} i_b^2 (r_p + R_l) \, d\alpha \qquad (3\text{-}10)$$

which may be written in the form

$$P_i = I_{\text{rms}}^2 (r_p + R_l) \qquad (3\text{-}11)$$

where the rms current has the value

$$I_{rms} = \sqrt{\frac{1}{2\pi} \int_0^{2\pi} i_b^2 \, d\alpha} = \sqrt{\frac{1}{2\pi} \int_0^{\pi} I_m^2 \sin^2 \alpha \, d\alpha} = \frac{I_m}{2} \qquad (3\text{-}12)$$

The efficiency of rectification is defined by the relation

$$\eta_r = \frac{P_{d\text{-}c}}{P_i} \times 100\% = \frac{I_{d\text{-}c}^2 R_l}{I_{rms}^2 (r_p + R_l)} \times 100\%$$

which becomes

$$\eta_r = \left(\frac{I_{d\text{-}c}}{I_{rms}}\right)^2 \frac{100}{1 + r_p/R_l} \qquad (3\text{-}13)$$

By combining this with Eqs. (12-6) and (12-11), there results

$$\eta_r = \left(\frac{I_m/\pi}{I_m/2}\right)^2 \frac{100}{1 + r_p/R_l} = \frac{40.6}{1 + r_p/R_l} \qquad \% \qquad (3\text{-}14)$$

This indicates that the theoretical maximum efficiency of the single-phase half-wave rectifier is 40.6 per cent.   But it may be shown that maximum power output occurs when $R_l = r_p$, with a corresponding theoretical plate-circuit efficiency of 20.3 per cent.

There are several features of such a rectifier circuit that warrant special attention.   Refer to Fig. 3-1, which shows the complete wiring diagram of the rectifier.   On the inverse cycle, i.e., on that part of the cycle during which the tube is not conducting, the maximum potential across the rectifier tube is equal to the transformer maximum value.   That is, the peak inverse potential across the tube is equal to the transformer maximum value.

Note also from the diagram that with the negative terminal of the output connected to ground the full transformer potential exists between the primary and the secondary windings of the filament heating transformer. This requires that the transformer insulation must be adequate to withstand this potential without rupture.   Evidently if the positive terminal is grounded, then the transformer need not have a high insulation strength.

3-3. Ripple Factor.   Although it is the object of a rectifier to convert a-c into d-c current, the simple circuit considered does not achieve this. Nor, in fact, do any of the more complicated rectifier circuits, either single-phase or polyphase, accomplish this exactly.   What is achieved is a unidirectional current, periodically fluctuating components still remaining in the output.   Filters are ordinarily used in rectifier systems in order to help decrease these fluctuating components, and these will receive detailed consideration below.   A measure of the fluctuating components is given by the ripple factor r, which is defined as

$$r = \frac{\text{rms value of a-c components of wave}}{\text{avg or d-c value of wave}}$$

and which may be written as

$$r = \frac{I'_{\text{rms}}}{I_{\text{d-c}}} = \frac{E'_{\text{rms}}}{E_{\text{d-c}}} \qquad (3\text{-}15)$$

where I'_{rms} and E'_{rms} denote the rms values of the a-c components only.

An analytical expression for the ripple factor is readily possible. It is noted that the instantaneous a-c component of the current is given by

$$i' = i - I_{\text{d-c}}$$

But by definition

$$I'_{\text{rms}} = \sqrt{\frac{1}{2\pi}\int_0^{2\pi}(i - I_{\text{d-c}})^2\,d\alpha} = \sqrt{\frac{1}{2\pi}\int_0^{2\pi}(i^2 - 2iI_{\text{d-c}} + I_{\text{d-c}}^2)\,d\alpha}$$

This expression is readily interpreted. The first term of the integrand when evaluated yields the square of the rms value of the total wave I_{rms}^2. The second term yields

$$\frac{1}{2\pi}\int_0^{2\pi}2iI_{\text{d-c}}\,d\alpha = 2I_{\text{d-c}}^2$$

The rms ripple current then becomes

$$I'_{\text{rms}} = \sqrt{I_{\text{rms}}^2 - 2I_{\text{d-c}}^2 + I_{\text{d-c}}^2} = \sqrt{I_{\text{rms}}^2 - I_{\text{d-c}}^2}$$

By combining these results with Eq. (3-15)

$$r = \frac{\sqrt{I_{\text{rms}}^2 - I_{\text{d-c}}^2}}{I_{\text{d-c}}} = \sqrt{\left(\frac{I_{\text{rms}}}{I_{\text{d-c}}}\right)^2 - 1} \qquad (3\text{-}16)$$

This expression is independent of the current waveshape and applies in general, since the development was not confined to a particular waveshape. In the case of the half-wave single-phase rectifier the ratio

$$\frac{I_{\text{rms}}}{I_{\text{d-c}}} = \frac{I_m/2}{I_m/\pi} = \frac{\pi}{2} = 1.57$$

and hence

$$r = \sqrt{1.57^2 - 1} = 1.21 \qquad (3\text{-}17)$$

This shows that the rms value of the ripple potential exceeds the d-c potential of the output. This merely tends to show that a single-phase half-wave rectifier without filter is a relatively poor device for converting a-c into d-c potential.

3-4. Single-phase Full-wave Rectifier. The circuit of the single-phase full-wave rectifier, given in Fig. 3-4, bears some resemblance to a push-pull circuit. Actually the circuit comprises two half-wave circuits which are so connected that conduction takes place through one tube during one half of the total power cycle and through the other tube during the second half of the power cycle. The output current

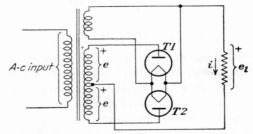

Fig. 3-4. Schematic wiring diagram of a single-phase full-wave rectifier.

through the load has the form illustrated in Fig. 3-5, where the portions of the wave marked 1 flow through tube $T1$ and the portions of the wave marked 2 flow through tube $T2$.

The d-c and rms values of the load current are found from Eqs. (3-7) and (3-12) to be

$$I_{d\text{-}c} = \frac{2I_m}{\pi}$$
$$I_{rms} = \frac{I_m}{\sqrt{2}}$$

$$(3\text{-}18)$$

where I_m is the peak value of the current wave. The d-c output power is then

$$P_{d\text{-}c} = I_{d\text{-}c}^2 R_l = \left(\frac{2}{\pi}\right)^2 \frac{E_m^2 R_l}{(r_p + R_l)^2}$$

$$(3\text{-}19)$$

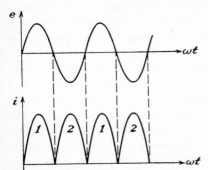

Fig. 3-5. The transformer potential and output load current in a single-phase full-wave rectifier.

By comparing this expression with Eq. (3-8) it is seen that the power delivered to the load is higher by a factor of 4 in the full-wave case. However, the power depends on the circuit parameters in the same way as for the half-wave circuit.

The input power from the a-c source is readily found to have the same form as Eq. (3-11), viz.,

$$P_i = I_{rms}^2 (r_p + R_l)$$

$$(3\text{-}20)$$

The efficiency of rectification is

$$\eta_r = \frac{81.2}{1 + r_p/R_l} \qquad \% $$

$$(3\text{-}21)$$

This expression shows a theoretical maximum that is twice that of the half-wave rectifier.

The ripple factor is readily found when it is noted that

$$\frac{I_{\mathrm{rms}}}{I_{\mathrm{d-c}}} = \frac{I_m/\sqrt{2}}{2I_m/\pi} = 1.11$$

From Eq. (3-16),

$$r = \sqrt{1.11^2 - 1} = 0.482 \tag{3-22}$$

Thus the ripple factor has dropped from 1.21 in the half-wave rectifier to 0.482 in the present case. What has been accomplished in the full-wave rectifier, therefore, is that the rectification process has become more efficient, with a higher percentage of the power supplied to the circuit being converted into the desired d-c power, and with a consequent smaller fraction remaining in a-c form, which, while producing heating of the load, does not contribute to the desired d-c power.

A study of Fig. 3-4 indicates that when one tube is conducting, say $T1$, then tube $T2$ is in the nonconducting state. Except for the tube drop $i_b r_p$ in $T1$, the peak inverse potential across $T2$ is $2E_m$, or twice the transformer maximum potential measured to the mid-point, or the full transformer potential. The potential stress between windings of the filament transformer is seen to be the full d-c potential, if the negative is grounded,

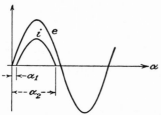

FIG. 3-6. The applied potential and the current waveshape in a half-wave rectifier circuit using a gas diode.

and is sensibly zero, if the positive is grounded.

3-5. Circuits with Gas Diodes. Gas diodes may be used in the half-wave and full-wave circuits discussed above. Owing to their different plate characteristics, the results are somewhat different. For these tubes a sensibly constant potential appears across the tube when the tube is conducting, but conduction does not begin until the applied potential exceeds the breakdown potential of the tube. The tube will consequently conduct for less than 180 deg in each cycle. The situation is illustrated in Fig. 3-6.

The equation of the potential across the load during conduction is obtained by applying Kirchhoff's law to the plate circuit,

$$e_l = i_b R_l = E_m \sin \alpha - E_0 \tag{3-23}$$

and the corresponding expression for the current is

$$i_b = \frac{E_m \sin \alpha - E_0}{R_l} \tag{3-24}$$

where E_0 is the constant tube drop during conduction.

The d-c plate current is found by taking the average value of the instantaneous current and is

$$I_{\text{d-c}} = \frac{1}{2\pi} \int_{\alpha_1}^{\alpha_2} \frac{E_m \sin \alpha - E_0}{R_l} \, d\alpha \tag{3-25}$$

where α_1 is the angle at which the tube fires and α_2 is the angle at which conduction ceases.   Ordinarily the applied plate potential is much larger than E_0, and the angles α_1 and $\pi - \alpha_2$ are very nearly zero.   Consequently the limits of the integral of Eq. (3-25) may be changed to 0 and π without appreciable error in the result.   When this is done and the integral is evaluated, it is found that

$$I_{\text{d-c}} = \frac{E_m}{\pi R_l} - \frac{E_0}{2R_l} = \frac{E_m}{\pi R_l} \left(1 - \frac{\pi}{2} \frac{E_0}{E_m} \right) \tag{3-26}$$

The load potential $E_{\text{d-c}}$ may be written as

$$E_{\text{d-c}} = \frac{E_m}{\pi} \left(1 - \frac{\pi}{2} \frac{E_0}{E_m} \right) \tag{3-27}$$

This equation does not contain the load current.   This means, of course, that $E_{\text{d-c}}$ is independent of the load current, with consequent perfect regulation.

To calculate the efficiency of rectification, it is necessary to calculate the input power to the plate circuit.   This is given by

$$P_i = \frac{1}{2\pi} \int_0^{\pi} e i_b \, d\alpha = \frac{1}{2\pi} \int_0^{\pi} E_m \sin \alpha \, \frac{E_m \sin \alpha - E_0}{R_l} \, d\alpha$$

where the limits are again taken as 0 and π.   This expression reduces to

$$P_i = \frac{E_m^2}{4R_l} \left(1 - \frac{4}{\pi} \frac{E_0}{E_m} \right) \tag{3-28}$$

The efficiency of rectification is then

$$\eta_r = \frac{P_{\text{d-c}}}{P_i} = \frac{4}{\pi^2} \frac{\left(1 - \dfrac{\pi}{2} \dfrac{E_0}{E_m} \right)^2}{1 - \dfrac{4}{\pi} \dfrac{E_0}{E_m}} \tag{3-29}$$

which may be reduced to the form

$$\eta_r = 40.6 \left(1 - 1.87 \frac{E_0}{E_m} \right) \qquad \% \tag{3-30}$$

Note that this value is independent of the load current or load resistance. To the same approximation, namely, $E_m \gg E_0$, the ripple factor is given by

$$r = 1.21 \left(1 + 0.5 \frac{E_0}{E_m} \right) \qquad (3\text{-}31)$$

which is slightly higher than the value with the vacuum diode. This increased ripple results because the tube conduction is less than 180 deg.

The corresponding properties of the full-wave circuit with gas tubes will follow a completely parallel development and yield results that bear the same relation to the vacuum-tube case that the foregoing results do to the corresponding half-wave vacuum-rectifier case.

3-6. Miscellaneous Single-phase Rectifier Circuits. A variety of other rectifier circuits exist which find widespread use. Among these are bridge rectifier circuits, potential-doubling circuits, and potential-multiply-

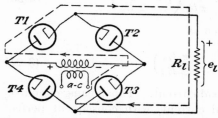

ing circuits. The bridge circuit finds extensive use both as a power rectifier and also as the rectifying system in rectifier-type a-c meters. The rectifiers for power use utilize thermionic diodes of both the vacuum and gas varieties, whereas those for instrument use are usually of the copper oxide or crystal types.

Fig. 3-7. Single-phase full-wave bridge rectifier circuit.

To examine the operation of the bridge circuit, refer to Fig. 3-7. It is observed that two tubes conduct simultaneously during one half of the cycle and the other two tubes conduct during the second half of the cycle. The conduction paths and directions are such that the resulting current through the load is substantially that shown in Fig. 3-5.

The primary features of the bridge circuit are the following: The currents drawn in both the primary and secondary of the plate-supply transformer are sinusoidal. This permits a smaller transformer to be used for a given output power than is necessary for the same power with the single-phase full-wave circuit of the two-tube type.* Also, the transformer need not have a center tap. Since each tube has only transformer potential across it on the inverse cycle, the bridge circuit is suitable for high-potential applications. However, the transformers supplying the heaters of the tubes must be properly insulated for the high potential.

A rectifier meter is essentially a bridge-rectifier system which utilizes copper oxide elements. The potential to be measured is applied through a multiplier resistance to two corners of the bridge, a d-c milliammeter being used as an indicating instrument across the other two corners.

---

* For a discussion of *transformer utilization factor*, see J. Millman and S. Seely. "Electronics," 2d ed., chap. 14, McGraw-Hill Book Company, Inc., New York, 1951,

But as the d-c milliammeter reads average values of current, the scale of the meter is calibrated to give rms values of sinusoidal waves by applying a sinusoidal potential to the input terminals. The indication on such an instrument is not correct for input signals that contain appreciable harmonics.

A common potential-doubling circuit is shown in Fig. 3-8. The output[1] from such a circuit is approximately equal to twice the transformer maximum potential. It operates by alternately charging each of the two capacitors to the transformer peak potential E_m, current being continually drained from the capacitors through the load. This circuit is characterized by poor regulation unless very large capacitors are used. The peak inverse potential is twice the transformer peak potential. If ordinary rectifiers are used, two separate filament sources are required.

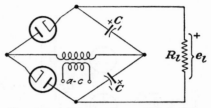

Fig. 3-8. A full-wave potential-doubling circuit.

If a relatively low potential system is built, and these are used extensively in a-c/d-c radio sets, special tubes such as 25Z5 are available. These tubes are provided with separate indirectly heated cathodes. The cathodes in these tubes are well insulated from the heaters, which are connected in series internally.

The regulation of the potential doubler can be improved, particularly at the higher loads, by employing a bridge doubler rectifier,[2] which is illustrated in Fig. 3-9. The feature of this rectifier circuit is that at

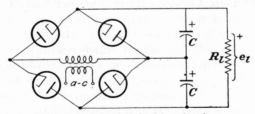

Fig. 3-9. A bridge doubler circuit.

light loads the output potential is approximately twice the transformer peak potential. However, the potential will never fall below the output of the bridge circuit at any load, nor will the ripple factor exceed that of the bridge circuit, viz., $r = 0.482$. Most other features of this circuit are like those in the normal bridge circuit, such as the peak inverse potential to which each tube is subjected, and the heater-cathode insulation problems.

An alternative potential-doubling circuit[3] is shown in Fig. 3-10. The output potential from this circuit, like that from Fig. 3-8, is approximately equal to twice the transformer maximum potential. It operates by charging capacitor C_1 during one half cycle through tube $T1$ to the transformer peak potential E_m and during the next half cycle charges C_2 through tube $T2$ to the potential determined by that across C_1 and the transformer in series, the peak being approximately $2E_m$. The peak inverse potential across each tube is twice the transformer peak potential.

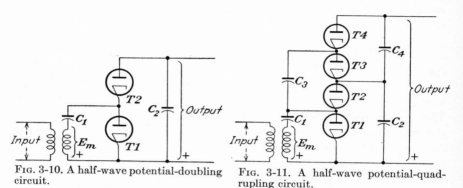

FIG. 3-10. A half-wave potential-doubling circuit.   FIG. 3-11. A half-wave potential-quadrupling circuit.

This circuit may be extended to a quadrupler by adding two tubes and two capacitors, as shown in Fig. 3-11. It may be extended to provide n-fold multiplication, odd or even.

FILTERS

3-7. The Harmonic Components in Rectifier Circuits. It is usually the requirement of a power supply to provide a relatively ripple-free source of d-c potential from an a-c line. However, as seen above, a rectifier actually provides an output which contains a-c components in addition to the d-c term that is desired, a measure of the a-c components being given by the ripple factor. It is customary to include a filter between the rectifier and the output to attenuate these ripple components. Often an electronic regulator is also included, if the potential output is to be substantially constant with load or if the ripple must be small.

The analysis of the action of such rectifier filters is complicated by the fact that the rectifier as a driving source is nonlinear, thus requiring the solution of circuits with nonlinear elements. It is possible in most cases to make reasonable assumptions in order to effect an approximate engineering solution. In consequence, the results obtained are only approximate.

An analytic representation of the output of the single-phase half-wave rectifier is obtained in terms of a Fourier series expansion. This series representation has the form

$$i = b_0 + \sum_{k=1}^{\infty} b_k \cos k\alpha + \sum_{k=1}^{\infty} a_k \sin k\alpha \qquad (3\text{-}32)$$

where $\alpha = \omega t$ and where the coefficients that appear in the series are given by the integrals

$$b_0 = \frac{1}{2\pi} \int_0^{2\pi} i \, d\alpha$$

$$b_k = \frac{1}{\pi} \int_0^{2\pi} i \cos k\alpha \, d\alpha \qquad (3\text{-}33)$$

$$a_k = \frac{1}{\pi} \int_0^{2\pi} i \sin k\alpha \, d\alpha$$

It should be recalled that the constant term b_0 that appears in this Fourier series is the average or d-c value of the current.

The explicit expression for the current in a half-wave rectifier circuit, which is obtained by performing the indicated integrations using Eqs. (3-5) over the two specified intervals, yields

$$i = I_m \left[\frac{1}{\pi} + \frac{1}{2} \sin \omega t - \frac{2}{\pi} \sum_{k=2,4,6,\ldots} \frac{\cos k\omega t}{(k+1)(k-1)} \right] \qquad (3\text{-}34)$$

where $I_m = E_m/(r_p + R_l)$ and E_m is the peak transformer potential. The lowest angular frequency that is present in this expression is that of the primary source. Also, except for this single term of frequency ω, all other terms that appear in the expression are even-harmonic terms.

The corresponding Fourier series representation of the output of the full-wave rectifier which is illustrated in Fig. 3-5 may be derived from Eq. (3-34). Thus, by recalling that the full-wave circuit comprises two half-wave circuits which are so arranged that one circuit is operating during the interval when the other is not operating, then clearly the currents are functionally related by the expression $i_2(\alpha) = i_1(\alpha + \pi)$. The total load current, which is $i = i_1 + i_2$, then attains the form

$$i = I_m \left[\frac{2}{\pi} - \frac{4}{\pi} \sum_{k=2,4,6,\ldots} \frac{\cos k\omega t}{(k+1)(k-1)} \right] \qquad (3\text{-}35)$$

where $I_m = E_m/(R_l + r_p)$ and where E_m is the maximum value of the transformer potential measured to the center tap.

A comparison of Eqs. (3-34) and (3-35) indicates that the fundamental angular-frequency term has been eliminated in the full-wave circuit, the lowest harmonic term in the output being 2ω, a second-harmonic term. This will be found to be a distinct advantage in filtering.

The Fourier series representation of the half-wave and full-wave circuits using gas diodes can be obtained in the same way as above, although the form will be more complex. This is so because conduction begins at some small angle φ_0 and ceases at the angle $\pi - \varphi_0$, when it is assumed that the breakdown and the extinction potentials are equal. But since these angles are usually small under normal operating conditions, it will be assumed that Eqs. (3-34) and (3-35) are applicable for circuits with vacuum or gas diodes. The Fourier series representation of the output of a controlled rectifier is also possible, although the result is quite complex. However, such controlled rectifiers are ordinarily used in services in which the ripple is not of major concern, and, as a result, no detailed analysis will be undertaken. Some results will be given below covering these rectifiers, however.

3-8. Inductor Filters. The operation of an inductor filter depends on the inherent property of an inductance to oppose any change of current

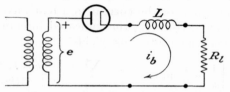

FIG. 3-12. Half-wave rectifier circuit with inductor filter.

that may tend to take place through it. That is, the inductor stores energy in its magnetic field when the current is above its average value and releases energy when the current falls below this value. Consequently any sudden changes in current that might otherwise take place in the circuit will be smoothed out by the action of the inductor.

In particular, suppose that an inductor is connected in series with the load in a single-phase half-wave circuit, as illustrated in Fig. 3-12. For simplicity, suppose that the tube and choke resistances are negligible. Then the controlling differential equation for the current in the circuit during the time of current conduction is

$$L \frac{di_b}{dt} + Ri_b = E_m \sin \omega t \tag{3-36}$$

A solution of this differential equation may be effected. This solution is complicated by the fact that current continues over only a portion of the cycle. The general character of the solution is shown graphically in Fig. 3-13, in which is shown the effect of changing the inductance on the waveform of the current. Since a simple inductance choke is seldom used with a half-wave circuit, further details of the analysis will not be given.

Suppose that an inductor filter is applied to the output of a full-wave rectifier. The circuit and a sketch of the output-current waveshape are given in Fig. 3-14. Since no cutout occurs in the current, the analysis assumes a different form from that for the half-wave case. Now, instead of considering the circuit differential equation, as in Eq. (3-36), and

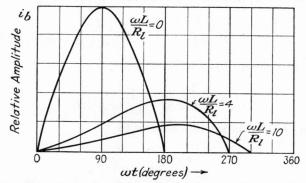

FIG. 3-13. The effect of changing inductance on the waveform of the current in a half-wave rectifier with inductor filter. The load R_l is assumed constant.

adjusting the initial conditions to fulfill the required physical conditions, an approximate solution is effected. It is supposed that the equation of the potential that is applied to the filter is given by Eq. (3-35). More-over, it is noted that the amplitudes of the a-c terms beyond the first, and this is of second-harmonic frequency, are small compared with that of the first term. In particular, the fourth-harmonic frequency term is only 20 per cent of the second-harmonic term. Furthermore, the impedance of the inductor increases with frequency, and better filtering action exists for the higher-harmonic terms. Conse-quently it is assumed that all higher-order terms may be neglected.

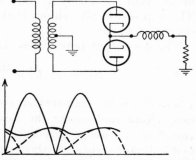

FIG. 3-14. Full-wave rectifier circuit with inductor filter, and the wave-shape of the load current.

In accordance with this discussion, it is supposed that the input potential to the filter and load has the approximate form

$$e = \frac{2E_m}{\pi} - \frac{4E_m}{3\pi} \cos 2\omega t \qquad (3\text{-}37)$$

The corresponding load current is, in accordance with a-c circuit theory,

$$i_l = \frac{2E_m}{\pi R_l} - \frac{4E_m}{3\pi} \frac{\cos (2\omega t - \psi)}{\sqrt{R_l^2 + 4\omega^2 L^2}} \qquad (3\text{-}38)$$

where

$$\tan \psi = \frac{2\omega L}{R_l} \tag{3-39}$$

The ripple factor, defined in Eq. (3-15), becomes

$$r = \frac{(4E_m/3\pi)(1/\sqrt{R_l^2 + 4\omega^2 L^2})}{2E_m/\pi R_l} = \frac{2R_l}{3\sqrt{2}} \frac{1}{\sqrt{R_l^2 + 4\omega^2 L^2}}$$

which may be expressed in the form

$$r = \frac{2}{3\sqrt{2}} \frac{1}{\sqrt{1 + (4\omega^2 L^2/R_l^2)}} \tag{3-40}$$

If the ratio $\omega L/R_l$ is large, this reduces to

$$r = \frac{1}{3\sqrt{2}} \frac{R_l}{\omega L} \tag{3-41}$$

This expression shows that the filtering improves with decreased load resistance or, correspondingly, with increased load current. At no load, $R_l = \infty$, and the filtering is poorest, with $r = 2/3\sqrt{2} = 0.47$. This is also the result which applies when no choke is included in the circuit. [Compare this result with Eq. (3-22), which gives 0.482. The difference arises from the terms in the Fourier series that have been neglected.] The expression also shows that large inductances are accompanied by decreased ripple.

The d-c output potential is given by

$$E_{\text{d-c}} = I_{\text{d-c}} R_l = \frac{2E_m}{\pi} = 0.637 E_m = 0.90 E_{\text{rms}} \qquad [(3-42)$$

where E_{rms} is the transformer secondary potential measured to the center tap. Note that under the assumptions made, viz., negligible power-transformer leakage reactance, transformer resistance, tube resistance, and inductor resistance, the output potential does not change with load, with consequent perfect regulation. Because the neglected effects are not negligible, the output potential actually decreases with increased current.

3-9. Capacitor Filter. Filtering is frequently effected by shunting the load with a capacitor. During the time that the rectifier output is increasing, the capacitor is charging to the rectifier output potential and energy is stored in the capacitor. During the time that the rectifier potential falls below that of the capacitor, the capacitor delivers energy to the load, thus maintaining the potential at a high level for a longer period than without the capacitor. The ripple is therefore considerably decreased. Clearly, the diode acts as a switch, permitting charge to flow into the capacitor when the rectifier potential exceeds the capacitor potential, and then acts to disconnect the power source when the potential falls below that of the capacitor.

To examine the operation in some detail, refer to Fig. 3-15, which shows a diagram of the circuit.   The tube current during the conducting portion of the cycle is

$$i_b = i_C + i_l \qquad (3\text{-}43)$$

where

$$i_l = \frac{e_l}{R_l} = \frac{e_C}{R_l} \qquad (3\text{-}44)$$

and where

$$i_C = \frac{dq_C}{dt} = C \frac{de_C}{dt} \qquad (3\text{-}45)$$

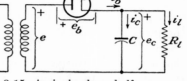

FIG. 3-15. A single-phase half-wave capacitor-filtered rectifier.

where q_C is the capacitor charge.   The controlling differential equation of the charging current through the tube is then

$$i_b = \frac{e_C}{R_l} + C \frac{de_C}{dt} \qquad (3\text{-}46)$$

But the potential e_C during the time that the tube is conducting is simply the transformer potential, if the tube drop is neglected.   Hence the

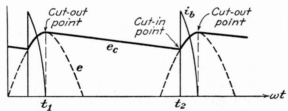

FIG. 3-16. The tube current and the load potential in a single-phase half-wave capacitor-filtered rectifier.

capacitor potential during this portion of the cycle is sinusoidal and is

$$e_C = e = E_m \sin \omega t$$

The corresponding tube current is

$$i_b = \frac{E_m}{R_l} \sin \omega t + \omega C E_m \cos \omega t$$

This may be written in the equivalent form

$$i_b = E_m \sqrt{\omega^2 C^2 + \frac{1}{R_l^2}} \sin (\omega t + \psi) \qquad (3\text{-}47)$$

where

$$\psi = \tan^{-1} \omega C R_l \qquad (3\text{-}48)$$

A sketch of the current wave is illustrated in Fig. 3-16.

Equation (3-47) shows that the use of large capacitances, in order to improve the filtering, is accompanied by large tube currents. Therefore, if a large capacitance is used for a given load in order to maintain the output potential more nearly constant, a very peaked current exists. In fact, for a certain required average current demand by the load, the tube-current pulse becomes more and more peaked as the capacitance is made larger. This imposes serious duty conditions on the tube, since the average current through the tube may be well within the tube rating and yet the large peak current may injure the cathode. Vacuum diodes would not be appreciably damaged by the high peak-current demands, since temperature-saturated currents may be drawn without seriously injuring the cathode. In the case of gas tubes, however, any attempt to draw higher than temperature-saturated current will usually be accompanied by severe positive-ion bombardment of the cathode, with consequent cathode disintegration. It is for this reason that large-capacitance input filters should not be used with rectifiers that employ gas diodes.

When the tube stops conducting, $i_b = 0$ and the controlling differential equation during the nonconducting portion of the cycle is, from Eq. (3-46),

$$C \frac{de_C}{dt} + \frac{e_C}{R_l} = 0 \tag{3-49}$$

The solution of this differential equation is

$$e_C = A e^{-t/R_l C} \tag{3-50}$$

This shows that the capacitor discharges exponentially through the load.

To determine the value of the constant A that appears in this expression, use is made of the fact that at the time $t = t_1$, the cutout time,

$$e_C = e = E_m \sin \omega t_1$$

Combining this result with Eq. (3-50) gives

$$A = E_m \sin \omega t_1 e^{t_1/R_l C} \tag{3-51}$$

and Eq. (3-50) becomes

$$e_C = E_m \sin \omega t_1 e^{-(t-t_1)/R_l C} \tag{3-52}$$

The quantity t_1 that appears in this expression is known, since at $t = t_1$ the tube current is zero. From Eq. (3-47) this requires

$$\sin (\omega t_1 + \psi) = 0$$

from which it follows that

$$\omega t_1 = \pi - \psi = \pi - \tan^{-1} \omega C R_l \tag{3-53}$$

If t_1 from Eq. (3-53) is substituted in Eq. (3-52), there results

$$e_C = E_m \sin \omega t_1 e^{-(\omega t + \psi - \pi)/\omega C R_l} \tag{3-54}$$

To find the "cutin" point, it is noted that e_C equals the impressed transformer potential e at this point. This requires

$$E_m \sin \omega t_2 = E_m \sin \omega t_1 e^{-(\omega t_2 - \psi - \pi)/\omega CR_l}$$

or

$$\sin \omega t_2 = \sin \omega t_1 e^{-(\omega t_2 - \psi - \pi)/\omega CR_l} \quad (3\text{-}55)$$

The evaluation of the cutin time t_2 cannot be solved explicitly, for this is a transcendental equation. Graphical methods can be used effectively in this evaluation. The results are given in Fig. 3-17. Included on this graph are a plot of Eq. (3-53) for the cutout angle and a plot of Eq. (3-55) for the cutin angle.

The foregoing analysis gives a complete specification of the operation of the capacitor filter, the current through the tube being given by Eqs. (3-47) and (3-48), the potential across the load resistor being given by

$$e_C = E_m \sin \omega t \\ \text{for } \omega t_2 < \omega t < \omega t_1 \quad (3\text{-}56a)$$

and by Eq. (3-54):

$$e_C = E_m \sin \omega t_1 e^{-(\omega t - \omega t_1)/\omega R_l C} \\ \text{for } \omega t_1 < \omega t < 2\pi + \omega t_2 \quad (3\text{-}56b)$$

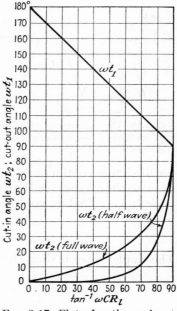

FIG. 3-17. Plot of cutin angle ωt_2 and cutout angle ωt_1 vs. circuit parameters for the capacitor filter.

With this information it is possible to evaluate the d-c output potential, the ripple factor, the peak tube current, etc. These quantities may then be plotted as functions of the parameters R_l, C, E_m. Such an analysis is quite involved, but it has been carried out,[4] and the results are given in graphical form.

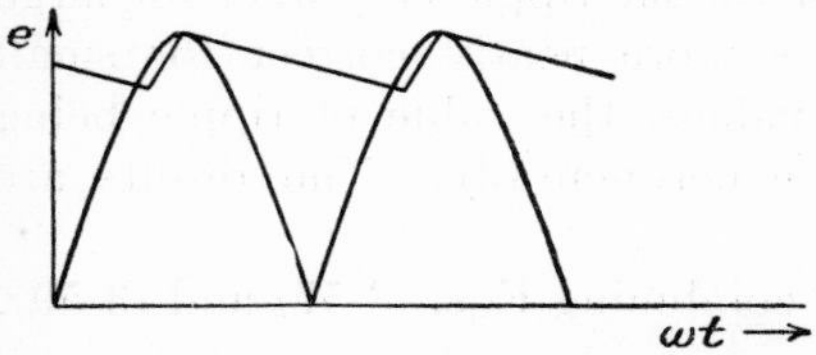

3-10. Approximate Analysis of Capacitor Filters. It is expedient to make several reasonable approximations in order to obtain an approximate analysis of the behavior of the capacitor filter. Such an approximate analysis possesses the advantage that the important factors of the operation are simply related to the circuit parameters. Moreover, the results are sufficiently accurate for most engineering applications. The character of the approximation is made evident by an inspection of Fig. 3-18, which shows the trace of an oscillogram of the load potential in a

FIG. 3-18. Oscillogram of the load potential in a single-phase full-wave capacitor-filtered rectifier.

single-phase full-wave capacitor filtered rectifier. The potential curve may be approximated by two straight-line segments, as shown in Fig. 3-19. If the total capacitor discharge potential is denoted as E_r, then,

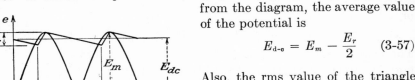

FIG. 3-19. The approximate load-potential waveform corresponding to the curves of Fig. 3-18.

from the diagram, the average value of the potential is

$$E_{\text{d-c}} = E_m - \frac{E_r}{2} \qquad (3\text{-}57)$$

Also, the rms value of the triangle ripple potential may be shown to be

$$E'_{\text{rms}} = \frac{E_r}{2\sqrt{3}} \qquad (3\text{-}58)$$

Also, if it is assumed that the capacitor discharge continues for the full half cycle at a constant rate which is equal to the average load current $I_{\text{d-c}}$, the fall in potential during this half cycle is E_r. That is, approximately

$$E_r = \frac{I_{\text{d-c}}}{2fC} \qquad (3\text{-}59)$$

The ripple factor is then given by

$$r = \frac{E'_{\text{rms}}}{E_{\text{d-c}}} = \frac{E_r}{2\sqrt{3}\,E_{\text{d-c}}} = \frac{I_{\text{d-c}}}{4\sqrt{3}\,fCE_{\text{d-c}}}$$

But since $E_{\text{d-c}} = I_{\text{d-c}}R_l$,

$$r = \frac{1}{4\sqrt{3}\,fCR_l} \qquad (3\text{-}60)$$

This expression shows that the ripple factor varies inversely with the load resistance and the filter capacitance. At no load, $R_l = \infty$, and the ripple is zero. As R_l decreases, corresponding to increasing current, the ripple becomes larger. Also, for given R_l, the ripple is smaller for large capacitances. Actually, Eq. (3-60) is more nearly correct for small values of ripple than for the larger values, the value of ripple being generally larger than that obtained experimentally. The results are adequate for most purposes.

The regulation curve is obtained by combining Eqs. (3-57) and (3-59). This yields

$$E_{\text{d-c}} = E_m - \frac{I_{\text{d-c}}}{4fC} \qquad (3\text{-}61)$$

This expression represents a linear fall in potential with d-c output current. Also, it shows that the simple capacitor filter will possess poor regulation unless the capacitance C is large.

Now refer to the circuit of Fig. 3-15 to ascertain the peak inverse potential across the tube.   It is seen to be twice the transformer peak potential. For the full-wave case, the peak inverse potential is also twice the transformer maximum potential, as measured from the mid-point to either end, or the full transformer potential.   Thus the presence of the capacitor increases the peak inverse potential in the half-wave circuit from E_m to $2E_m$ but does not affect the peak inverse potential in the full-wave circuit.

3-11. L-section Filter.   An L-section filter consists of a series inductor and a shunt capacitor, as shown in Fig. 3-20.   This filter is so arranged that the inductor offers a high impedance to the harmonic terms, and the capacitor shunts the load, so as to by-pass the harmonic currents.   The resulting ripple is markedly reduced over that of the relatively simple filters of Secs. 3-8 and 3-9.

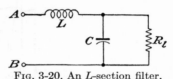

FIG. 3-20. An L-section filter.

The ripple factor is readily approximated by taking for the potential applied to the input terminals of the filter the first two terms in the Fourier series representation of the output potential of the rectifier, viz.,

$$e = \frac{2E_m}{\pi} - \frac{4E_m}{3\pi} \cos 2\omega t \qquad (3\text{-}62)$$

But since the filter elements are chosen to provide a high series impedance and a very low shunting impedance, certain plausible approximations may be made.   Thus, since the choke impedance is high compared with the effective parallel impedance of the capacitor and load resistor, the net impedance between terminals AB is approximately X_L and the a-c current through the circuit is

$$I'_{\text{rms}} \doteq \frac{4E_m}{3\sqrt{2}\,\pi} \frac{1}{X_L} = \frac{\sqrt{2}}{3} E_{\text{d-c}} \frac{1}{X_L} \qquad (3\text{-}63)$$

Likewise, since the a-c impedance of the capacitor is small compared with R_l, it may be assumed that all the a-c current passes through the capacitor and none through the resistor.   The a-c potential across the load (the ripple potential) is the potential across the capacitor and is

$$E'_{\text{rms}} \doteq \frac{\sqrt{2}}{3} E_{\text{d-c}} \frac{X_C}{X_L} \qquad (3\text{-}64)$$

The ripple factor is then given by

$$r = \frac{\sqrt{2}}{3} \frac{X_C}{X_L} = \frac{\sqrt{2}}{3} \frac{1}{2\omega C} \frac{1}{2\omega L} \qquad (3\text{-}65)$$

which may be written, at 60 cps, with L in henrys and C in microfarads

$$r = \frac{0.830}{LC} \tag{3-66}$$

It should be noted that the effect of combining the decreasing ripple of the inductor filter and the increasing ripple of the simple capacitor filter for increasing loads is a constant ripple circuit, independent of load.

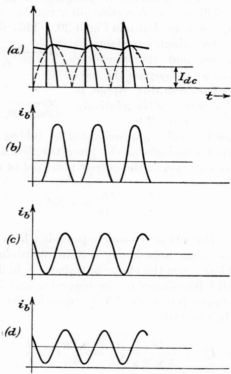

FIG. 3-21. The tube-current waveform in the full-wave rectifier with an L-section filter, when (a) $L = 0$, (b) $L < L_c$, (c) $L = L_c$, (d) $L > L_c$, for constant I_{d-c}.

The above analysis assumes that no current cutout exists at any time of the cycle. If it did, the analysis would follow along the lines of Sec. 3-9 and Eq. (3-62) for the potential would not apply. But since with no inductance in the filter cutout will occur, whereas with sufficient inductance there will be no cutout, it would be expected that there would be some minimum inductance for a given current below which cutout would occur, although for larger values than this critical value the conduction would continue for the full cycle. The situation is best illustrated graphically. Figure 3-21 shows the expected tube current for various amounts of series inductance L.

If the rectifier is to pass current throughout the entire cycle, the peak current delivered must not exceed the d-c component. But the d-c value is E_{d-c}/R_l. Also, the peak a-c current is $(2E_{d-c}/3)(1/X_L)$. Hence for current flow during the full cycle it is necessary that

$$\frac{E_{d-c}}{R_l} \geq \frac{2E_{d-c}}{3}\frac{1}{X_L}$$

or

$$X_L \geq \frac{2R_l}{3} \tag{3-67}$$

from which the value for the critical inductance is found to be

$$L_c = \frac{2R_l}{3\omega}$$

which has the value

$$L_c = \frac{R_l}{1,130} \tag{3-68}$$

for a 60-cps power frequency, where R_l is in ohms and L_c is in henrys. However, owing to the approximations that have been made in this analysis, it is advisable for conservative design to use a larger value of L_c than that given in Eq. (3-68). A good practical figure is to choose the denominator as 1,000 instead of 1,130.

The effect of the cutout is illustrated in Fig. 3-22, which shows a regulation curve of the system, for constant R_l and varying series inductance. Clearly, when the series inductance is zero, the filter is of the simple capacitance type and the output potential is approximately E_m. With increasing inductance, the potential falls, until

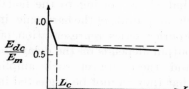

FIG. 3-22. The regulation curve of a rectifier with L-section filter as a function of series inductance, for constant output current.

at $L = L_c$ the output potential is that corresponding to the simple L filter with no cutout, or $0.637E_m$. For values of L greater than L_c, there is no change in potential, except for the effects of the resistances of the various elements of the circuit.

It is not possible to satisfy the conditions of Eq. (3-68) for all values of load, since at no load this would require an infinite inductance. However, when good potential regulation is desired, it is customary to use a bleeder resistance across the load so as to maintain the conditions of Eq. (3-68) even if this respresents a power loss.

A more efficient method than using a high bleeder current, with its attendant power dissipation, is to make use of the fact that the inductance of an iron-core reactor depends, among other things, on the amount of d-c current in the winding. Chokes for which the inductance is high at low values of d-c current and which decrease markedly with increased d-c currents are called "swinging" chokes. The swinging choke is provided with a closed iron core, whereas the core of the inductor which is to possess a more nearly constant inductance is provided with a narrow air gap. A typical curve for such a reactor is illustrated in Fig. 3-23. The advantage of such a choke is that for high R_l, and therefore low d-c current, the inductance is high. As a result, the conditional equation (3-68) is satisfied over a wider range of R_l. Clearly, however, when a swinging choke is used, the ripple factor is no longer independent of the load.

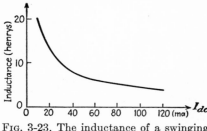

Fig. 3-23. The inductance of a swinging choke as a function of the d-c current through it.

The above analysis for the critical inductance of the L-type filter applies for the full-wave rectifier for which conduction continues for 180 deg in each cycle. Consequently the results so obtained are not applicable when an L-section filter is used with a controlled rectifier. The analysis for a full-wave controlled rectifier is considerably more complicated than that above, owing to the fact that the amplitude of the harmonics in the Fourier series representation of the output depends on the delay angles, and these are of such amplitude that they cannot be neglected in the analysis. The results of such an analysis are given graphically[1] in Fig. 3-24. The curves give a measure of both the critical inductance and the output potential.

3-12. Multiple L-section Filters. If it is desired to limit the ripple to a value that is less than that possible with a single L-section filter using commercially available elements, two or more L-section filters may be con-

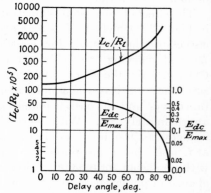

Fig. 3-24. Critical inductance and d-c output potential as a function of the delay angle in a full-wave controlled rectifier.

nected in cascade, as shown in Fig. 3-25. An approximate solution is possible by following the methods of Sec. 3-11. It is assumed, therefore, that the choke impedances are much larger than the reactances of the capacitors. Also, it is assumed that the reactance of the last capacitor is small compared with the resistance of the load. Under these

assumptions, the impedance between A_3 and B_3 is X_{C2}. The impedance between A_2 and B_2 is X_{C1}, and the impedance between A_1 and B_1 is
X_{L1}, approximately.

The a-c current I_1 is approximately

$$I_1 = \frac{\sqrt{2}}{3} E_{\text{d-c}} \frac{1}{X_{L1}}$$

The a-c potential across C_1 is approximately

$$E_{A_2B_2} = I_1 X_{C1}$$

The a-c current I_2 is approximately

$$I_2 = \frac{E_{A_2B_2}}{X_{L2}}$$

The a-c potential across the load is approximately

$$I_2 X_{C2} = I_1 X_{C2} \frac{X_{C1}}{X_{L1}} = \frac{\sqrt{2}}{3} E_{\text{d-c}} \frac{X_{C1}}{X_{L1}} \frac{X_{C2}}{X_{L2}}$$

The ripple factor is given by the expression

$$r = \frac{\sqrt{2}}{3} \frac{X_{C1}}{X_{L1}} \frac{X_{C2}}{X_{L2}} \tag{3-69}$$

A comparison of this expression with Eq. (3-64) indicates the general-
ization that should be made in obtaining an expression for the ripple
factor of a cascaded filter of n sec-
tions.   The expression would have
the form

$$r = \frac{\sqrt{2}}{3} \frac{X_{C1}}{X_{L1}} \frac{X_{C2}}{X_{L2}} \cdots \frac{X_{Cn}}{X_{Ln}} \tag{3-70}$$

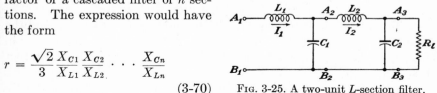

FIG. 3-25. A two-unit L-section filter.

If the sections are all similar, then Eq. (3-70) becomes

$$r = \frac{\sqrt{2}}{3} \left(\frac{X_C}{X_L}\right)^n = \frac{\sqrt{2}}{3} \frac{1}{(16\pi^2 f^2 LC)^n} \tag{3-71}$$

It follows from this that the required LC product for a specified ripple
factor r is given by

$$LC = 1.76 \left(\frac{0.471}{r}\right)^{1/n} \tag{3-72}$$

Note also that, to the approximation that the impedance between A_2
and B_2 is simply X_{C1}, the critical inductance is given by Eq. (3-68), as
for the single-section unit.

3-13. Π-section Filter. The use of a Π-section filter provides an output potential that approaches the peak value of the a-c potential of the source, the ripple components being very small. Such a filter is illustrated in Fig. 3-26. Although such filters do provide a higher d-c output potential than is possible with an L-section filter, the tube currents are peaked and the regulation is generally poor, these results being common with the simple capacitor filter.

A study of the oscilloscope patterns at various points of such a filter shows that the action can be understood by considering the inductor and

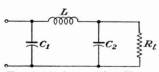

FIG. 3-26. A Π-section filter.

the second capacitor as an L-section filter that acts on the triangular output potential wave from the first capacitor. The output potential is then approximately that from the input capacitor, the ripple contained in this output being reduced by the L-section filter. That is, the ripple factor of the Π-section filter is given approximately by

$$r_\pi = r_C r_L \tag{3-73}$$

where r_C is given by Eq. (3-60) and r_L is given by Eq. (3-65). This becomes

$$r_\pi = 0.855 \frac{X_{C1}X_{C2}}{X_L R_l} \tag{3-74}$$

with all reactances calculated at the second-harmonic frequency. For a 60-cps power source, this is

$$r_\pi = \frac{2 \times 10^3}{C_1 C_2 L R_l} \tag{3-75}$$

with the capacitances in microfarads, the inductance in henrys, and the resistance in ohms. This result is only approximate, since it assumes in effect that the ripple output from the capacitor filter is sinusoidal rather than triangular.

A somewhat more accurate evaluation of the ripple factor, due to Arguimbau,[6] is possible. The technique employed is similar to that used to evaluate the grid driving power of a class C amplifier. For the filter connected to a rectifier at the power frequency ω, the important ripple term is of second-harmonic frequency. Consequently, it is required to find the peak value of the second-harmonic current I'_{2m} to the input capacitor of the Π filter. This is given by the Fourier component

$$I'_{2m} = \frac{1}{\pi} \int_0^{2\pi} i_b \cos 2\omega t \, d(\omega t) \tag{3-76}$$

Now assume that the current pulse is significant only near the peak value of the cosine curve. Therefore, the $\cos 2\omega t$ factor appearing in the integral is replaced by unity, and approximately

$$\sqrt{2}\, I_2' \doteq \frac{1}{\pi} \int_0^{2\pi} i_b\, d(\omega t) = 2I_{\text{d-c}} \tag{3-77}$$

Hence, the upper limit of the rms second-harmonic potential is

$$E_2' = I_2' X_{C1} = \sqrt{2}\, I_{\text{d-c}} X_{C1} \tag{3-78}$$

But the potential E_2' is applied to the L section, so that, by the same logic as before, the output ripple is $E_2' X_{C2}/X_L$. Hence, the ripple factor is

$$r_\pi = \sqrt{2}\, \frac{I_{\text{d-c}} X_{C1} X_{C2}}{E_{\text{d-c}} X_L} = \sqrt{2}\, \frac{X_{C1}}{R_l} \frac{X_{C2}}{X_L} \tag{3-79}$$

where all reactances are calculated at the second-harmonic frequency. At 60-cps primary frequency, this reduces to

$$r_\pi = \frac{3.3 \times 10^3}{C_1 C_2 L R_l} \tag{3-80}$$

Note that here, as in the previous analysis, the effects of higher harmonics than the second have been neglected. This result is probably more accurate than that given in Eq. (3-75) owing to the more reasonable approximation in the analysis.

If the inductor of the Π-section filter is replaced by a resistor, a practice that is often used with low-current-drain power supplies, the ripple factor is given by Eq. (3-79) with X_L replaced by R. Thus

$$r_\pi = \sqrt{2}\, \frac{X_{C1} X_{C2}}{R R_l}$$

or

$$r_\pi = \frac{2.5 \times 10^6}{C_1 C_2 R R_l} \tag{3-81}$$

REFERENCES

1. For an analysis of the operation, see Waidelich, D. L., *Proc. IRE*, **29**, 554 (1941).
2. Corbyn, D. B., *Electronic Eng.*, **24**, 418 (1952).
3. Cockroft, J. D., and E. T. S. Walton, *Proc. Roy. Soc.* (*London*), **136**, 619 (1932).
   Waidelich, D. L., *Proc. IRE*, **30**, 534 (1942).
   Mitchell, R. G., *Wireless Eng.*, **22**, 474 (1945).
4. Waidelich, D. L., *Trans. AIEE*, **60**, 1161 (1941).
   Schade, O. H., *Proc. IRE*, **31**, 341 (1943).
5. Overbeck, W. P., *Proc. IRE*, **27**, 655 (1939).
6. Arguimbau, L., "Vacuum Tube Circuits," John Wiley & Sons, Inc., New York, 1948.

PROBLEMS

3-1. A type 5U4G is connected in a half-wave circuit to supply power to a 1,500-ohm load from a 350-volt rms source of potential.

a. On a plate characteristic of the tube, plot the load line, and from this find the dynamic curve.

b. Obtain a plot of the output-current waveshape for a sinusoidal applied potential.

c. Estimate the value of the plate resistance r_p from the static characteristic at four different values of current (50, 100, 150, 200 ma). Use the average of these as the r_p of the tube.

d. Plot on the curve in part *b* the value obtained from Eq. (3-5), and compare.

3-2. The two sections of a 6X5 diode are connected in parallel and supply power to a 5,000-ohm load from a 325-volt rms source of potential. The effective plate resistance of the parallel combination of diodes is approximately 125 ohms. Calculate the following:

a. The d-c load current.

b. The a-c current (rms).

c. The reading of a d-c voltmeter placed across the diode terminals.

d. The total input power to the plate circuit.

e. The efficiency of rectification.

f. The regulation from no load to the given load.

g. The ripple factor.

3-3. Suppose that a 6X5 tube supplies power to a 5,000-ohm load from a 325-0-325 transformer. Repeat Prob. 3-2 under these conditions.

3-4. Show that the input power to a rectifier using gas diodes may be expressed in the form

$$P_i = I_{rms}^2 R_L + E_0 I_{d\text{-}c}$$

3-5. A gas diode for which the breakdown and maintaining potential is taken to be 10 volts supplies power in a half-wave rectifier circuit to a 1,000-ohm load from a 325-volt rms source. Calculate the following:

a. The d-c current through the load.

b. The a-c (rms) current through the load.

c. The reading of a d-c voltmeter placed across the diode.

d. The reading of an rms a-c voltmeter across the diode.

e. The power input to the plate circuit.

f. The efficiency of rectification.

g. The ripple factor.

3-6. The peak inverse plate potential rating of a 2X2/879 half-wave high-vacuum rectifier is 12,500 volts. Calculate the maximum d-c potential possible to a load, without exceeding the peak inverse potential, when such tubes are used in:

a. A half-wave circuit.

b. A full-wave circuit.

c. A full-wave bridge circuit.

d. A full-wave potential-doubling circuit.

e. A half-wave potential-doubling circuit.

f. Specify in each case the insulation strength of each filament transformer when the positive terminal is grounded.

3-7. Analyze the operation of the potential-quadrupling circuit of Fig. 3-11. Calculate:

a. The maximum possible potential across each capacitor.

b. The peak inverse potential of each tube.

c. The required insulation strength of each filament transformer.

3-8. It is planned to use a type 83 gas diode in a single-phase full-wave rectifier circuit with capacitor filter. The transformer potential is 350 volts rms to center tap. The load consists of a 16-μf capacitor in parallel with a 2,500-ohm resistor. The tube drop and the transformer resistance and leakage reactance may be neglected.

a. Calculate the cutout angle.

b. Determine the cutin point.

c. Calculate the peak tube current. Should the type 83 tube be used? Compare the peak current per plate with that given (1 amp) in the tube manual.

3-9. Given two 20-henry chokes and two 16-μf capacitors. Calculate the output potential and ripple factor under each of the following conditions:

a. The two chokes are connected in series with the load.

b. The two capacitors are connected across the load.

c. A single L-section filter, consisting of the two chokes in series and the two capacitors in parallel, is used.

d. A double L-section filter, consisting of two sections, each of one choke and one capacitor, is used.

The load is 2,000 ohms, and a 375-0-375 transformer is used in a full-wave circuit. Assume a 25-volt drop occurs across the tube.

3-10. A power supply has the form shown in the diagram.

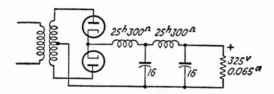

a. Determine the approximate secondary potential of the power transformer.

b. What would be the ripple potential if the power frequency is 60 cps; 400 cps?

3-11. In the power supply shown in the figure:

a. What is the output d-c potential?

b. What is the ripple potential in the output?

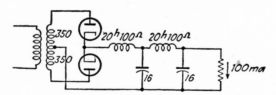

c. What is the minimum load current below which current cutout in the filter occurs? What is the corresponding load potential?

Note: Make allowance for the tube drop, but assume a perfect transformer.

3-12. A typical circuit for the high-potential supply for a cathode-ray tube is shown in the diagram. Estimate the output ripple potential.

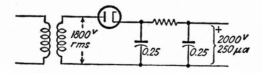

3-13. The circuit shown in the accompanying diagram is to supply two different potentials. If the transformer is 375-0-375, what are the output potentials?

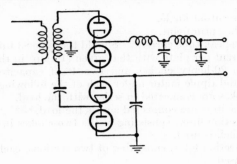

CHAPTER 4

VACUUM TRIODES AS CIRCUIT ELEMENTS

4-1. Introduction. The analysis of the behavior of a vacuum-tube circuit may be accomplished by two different methods, both of which are to be examined in some detail. In one method, use is made of the static characteristics of the tube. The second method achieves two forms. In one, the tube is replaced by an equivalent potential source and a series resistance. The source potential depends on the amplitude of the input signal, the internal resistance depending on the tube that is used. In the other form, the tube is replaced by an equivalent current source and a shunting conductance. The magnitude of the source current depends on the amplitude of the input signal, the shunting conductance depending on the tube that is used.

Although the second methods assume that the tube characteristics are linear, the ultimate analyses allow a very clear insight into the operation of the circuit. Because of this, the equivalent-circuit methods of analysis are usually considerably more important than the method involving the tube characteristics. Moreover, it is possible to estimate the inaccuracies in the method, when large signal operation is involved. Actually, the form of analysis is dictated in large measure by the bias of the tube, the signal amplitudes, and the characteristics of the load. It must be noted that the equivalent-circuit techniques provide no means for establishing d-c bias and current levels, and direct recourse to the static characteristics is necessary for this purpose.

An introduction of the methods will be made in terms of the operation of the triode, but these will later be extended to the operation of other types of tubes.

4-2. Symbols and Terminology. The simple triode amplifier is illustrated in Fig. 4-1. Before proceeding with the analysis, it is necessary to discuss the meaning of the symbols and the general terminology of vacuum-tube circuits.

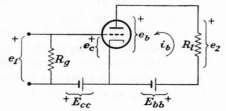

FIG. 4-1. The basic circuit of a triode amplifier.

The input circuit of the amplifier usually refers to all the elements of the circuit that exists between the grid and the cathode terminals of the tube. Similarly, the output, or plate, circuit usually refers to the elements that are connected between the cathode and the plate terminals of the tube. In the circuit illustrated, the input circuit comprises the input potential source e_1, the grid resistor R_g, and the bias battery E_{cc}. The plate circuit consists of the load resistor R_l and the plate-supply battery E_{bb}. In many applications, the input signal e_1 is a sinusoidally varying potential, although the waveshape may be nonsinusoidal, and is frequently very carefully chosen for a particular application.

A variety of potentials, both d-c and varying, are involved simultaneously in a vacuum-tube circuit, making it necessary that a precise method of labeling such quantities be established. In what follows, lowercase letters will be used to designate instantaneous values, and capital letters will denote either d-c or rms values of sinusoids. The subscripts c and g will refer to the grid circuit, and the subscripts b and p will refer to the plate circuit. Examples of the notation follow:

E_{cc} = d-c grid, or C bias

E_{bb} = d-c plate supply, or B supply

E_1 = rms value of a-c input excitation potential if this excitation is sinusoidal

E_2 = rms value of a-c output potential for a sinusoidal output

e_1 = instantaneous input signal potential; measured with respect to the input terminals

e_c = instantaneous potential that appears between grid and cathode of tube

e_g = instantaneous-signal component that appears between grid and cathode of tube

e_2 = instantaneous signal potential that appears across output element of circuit

e_b = instantaneous potential between plate and cathode of tube

i_p = instantaneous-signal component of plate current; positive in direction from cathode to plate through load

i_b = instantaneous total plate current; positive in direction from cathode to plate through load

I_b = average or d-c current in plate circuit

E_b = average or d-c potential from plate to cathode

Figure 4-1 illustrates the reference positive-potential polarities and the reference direction of current. These reference conditions are an essential part of the diagram.

As a specific illustration of the notation, suppose that the input signal potential to the amplifier of Fig. 4-1 is

$$e_1 = e_g = \sqrt{2}\, E_g \sin \omega t$$

Then the instantaneous grid-cathode potential is

$$e_c = E_{cc} + \sqrt{2}\, E_g \sin \omega t$$

Circuits will be discussed in which no such simple relation between grid driving signal and grid-cathode potential exists, owing to an involved interconnection of circuit elements among the tube elements.

4-3. Graphical Analysis. Refer to Fig. 4-1, and suppose that the grid input signal $e_1 = 0$. Owing to the d-c sources E_{cc} and E_{bb}, it will be supposed that there is a current in the plate circuit. This is true only if the plate supply E_{bb} and the grid supply E_{cc} are properly chosen. The value of this current may be found graphically. In fact, it is essential that a graphical solution be used. This follows from the fact that the plate circuit of Fig. 4-1 yields the relation

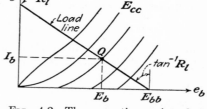

$$e_b = E_{bb} - i_b R_l \qquad (4\text{-}1)$$

However, this one equation is not sufficient to determine the current corresponding to the potential E_{bb}, since there are two unknown quantities in the expression, e_b and i_b.

FIG. 4-2. The operating point Q is located at the intersection of the load line and the plate characteristic for $e_c = E_{cc}$.

A second relation between e_b and i_b is given by the plate characteristics of the triode. The simultaneous solution of Eq. (2-1) and the plate characteristics will yield the desired current. This is accomplished by drawing Eq. (4-1) on the plate characteristics, in the manner illustrated in Fig. 4-2. The line that passes through the points

$$i_b = 0 \qquad e_b = E_{bb}$$
$$i_b = \frac{E_{bb}}{R_l} \qquad e_b = 0 \qquad\qquad (4\text{-}2)$$

is known as the *load line*. It is obviously independent of the tube characteristics, for it depends only upon elements external to the tube. The intersection of this line with the curve for $e_c = E_{cc}$ is called the *operating*, or *quiescent*, point Q. The grid-bias supply E_{cc} is usually such as to maintain the grid negative relative to the cathode. The Q current in the external circuit is I_b, and the corresponding plate-cathode potential is E_b.

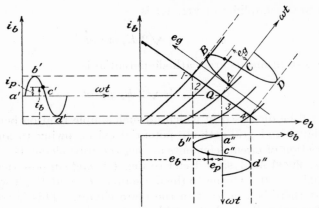

Fig. 4-3. The output current and potential waveforms for a given input grid signal.

Suppose that the grid-cathode potential is

$$e_c = E_{cc} + \sqrt{2}\, E_g \sin \omega t$$

The maximum and minimum values of e_c will be $E_{cc} + \sqrt{2}\, E_g$ and $E_{cc} - \sqrt{2}\, E_g$, respectively. The plate current and the plate potential will vary about the values of I_b and E_b. The graphical construction of Fig. 4-3 shows the details of the variations. The values of e_b and i_b for any given value of e_c are obtained from the intersection of the load line and the i_b-e_b curve for the specified e_c. The points a', b', c', etc., of the output current and the points a'', b'', c'', etc., of the output-potential wave correspond, respectively, to the points A, B, C, etc., of the input-grid-signal waveform.

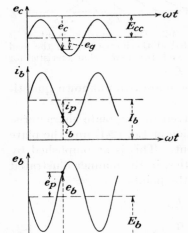

It is instructive to show the several waveshapes in their proper phase relation. This is done in Fig. 4-4. It should be noted in particular that the variations about the quiescent values have been labeled. The quantities so labeled are

Fig. 4-4. The grid input waveshape and the corresponding output current and potential waveshapes.

$$
\begin{aligned}
e_g &= e_c - E_{cc} \\
e_p &= e_b - E_b \qquad (4\text{-}3) \\
i_p &= i_b - I_b
\end{aligned}
$$

These quantities give a measure of the amplification property of the amplifier, as it is a direct measure of the a-c output variations for a given a-c input variation.

The curves of Fig. 4-4 indicate the following very significant results: If the current i_p is sinusoidal, then i_p and e_p are 180 deg out of phase with each other. Also, the grid driving potential e_g and the plate current i_p are in phase with each other. This simply states that, when a positive signal is applied to the grid, the tube current increases. Moreover, with an increased current in the plate circuit, the potential of the plate falls.

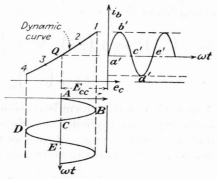

A curve of the intersection of the load line with the static-characteristic curves, which is a measure of the current i_b as a function of e_c for the specified E_{bb} and load R_l, is important. It is known as the "dynamic" characteristic of the tube circuit and yields directly the output current for a given input signal. The construction is directly related

FIG. 4-5. The dynamic curve and its use in determining the output waveshape for a given input signal.

to the construction of Fig. 4-3 and is given in Fig. 4-5. The corresponding points on both curves are similarly marked.

4-4. Potential-source Equivalent Representation of a Triode. In most electron-tube problems, one is interested in the "a-c response" of the tube, rather than in the total instantaneous variation of the potentials and current. That is, the values of i_p and e_p for a given e_g are ordinarily desired. It is possible to deduce this information directly from the static characteristics of the tube, as discussed in Sec. 4-3. Of course, if the potential variations are small, the accuracy of the results will be poor, as small changes cannot be read with any degree of accuracy from the curves. Moreover, the process may become quite tedious to perform, particularly for a reactive load, since the load curve is no longer a straight line.

For small variations in the input potential, the tube parameters μ, r_p and g_m will remain substantially constant over the operating range. Under such conditions, it will be shown that the graphical solution may be replaced by an analytic one. Actually, the equivalent analytical solution depends on the constancy of the tube parameters, rather than on the magnitude of the signals involved. The analytic method may be used even under large signal operation provided that the tube parameters remain substantially constant.

Reference is made to Eqs. (2-17) and (2-18), which specify the variation in current about the quiescent point in terms of the variation resulting from the changes in the plate and grid potentials. This expression,

which is

$$\Delta i_b = \left(\frac{\partial i_b}{\partial e_b}\right)_{E_c} \Delta e_b + \left(\frac{\partial i_b}{\partial e_c}\right)_{E_b} \Delta e_c \qquad (4\text{-}4)$$

is only approximate. It specifies only the first two terms of the Taylor expansion of the function $i_b = i_b(e_b, e_c)$. In the general case, the result is

$$\Delta i_b = \left(\frac{\partial i_b}{\partial e_b}\right)_{E_c} \Delta e_b + \left(\frac{\partial i_b}{\partial e_c}\right)_{E_b} \Delta e_c + \frac{1}{2!}\left(\frac{\partial^2 i_b}{\partial e_b^2}\right)_{E_c} (\Delta e_b)^2$$
$$+ \frac{1}{2!}\left(\frac{\partial^2 i_b}{\partial e_c^2}\right)_{E_b} (\Delta e_c)^2 + \frac{\partial^2 i_b}{\partial e_b \, \partial e_c} \, \partial e_b \, \partial e_c + \cdots \qquad (4\text{-}5)$$

A more informative form is possible, by relating the higher-order terms in the expansion explicitly as variations in the plate resistance r_p or in the mutual conductance g_m. Consider the third term in the expansion. By combining this with Eq. (1-18), there results

$$\frac{1}{2}\left(\frac{\partial^2 i_b}{\partial e_b^2}\right)_{E_c} (\Delta e_b)^2 = \frac{1}{2}\left[\frac{\partial(1/r_p)}{\partial e_b}\right]_{E_c} (\Delta e_b)^2 \qquad (4\text{-}6)$$

When the tube parameters are sensibly constant over the operating range of Δe_b and Δe_c, Eq. (4-4) is an adequate representation of the variation. This may be written, by Eqs. (2-17) and (2-18), as

$$\Delta i_b = \frac{1}{r_p} \Delta e_b + g_m \, \Delta e_c \qquad (4\text{-}7)$$

But as the changes about the quiescent values are, respectively,

$$\begin{aligned}
\Delta i_b &= i_b - I_b = i_p \\
\Delta e_c &= e_c - E_{cc} = e_g \\
\Delta e_b &= e_b - E_{bb} = e_p
\end{aligned} \qquad (4\text{-}8)$$

then Eq. (4-7) becomes

$$i_p = \frac{1}{r_p} e_p + g_m e_g \qquad (4\text{-}9)$$

or

$$e_p = -\mu e_g + i_p r_p \qquad (4\text{-}10)$$

This expression shows that the potential e_p comprises two components; one is an equivalent generated emf, or electromotance, which is μ times as large as the grid-cathode potential e_g, and the second is a potential difference across the tube resistance r_p resulting from the current i_p through it.

Equation (4-10) may be used as the basis for drawing an equivalent network for the tube. This is done in Fig. 4-6. Observe that the plate circuit of the tube is replaced by a fictitious potential source with an electromotance μe_g and an internal resistance r_p. Two points are emphasized. First, the reference positive polarities and reference current direction are essential parts of the equivalent-network representation. Second, no d-c quantities appear on the diagram, since the equivalent-circuit representation applies only for *changes* about the Q point.

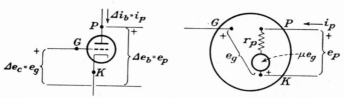

Fig. 4-6. The vacuum triode and its a-c potential-source equivalent representation.

4-5. Current-source Equivalent Representation of a Triode. The current-source equivalent representation of a triode replaces the tube by a constant-current source shunted by a conductance, instead of the potential source with a series resistance. The form of the result is easily obtained by rearranging Eq. (4-9) into the form

$$g_m e_g = i_p - \frac{e_p}{r_p} \tag{4-11}$$

This expression shows that the current i_p comprises two components; one is a generated current which is g_m as large as the grid-cathode potential e_g, and the second is a current through the shunting tube resistance r_p because of the potential e_p across it.

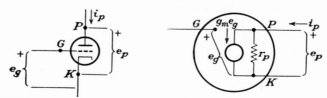

Fig. 4-7. The vacuum triode and its current-source equivalent representation.

Equation (4-11) may be used as the basis for drawing the equivalent network of the tube. This is done in Fig. 4-7. Observe that the plate circuit of the tube is replaced by a current source with generated current $g_m e_g$ and a shunting resistance r_p. Note also that the reference positive polarities and the reference current direction are essential parts of the equivalent-network representation, as before.

The reader will observe a striking parallel between the discussion in this section and that in the previous section, except that one section confines itself to a potential source and a series internal resistance, whereas the present section confines itself to a current source and a shunt conductance (or resistance). This is actually part of a larger pattern which exists in general network analysis and which is given the name of *duality*.*

If the varying quantities are sinusoidally varying ones, and this will ordinarily be assumed unless otherwise explicitly stated, the analysis proceeds most easily in terms of the phasors (sinors and complex-number representation for impedances) of elementary a-c circuit theory. The circuit notation and certain elements of general network analysis which will be found useful in this text are discussed in Appendix A. The reader is urged to refer to this appendix before proceeding. For sinusoidally varying signals, therefore, the tube potentials are expressed in terms of the symbols E_g, E_p, and I_p, where these boldface symbols are employed to denote sinor quantities, a symbolism that is adopted in this text. For sinusoidally varying quantities, the vacuum triode is given in the accompanying two equivalent forms (see Fig. 4-8).

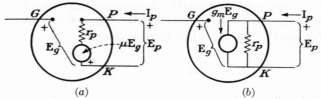

(a)   (b)

FIG. 4-8. (a) The potential-source and (b) the current-source equivalent circuits of the triode for sinusoidally varying quantities.

4-6. Linear Analysis of Electron-tube Circuits. As discussed in Sec. 4-4, it is possible to determine the a-c response of a vacuum-tube circuit, when the parameters of the tube remain substantially constant over the range of operation, by replacing the tube by either its potential-source equivalent or its current-source equivalent, and then employing the techniques of general network analysis in the complete analysis of the circuit.

The technique of drawing the equivalent network of any tube circuit is a straightforward process, although care must be exercised in carrying out the details. To avoid error, the following simple rules will be found helpful:

1. Draw the actual diagram neatly.

2. Mark the points G, P, and K on this diagram. Locate these points as the start of the equivalent circuit. Maintain the same relative position as in the original circuit.

3. Between points P and K include either the potential-source representation of Fig. 4-8a or the current-source representation of Fig. 4-8b, depending on the preferred form.

---

* Some amplification of the principles of duality is given in Appendix A. For an extensive discussion see W. LePage and S. Seely, "General Network Analysis," McGraw-Hill Book Company, Inc., New York, 1952.

4. Transfer all circuit elements from the actual circuit to the equivalent circuit, without altering the relative positions of these elements.

5. Replace each d-c source by its internal resistance, if any.

Several examples will be given to illustrate the foregoing techniques.

Example 1.   Calculate the output potential E_2 of the simple amplifier circuit given in Fig. 4-9.   Note that the technique of drawing the equivalent circuit is in accord with the rules given above.

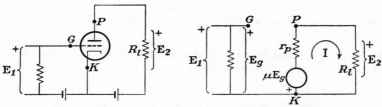

FIG. 4-9. A simple amplifier circuit and its a-c equivalent. The potential-source equivalent of the tube has been used.

A direct application of the Kirchhoff potential law, which requires that the algebraic sum of the potential rises and falls in completing a closed loop must be zero, yields directly

$$\mu E_g + I(r_p + R_l) = 0 \tag{4-12}$$

Note also that

$$E_g = E_1 \tag{4-13}$$

It therefore follows that

$$I = - \frac{\mu E_1}{r_p + R_l} \tag{4-14}$$

and the output potential E_2 is given by

$$E_2 = IR_l = - \frac{\mu R_l E_1}{r_p + R_l} = \frac{-\mu}{1 + r_p/R_l} E_1 \tag{4-15}$$

The ratio of the output to input potentials E_2/E_1 is the amplification, or gain, **K** of the amplifier.   Therefore

$$K = \frac{E_2}{E_1} = \frac{-\mu}{1 + r_p/R_l} \tag{4-16}$$

It is of interest to plot this expression, which has the form given in Fig. 4-10. It should be observed from this diagram that gains which approach μ are quite feasible with moderate R_l/r_p ratios.   For values of the ratio $-K/\mu$ which are nearly unity, it is required

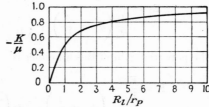

FIG. 4-10. The gain of the amplifier of Fig. 4-9 as a function of load resistance.

that R_l be large.   In this case, however, for the tube to be operated at the proper d-c quiescent levels, the source E_{bb} must be large, and the heating of the tube or load resistor may become unduly high.

Example 2. Calculate the output potential $\mathbf{E}_2$ of the amplifier circuit given in Fig. 4-11.

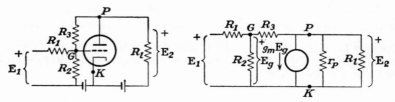

FIG. 4-11. A simple amplifier circuit and its a-c equivalent. The current-source equivalent has been used.

The Kirchhoff current law is applied to the two junctions. This law requires that the algebraic sum of the currents at any junction must be zero. The equations are

$$\text{Junction } G: \qquad \frac{\mathbf{E}_2 - \mathbf{E}_g}{R_3} - \frac{\mathbf{E}_g}{R_2} - \frac{\mathbf{E}_g - \mathbf{E}_1}{R_1} = 0$$

$$\text{Junction } P: \qquad -\frac{\mathbf{E}_2 - \mathbf{E}_g}{R_3} - g_m\mathbf{E}_g - \frac{\mathbf{E}_2}{r_p} - \frac{\mathbf{E}_2}{R_l} = 0 \tag{4-17}$$

Collecting terms gives two equations,

$$\frac{\mathbf{E}_1}{R_1} + \frac{\mathbf{E}_2}{R_3} - \mathbf{E}_g\left(\frac{1}{R_1} + \frac{1}{R_2} + \frac{1}{R_3}\right) = 0$$

$$\mathbf{E}_2\left(\frac{1}{R_3} + \frac{1}{r_p} + \frac{1}{R_l}\right) + \mathbf{E}_g\left(g_m - \frac{1}{R_3}\right) = 0 \tag{4-18}$$

Combine the equations to get, by eliminating $\mathbf{E}_g$,

$$\frac{\mathbf{E}_1}{R_1} + \mathbf{E}_2\left[\frac{1}{R_3} + \frac{\left(\dfrac{1}{R_1} + \dfrac{1}{R_2} + \dfrac{1}{R_3}\right)\left(\dfrac{1}{R_3} + \dfrac{1}{r_p} + \dfrac{1}{R_l}\right)}{g_m - 1/R_3}\right] = 0 \tag{4-19}$$

The output potential is

$$\mathbf{E}_2 = \frac{-(g_m - 1/R_3)(1/R_1)}{\dfrac{1}{R_3}\left(g_m - \dfrac{1}{R_3}\right) + \left(\dfrac{1}{R_1} + \dfrac{1}{R_2} + \dfrac{1}{R_3}\right)\left(\dfrac{1}{R_3} + \dfrac{1}{r_p} + \dfrac{1}{R_l}\right)}\mathbf{E}_1 \tag{4-20}$$

The potential gain of this amplifier is

$$\mathbf{K} \equiv \frac{\mathbf{E}_2}{\mathbf{E}_1} = \frac{-(g_m - 1/R_3)(1/R_1)}{\left(g_m - \dfrac{1}{R_3}\right)\dfrac{1}{R_3} + \left(\dfrac{1}{R_1} + \dfrac{1}{R_2} + \dfrac{1}{R_3}\right)\left(\dfrac{1}{R_3} + \dfrac{1}{r_p} + \dfrac{1}{R_l}\right)} \tag{4-21}$$

It should be noted that if the resistors R_1 and R_3 were absent, the circuit will reduce to that of Example 1. Thus, by setting $R_1 = 0$ and $R_3 = \infty$ in Eq. (4-21), the result reduces to that given in Eq. (4-16). Because of the presence of R_1 and R_3, the gain of this amplifier stage is lower than that given in Example 1.

A discussion of the effects of introducing these resistors, which have introduced what is known as *negative feedback*, will be deferred until Chap 7.

4-7. Measurement of Triode Coefficients.   As several additional illustrations of the methods of analysis just discussed, the circuits for obtaining the values of μ, r_p, and g_m of a triode will be analyzed.   It should be recalled that the triode coefficients, first discussed in Sec. 2-13, were shown to be related to the slope of the static-characteristic curves, according to Figs. 2-14 to 2-16.   However, the accuracy with which these quantities can be measured in this way is not high.   Not only do the methods now to be discussed yield results which are made under dynamic conditions, but the results are usually more accurate than those deduced from the static characteristics.

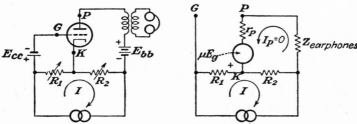

Fig. 4-12. The Miller bridge and its equivalent circuit for determining the amplification factor of a triode under operating conditions.

The amplification factor μ is readily determined by means of the circuit given in Fig. 4-12.   The operations involved in balancing the bridge consist simply in varying R_1 and R_2 until no signal from the oscillator is heard in the earphones.   When this condition prevails, the plate current $I_p = 0$.   Then the potential $\mathbf{E}_g = \mathbf{I}R_1$.   By applying Kirchhoff's law to the plate circuit,

$$-\mu\mathbf{E}_g + \mathbf{I}R_2 = 0$$

or

$$+\mu\mathbf{E}_g = \mathbf{I}R_2 = \mu\mathbf{I}R_1$$

It follows from this that

$$\mu = \frac{R_2}{R_1} \tag{4-22}$$

This measurement may be effected for any desired d-c current in the tube simply by adjusting the grid bias E_{cc}.

The transconductance g_m is measured by means of a bridge circuit that is a slight modification of Fig. 4-12.   The addition of a resistor R_3 between the plate and cathode makes this measurement possible.   The schematic and equivalent circuits of this bridge network are given in Fig. 4-13.   The measurement is accomplished by adjusting the resistors until no signal is heard in the earphones.

By applying Kirchhoff's law to the several meshes, there results

$$\mathbf{I}_p R_3 + \mathbf{I}_p r_p - \mu \mathbf{E}_g = 0$$

But the potential $\mathbf{E}_g$ is

$$\mathbf{E}_g = \mathbf{I} R_1$$

Then

$$\mathbf{I}_p(R_3 + r_p) = \mu \mathbf{I} R_1 \tag{4-23}$$

Also, it follows that

$$\mathbf{I} R_2 - \mathbf{I}_p R_3 = 0$$

or

$$\mathbf{I} R_2 = \mathbf{I}_p R_3 \tag{4-24}$$

The ratio of Eq. (4-23) to Eq. (4-24) is

$$\frac{R_3 + r_p}{R_3} = \mu \frac{R_1}{R_2}$$

from which

$$r_p = R_3 \left(\mu \frac{R_1}{R_2} - 1 \right) \tag{4-25}$$

Although this bridge may be used to evaluate r_p, the result would be dependent on the measurement of μ. If, however, R_1 is chosen in such

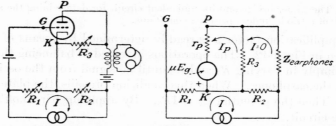

Fig. 4-13. The Miller bridge for determining the transconductance of a triode under operating conditions.

a way that $\mu R_1/R_2 \gg 1$, then approximately

$$r_p \doteq \mu \frac{R_3 R_1}{R_2}$$

or

$$g_m = \frac{\mu}{r_p} = \frac{R_2}{R_3 R_1} \tag{4-26}$$

The plate resistance r_p of the tube can be measured directly by incorporating the plate circuit of the tube as the fourth arm of a Wheatstone bridge, as shown in Fig. 4-14. When the bridge is balanced,

$$r_p = \frac{R_2 R_3}{R_1} \tag{4-27}$$

The above circuits do not yield perfect balance owing to the capacitive effects of the tube, and it is sometimes necessary to provide a means for balancing these effects. Basically, however, the circuits are those given.

4-8. Harmonic Generation in a Tube. The equivalent-linear-circuit analysis of Sec. 4-4 usually permits an adequate solution of an amplifier circuit when the limitations of the method are not exceeded or if relatively slight differences are considered of no importance. There are occasions when it is desirable to examine critically the effects of the assumptions.

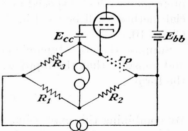

Fig. 4-14. A Wheatstone bridge for determining the plate resistance of a triode under operating conditions.

The assumption of linear operation, which is implied in Eq. (4-4) and which assumed that higher-order terms in the Taylor expansion of the current $i_b(e_b,e_c)$ are negligible, is not always valid. This assumption, which allowed the graphical solution of Fig. 4-5 to be replaced by the analytical one of Fig. 4-6, requires that the dynamic characteristic of the amplifier circuit be linear over the range of operation. Actually, the dynamic characteristic is not linear in general but contains a slight curvature. This nonlinear characteristic arises because the (i_b,e_b) static characteristics (see Fig. 4-3) are not equidistant lines for constant e_c intervals over the range of operation. The effect of this nonlinear dynamic characteristic is a nonsinusoidal output waveshape when the input wave is sinusoidal. Such an effect is known as *nonlinear*, or *amplitude*, distortion.

It is possible to obtain a measure of the degree of nonlinearity that results from the existence of the nonlinear dynamic curve. To do this, it is observed that the dynamic curve with respect to the Q point may be expressed by a power series of the form

$$i_p = a_1 e_g + a_2 e_g^2 + a_3 e_g^3 + \cdots \tag{4-28}$$

Clearly, if all terms in this series vanish except the first, then the linear assumptions of the equivalent-circuit concept result. It will be found that triodes, when operated under normal conditions, may be adequately expressed by retaining the first two terms in the expansion. When a triode is operated with such a large signal that the instantaneous grid-cathode potential becomes positive, or if the triode is operated with such a bias that the very curved portions of the plate characteristics must be employed, more than two terms must be retained in the expansion. Likewise, it is found that the parabolic approximation is not adequate to represent the dynamic curve of a tetrode or a pentode under normal operating conditions. If the dynamic curve contains an extreme curvature or if the operation is over an extreme range, it is sometimes found preferable to devise special methods of analysis. For example, such special methods will be used in the analysis of a tuned class C amplifier in Chap. 10.

Suppose that the dynamic curve may be represented as in Eq. (4-28), and consider that the input wave is a simple cosine function of time, of the form

$$e_g = E_{gm} \cos \omega t \qquad (4\text{-}29)$$

By combining this expression with Eq. (4-28) and expanding the higher-order powers of the cosine that appear in the resulting series, the result may be shown to have the form

$$i_b = I_b + B_0 + B_1 \cos \omega t + B_2 \cos 2\omega t + B_3 \cos 3\omega t + \cdots \qquad (4\text{-}30)$$

If it is assumed that the excitation potential is a sine function of the time instead of the cosine form chosen, the resulting Fourier series representing the output current will be found to contain odd sine components and even cosine components.

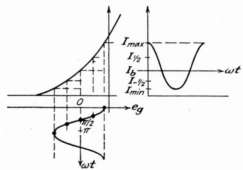

FIG. 4-15. The construction for obtaining the plate-current values to be used in the five-point schedule for determining the Fourier coefficients.

A number of different methods exist for obtaining the coefficients B_0, B_1, B_2, etc. One of the more common methods is best discussed by reference to Fig. 4-15. It will be assumed for convenience that only five terms, B_0, B_1, B_2, B_3, B_4, exist in the resulting Fourier series. In order to evaluate these five coefficients, the values of the current at five different values of e_g are required. The values chosen are I_{max}, $I_{\frac{1}{2}}$, I_b, $I_{-\frac{1}{2}}$, and I_{min} and correspond, respectively, to the following values of e_g: the maximum positive value; one-half the maximum positive value; zero; one-half the maximum negative value; the maximum negative value.

It is evident from the figure that the currents are those chosen as shown at the angles

$$\omega t = 0 \qquad i_b = I_{\text{max}}$$

$$\omega t = \frac{\pi}{3} \qquad i_b = I_{\frac{1}{2}}$$

$$\omega t = \frac{\pi}{2} \qquad i_b = I_b \tag{4-31}$$

$$\omega t = \frac{2\pi}{3} \qquad i_b = I_{-\frac{1}{2}}$$

$$\omega t = \pi \qquad i_b = I_{\text{min}}$$

By combining these results with Eq. (4-30), five equations containing five unknowns are obtained. The simultaneous solution of these equations yields

$$B_0 = \tfrac{1}{6}\,(I_{\text{max}} + 2I_{\frac{1}{2}} + 2I_{-\frac{1}{2}} + I_{\text{min}}) - I_b$$
$$B_1 = \tfrac{1}{3}\,(I_{\text{max}} + I_{\frac{1}{2}} - I_{-\frac{1}{2}} - I_{\text{min}})$$
$$B_2 = \tfrac{1}{4}\,(I_{\text{max}} - 2I_b + I_{\text{min}}) \tag{4-32}$$
$$B_3 = \tfrac{1}{6}\,(I_{\text{max}} - 2I_{\frac{1}{2}} + 2I_{-\frac{1}{2}} - I_{\text{min}})$$
$$B_4 = \tfrac{1}{12}\,(I_{\text{max}} - 4I_{\frac{1}{2}} + 6I_b - 4I_{-\frac{1}{2}} + I_{\text{min}})$$

The percentage of harmonic distortion is defined as

$$D_2 = \frac{B_2}{B_1} \times 100\% \qquad D_3 = \frac{B_3}{B_1} \times 100\% \qquad D_4 = \frac{B_4}{B_1} \times 100\% \tag{4-33}$$

where D_s ($s = 2, 3, 4, \ldots$) represents the per cent distortion of the sth harmonic and the total distortion is defined as

$$D = \sqrt{D_2^2 + D_3^2 + D_4^2 + \cdots} \tag{4-34}$$

For the case where a three-point schedule is sufficient, and, as already indicated, this would apply for a triode under normal operating conditions, the analysis yields the expressions

$$B_1 = \tfrac{1}{2}\,(I_{\text{max}} - I_{\text{min}})$$
$$B_2 = B_0 = \tfrac{1}{4}\,(I_{\text{max}} - 2I_b + I_{\text{min}}) \tag{4-35}$$

PROBLEMS

4-1. A 6C5 triode is used in the circuit of Fig. 4-1, the plate characteristics of which are given in Appendix B.

a. With $E_{bb} = 300$ volts, $E_{cc} = -8$ volts, $R_l = 20$ kilohms, draw the load line, and locate the operating point. Plot the dynamic characteristic of the circuit.

b. If $e_1 = 6 \sin 10{,}000t$, determine the output current graphically, and plot the curve as a function of ωt.

c. From these curves, determine and plot the instantaneous plate potential for the same interval as in part *b*. Check the phase relation between a-c components of grid potential, plate current, and plate potential.

4-2. The characteristics of a given triode may be represented by the expression

$$i_b = 8.8 \times 10^{-3}(e_b + 16e_c)^{1.5} \qquad \text{ma}$$

It is to be operated at a plate potential $E_b = 250$ volts and a grid-bias potential $E_c = -9$ volts.

a. Calculate the plate resistance of the tube.

b. If this tube is used in the circuit of Fig. 4-1 with a load resistance $R_l = 10$ kilohms, determine the plate supply potential necessary for the tube to be operating under the specified conditions.

c. Suppose that the grid driving source applies a potential $e_1 = 8 \sin \omega t$ to the grid. Determine the a-c potential across the load resistor.

4-3. Draw the potential-source equivalent circuit of the electron-tube circuits in the accompanying diagrams.

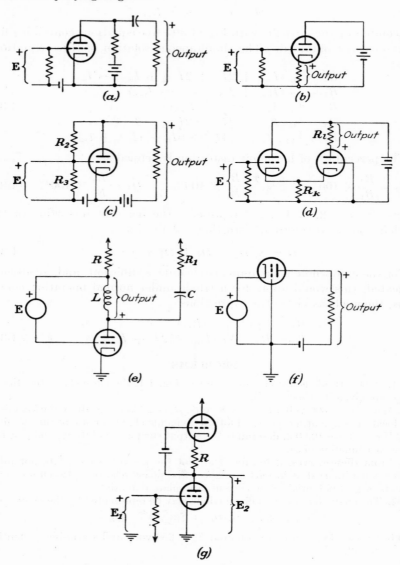

4-4. A type 6A3 triode is used in an amplifier circuit to supply power to a 3,000-ohm resistor. In this circuit $E_{cc} = -45$ volts, $E_{bb} = 350$ volts. A 45-volt peak a-c signal is applied to the grid.

a. Plot the dynamic curve of the tube.

b. Assume that only the fundamental and a second harmonic exist in the output. Determine the magnitudes of each.

c. Plot a curve showing the output current for the sinusoidal input. On the same sheet, plot the corresponding results from the calculations in part b.

4-5. It is possible to obtain a five-point schedule for determining the coefficients B_0, B_1, B_2, B_3, B_4 by almost any sensible choice of angle. Determine the five-point schedule for determining the coefficients B in terms of I_{max}, $I_{0.707}$, I_b, $I_{-0.707}$, I_{min}.

CHAPTER 5

BASIC AMPLIFIER PRINCIPLES

5-1. Classification of Tubes and Amplifiers. The classification of an amplifier is usually somewhat involved, owing to the fact that a complete classification must include information about the tubes that are used, the conditions of the bias, the character of the circuit elements connected to the tubes, the function of the circuit, and the range of operation. Certain of these factors will be discussed here, but many will be deferred for later discussion.

Apart from the wide variety of vacuum tubes of the diode, triode, tetrode, pentode, beam, hexode, heptode, and multiunit types and the varied power capacities of each type, it is possible to classify the tubes according to their principal applications. Tubes may be classified roughly into five groups, viz., potential-amplifier tubes, power-amplifier tubes, current-amplifier tubes, general-purpose tubes, and special-purpose tubes.

1. Potential-amplifier tubes have a relatively high amplification factor and are used where the primary consideration is one of high potential gain. Such tubes usually operate into high impedance loads, either tuned or untuned.

2. Power-amplifier tubes are those which have relatively low values of amplification factor and fairly low values of plate resistance. They are capable of controlling appreciable currents at reasonably high plate potentials.

3. Current-amplifier tubes are those which are designed to give a large change of plate current for a small grid potential; i.e., they possess a high transconductance. These tubes may be required to carry fairly large plate currents. Such tubes find application as both potential and power amplifiers, depending on the tube capacity.

4. General-purpose amplifier tubes are those whose characteristics are intermediate between the potential- and the power-amplifier tubes. They must have a reasonably high amplification factor and yet must be able to supply some power.

5. Special-purpose tubes include a wide variety of types. The hexode, heptode, and multiunit tubes are of this type.

100

Amplifiers are classified according to their frequency range, the method of tube operation, and the method of interstage coupling.   For example, they may be classed as direct-coupled amplifiers, audio-frequency (a-f) amplifiers, video amplifiers, or tuned r-f amplifiers if some indication of the frequency of operation is desired.   Also, the position of the quiescent point and the extent of the tube characteristic that is being used will determine the method of tube operation.   This will specify whether the tube is being operated in class A, class AB, class B, or class C.   These definitions are illustrated graphically in Fig. 5-1.

1. A class A amplifier is an amplifier in which the grid bias and the a-c grid potentials are such that plate current flows in the tube at all times.

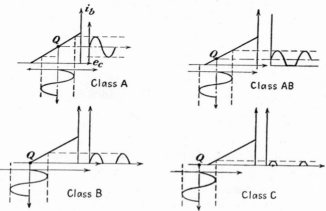

Fig. 5-1. Amplifier classification in terms of the position of the quiescent point of the tube.

2. A class AB amplifier is one in which the grid bias and the a-c grid potentials are such that plate current flows in the tube for appreciably more than half but less than the entire electrical cycle.

3. A class B amplifier is one in which the grid bias is approximately equal to the cutoff value of the tube, so that the plate current is approximately zero when no exciting grid potential is applied, and such that plate current flows for approximately one-half of each cycle when an a-c grid potential is applied.

4. A class C amplifier is one in which the grid bias is appreciably greater than the cutoff value, so that the plate current in each tube is zero when no a-c grid potential is applied, and such that plate current flows for appreciably less than one-half of each cycle when an a-c grid potential is applied.

To indicate that grid current does not flow during any part of the input cycle, the subscript 1 is frequently added to the letter or letters of the class identification.   The subscript 2 is added to denote that grid current does flow during some part of the cycle. For example, the designation class AB₁ indicates that the amplifier operates under class AB conditions and that no grid current flows during any part of the input cycle.

Potential amplifiers, whether tuned or untuned, generally operate in class A. Low-power audio amplifiers may be operated under class A and with special connections, under class AB or class B conditions. Tuned r-f power amplifiers are operated either under class B or under class C conditions. Oscillators usually operate under class C conditions. A detailed discussion is deferred until the appropriate points in the text. When a tube is used essentially as a switch, no classification is ordinarily specified.

5-2. Distortion in Amplifiers. The application of a sinusoidal signal to the grid of an ideal class A amplifier will be accompanied by a sinusoidal output wave. Frequently the output waveform is not an exact replica of the input-signal waveform because of distortion that results either within the tube or from the influence of the associated circuit. The distortions that may exist either separately or simultaneously are nonlinear distortion, frequency distortion, and delay distortion. These are defined as follows:

1. Nonlinear distortion is that form of distortion which occurs when the ratio of potential to current is a function of the magnitude of either.

2. Frequency distortion is that form of distortion in which the change is in the relative magnitudes of the different frequency components of a wave, provided that the change is not caused by nonlinear distortion.

3. Delay distortion is that form of distortion which occurs when the phase angle of the transfer impedance with respect to two chosen pairs of terminals is not linear with frequency within a desired range, the time of transmission, or delay, varying with frequency in that range.

In accordance with definition 1, nonlinear distortion results when new frequencies appear in the output which are not present in the input signal. These new frequencies arise from the existence of a nonlinear dynamic curve and were discussed in Sec. 4-8.

Frequency distortion arises when the components of different frequency are amplified by different amounts. This distortion is usually a function of the character of the circuits associated with the amplifier. If the gain vs. frequency characteristic of the amplifier is not a horizontal straight line over the range of frequencies under consideration, the circuit is said to exhibit frequency distortion over this range.

Delay distortion, also called *phase-shift distortion*, results from the fact that the phase shift of waves of different frequency in the amplifier is different. Such distortion is not of importance in amplifiers of the a-f type, since delay distortion is not perceptible to the ear. It is very objectionable in systems that depend on waveshape for their operation, as, for example, in television or facsimile systems.   If the phase shift is proportional to the frequency, a time delay will occur although no distortion is introduced.   To see this, suppose that the input signal to the amplifier is periodic and may be expressed analytically by

$$e_1 = E_{m1} \sin (\omega t + \theta_1) + E_{m2} \sin (2\omega t + \theta_2) + \cdots \qquad (5\text{-}1)$$

If the gain K is constant in magnitude but possesses a phase shift that is proportional to the frequency, the output will be of the form

$$e_2 = KE_{m1} \sin (\omega t + \theta_1 + \psi) + KE_{m2} \sin (2\omega t + \theta_2 + 2\psi) + \cdots$$

This output potential has the same waveshape as the input signal, but a time delay between these two waves exists.   By writing

$$\omega t' = \omega t + \psi$$

then

$$e_2 = KE_{m1} \sin (\omega t' + \theta_1) + KE_{m2} \sin (2\omega t' + \theta_2) + \cdots \qquad (5\text{-}2)$$

This is simply the expression given by Eq. (3-1), except that it is referred to a new time scale t'.   Delay distortion, like frequency distortion, arises from the frequency characteristics of the circuit associated with the vacuum tube.

It is not possible to achieve such a linear phase characteristic with simple networks, but it may be approximated with special phase-equalizing networks.

5-3. The Decibel; Power Sensitivity.   In many problems where two power levels are to be compared, it is found very convenient to compare the relative powers on a logarithmic rather than on a direct scale.   The unit of this logarithmic scale is called the *bel*.   A *decibel*, which is abbreviated db, is $\frac{1}{10}$ bel.   By definition, the logarithm to the base 10 of the ratio of two powers is N bels; that is,

$$\text{Number of bels} = \log_{10} \frac{P_2}{P_1}$$

$$(5\text{-}3)$$

or

$$\text{Number of db} = 10 \log_{10} \frac{P_2}{P_1}$$

It should be emphasized that the bel or the decibel denotes a power ratio. Consequently the specification of a certain power in decibels is meaningless unless a reference level is implied or is explicitly specified.   In communication applications, it is usual practice to specify 6 mw as the zero reference level.   However, any power may be designated as the zero reference level in any particular problem.

Suppose that these considerations are applied to a power amplifier, with P_2 the output power and P_1 the input power.   This assumes that the input circuit to the amplifier absorbs power.   If the grid circuit does not absorb an appreciable power, then the term *decibel gain* of the amplifier means nothing.   Under such conditions, it is customary to speak of *power sensitivity,* which is defined as the ratio of the power output to the square of the input signal potential.   Thus

$$\text{Power sensitivity} \equiv \frac{P_2}{E_1^2} \qquad \text{mhos} \qquad (5\text{-}4)$$

where P_2 is the power output in watts and E_1 is the input signal rms volts.

If the input and output impedances are equal resistances, then $P_2 = E_2^2/R$ and $P_1 = E_1^2/R$, where E_2 and E_1 are the output and input potentials.   Under this condition, Eq. (5-3) reduces to

$$\text{Number of db} = 20 \log_{10} \frac{E_2}{E_1} \qquad (5\text{-}5)$$

In general, the input and output resistances are not equal.   Despite this, this expression is adopted as a convenient definition of the decibel potential gain of an amplifier.   It is essential, however, when the gain of an amplifier is discussed, that it be clearly stated whether one is referring to potential gain or power gain, as these two figures will be different, in general.

Many of the considerations of the foregoing sections are best illustrated by several examples.

Example 1.   Calculate the gain of the grounded-grid amplifier circuit of Fig. 5-2.

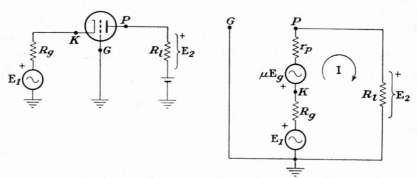

Fig. 5-2. Schematic and equivalent circuits of a grounded-grid amplifier.

Solution.   The equivalent circuit of the amplifier is drawn according to the rules of Sec. 4-6 and is that shown in Fig. 5-2b.   The application of the Kirchhoff potential law to the equivalent circuit yields

$$\mathbf{E}_1 - \mu\mathbf{E}_g - \mathbf{I}(r_p + R_g + R_l) = 0 \qquad (5\text{-}6)$$

Also from the diagram

$$\mathbf{E}_g = -\mathbf{E}_1 + \mathbf{I}R_g \qquad (5\text{-}7)$$

Combine the two equations to find

$$\mathbf{E}_1 - \mu(-\mathbf{E}_1 + \mathbf{I}R_g) - \mathbf{I}(r_p + R_g + R_l) = 0$$

The plate current is then given by

$$\mathbf{I} = \frac{\mathbf{E}_1(\mu + 1)}{r_p + (\mu + 1)R_g + R_l} \tag{5-8}$$

The corresponding output potential is

$$\mathbf{E}_2 = \mathbf{I}R_l = \frac{(\mu + 1)R_l\mathbf{E}_1}{(\mu + 1)R_g + r_p + R_l} \tag{5-9}$$

The gain, or potential amplification of this amplifier, which is the ratio of the output to the input potential, is

$$\mathbf{K} = \frac{\mathbf{E}_2}{\mathbf{E}_1} = \frac{R_l}{R_g + \dfrac{r_p + R_l}{\mu + 1}} \tag{5-10}$$

The input impedance is given as the ratio $\mathbf{E}_1/\mathbf{I}$ and is

$$\mathbf{Z}_i = \frac{\mathbf{E}_1}{\mathbf{I}} = \frac{r_p + R_l}{\mu + 1} + R_g \tag{5-11}$$

which, for small R_g, is quite small. This means, of course, that heavy loading of the driving source may exist if R_g is small.

It is of interest to compare the results of this example with Example 1 of Sec. 4-6. Observe that it is possible to apply the signal either in the grid circuit or in the cathode circuit and still achieve operation of the tube, although the input impedance is different in the two cases.

Example 2. A type 6J5 triode for which $\mu = 20$, $r_p = 7,700$ ohms is employed in an amplifier, the load of which consists of an inductor for which $R_L = 1,000$ ohms and $L = 1$ henry. Calculate the gain and phase shift of the amplifier at $\omega = 2,000$ rad/sec and $\omega = 10,000$ rad/sec. Draw the complete sinor diagram of the system. The input signal is 6 volts rms.

Solution. The schematic and equivalent circuits are shown in the accompanying diagrams. At $\omega = 2,000$ rad/sec,

$$\mathbf{I} = \frac{120 + j0}{7,700 + (1,000 + j2,000)} = 13.1 - j3.01 \text{ ma}$$

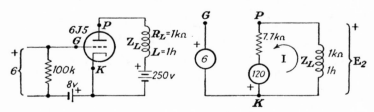

The output potential is

$$E_2 = -(1,000 + j2,000)(13.1 - j3.01) \times 10^{-3}$$
$$= -(19.1 + j23.2) = 30.1\underline{/-129.5°}$$

The gain is given by

$$K = \frac{E_2}{E_1} = \frac{30.1\underline{/-129.5°}}{6\underline{/0}} = 5.01\underline{/-129.5°}$$

The potential sinor diagram has the form shown in the sketch.

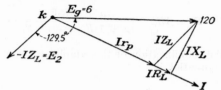

At $\omega = 10,000$ rad/sec,

$$I = \frac{120 + j0}{7,700 + (1,000 + j10,000)} = 5.94 - j6.83 \text{ ma}$$

The output potential is

$$E_2 = -(1,000 + j10,000)(5.94 - j6.83) \times 10^{-3}$$
$$= -(74.2 + j52.6)$$
$$= 90.8\underline{/-144.7°}$$

The gain is given by

$$K = \frac{90.8\underline{/-144.7°}}{6\underline{/0}} = 15.1\underline{/-144.7°}$$

The potential sinor diagram has the form of the accompanying diagram.

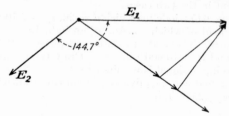

The results are tabulated for convenience. An examination of the results indicates the presence of frequency distortion, since the gain at $\omega = 2,000$ rad/sec is different from that at $\omega = 10,000$ rad/sec. Also, phase-shift distortion exists in this amplifier.

ω	Gain and phase	Potential db gain
2,000	$5.01\underline{/-129.5°}$	14 db
10,000	$15.1\underline{/-144.7°}$	23.6 db

5-4. Interelectrode Capacitances in a Triode. It was assumed in the foregoing discussions that, with a negative bias on the grid, the grid driving-source current was negligible. This is generally true if one examines only the current intercepted by the grid because of its location within the region of the electron stream. Actually though, owing to the physical proximity of the elements of the tube, interelectrode capacitances between pairs of elements exist. These capacitances are important in the behavior of the circuit, as charging currents do exist.

Owing to the capacitance that exists between the plate and the grid, it is not true that the grid circuit is completely independent of the plate circuit. Since the capacitance between plate and grid is small, the approximation that the plate circuit is independent of the grid circuit is valid at the lower frequencies. However, at the higher frequencies, interelectrode capacitances may seriously affect the operation.

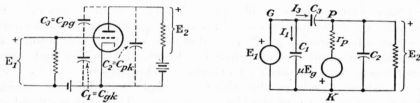

FIG. 5-3. Schematic and equivalent circuits of an amplifier, including the interelectrode capacitances.

A more complete schematic diagram and its equivalent circuit are given in Fig. 5-3. In this circuit, C_{gp} denotes the capacitance between the grid and the plate, C_{gk} is the grid-cathode capacitance, and C_{pk} is the capacitance between the plate and the cathode. The solution for the gain of this circuit is readily obtained with the aid of the Millman theorem (see Appendix A, Sec. A-5b). The point O' corresponds to the plate terminal P, and the point O is the cathode terminal K. Four branches must be considered between these points: the load impedance with zero potential; the capacitor C_2 with zero potential; the potential rise μE_g in series with r_p; the potential $\mathbf{E}_1$ in series with C_3. The capacitor C_1 which exists across the input $\mathbf{E}_1$ does not appear in the equation. The result is]

$$\mathbf{E}_2 = \frac{-\mu E_g \mathbf{Y}_p + \mathbf{E}_1 \mathbf{Y}_3}{\mathbf{Y}_p + \mathbf{Y}_l + \mathbf{Y}_2 + \mathbf{Y}_3} \tag{5-12}$$

where $\mathbf{Y}_p = 1/r_p$ is admittance corresponding to r_p

$\mathbf{Y}_2 = j\omega C_2$ is admittance corresponding to C_2

$\mathbf{Y}_3 = j\omega C_3$ is admittance corresponding to C_3

$\mathbf{Y}_l = 1/\mathbf{Z}_l$ is admittance corresponding to $\mathbf{Z}_l$

$\mathbf{E}_2 =$ potential difference between P and K, or potential across load impedance

Note that $E_1 = E_g$. The potential gain is given by

$$K = \frac{\text{output potential}}{\text{input potential}} = \frac{E_2}{E_1}$$

and may be written in the form

$$K = \frac{Y_3 - g_m}{Y_p + Y_l + Y_2 + Y_3} \qquad (5\text{-}13)$$

In this expression use has been made of the fact that $g_m = \mu/r_p$.

In this analysis a number of factors have been neglected. It has been assumed that no conduction or leakage currents exist between tube terminals. Such leakage current will depend upon many variable factors, such as the spacing between electrodes, the materials of the base, the conditions of the surface of the glass and the tube base, and perhaps the surface leakage between connecting wires. Ordinarily the error is small in neglecting the effects of this surface leakage. If this assumption is not true, the effect can be taken into acount by writing for each interelectrode admittance $g_s + j\omega C_s$ instead of $j\omega C_s$, where g_s takes account of the leakage current and also dielectric losses. Interwiring and stray capacitances must be taken into account. This may be done by considering them to be in parallel with C_1, C_2, and C_3. Additional considerations are necessary at the high frequencies. These are discussed in Sec. 5-8.

The error made in the calculation of the gain by neglecting the interelectrode capacitances is very small over the a-f spectrum. These interelectrode capacitances are usually 10 $\mu\mu f$ or less, which corresponds to admittances of less than 2 μmhos at 20,000 cps. This is to be compared with the mutual conductance of the tube of, say, 1,500 μmhos at the normal operating point. Likewise $Y_2 + Y_3$ is usually negligible compared with $Y_p + Y_l$. Under these conditions, the expression for the gain [Eq. (5-13)] reduces to Eq. (4-16).

5-5. Input Admittance of a Triode. Owing to the presence of the interelectrode capacitances, the grid circuit is no longer isolated from the plate circuit. In fact, with a positive signal on the grid and with the consequent negative potential on the plate, an appreciable change of potential appears across the capacitance C_{gp}, with a consequent appreciable current flow. Also, the potential change across the capacitance C_{gk} is accompanied by a current flow. Clearly, therefore, the input-signal source must supply these currents. To calculate this current, it is noted from the diagram that

$$I_1 = E_1 Y_1$$

and

$$I_3 = E_{gp} Y_3 = (E_1 - E_2) Y_3$$

But from the fact that

$$E_2 = KE_1$$

then the total input current is

$$I_i = I_1 + I_3 = [Y_1 + (1 - K)Y_3]E_1$$

The input admittance, given by the ratio $Y_i = I_i/E_1$, is

$$Y_i = Y_1 + (1 - K)Y_3 \qquad (5\text{-}14)$$

If Y_i is to be zero, evidently both Y_1 and Y_3 must be zero, since K cannot, in general, be $1/\underline{0}$ deg. Thus, for the system to possess a negligible input admittance over a wide range of frequencies, the grid-cathode and the grid-plate capacitances must be negligible.

Consider a triode with a pure resistance load. At the lower frequencies, the gain is given by the simple expression [Eq. (4-16)]

$$K = \frac{-\mu R_l}{R_l + r_p}$$

In this case, Eq. (5-14) becomes

$$Y_i = j\omega \left[C_1 + \left(1 + \frac{\mu R_l}{R_l + r_p}\right) C_3 \right] \qquad (5\text{-}15)$$

Thus the input admittance is that from a capacitor between grid and cathode of magnitude

$$C_i = C_1 + \left(1 + \frac{\mu R_l}{R_l + r_p}\right) C_3 \qquad (5\text{-}16)$$

Attention is called to the very large contribution to the input capacitance by the grid-plate capacitance C_3, owing to the fact that its magnitude is multiplied by the amplifier gain. As a result, the total input capacitance is very much higher than any of the interelectrode capacitances. The presence of this input capacitance will be found to affect the operation of the amplifier, and often will make operation impossible, especially at the higher frequencies. Methods of compensation have been devised to overcome this effect, and these will be examined later.

For the general case when the gain of the amplifier K is a complex quantity, the input admittance will consist of two terms, a resistive and a reactive term. For the case of an inductive load, the gain K may be written in the form (see Sec. 5-3, Example 2)

$$K = -(k_1 + jk_2) \qquad (5\text{-}17)$$

and Eq. (5-14) becomes

$$Y_i = -\omega C_3 k_2 + j\omega[C_1 + (1 + k_1)C_3] \qquad (5\text{-}18)$$

This expression indicates that the equivalent input circuit comprises a resistance (which is negative in this particular case, although it will be positive for a capacitive load) in parallel with a capacitance C_i, as shown in Fig. 5-4.   The equivalent elements have the form

$$R_i = -\frac{1}{\omega C_3 k_2} \qquad (5\text{-}19)$$

and the capacitor

$$C_i = C_1 + (1 + k_1)C_3 \qquad (5\text{-}20)$$

Fig. 5-4. The equivalent input circuit of a triode.

As indicated in the above development, it is possible for the term k_2 to be negative (with an inductive load).

Under these circumstances the input resistance R_i will be negative.   Physically, this means that power is being fed back from the output circuit into the grid circuit through the coupling provided by the grid-plate capacitance.   If this feedback reaches an extreme stage, the amplifier will oscillate.   These feedback effects in an amplifier will be examined in some detail in Chap. 7.

5-6. Input Admittance of a Tetrode.   The equivalent circuit of the tetrode is essentially that of the triode, even though a screen grid exists in the tetrode.   A schematic diagram of a simple amplifier circuit employing a tetrode is given in Fig. 5-5.   In drawing the equivalent

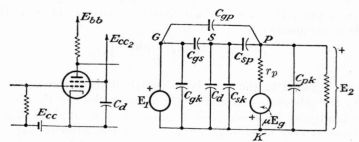

Fig. 5-5. Schematic and equivalent circuits of a tetrode in an amplifier circuit.

circuit, the rules given in Sec. 4-6 have been appropriately extended and employed.   This requires the introduction of a point S, the screen terminal, in addition to the points K, G, and P.

Notice that the screen potential is maintained at a fixed d-c potential with respect to cathode and is at zero potential in so far as a-c variations about the Q point are concerned.   As indicated in the figure, this effectively places a short circuit across C_{ks} and puts C_{gk} and C_{gs} in parallel. This parallel combination is denoted C_1.   The capacitance C_{ps} now appears from plate to cathode and is effectively in parallel with C_{pk}. This parallel combination is denoted C_2.   Also, from the discussion in Sec. 2-14, the shielding action of the screen is such that the capacitance

C_{pg} between grid and plate is very small. If this capacitance is assumed to be negligible, and it is less than 0.001 $\mu\mu f$ in the average potential tetrode, then Fig. 5-5 may be redrawn in the form shown in Fig. 5-6. In this figure, the capacitances have the values

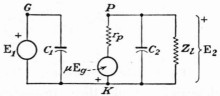

$$C_1 = C_{gk} + C_{gs}$$
$$C_2 = C_{ps} + C_{pk} \qquad (5\text{-}21)$$

The input admittance of the tube is then

$$\mathbf{Y}_i = j\omega C_1 \qquad (5\text{-}22)$$

Fig. 5-6. The ideal equivalent circuit of a tetrode amplifier.

The mere substitution of a tetrode for a triode may not result in a very marked improvement in the amplifier response. This follows from the fact that the stray and wiring capacitances external to the tube may allow significant grid-plate coupling. It is necessary that care be exercised in order that plate and grid circuits be shielded or widely separated from each other in order to utilize the inherent possibilities of the tube.

5-7. Input Admittance of a Pentode. The discussion in Sec. 2-14 showed that, even though the tetrode had a significantly smaller grid-plate capacitance than the triode, the presence of the screen grid was accompanied by the effects of secondary emission from the plate when the instantaneous plate potential fell below the screen potential. As discussed, the effect of this is overcome by the insertion of a suppressor grid between the screen grid and the plate.

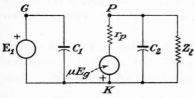

Fig. 5-7. The equivalent circuit of a pentode amplifier.

When used in a circuit as a potential amplifier, the pentode is connected in the circuit exactly like the tetrode with the addition that the suppressor grid is connected to the cathode. By drawing the complete equivalent circuit of the pentode amplifier, by appropriately extending the rules of Sec. 4-6, and by including all tube capacitances, it is easy to show that the equivalent circuit reduces to that shown in Fig. 5-7. In this diagram

$$C_1 = C_{gk} + C_{gs}$$
$$C_2 = C_{pk} + C_{ps} + C_{p3} \qquad (5\text{-}23)$$

where C_{p3} is the plate-grid No. 3 capacitance.

The plate load impedance $\mathbf{Z}_l$ is frequently much smaller than the plate resistance of the tube, and it is convenient to use the current-source equivalent-circuit representation of the tube, as shown. For the range of frequencies over which the input and output capacitances C_1 and C_2 are negligible, and with $r_p \gg Z_l$, the total generator current passes

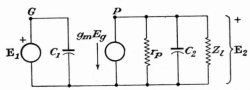

FIG. 5-8. The current-source equivalent circuit of the pentode amplifier.

through Z_l. Under these circumstances the output potential is

$$\mathbf{E}_2 = -g_m \mathbf{E}_1 \mathbf{Z}_l$$

and the gain is given by the simple form

$$\mathbf{K} = -g_m \mathbf{Z}_l \qquad (5\text{-}24)$$

If the assumed conditions are not valid, the gain becomes

$$\mathbf{K} = -g_m \mathbf{Z} \qquad (5\text{-}25)$$

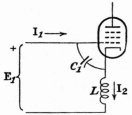

FIG. 5-9. Circuit for examining the effect of cathode lead inductance in a pentode.

where $\mathbf{Z}$ is the combined parallel impedance in the output circuit.

5-8. High-frequency (H-F) Considerations. In addition to the effects of the interelectrode capacitances in affecting the performance of an amplifier, several other factors are of importance, particularly at the higher frequencies. These were mentioned in Sec. 5-7 and include the effects of lead inductances and also the effects due to transit time.

To examine the effect of the cathode lead inductance, Fig. 5-9 is analyzed. For convenience, it will be assumed that the grid is negative throughout the cycle and that transit-time effects are negligible. Then for $\mathbf{I}_2 \gg \mathbf{I}_1$

$$\mathbf{I}_2 = g_m \mathbf{E}_g$$

and

$$\mathbf{E}_g = \frac{\mathbf{I}_1}{j\omega C_1}$$

Also

$$\mathbf{E}_1 = \frac{\mathbf{I}_1}{j\omega C_1} + j g_m \mathbf{E}_g \omega L$$

Combine equations to get

$$\mathbf{E}_1 = \frac{\mathbf{I}_1}{j\omega C_1} + j g_m \omega L \frac{\mathbf{I}_1}{j\omega C_1}$$

$$= \frac{\mathbf{I}_1}{j\omega C_1} (1 + j g_m \omega L)$$

The input admittance is

$$\mathbf{Y}_i = \frac{\mathbf{I}_1}{\mathbf{E}_1} = \frac{j\omega C_1}{1 + jg_m\omega L} = \frac{j\omega C_1(1 - j\omega g_m L)}{1 + \omega^2 g_m^2 L^2} \qquad (5\text{-}26)$$

If $\omega^2 g_m^2 L^2 \ll 1$, then

$$\mathbf{Y}_i = \omega^2 g_m L C_1 + j\omega C_1 \qquad (5\text{-}27)$$

Observe, therefore, that the cathode lead inductance introduces an input conductance of amount $\omega^2 g_m L C_1$.

A second component of input conductance arises because of the transit time of the electrons between cathode and plate. An exact calculation is difficult, but a qualitative explanation is possible which indicates the grid-loading effects involved. To understand grid loading, consider an electron that has left the cathode and is approaching the grid in its flight to the anode. Suppose that the grid potential is negative relative to the cathode so that no electrons are collected by the grid. As the electron approaches the grid, a changing image-charge density will be induced on the grid (see Sec. 2-4 for a discussion of image charges). This changing image charge represents an instantaneous grid current, the direction of flow of charge being such as to charge the bias battery. The power for this charging process is supplied by the moving electron, and as a result the electron is decelerated.

Once the electron has passed the grid, the process is reversed, and the moving electron receives energy from the grid, and it is accelerated thereby. The amount of energy lost by the electron as it approaches the grid is just equal to that which it gains as it moves away, and the net energy change is zero. As a result, the net grid loading is zero.

If the transit time of the electron in the cathode-anode space is of the order of the period of the applied grid potential, the grid loading becomes important, for now the electron can no longer be considered to be in a field which is constant in time. It is possible for the energy that is supplied to the grid by the moving electron to exceed the amount of energy that is returned by the grid in its interelectrode flight, with a resultant net energy loss in the grid circuit. This energy is supplied by the grid driving source, and it represents a load on this source.

From a circuits point of view, the foregoing may be described in terms of an induced current in the grid. At the lower frequencies, the induced grid current is 90 deg out of phase with the grid potential, with a consequent zero net power loss. At the higher frequencies, an inphase component exists. This inphase component reduces the input resistance, and this may produce an appreciable loading of the input circuit.

The foregoing concepts may be employed to indicate in a qualitative way the effect of the various factors on the input resistance. If T

denotes the transit time, f denotes the frequency of the applied grid potential, and g_m is the mutual conductance of the tube, it is expected that the grid current I_g is proportional to T and f, since I_g is small if either of these is small. Also, I_g should be proportional to g_m, since g_m determines the a-c component of plate current for a specified E_g, and the total grid current is proportional to this a-c component of the plate current. If α denotes the transit angle, which is now less than 90 deg, then the inphase component of I_g is $I_g \sin \alpha$, which is simply $I_g \alpha$ for small deviations from 90 deg. But α is also proportional to T and f. Thus the inphase component of I_g is proportional to $g_m T^2 f^2$, or

$$g_i = k g_m f^2 T^2 \tag{5-28}$$

where k is a constant depending on the geometry of the tube and electrode potentials. This relationship agrees with the complete analysis of Ferris.[1]

It will be seen from Eqs. (5-27) and (5-28) that g_i and the conductance component of the cathode inductance depend on the frequency in the same way. Consequently, these components cannot be separated readily in measurement of input resistance or conductance.

Tubes for use at the high frequencies are made in a manner to reduce transit time, interelectrode capacitances, and lead inductances. This is done by means of very close electrode spacing, and generally small physical dimensions of electrodes. Among such tubes are the so-called "acorn," "doorknob," "pencil," and "disk-seal," or "lighthouse," tubes, with upper limits in frequency of approximately 2,000, 1,700, 3,000, and 3,500 Mc, respectively. These names are indicative of the external envelope shape, the first three possessing essentially cylindrical electrode structures, the last being essentially of a planar construction. The first two have the leads brought out of the envelopes at widely spaced points, in order to reduce capacitances. The latter two bring the leads out in the form of disks. At the higher frequencies these tubes are incorporated in coaxial line resonators, lead inductances being unimportant as these form part of the resonant cavities.

5-9. Potential Sources for Amplifiers. A number of different potential sources are required in an amplifier. These are the following: the filament, or A, supply; the plate, or B, supply E_{bb}; the grid-bias, or C, supply E_{cc}; the screen supply E_{cc2}. These potentials are supplied in different ways.

The Filament, or A, Supply. The most common method of heating the cathodes of indirectly heated tubes is from a low-potential winding on a transformer which operates from the a-c supply lines. Storage batteries may be used if d-c heating is necessary, but this is ordinarily not necessary except in special applications.   Special low-drain tubes are available for use in portable radio sets and are fed from dry batteries.

The Plate, or B, Supply E_{bb}.   Most equipments involving the use of electron tubes are operated from the a-c supply mains, and the d-c plate supply is then secured by means of a rectifier and filter unit (see Chap. 3 for details).   For applications with severe requirements on regulation or low ripple, the power supply must be electronically regulated. For low-drain requirements, dry batteries may be used.

The Grid, or C, Supply E_{cc}.   The grid circuit of most amplifiers ordinarily requires very little current, and hence low-power dry batteries may be used.   In most cases, however, self-bias is used (although this is restricted to class A and class AB amplifiers).   Self-bias is achieved by including a resistor R_k in the cathode of the amplifier tube and shunting this resistor with a capacitor C_k, the reactance of which is small compared with R_k over the operating frequency range.   The quiescent current I_b flows through this resistor, and the potential difference

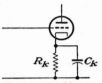

Fig. 5-10. Obtaining self-bias by means of a cathode resistor.

provides the grid bias.   The correct self-biasing resistor $R_k = E_{cc}/I_b$.

The capacitor C_k serves to by-pass any a-c components in the plate current, so that no a-c component appears across the resistor R_k.   If such an a-c component, or varying bias, does exist, then clearly there is a reaction between the plate circuit and the input circuit.   Such a "feedback" effect will receive detailed consideration in Chap. 7.   If this effect is to be avoided, large-capacitance capacitors may be required, particularly if the frequency is low.   High-capacitance low-potential electrolytic capacitors are available for this specific service and are quite small physically.

The Screen Supply E_{cc2}.   The screen supply is ordinarily obtained from the plate-supply source.   In many cases the screen potential is lower than the plate supply, and it is usual practice to connect the screen to the plate supply through a resistor.   The resistor is chosen of such a size that the potential drop across it due to the screen current will set the screen at the desired potential.   A capacitor is then connected from the screen to the cathode so as to maintain this potential constant and independent of B-supply variations or variations in the screen current.

It is customary to use a common B supply for all tubes of a given amplifier circuit.   Because of this, the possibility for interactions among the stages through this common plate supply does exist and might be troublesome unless the effective output impedance of the power-supply unit is very small.   It is necessary in some applications to include RC combinations known as *decoupling filters* so as to avoid this interaction.

A typical resistance-capacitance coupled-amplifier circuit which is provided with self-bias, decoupling filters, and screen dropping resistors is illustrated in Fig. 5-11.

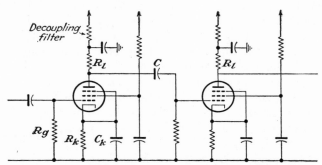

Fig. 5-11. Resistance-capacitance coupled amplifier, with self-bias, decoupling filters, and screen dropping resistors.

REFERENCE

1. Ferris, W. R., *Proc. IRE*, **24**, 82 (1936).

PROBLEMS

5-1. Two waves, one of amplitude 10 volts and frequency 1,000 cps, the second of amplitude 5 volts and frequency 3,000 cps, are applied to the input of a certain network. The two waves are so phased that they both pass through zero in the positive direction together.

a. Sketch the resulting input potential.

b. Suppose that the fundamental component suffers a phase delay of 10 deg on the fundamental scale and that the third-harmonic component suffers a 50-deg delay on the third-harmonic scale, although neither amplitude is effected. Sketch the output wave.

5-2. *a.* The output potential of a given amplifier is 18 volts, when the input potential is 0.2 volt at 5,000 cps. What is the decibel potential gain of the amplifier?

b. The output potential is 7 volts when the input potential is 0.2 volts at 18,000 cps. By how many decibels is the response of the amplifier at 18 kc below that at 5 kc?

5-3. Prepare a table giving the power sensitivity of the following tubes (assume that the output power and the grid excitation are those specified in the tube manual): 6A3, 6F6, 6V6, 6L6, 6AG7.

5-4. An a-c excitation potential of 5 volts rms at a frequency of 2,000 cps is applied to a 6J5 tube for which $\mu = 20$, $r_p = 7,700$ ohms. The load is a pure resistance of 15,000 ohms. Calculate the following:

a. The a-c current in the plate circuit.

b. The a-c output potential.

c. The gain of the amplifier.

d. The a-c power in the load resistor.

5-5. Repeat Prob. 5-4 if the load is an inductive reactance of 15,000 ohms.

5-6. Find expressions for the indicated quantity in the accompanying circuits.

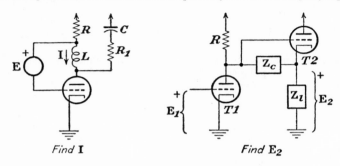

Find **I**   Find **E₂**

5-7. A type 6SF5 high-mu triode is operated as a simple amplifier under specified conditions at 30,000 cps. The important factors are

$$\mu = 100 \qquad r_p = 66,000 \text{ ohms} \qquad C_{gp} = 2.4 \ \mu\mu\text{f} \qquad C_{gk} = 4.0 \ \mu\mu\text{f}$$
$$C_{pk} = 3.6 \ \mu\mu\text{f}$$

a. Calculate the input capacitance and the input resistance of the tube alone
when the load is a resistor $R_l = 100$ kilohms.

b. Repeat when the load impedance is of the form $60,000 + j60,000$ ohms.

5-8. A type 6J5 triode is operated as a simple amplifier under specified conditions at 22,000 cps. The important factors are

$$\mu = 20 \qquad r_p = 7,700 \text{ ohms} \qquad C_{gp} = 3.4 \ \mu\mu\text{f} \qquad C_{gk} = 3.4 \ \mu\mu\text{f}$$
$$C_{pk} = 3.6 \ \mu\mu\text{f}$$

a. Calculate the input capacitance and the input resistance of the tube when
the load is a resistor $R_l = 20$ kilohms.

b. Repeat when the load is an impedance of the form $10,000 + j10,000$ ohms.

5-9. A type 6J5 tube is operated in the circuit of the accompanying diagram.
Calculate the output potential. (See Prob. 5-8 for the important factors of the
tube.)

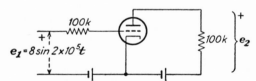

5-10. Show that Fig. 5-7 does represent the complete equivalent circuit of the
pentode.

5-11. A type 6SJ7 pentode is operated as a simple amplifier under specified
conditions.

a. When connected as a pentode, with $R_l = 25$ kilohms, the important factors
are

$$g_m = 1,575 \ \mu\text{mhos} \qquad r_p = 0.7 \text{ megohms} \qquad C_{gp} = 0.005 \ \mu\mu\text{f} \qquad C_{\text{input}} = 6.0 \ \mu\mu\text{f}$$
$$C_{\text{output}} = 7.0 \ \mu\mu\text{f}$$

Calculate the input capacitance of the amplifier.

b. When this tube is reconnected as a triode, the factors become

$$\mu = 19 \qquad r_p = 8,000 \text{ ohms} \qquad C_{gp} = 2.8 \ \mu\mu\text{f} \qquad C_{gk} = 3.4 \ \mu\mu\text{f} \qquad C_{pk} = 11 \ \mu\mu\text{f}$$

Calculate the input capacitance with $R_l = 25$ kilohms, and compare with the results of part *a*.

5-12. A 6AC7 pentode is to be used as a class A amplifier with $E_b = 250$ volts. Determine the value of the self-biasing cathode resistor to set $E_{cc} = -2$ volts; the screen dropping resistor to set E_{c2} at 150 volts if $E_{bb} = 350$.

CHAPTER 6

UNTUNED POTENTIAL AMPLIFIERS

6-1. Basic Considerations. It is frequently necessary to achieve a higher gain in an amplifier than is possible with a single amplifier stage. In such cases, the amplifier stages are cascaded to achieve this higher gain, the output potential from one stage serving as the input potential to the next stage.

A number of factors influence the number and the characteristics of the individual stages which must be used to meet certain previously specified requirements. Among the factors which must be taken into account in amplifier design are the total over-all gain required, the shape of the frequency-response characteristic, and the over-all bandwidth. Certain factors exist which impose limits to the sensitivity which may be achieved, among these being the inherent noise generated in such devices. The requirements for stability of operation impose severe practical restrictions on the techniques of construction. Because of the several factors that play a part in amplifier design, gains in excess of about 10^6, or 120 db potential gain, are extremely difficult to achieve. Depending on the bandwidth considerations, amplifiers seldom exceed six to nine stages in cascade for stable operation. Extreme caution is required in the design of such multistage amplifiers.

To calculate the over-all gain and frequency response of a multistage amplifier, the equivalent circuit of the amplifier must be drawn. The rules for accomplishing this are given in Sec. 4-6. The resultant equivalent network is then analyzed as a conventional problem in a-c circuit analysis.

A variety of coupling networks between the cascaded stages are possible, and a few have become very common, either because of their simplicity or because of some especially desirable characteristic. A number of the more common types will be considered in this chapter in some detail.

6-2. Resistance-Capacitance *(RC)* **Coupled Amplifier.** The resistance-capacitance *(RC)* coupled amplifier, illustrated in Fig. 6-1, is one of the more common and more important amplifier circuits. This amplifier circuit is used when a sensibly constant amplification over a wide range of frequencies is desired. By the use of tubes with high amplifica-

119

tion factors, it is possible to achieve a gain of 50 or more per stage. It will be found that high-gain triodes possess certain inherent disadvantages, and it is frequently desirable to use pentodes instead. If pentodes are used, the screen potential must remain constant; otherwise the following analysis will no longer be valid.

The capacitors C_1, C_2, and C_3 in this schematic diagram are known as *coupling*, or *blocking*, capacitors and serve to prevent any d-c potentials that are present in one stage from appearing in another stage. That is, capacitor C_1 serves to prevent any d-c potential in the input from appearing across the grid resistor R_{g1} and thus changing the d-c operating level of the amplifier. Capacitor C_2 serves a similar function in coupling stage 1 to stage 2. The value of the coupling capacitors is determined primarily by the l-f amplification. They ordinarily range from about 0.001 μf to 0.1 μf for conventional a-f stages. The resistor R_g, which is

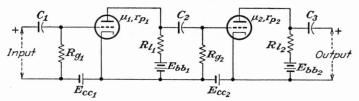

Fig. 6-1. Schematic diagram of a two-stage RC coupled amplifier.

known as the *grid resistor*, furnishes a path by which the grid-bias supply is applied to the grid. It also serves as a leak path through which any electrons that may be collected by the grid from the electron stream within the tube may be returned to the cathode. If such a leak path were not provided, the grid would acquire a negative potential with the collection of the electrons, thus influencing the operation of the tube. A negative-bias supply potential is ordinarily used, and the grid current is usually very small. This permits the use of relatively large resistances for R_g, say from 50 kilohms to 2 megohms. Large values of R_g are desirable in achieving a wide frequency response. The load resistor R_l is determined principally by the gain and the frequency bandwidth that are desired, as will be shown below.

The equivalent circuit of the amplifier of Fig. 6-1 is shown in Fig. 6-2. This circuit is valid for triodes, tetrodes, or pentodes provided that the screen potential of the latter two is maintained constant. In this circuit E_1 denotes the a-c input potential applied to the grid of the first stage. This potential appears across the parallel combination consisting of the resistor R_{g1} in parallel with the input impedance to the amplifier. The interelectrode capacitances are not shown on the diagram, but their effect is contained in the effective input capacitance C_g to each stage. That is, the input impedance of the stage is considered to comprise a resistance (assumed positive) in parallel with the input capacitance. It is also supposed that the impedance of the driving source is low, so that the loading by the total input impedance of the first stage does not affect the input potential. The output circuit of the first stage consists of the load resistance, the coupling capacitance C_2, output tube and wiring capacitances, and the total input impedance of the second stage. This is denoted as R_g and C_g for the total resistive and capacitive components. The output of the amplifier is the potential across the output impedance, which is denoted by the symbol **Z**. This impedance cannot be specified more completely until the nature of the output circuit is known.

The coupling between the grid and the plate of the tubes through the interelectrode capacitances can be neglected over a wide frequency range

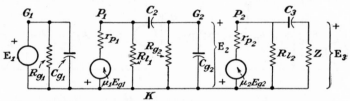

FIG. 6-2. The equivalent circuit of the RC amplifier of Fig. 6-1.

with pentodes and over the a-f range with triodes. Consequently each stage may be considered as independent of the following stage, but the output of one stage is the input to the next stage. As a result, it follows that since

$$\mathbf{K}_1 = \frac{\mathbf{E}_2}{\mathbf{E}_1} = \frac{\text{output potential of 1st stage}}{\text{input potential to 1st stage}}$$

and

$$\mathbf{K}_2 = \frac{\mathbf{E}_3}{\mathbf{E}_2} = \frac{\text{output potential of 2d stage}}{\text{input potential to 2d stage}}$$
$$= \frac{\text{output potential of 2d stage}}{\text{output potential of 1st stage}}$$

then the resultant over-all gain is

$$\mathbf{K} = \frac{\mathbf{E}_3}{\mathbf{E}_1} = \frac{\text{output potential of 2d stage}}{\text{input potential to 1st stage}}$$

It follows from these expressions that

$$\mathbf{K} = \mathbf{K}_1\mathbf{K}_2 \tag{6-1}$$

By taking twenty times the logarithm of the magnitude of this expression

$$20 \log_{10} K = 20 \log_{10} K_1 + 20 \log_{10} K_2 \tag{6-2}$$

It follows from this that the total decibel potential gain of the multistage amplifier is the sum of the decibel potential gains of the separate stages. This fact is independent of the type of interstage coupling.

6-3. Analysis of *RC* Coupled Amplifier. A typical stage of the *RC* coupled amplifier is considered in detail. This stage might represent any of a group of similar stages of an amplifier chain, except perhaps the output stage. Representative subscripts have been omitted. The equivalent circuit is given in its two forms in Figs. 6-3.

The typical stage will be analyzed by two methods in order to show the features of the methods. One method will employ the Millman theorem, as applied to Fig. 6-3a. The second method will employ a straightforward junction solution of Fig. 6-3b.

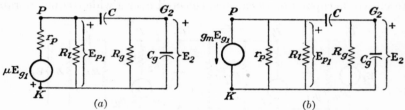

FIG. 6-3. A typical stage of an *RC* coupled amplifier. (a) Potential-source and (b) current-source equivalents.

A direct application of the Millman theorem between the points G_2 and K yields the expression

$$\mathbf{E}_2 = \frac{\mathbf{E}_{p1}\mathbf{Y}_C}{\mathbf{Y}_C + \mathbf{Y}_{R_g} + \mathbf{Y}_{C_g}} \tag{6-3}$$

where $\mathbf{Y}_C = j\omega C$, $\mathbf{Y}_{R_g} = 1/R_g$, $\mathbf{Y}_{C_g} = j\omega C_g$. An application of this theorem between the points P and K yields the expression

$$\mathbf{E}_{p1} = \frac{-\mu\mathbf{E}_{g1}\mathbf{Y}_p + \mathbf{E}_2\mathbf{Y}_C}{\mathbf{Y}_p + \mathbf{Y}_l + \mathbf{Y}_C} \tag{6-4}$$

where $\mathbf{Y}_p = 1/r_p$ and $\mathbf{Y}_l = 1/R_l$. By combining Eq. (6-3) with Eq. (6-4) and solving for the gain $\mathbf{K} = \mathbf{E}_2/\mathbf{E}_{g1}$, since $\mathbf{E}_{g1} = \mathbf{E}_1$, there results

$$\mathbf{K} = \frac{-\mu\mathbf{Y}_p\mathbf{Y}_C}{(\mathbf{Y}_C + \mathbf{Y}_{R_g} + \mathbf{Y}_{C_g})(\mathbf{Y}_p + \mathbf{Y}_l) + \mathbf{Y}_C(\mathbf{Y}_{R_g} + \mathbf{Y}_{C_g})} \tag{6-5}$$

This is the complete expression for the potential gain of such an amplifier stage. If the constants of the circuit are known, the gain and phaseshift characteristics as a function of frequency may be calculated.

Now refer to Fig. 6-3b, and apply the standard techniques of junction analysis. The controlling equations, obtained from considerations of the Kirchhoff current law, are

$$(\mathbf{Y}_p + \mathbf{Y}_l + \mathbf{Y}_C)\mathbf{E}_{p1} - \mathbf{Y}_C\mathbf{E}_2 = -g_m\mathbf{E}_{g1} \tag{6-6}$$
$$-\mathbf{Y}_C\mathbf{E}_{p1} + (\mathbf{Y}_C + \mathbf{Y}_{C_g} + \mathbf{Y}_{R_g})\mathbf{E}_2 = 0$$

By determinantal methods, it follows that

$$K = \frac{E_2}{E_1} = \frac{\begin{vmatrix} Y_p + Y_l + Y_C & -g_m \\ -Y_C & 0 \end{vmatrix}}{\begin{vmatrix} Y_p + Y_l + Y_C & -Y_C \\ -Y_C & Y_C + Y_{C_g} + Y_{R_g} \end{vmatrix}} \qquad (6\text{-}7)$$

The expansion of these determinants by Cramer's rule yields Eq. (6-5), as it must.

It will be found convenient to analyze the response of the amplifier for limiting regions of frequency instead of attempting an interpretation of

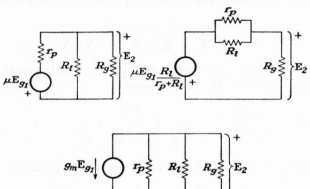

Fig. 6-4. The mid-frequency equivalent circuits of the RC amplifier.

Eq. (6-5) directly. In fact, in many cases it is more convenient to analyze the appropriate equivalent circuit, rather than attempting the analysis from Eq. (6-5).

Intermediate Frequencies. The intermediate frequencies, or mid-frequencies, are those for which Y_C is large and Y_{C_g} is small. Subject to these conditions, the equivalent circuits of Fig. 6-3 reduce to those shown in Fig. 6-4.

For the range of frequencies over which this equivalent circuit is valid, the expression for the gain becomes

$$K = K_0 = \frac{-g_m}{Y_p + Y_l + Y_{R_g}} \qquad (6\text{-}8)$$

This expression for the gain is independent of the frequency, since no reactive elements appear in the circuit. Each parameter in the equation is a conductance, and because of the negative sign the relative phase angle between the input and output potentials is constant and equal to 180 deg.

L-F Region. At the low frequencies the effect of C_g is negligible, and Y_{C_g} may be made zero. The effect of the coupling capacitor C becomes

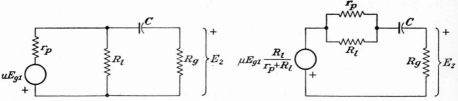

Fig. 6-5. The l-f equivalent circuit of the *RC* amplifier.

very important. The equivalent circuit under these conditions has the form shown in Fig. 6-5. The general expression for the gain [Eq. (6-5)] reduces to

$$\mathbf{K} = \mathbf{K}_1 = \frac{-\mu \mathbf{Y}_p \mathbf{Y}_C}{\mathbf{Y}_C(\mathbf{Y}_p + \mathbf{Y}_l + \mathbf{Y}_{R_g}) + \mathbf{Y}_{R_g}(\mathbf{Y}_p + \mathbf{Y}_l)} \quad (6\text{-}9)$$

It is found convenient to examine the l-f gain relative to the mid-frequency gain. The ratio $\mathbf{K}_1/\mathbf{K}_0$ becomes

$$\frac{\mathbf{K}_1}{\mathbf{K}_0} = \frac{1}{1 + \dfrac{\mathbf{Y}_{R_g}(\mathbf{Y}_p + \mathbf{Y}_l)}{\mathbf{Y}_C(\mathbf{Y}_p + \mathbf{Y}_l + \mathbf{Y}_{R_g})}} \quad (6\text{-}10)$$

This may be written in the simple form, for any frequency f,

$$\frac{\mathbf{K}_1}{\mathbf{K}_0} = \frac{1}{1 - j\mathbf{f}_1/f} \quad (6\text{-}11)$$

where

$$\mathbf{f}_1 \equiv \frac{\mathbf{Y}_{R_g}(\mathbf{Y}_p + \mathbf{Y}_l)}{2\pi C(\mathbf{Y}_p + \mathbf{Y}_l + \mathbf{Y}_{R_g})} \quad (6\text{-}12)$$

Equations (6-11) and (6-12) are meaningful only if the load is a pure resistance, since then $\mathbf{f}_1$ is a real number and the magnitude of the relative gain becomes

$$\frac{K_1}{K_0} = \frac{1}{\sqrt{1 + (f_1/f)^2}}$$
$$\qquad (6\text{-}13)$$

where
$$f_1 = \frac{1}{2\pi C\,[R_g + r_p R_l/(r_p + R_l)]}$$

This shows that the parameter f_1 represents the frequency at which the gain falls to $1/\sqrt{2}$, or 70.7 per cent of its mid-frequency value. This frequency is usually referred to as the *l-f cutoff* frequency of the amplifier. The relative phase angle θ_1 is given by

$$\tan\theta_1 = \frac{f_1}{f} \quad (6\text{-}14)$$

This approaches 90 deg as the frequency approaches zero.

It should be noted that the l-f cutoff value [Eq. (6-12)] depends, among other terms, on the size of the coupling capacitor C. Since the value of C appears in the denominator of the expression for f_1, then, for a decreased l-f cutoff, larger values of C must be chosen. Of course, the gain must ultimately fall to zero at zero frequency.

There are several practical limitations to the size of the coupling capacitance that may be used. The capacitor must be of high quality so that any leakage current will be small. Otherwise a conduction path from the plate of one stage to the grid of the next stage may exist. But good-quality capacitors in sizes greater than 0.1 μf are physically large and are relatively expensive. Also, if the coupling capacitance is large, a phenomenon known as *blocking* may result if grid current flows. This arises when the time constant CR_g is much larger than the period of the highest frequency to be passed by the amplifier. Thus if an appreciable charge

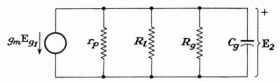

Fig. 6-6. The h-f equivalent circuit of the RC amplifier.

flows into the capacitor with the application of the input signal and if this cannot leak off quickly enough, a charge will build up. This may bias the tube highly negatively, perhaps even beyond cutoff. The amplifier then becomes inoperative until the capacitor discharges. This condition is sometimes desirable in special electron-tube circuits. However, it is a condition that must be avoided in an amplifier that is to reproduce the input signal in an amplified form.

The grid resistance R_g must be made high to keep the gain high, since R_g of one stage represents a loading across the plate resistance R_l of the previous stage. The upper limit to this value is set by the grid current. Ordinarily the grid current is small, particularly when the grid bias is negative. But if the grid resistance is made too high, and several megohms is the usual limit, the potential across this resistance will act as a spurious bias on the tube. While special low-grid-current tubes are available, these are designed for special operations and would not ordinarily be used in conventional circuits.

H-F Region. At the high frequencies, the admittance of C is very large, and the admittance of C_g becomes important. The equivalent circuit corresponding to these conditions becomes that shown in Fig. 6-6. The general expression for the gain reduces to

$$\mathbf{K} = \mathbf{K}_2 = \frac{-\mu \mathbf{Y}_p}{\mathbf{Y}_p + \mathbf{Y}_l + \mathbf{Y}_{R_g} + \mathbf{Y}_{C_g}} \qquad (6\text{-}15)$$

The gain ratio $\mathbf{K}_2/\mathbf{K}_0$ becomes

$$\frac{\mathbf{K}_2}{\mathbf{K}_0} = \cfrac{1}{1 + \cfrac{\mathbf{Y}_{C_g}}{\mathbf{Y}_p + \mathbf{Y}_l + \mathbf{Y}_{R_g}}} \tag{6-16}$$

This expression may be written in a form similar to Eq. (6-11) for the l-f case. It becomes

$$\frac{\mathbf{K}_2}{\mathbf{K}_0} = \frac{1}{1 + jf/\mathbf{f}_2} \tag{6-17}$$

where

$$\mathbf{f}_2 \equiv \frac{\mathbf{Y}_p + \mathbf{Y}_l + \mathbf{Y}_{R_g}}{2\pi C_g} \tag{6-18}$$

In this expression C_g denotes the total capacitance from grid to cathode and comprises the input capacitance of the following stage, the output wiring, and the output tube capacitance.

In Eqs. (6-17) and (6-18), as in Eqs. (6-11) and (6-12), the expressions are meaningful only if the load is a pure resistance. Then $\mathbf{f}_2$ is a real number, and the magnitude of the relative gain becomes

$$\frac{K_2}{K_0} = \sqrt{\frac{1}{1 + (f/f_2)^2}} \tag{6-19}$$

It follows from this that f_2 represents that frequency at which the h-f gain falls to $1/\sqrt{2}$, or 70.7 per cent, of its mid-frequency value. This frequency is usually referred to as the *h-f cutoff* of the amplifier. The relative phase angle θ_2 is given by

$$\tan \theta_2 = -\frac{f}{f_2} \tag{6-20}$$

This angle approaches -90 deg as the frequency becomes very large compared with f_2.

Note from Eq. (6-18) that the h-f cutoff value depends on the value of C_g, among other factors. Since the value of C_g appears in the denominator of the expression, then clearly a high h-f cutoff requires a small value of C_g. Moreover, since the input capacitance of a pentode is appreciably less than that of a triode, the pentode possesses inherently better possibilities for a broad frequency response than does the triode. Note above that the h-f cutoff is improved by the use of large Y_p, Y_l, and Y_{R_g}, which implies the use of small values of resistance R_l, R_g and a tube with a small plate resistance.

6-4. Universal Amplification Curves for *RC* Amplifiers.[1] The foregoing analysis shows that the gain of an *RC* coupled amplifier is substantially constant over a range of frequencies and falls off at both the high and the low frequencies. A typical frequency-response curve has the form sketched in Fig. 6-7.

Since the relative gain and the relative phase-shift characteristics depend only upon the two parameters f_1 and f_2, it is possible to construct curves which are applicable to any such amplifier. Such universal curves are given in Fig. 6-8.

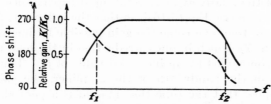

Fig. 6-7. A typical frequency response and phase characteristic of an RC coupled amplifier.

The frequency-response characteristics of any RC coupled amplifier can easily be obtained with the aid of these curves. The first step in the analysis is to calculate the values of the parameters f_1 and f_2 from Eqs. (6-12) and (6-18). Then the values of the relative gain and the relative phase angle are obtained from the curves for a number of values of the ratio f_1/f and f/f_2. These are plotted as a function of f. It must be remembered in using Fig. 6-8 that the ordinate is K_1/K_0 or θ_1 when the abscissa is f_1/f. Also, the ordinate is K_2/K_0 or θ_2 when the abscissa is f/f_2.

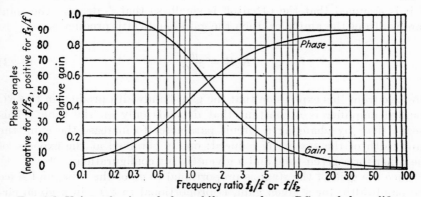

Fig. 6-8. Universal gain and phase-shift curves for an RC coupled amplifier.

6-5. Gain-Bandwidth Product. Suppose that it is desired to extend the h-f response of an RC coupled amplifier. According to the universal gain characteristic, this requires that the quantity f_2 be increased. By Eq. (6-18) this increase in f_2 may be accomplished by increasing any of the terms Y_p, Y_l, or Y_{R_g} or by decreasing C_g. It is desired to examine the effect of varying these parameters.

Consider the factor $\mathbf{Y}_p$. An increase in $\mathbf{Y}_p$ implies that the plate resistance r_p is reduced. This would seem to favor the use of triodes with low values of r_p. However, tubes of this type are power triodes, which are low-μ tubes. Consequently, in addition to the low gain inherent in such tubes, and the corresponding high grid driving signal that would be required for reasonable output potential, the use of a triode is inadvisable because of the relatively large total input capacitance which such a stage would possess [see Eq. (5-16)], so that the influence of the increase in C_g would more than overcome the gain possible by increasing $\mathbf{Y}_p$.

An increase in $\mathbf{Y}_l$, which implies a reduction in the load resistance R_l, will also be accompanied by an increased value of f_2. Thus while there is an increase in the bandwidth of the amplifier, the gain is thereby reduced. Suppose that the tube that is used is a pentode, and this is generally the case for a broad-band amplifier. For the pentode, since r_p is large (and of the order of 1 megohm) and R_g may also be made large, the h-f cutoff value is given with good approximation by

$$f_2 = \frac{Y_l}{2\pi C_g} = \frac{1}{2\pi R_l C_g} \tag{6-21}$$

Moreover, for the pentode, the gain of the stage is given with good approximation by

$$K_2 = g_m R_l \tag{6-22}$$

If it is assumed that the l-f cutoff is small, so that f_2 denotes the total bandwidth of the amplifier, then the gain-bandwidth product is

$$K_2 B = \frac{g_m}{2\pi C_g} \tag{6-23}$$

Observe from this expression that the gain-bandwidth product of the RC coupled amplifier is a constant that depends only on the tube. This means that, by changing a circuit parameter to increase the gain, the bandwidth of the system is reduced; one is obtained at the expense of the other for a given tube and a given circuit configuration.

Since the gain of the stage is proportional to g_m of the tube, and since the bandwidth, for a given gain, is proportional to $1/C_g$ in a given circuit configuration, the limit to the bandwidth is dictated fundamentally by the interelectrode capacitances of the tube. Thus even if the wiring and socket capacitances were reduced to zero, an impossible practical situation, the sum of the output capacitance of the one tube and the input capacitance to the following stage would provide the ultimate limitation. That is, the ultimate limit is imposed by an effective capacitance C_t, which is the output capacitance of one tube and the input capacitance to the next tube, or

$$K_2 B = \frac{g_m}{2\pi(C_{\text{in}} + C_{\text{out}})} = \frac{g_m}{2\pi C_t} \tag{6-24}$$

From this expression, a quantity M is defined as

$$M \equiv \frac{g_m}{C_t} \tag{6-25}$$

M is known as the *figure of merit* of the tube.

For service requiring a large gain-bandwidth product, the tube should possess a large transconductance in proportion to the input plus output electrode capacitances. The 6AK5 and the 6AC7 are both highly satisfactory in this respect, the 6AK5 being slightly superior to the 6AC7. When allowance is made for socket and wiring capacitances, an average 6AK5 has a gain-bandwidth product of approximately 55 Mc (for the tube capacitances alone this figure is approximately 117 Mc) and an average 6AC7 has a corresponding value of 50 Mc.

6-6. Cascaded Stages. When identical stages are connected in cascade, a higher gain is provided, as required by Eq. (6-1). However, this higher gain is accompanied by a narrower bandwidth. It is desired to obtain expressions which show the effect of cascading identical amplifiers. This is done piecewise for the important frequency regions.

Consider that n identical stages are connected in cascade. In the mid-frequency range the resultant gain is constant and is given by

$$K_{\text{on}} = (K_0)^n \tag{6-26}$$

For the l-f region, the relative gain for the n stages is given by

$$\left(\frac{K_1}{K_0}\right)^n = \frac{1}{[1 + (f_1/f)^2]^{n/2}} \tag{6-27}$$

The resulting l-f cutoff value is defined as that value for which the relative gain is reduced by $1/\sqrt{2}$. This requires that

$$\left[1 + \left(\frac{f_1}{f}\right)^2\right]^{n/2} = 2^{1/2} \tag{6-28}$$

from which

$$1 + \left(\frac{f_1}{f}\right)^2 = 2^{1/n}$$

so that the ratio of single to n cascade stages is

$$\frac{f_1}{f_{1n}} = \sqrt{2^{1/n} - 1} \tag{6-29}$$

The relative h-f gain for the n-stage amplifier is obtained exactly as for the l-f region and is given by

$$\left(\frac{K_2}{K_0}\right)^n = \frac{1}{[1 + (f/f_2)^2]^{n/2}} \tag{6-30}$$

The corresponding relative h-f cutoff-value ratio is then

$$\frac{f_{2n}}{f_2} = \sqrt{2^{1/n} - 1} \tag{6-31}$$

Table 6-1 gives the values of the cutoff frequency reduction function

TABLE 6-1

BANDWIDTH REDUCTION FACTOR $\sqrt{2^{1/n} - 1}$

n	$\sqrt{2^{1/n} - 1}$
1	1.0
2	0.643
3	0.510
4	0.435
5	0.387
6	0.350

$\sqrt{2^{1/n} - 1}$. It is seen, for example, that the h-f cutoff value of two identical stages in cascade is reduced by a factor 0.643. Correspondingly, the l-f cutoff value is increased by this same factor. This means, of course, that the total bandwidth of the amplifier decreases as the number of cascaded stages increases. To achieve specified over-all h-f and l-f cutoff values, the single-stage cutoff values must be correspondingly high and low, respectively.

6-7. Direct-coupled Amplifier.[2] It is possible to build a type of cascaded amplifier without reactive elements and, in principle at least, secure a very broad-band amplifier. The potential gain of such an amplifier does not depend on the frequency, at least to a first approximation. However, the effect of tube and wiring capacitances imposes the same limitations on the h-f cutoff of the amplifier as in the RC coupled amplifier. It might appear that such amplifiers would find very widespread use because of these desirable characteristics. However, such amplifiers do possess certain disadvantages, and their use is limited, though they find extensive employment as d-c amplifiers and as amplifiers for very slowly varying inputs.

A battery-coupled cascade-amplifier circuit of basic design, together with the equivalent plate circuit for small changes in voltage and current, is shown in Fig. 6-9. The gain of such an amplifier stage is readily found to be

$$\mathbf{K} = \frac{-\mu R_l}{r_p + R_l} \tag{6-32}$$

It will be observed that the circuits are quite like the RC coupled amplifier except that the coupling (blocking) capacitors are absent. Because of the fact that the grid of one stage is directly connected to the plate circuit of the previous stage, it is necessary to include d-c sources at the various critical points in the circuit in order that the quiescent conditions be those of class A operation.

The battery-coupled amplifier has the outstanding feature that it will amplify a steady component in the input voltage, but it suffers from three main disadvantages. The first is the cost of the relatively high-potential grid-bias batteries. These are required when a common plate and a common filament supply are used. In an alternative arrangement, indirectly heated cathodes having different potentials are used, thus obviating the necessity for large grid-bias potentials. However, separate plate supplies are required in this case.

The second disadvantage of the direct-coupled amplifier is the inherent instability associated with direct coupling. The characteristics of the tubes in the circuit change slightly with time; the battery potentials, or the a-c line-operated rectified power supplies, likewise change with time. Since such changes are amplified, the d-c amplifier is not feasible unless precautions can be taken which tend to overcome this instability. For this reason, balanced circuits and circuits with degenerative feedback are used, since they tend to minimize this difficulty.

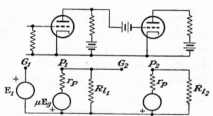

FIG. 6-9. Basic battery-coupled amplifier circuits.

The third disadvantage arises from the capacitance between the grid-bias batteries and the cathodes. This, plus the interelectrode capacitances, stray wiring capacitance, and stray inductance, influences the transient-response time and materially affects the rapidity with which the amplifier output responds to rapid changes of input potential. In consequence, even though the amplifier is direct-coupled, precautions must be taken to ensure a broad h-f response in order to provide a short response time.

It is possible to build a direct-coupled amplifier that uses a positive plate supply, a negative bias supply, and resistance coupling networks. This overcomes the first disadvantage. The circuit of such an amplifier is illustrated in Fig. 6-10. The equivalent circuit of a typical stage of this amplifier is given in Fig. 6-11. The gain of such an amplifier is readily found to be

$$K = -\frac{\mu R_{g2}\dfrac{R_{l1}}{R_{l1} + R_{c1} + R_{g2}}}{r_p + \dfrac{R_{l1}(R_{c1} + R_{g2})}{R_{l1} + R_{c1} + R_{g2}}} \qquad (6\text{-}33)$$

For an appreciable potential gain, the parallel combination of R_{l1} and $R_{c1} + R_{g2}$ should be large compared with r_p, and R_{g2} should be large compared with R_{c1}. This will necessitate the use of a large bias supply.

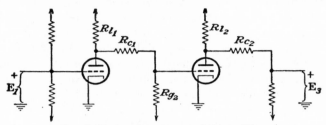

FIG. 6-10. A resistance-coupled amplifier.

Direct-coupled amplifiers are used extensively as the amplifier in a circuit the grid exciting source of which has a very high internal resistance or which is capable of supplying only a very small current. In this case, the grid current must be very small. In particular, the grid current is significant when the grid-cathode resistance of the tube, though high, might not be large in comparison with the resistance of the circuit that supplies the grid signal voltage. Special electrometer tubes in which the grid current is of the order of 10^{-15} amp are available for such applications. The grid current of the typical negative-grid tube is of the order of 10^{-8} amp with normal rated potential applied to the tube electrodes. With the electrode potentials at very low values, the grid current may be reduced as low as 10^{-12} amp.

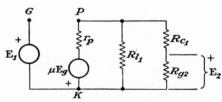

FIG. 6-11. The equivalent circuit of a typical stage of the resistance-coupled amplifier of Fig. 6-10.

6-8. The Cathode-coupled Amplifier. A two-tube circuit which is used extensively as a direct-coupled amplifier, owing to certain self-balancing features, and which is often used as an a-c amplifier, is illustrated in Fig. 6-12. This circuit overcomes the first disadvantage of the previous section and permits the use of a common battery supply for all stages.

To analyze the operation of the circuit, the Kirchhoff potential law is applied to the loop circuits shown. The tubes are assumed to be identical. Hence, there follows

$$\begin{aligned}
\mathbf{E}_{g1} &= \mathbf{E}_1 - \mathbf{E}_k = \mathbf{E}_1 - (\mathbf{I}_1 - \mathbf{I}_2)R_k \\
\mathbf{E}_{g2} &= -\mathbf{E}_k = -(\mathbf{I}_1 - \mathbf{I}_2)R_k \\
&\mathbf{I}_1 r_p - \mu\mathbf{E}_{g1} + \mathbf{E}_k = 0 \\
&\mathbf{I}_2(r_p + R_l) + \mu\mathbf{E}_{g2} - \mathbf{E}_k = 0
\end{aligned} \tag{6-34}$$

Write the equations in the form

$$\begin{aligned}
\mathbf{I}_1[r_p + (\mu + 1)R_k] - \mathbf{I}_2(\mu + 1)R_k &= \mu\mathbf{E}_1 \\
-\mathbf{I}_1(\mu + 1)R_k + \mathbf{I}_2[r_p + (\mu + 1)R_k + R_l] &= 0
\end{aligned}$$

The solution of these equations yields, for current $\mathbf{I}_2$,

$$\mathbf{I}_2 = \frac{\mu(\mu + 1)R_k\mathbf{E}_1}{[r_p + (\mu + 1)R_k][r_p + (\mu + 1)R_k + R_l] - [(\mu + 1)R_k]^2} \tag{6-35}$$

The output potential $\mathbf{E}_2$ is

$$\mathbf{E}_2 = \mathbf{I}_2 R_l = \frac{\mu(\mu + 1)R_k R_l\mathbf{E}_1}{[r_p + (\mu + 1)R_k][r_p + (\mu + 1)R_k + R_l] - [(\mu + 1)R_k]^2} \tag{6-36}$$

Now write this as

$$\mathbf{E}_2 = \frac{\mu R_l\mathbf{E}_1}{2r_p + \dfrac{r_p(r_p + R_l)}{(\mu + 1)R_k} + R_l} \tag{6-37}$$

If the parameters are so chosen that $r_p + R_l \ll (\mu + 1)R_k$, then approximately

$$\mathbf{E}_2 = \frac{\mu R_l\mathbf{E}_1}{2r_p + R_l} \tag{6-38}$$

which is a form quite like that for the ordinary single-tube amplifier, except for the appearance of the factor $2r_p$ in the denominator instead of

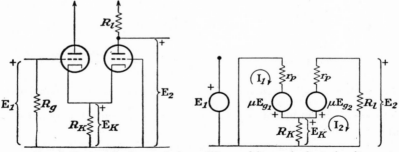

Fig. 6-12. A cathode-coupled amplifier and its equivalent circuit.

simply r_p. Note also that the output potential has the same phase as the input potential. A typical circuit showing cascade cathode-coupled amplifiers is given in Fig. 6-13.

It may be shown that the h-f cutoff value for cascaded stages, which results from the effects of the interelectrode, wiring, and distributed capacitances, is considerably higher than in a single-tube amplifier. However, such amplifier stages are not used for broad-band or video amplifiers, since a pentode proves to be superior, both as regards gain and bandwidth possibilities. Moreover, pentodes are seldom used in this circuit from bandwidth considerations alone. Such cathode-coupled amplifiers are used for very l-f or d-c amplifier service.

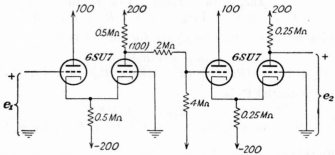

FIG. 6-13. A multistage d-c amplifier employing cathode-coupled amplifiers.

6-9. Inductance-Capacitance (LC) Coupled Amplifier. The circuit of the inductance-capacitance coupled amplifier differs from that of the resistance-capacitance coupled amplifier only in the use of an inductor plate load instead of a plate resistor. The schematic diagram of the amplifier is given in Fig. 6-14. The use of an inductor instead of a resistor in the plate circuit makes possible the use of a smaller plate-supply potential for a particular tube operating condition, since the d-c

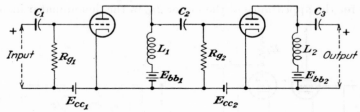

FIG. 6-14. Schematic diagram of an inductance-capacitance coupled amplifier.

resistance of the inductor is small and the d-c potential drop across this inductor is also small.

The equivalent circuit of one stage of this amplifier is given in Fig. 6-15. Observe that this circuit differs from the corresponding equivalent circuit of Fig. 6-3 only in the plate-circuit impedance. Consequently the analysis leading to Eq. (6-5) is valid in the present case provided that the plate-circuit admittance is interpreted to be

$$\mathbf{Y}_l = j\omega C_L + \frac{1}{R_L + j\omega L} \tag{6-39}$$

Here C_L is the distributed winding capacitance, which has been assumed to shunt the inductor, and R_L is the resistance of the inductor.

The frequency-response characteristic of this amplifier may be examined in the same way as that for the RC system. The analysis shows that the response is generally similar to that for the RC amplifier, except that the sensibly flat region is narrower, although the mid-frequency gain is somewhat higher. The gain drops off more rapidly than for the RC amplifier at the low frequencies owing to the low reactance of L in addition to the high reactance of C. The gain drops off more rapidly than for the RC amplifier at the high frequencies because of the shunting effects of both C_L and C_g. The mid-frequency gain is higher than for the RC amplifier

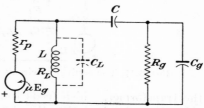

FIG. 6-15. The equivalent circuit of a typical stage of an LC coupled amplifier.

provided that the impedance of the inductor at these frequencies is higher than the resistance of the plate load of the RC amplifier.

The LC coupled amplifier is seldom used as a potential amplifier owing to the narrow frequency band and the cost of the inductor. This type of coupling, which is also referred to as *shunt-* or *parallel-feed* coupling, is frequently used in power amplifiers.

6-10. Transformer-coupled Amplifiers. The circuit of a transformer-coupled amplifier is given in Fig. 6-16. The transformer as a coupling

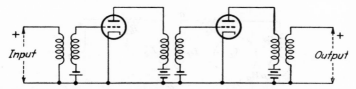

FIG. 6-16. Schematic diagram of a transformer-coupled amplifier.

device possesses several desirable features. Owing to the step-up character of the transformer, a total amplification per stage greater than the μ of the tube can be achieved. Also, the d-c isolation provided by transformer automatically removes the requirement for a blocking capacitor. High-quality interstage transformers generally have potential ratios of 1:3 or less. Higher transformation ratios usually are accompanied by distributed winding capacitances and by interwinding capacitances that are excessive. The effects of these capacitances will be considered below.

The equivalent circuit of a typical transformer-coupled stage is given in Fig. 6-17.

Mid-frequency Response. An approximate expression for the gain per stage may readily be found if it is assumed that the transformer is ideal. An ideal transformer is one for which unity coupling exists between primary and secondary windings and in which the losses and stray capacitances are negligible. If it is assumed that the secondary of

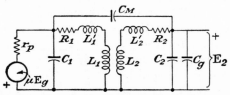

FIG. 6-17. The equivalent circuit of a typical transformer-coupled stage.

the transformer, which feeds the grid of the following stage, is essentially open-circuited, then the plate-circuit impedance is infinite. Consequently the full effective potential μE_g of the stage appears across the transformer primary. The corresponding output potential at the secondary terminals is $n\mu E_g$, where n is the transformation ratio of the transformer. The gain of the stage is then simply

$$\mathbf{K} = \mathbf{K}_0 = n\mu \qquad (6\text{-}40)$$

a constant, independent of the frequency.

L-F Region. The foregoing considerations are only approximate, owing to the character of the assumptions that were made. To examine the response at the lower frequencies, the effective distributed winding

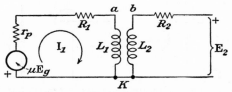

FIG. 6-18. The l-f equivalent circuit of a transformer-coupled amplifier.

capacitances and leakage inductances may be neglected. The corresponding equivalent circuit has the form shown in Fig. 6-18. The resistance of the primary winding is denoted as R_1, and its inductance is L_1. Similarly, R_2 and L_2 represent the secondary resistance and inductance, respectively.

It is evident from this diagram that the primary current is

$$\mathbf{I}_1 = \frac{\mu E_g}{r_p + R_1 + j\omega L_1}$$

The potential difference across the primary inductance is

$$\mathbf{E}_{ak} = \frac{-\mu \mathbf{E}_g}{1 - j(r_p + R_1)/\omega L_1} \tag{6-41}$$

But the potential that appears across the secondary winding $\mathbf{E}_{bk}$ is n times as large as $\mathbf{E}_{ak}$. The secondary voltage may be in phase or 180 deg out of phase with $\mathbf{E}_{ak}$ and depends upon the relative winding direction of the primary and secondary windings. The gain of the transformer-coupled stage is then

$$\mathbf{K}_1 = \frac{\mathbf{E}_{bk}}{\mathbf{E}_g} = \pm \frac{n\mu}{1 - j(r_p + R_1)/\omega L_1} \tag{6-42}$$

The ratio of l-f to mid-frequency gain is then

$$\frac{\mathbf{K}_1}{\mathbf{K}_0} = \pm \frac{1}{1 - j(r_p + R_1)/\omega L_1} \tag{6-43}$$

which may be written in the form

$$\frac{\mathbf{K}_1}{\mathbf{K}_0} = \pm \frac{1}{1 - jf_1/f} \tag{6-44}$$

where

$$f_1 \equiv \frac{r_p + R_1}{2\pi L_1} \tag{6-45}$$

Observe that the gain ratio has the same general form as for the RC coupled amplifier. Now the gain drops off at the lower frequencies because the reactance of the primary winding decreases and no longer will be large compared with the total resistance of the primary circuit $r_p + R_1$.

Equation (6-45) contains an explanation why high-gain tubes, which inherently possess high plate resistances, are not employed in transformer-coupled amplifiers. If such high-gain tubes were used, then the l-f response would be very poor. If an attempt were made to improve the l-f response by designing the transformer to have a very high primary inductance, the associated distributed capacitances would become excessive. The alternative method of obtaining high primary inductance through the use of core material of very high permeability has led to the development of high-permeability alloys such as permalloy and hiperm.

H-F Region. At the high frequencies the shunting effects of the primary and secondary windings may be neglected. However, the effects of the leakage inductances, and also the interwinding and distributed capacitances, are important. The circuit of Fig. 6-17 appears in Fig. 6-19a with the transformer replaced by its T equivalent, and referred to the primary. At the high frequencies the circuit reduces to that of

Fig. 6-19b, in which the winding, interwinding, interelectrode, and stray wiring capacitances are lumped into an equivalent capacitance C across the primary of the transformer.

The total effective shunting capacitance is related to the several components by the approximate expression

$$C = [(1 \pm n)^2 C_m + n^2 C_2] + n^2 C_g \tag{6-46}$$

The $\pm$ sign depends on the relative disposition and connection of the primary and secondary coils. When properly connected, the minus sign usually applies. To justify this expression, examine Fig. 6-19a. If

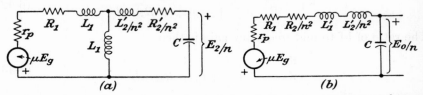

FIG. 6-19. The complete and approximate h-f equivalent circuit of a transformer-coupled stage.

the potential across the input terminals is $\mathbf{E}_1$, and that across the output terminals is $\mathbf{E}_2$, the difference of potential across C_m is

$$\mathbf{E}_{Cm} = \mathbf{E}_1 \pm \mathbf{E}_2 \doteq \mathbf{E}_1(1 \pm n)$$

where $n = N_2/N_1$. The energy stored in this capacitor per cycle is

$$W = \frac{C_m E_{Cm}^2}{2} = \frac{C_m}{2}(1 \pm n)^2 E_1^2$$

The equivalent capacitor across the primary terminals which will store the same energy per cycle will be $(1 \pm n)^2 C_m$. The other capacitances in the secondary are reflected into the primary as $n^2(C_2 + C_g)$. The total shunting capacitance is that given in Eq. (6-46).

An analysis of the approximate equivalent circuit yields for the gain of the amplifier the expression

$$\mathbf{K}_2 = \pm \frac{jn\mu X_C}{R + j(X_L - X_C)} \tag{6-47}$$

where $R = r_p + R_1 + R_2/n^2$; $L = L_1' + L_2'/n^2$; $X_L = \omega L$; $X_C = 1/\omega C$. The primary leakage inductance is L_1', and the secondary leakage inductance is L_2'. The gain ratio may be written in the form

$$\frac{\mathbf{K}_2}{\mathbf{K}_0} = \pm \frac{jX_C}{R + j(X_L - X_C)} \tag{6-48}$$

The magnitude of the gain ratio is

$$\frac{K_2}{K_0} = \frac{X_C}{\sqrt{R^2 + (X_L - X_C)^2}} \tag{6-49}$$

At the lower end of the region of frequencies where this analysis is valid, X_L is small and X_C is large, so that the gain ratio approaches unity, as it should.   At the higher frequencies, X_C is small, X_L is large, and the gain falls to zero.   Notice, however, that the secondary circuit may pass through a maximum, owing to a resonance condition that exists.   The maximum is found to occur when

$$X_C = \frac{2X_L^2 + R^2}{2X_L}$$

Usually R will be much smaller than X_L, and the maximum occurs when $X_C = X_L$, the condition for series resonance.   But as the frequency at which this resonance occurs is

$$\omega_0 = \frac{1}{\sqrt{LC}}$$

then the corresponding value of the gain is

$$\left(\frac{K_2}{K_0}\right)_{max} = \frac{1}{\omega_0 C R} = \frac{1}{R}\sqrt{\frac{L}{C}} \tag{6-50}$$

A typical frequency-response curve, the dependence on the primary inductance L_1, and the total leakage inductance L are illustrated in Fig. 6-20.

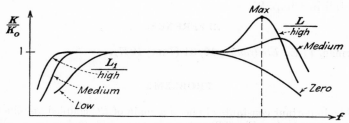

FIG. 6-20. A typical frequency-response characteristic of a transformer-coupled amplifier.

The peaking of the transformer-coupled-amplifier frequency-response curve may be suppressed to a considerable extent by several methods. The simplest way consists in shunting the secondary of the transformer with an appropriately chosen resistance.   This reduces the height of the resonant peak, although it also causes the mid-frequency gain to be less than $n\mu$.   Another method for improving the response characteristic is in the design of the transformer.   In modern transformers the shunt capacitance is decreased by decreasing the contributing factors.   The use of a grounded shield between windings reduces the interwinding capacitance.   The design of the windings reduces the distributed capacitances. Further, the leakage inductance is reduced, so that the peaking will occur at frequencies beyond the normal operating range of the amplifier. This reduction has been accomplished both by proper design of the windings and by use of suitable high-permeability core materials. Also, the use of a high-resistance secondary winding tends to suppress the resonant peak. A high-resistance primary winding is to be avoided owing to the adverse effect on the l-f response. High-quality transformers are available that are flat within 1 db over a range of frequencies from approximately 20 to 10,000 cps. The peaking may also be reduced materially through the use of inverse feedback in the amplifier, as will be shown in Chap. 7.

Transformers are seldom used as interstage coupling devices merely to obtain higher gain. This follows because the use of a pentode in an *RC* coupled amplifier will ordinarily provide a higher gain than is possible with a triode with a step-up transformer. Furthermore, the *RC* coupled stage requires less space and makes use of relatively inexpensive equipment. The principal uses of transformers are as the coupling stage between the driver and a push-pull amplifier, so as to provide the required two potentials that are 180 deg apart in phase (although this application is largely being supplanted by tube circuits), and also as the output transformer in a power amplifier. Here the principal function is one of impedance matching and permits the matching of low impedance loads to high-internal-resistance tubes. These applications will be discussed in some detail in Chap. 8.

REFERENCES

1. Terman, F. E., *Electronics*, **10**, 34 (June, 1937).

PROBLEMS

6-1. The important constants of one of a chain of *RC* coupled amplifier stages employing pentodes (see Fig. 6-3) are

$$R_l = 75 \text{ kilohms} \qquad r_p = 10^6 \text{ ohms} \qquad g_m = 1{,}600 \text{ } \mu\text{mhos} \qquad C = 0.01 \text{ } \mu\text{f}$$
$$C_{gk} = 11 \text{ } \mu\mu\text{f} \qquad C_{pk} = 8 \text{ } \mu\mu\text{f} \qquad R_g = 500 \text{ kilohms}$$

a. Calculate the mid-frequency gain and the upper and lower cutoff frequencies.

b. Between what frequencies is the amplifier-stage phase 180 ± 15 deg?

6-2. The frequency response of a three-stage cascaded *RC* amplifier employing pentodes is to be constant within 0.5 db up to 18 kc. Calculate the h-f cutoff of each stage.

6-3. Consider a chain of similar triode circuits in cascade. Show that the limiting gain-bandwidth product is given by

$$K^2 B = \frac{g_m}{2\pi C_t}$$

What can be said about the use of triodes in a cascade chain?

6-4. Compute the figure of merit of the following tubes: 6AK5, 6AC7, 6J6, 6F4 triodes; 6AK5, 6AC7 pentodes. (See any tube handbook for characteristics.)

6-5. Refer to Fig. 6-10 showing a resistance-coupled amplifier. The circuit constants are

$$R_{l1} = 250 \text{ kilohms} \qquad R_{g2} = 500 \text{ kilohms} \qquad R_{c1} = 500 \text{ kilohms}$$

If $I_{b1} = 0.5$ ma, $E_{bb} = 300$ volts, what must be the value of E_{cc} if E_c of $T2$ is to be -8 volts?

6-6. Calculate the gain of the series balanced d-c amplifier shown in the diagram.

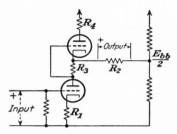

6-7. The LC coupled amplifier of Fig. 6-14 uses a triode. The important factors are

$$r_p = 10 \text{ kilohms} \qquad g_m = 2,000 \ \mu\text{mhos} \qquad R_g = 10^6 \text{ ohms} \qquad C = 0.01 \ \mu\text{f}$$
$$L = 40 \text{ henrys} \qquad \text{Distributed capacitance} = 200 \ \mu\mu\text{f}$$

Determine the upper and lower cutoff frequencies and the maximum gain.

6-8. A transformer-coupled amplifier is to be constant within 3 db over the frequency range from 100 to 8,400 cps.

a. Specify the required values of primary inductance, leakage inductance (reduced to unity turns ratio), and frequency of secondary resonance. The tube is a 6J5 with $r_p = 7,700$ ohms. Neglect the winding resistance in the calculations.

b. If the turns ratio is 3 and the total input and wiring capacitance of the next tube is 25 $\mu\mu$f, what is the permissible equivalent capacitance across the secondary of the transformer?

6-9. Obtain an expression for the output potentials of the cathode-coupled two-tube circuit shown in the figure. Compare the results with Eq. (6-38) when R_l of $T1$ is zero.

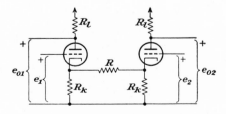

6-10. Calculate the input admittance and the output-terminal impedance of the cathode-coupled amplifier when connected as shown in Fig. 6-12. Neglect tube and wiring capacitances.

6-11. The circuit of an inverted amplifier is illustrated in the accompanying diagram. Calculate the following:

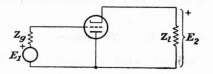

a. The gain.
b. Input impedance.
c. Ratio of output to input power if Z_g and Z_l are resistors

CHAPTER 7

SPECIAL AMPLIFIER CONSIDERATIONS

NOISE

7-1. Noise in Amplifiers. The term *noise* is used to describe any spurious signals which ultimately appear in the output of an amplifier. Noise may be produced by causes which may be external to, or which might be internal to, the system.

External noise, which will be only superficially examined, includes atmospheric interference with reception and occasional large amplitude pulses. Atmospheric interference arises principally from lightning discharges in the lower atmosphere. Owing to the magnitude of the fields involved, the effective area of disturbance is very large. However, such interference is most troublesome at the longer wavelengths, although considerable energy exists even in the short-wave band. Since the noise is present at all frequencies, the wider the bandwidth of the receiver, the greater will be the energy picked up from the atmospheric disturbance.

If the interference arises from short pulses, it proves most desirable to have a relatively wide band system, in order to avoid having the system extend the pulse. It is possible to provide suppression circuits in a receiver to overcome to a considerable extent noise from this cause.

External noise may also be of the man-made variety and arises when sparking of any sort exists, as, for example, the sparking at the brushes of a motor. Also, poorly shielded electronic equipment may be the source of considerable external noise. Diathermy machines, which are generally simple power oscillators, often with inadequately filtered power supplies, produce considerable amounts of noise over a relatively broad band.

The ignition systems of automobiles and aircraft engines are strong sources of noise. The noise from such sources is most severe in the 30- to 100-Mc frequency band. While screening of the ignition leads will reduce this type noise, this is generally not done, except in mobile systems which are directly affected.

In addition to the external sources of noise, a number of internal sources of noise exist. It might happen that the amplifier is oscillating because some part of the output is being fed back into the input. This may be caused by a common impedance between stages, for example,

through a common plate supply.   Appropriately placed decoupling filters
will usually prevent such interaction.   Coupling may occur through the
interelectrode capacitances of the tubes.   Methods of neutralization have
been developed for avoiding this.   If the coupling occurs through stray
wiring capacitances, electrical shielding is usually resorted to in order to
prevent such coupling.

Some noise may appear in amplifiers the cathode heaters of which are
fed from the a-c lines.   If the heat capacity of the cathode-heater assembly is too low, there may be some variation in cathode current due to the
fluctuations in temperature of the cathode.   This is usually low in indirectly heated cathode tubes, although it may be appreciable in tubes
of the directly heated type which are fed from an a-c source.

Noise, related to the power-line frequency, may also appear in an
amplifier if the rectifier power supply is not adequately filtered.   Such
ripple hum is often detectable in the average home radio receiver.

Microphonics, which causes output potentials due to the vibration
of the electrodes produced by acoustic or mechanical jarring of the tube,
may be very serious in high-gain systems.   The microphonic property
of a tube depends on the character of its construction, certain tubes being
considerably more microphonic than others.   Special low-microphonic
tubes are available.   The judicious use of shock mounts, loaded supports,
or special vibration-isolation methods will usually overcome this problem.

7-2. Internal Noise.   Even with the elimination of the foregoing
sources of noise, a limitation exists to the useful amplification possible
with an amplifier.   The noise generated in the receiver itself sets a
limit to the minimum amplitude that can be amplified if a satisfactory
signal/noise ratio is to be obtained in the output.

There are two fundamental sources of internal noise.   The first results
from the fact that the electrons in the circuit elements of the amplifier are
in a state of continuous agitation.   This activity produces fluctuations
in the electron distribution within the elements, and this appears as a
thermal-agitation potential.   The second cause arises within the tube
itself and is produced by the random motion of the electrons in the
cathode-anode space.

Thermal-agitation Noise.   The free or conduction electrons in a conductor are all in random motion, the amplitude of the motion being
dependent upon the temperature of the circuit.   Because of this random
motion, slight deviations exist in the statistical most-probable distribution, with the result that small fluctuating potentials are produced within
the conductor.   The small-fluctuation, or thermal-agitation, potentials in
the input circuit of an amplifier will give rise to an appreciable output if a
high-gain system is used.

Since these thermal-agitation motions are random, it is reasonable to expect that thermal-agitation potentials of all frequencies are produced. Consequently, the total rms potential expected in a circuit which is frequency-sensitive will depend upon the bandwidth of the circuit, among other factors.   An analysis of this problem by Johnson[1] and Nyquist[2] shows that the square of the rms potential produced in a circuit component having constant resistance R over the frequency band used is given by

$$\overline{E^2} = 4kTRB \tag{7-1}$$

where k is the Boltzmann constant ($= 1.38 \times 10^{-23}$ joule/$^\circ$K), T is the temperature of the resistor in degrees Kelvin, R is the resistance in ohms, and B is the pass band of the channel over which the noise is evaluated, measured to the 3-db, or half-power, points.   This expression is a special case of the following more general expression,

$$\overline{E^2} = 4kT \int_0^\infty \mathrm{Re}\,(\mathbf{Z})\,df \tag{7-2}$$

where $\mathrm{Re}\,(\mathbf{Z})$ denotes the real part of the impedance element in which noise is being produced and is the effective resistance component of the circuit.

If the measuring circuit is an amplifier having a gain characteristic $K(f)$, or if the noise source is the input circuit to the amplifier of gain characteristic $K(f)$, then the total rms noise is given by the expression

$$\overline{E^2} = 4kT \int_0^\infty K^2(f)\,\mathrm{Re}\,(\mathbf{Z})\,df \tag{7-3}$$

Of course, noise is generated in all resistance elements of the circuit. However, it is usually only the potential produced across the input terminals which is of importance, since it is this potential which is subject to the full amplification of the amplifier stages.   If this Johnson noise is sufficiently below the level of the input signal, then noise in subsequent stages will be negligible compared with the amplified output signal.

To get some idea of the magnitude of the potentials that are produced by this source of noise, choose the following values:

$$k = 1.38 \times 10^{-23} \text{ joule/}^\circ\text{K} \quad T = 300^\circ\text{K} \quad R = 10^5 \text{ ohms} \quad B = 100 \text{ kc}$$

then it is found that

$$E_{\mathrm{rms}} = 4.0 \ \mu\mathrm{v}$$

Shot Noise.   Among the various sources of noise in the tube itself, shot noise is most important.   The shot effect results from the fact that the current from the cathode to the anode consists of the flow of electrons, and since the electron emission from the cathode surface may not be completely uniform for a given cathode temperature, instantaneous fluctuations may occur, even if the time average current is constant.   If the tube is operating under space-charge-limited conditions, the irregularities in the cathode emission, and so in the arrival of the electrons at the anode, are considerably reduced.

The magnitude of the shot noise in a temperature-limited diode can be calculated, and as a result, temperature-limited diodes have been used as sources of noise. An analysis of this problem yields the following expression for the noise produced in such a temperature-saturated diode,[3]

$$\overline{I^2} = \Gamma^2(2eI_bB) \tag{7-4}$$

where I_b = d-c current, e = electronic charge, B = bandwidth, and Γ = constant depending on the randomness of the electron flow (= 1 for a completely random distribution as exists in a temperature-limited diode, and less than 1 if some degree of space-charge limitation occurs).

A quantitative treatment of shot noise in multielectrode tubes working under normal conditions is difficult. It is possible to deduce certain significant results from physical reasoning. The total shot noise will be proportional to the anode current. On the other hand, the signal in the output will depend on the transconductance g_m. It appears, therefore, that for a large signal/noise ratio the tube should have large g_m and yet draw a small anode current. It is likewise found that the partition of the cathode current between the screen and the anode also produces noise. Consequently pentodes with small screen current are best from this point of view (the beam tube is probably best in this regard.) In general, triodes operate with a lower noise than a comparable-type pentode.

If is often convenient to specify the shot and partition noises produced in a tube in terms of a fictitious resistance R_{eq} which, when placed in the grid line, will produce in the plate circuit the same noise by thermal agitation as is produced by the shot noise. If R denotes the parallel combination of r_p and R_l of the given amplifier, the equivalent noise potential squared in the output is

$$\overline{I^2}R^2 = \Gamma^2(2eI_bB)R^2$$

But from Eq. (7-1) for a noise resistance R_{eq} in the input, the corresponding potential squared in the output is

$$K^2\overline{E^2} = (4kTR_{eq}B)g_m^2R^2$$

If these expressions are equated, the equivalent grid noise resistance is found to be

$$R_{eq} = \frac{\Gamma^2 eI_b}{2kTg_m^2}$$

But since I_b varies directly with g_m, it would be expected that R_{eq} should vary inversely with g_m.   It has been shown, in fact, that for triodes[4]

$$R_{eq} \doteq \frac{2.5}{g_m} \qquad \text{ohms} \qquad (7\text{-}5)$$

As noted above, tetrodes and pentodes have more shot noise than do triodes, owing to the random interception of electrons by the screen grid. The expression for the equivalent noise resistance R_{eq} has been shown to be[4]

$$R_{eq} \doteq \frac{I_b}{I_b + I_{c2}} \left(\frac{2.5}{g_m} + \frac{20 I_{c2}}{g_m^2} \right) \qquad (7\text{-}6)$$

where I_b is the plate current in amperes, I_{c2} is the screen current in amperes, and g_m is the transconductance in mhos.   These formulas enable a direct comparison to be made between the input circuit noise and the shot and partition noise.   Typical values follow:

Type tube	R_{eq}, ohms
Triode	200–1,000
Tetrode and pentode	5,000–20,000
Mixer and converter	200,000–300,000

Other Noise.   Another important source of noise in the grid circuit arises from the motion of charges in the grid circuit due to the motion of electrons between cathode and anode.   The following formula has been developed for the mean square induced grid noise,[5]

$$\overline{I_g^2} = 4kT G_g \beta B \qquad (7\text{-}7)$$

where I_g is the noise current in amperes and G_g is the electronic portion of the input conductance in mhos.   This implies that, for noise purposes, the induced grid noise is represented by a current generator I_g shunted by a conductance G_g.   The value of β is approximately 5.

As indicated in the table above, a tube used as a mixer or converter is noisier than the same tube used as an amplifier.   This greater noise arises from the effects of the local oscillator injection.   As is discussed in Sec. 13-13, the oscillator provides several volts to the converter grid.   As a result, the g_m of the tube varies over a very wide range.   Since the equivalent noise resistance R_{eq} and the average input conductance G_g depend upon the average g_m of the tube during the injection cycle, then because of the wide excursions in g_m the resulting noise is high.

Another important source of noise in vacuum tubes is the *flicker* effect. This effect arises from the changes of emission from various portions of the cathode surface.   It has been found that the flicker effect produces noise components that are most important at the lower frequencies, and the resultant noise varies roughly inversely with the frequency.   It may be large in oxide-coated cathode tubes, where it overshadows the regular shot noise.

Another source of noise arises from the random neutralization of space charge by the comparatively few molecules normally present in a vacuum tube. In a tube with a good vacuum this effect produces about as much noise as thermal-agitation noise in the plate circuit of the tube. Secondary emission from the plate and grids in a vacuum tube also introduces some noise.

7-3. Noise Figure. It is customary to specify the quality of a receiver in terms of its noise figure. This quantity measures the noise generation within the receiver circuits. The noise figure F is a measure of the ratio of the actual available noise power output of a receiver to that of an ideal receiver which is free of noise sources, the only source of noise being the thermal-agitation noise that has been applied to the input terminals of the receiver by the antenna. The term "available" denotes that the power source is matched to the load for optimum power transfer. By definition, F is the ratio of the available signal to noise power at the input (S_i/N_i) to the available signal/noise power at the output (S_o/N_o); thus

$$F = \frac{S_i/N_i}{S_o/N_o} \qquad (7\text{-}8)$$

But the available power gain K_p of the receiver is the ratio S_o/S_i. Moreover, by definition, the available noise power input N_i is kTB. Thus Eq. (7-8) may be written as

$$F = \frac{N_o}{K_p kTB} \qquad (7\text{-}9)$$

This expression shows that the noise figure is the ratio of the available output noise power of the actual receiver to the available output noise power of an otherwise ideal receiver. The noise figure is often expressed in decibels, as $F_{db} = 10 \log_{10} F$.

Many factors contribute to the over-all noise figure of a receiver; the input circuit, the mixer (in a superheterodyne receiver), the beat-frequency oscillator, and others. The mixing problem becomes more difficult at the higher frequencies, with the result that receivers for very h-f use (in the microwave bands) usually have higher noise figures at the higher frequencies. For example, a representative noise figure of a radar receiver having a gain of 120 db and a bandwidth of 2 Mc and operating at 3,000 Mc is 15 db. Of this figure several decibels of noise arise in the mixer.

7-4. Noise Figure of Networks in Cascade. Suppose that a network of noise figure F_1 is cascaded with a network of noise figure F_2. An expression is desired for the noise figure F_{12} of the combination. As already discussed in Sec. 7-2, the noise in the input circuit to the first

network is usually the most significant source of noise, and it is anticipated, therefore, that the noise figure F_{12} of the combination will be very
nearly equal to F_1, particularly if the power gain K_{p1} of the first, or input,
network is large.   To examine the matter in some detail, refer to Fig. 7-1.

In Fig. 7-1 two networks are shown in cascade.   The input to the first
network is shown as an equivalent noise resistance and would be the
equivalent output-terminal noise resistance of the antenna or other noise
source.   This resistance supplies an available noise power kTB to the
first network.   The available power at the input terminals of the second
network is evidently $kTBF_1K_{p1}$, and the available output power at the
output of the second network is $kTBF_1K_{p1}K_{p2}$.

In addition to the noise produced in the input circuit to network 1
there is an available noise power produced in the input circuit to network
2.   This results in a component available power at the output of network 2 of $kTBF_2K_{p2}$.   However, a certain part of this latter available

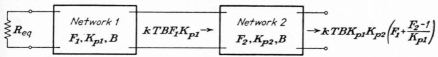

FIG. 7-1. Determination of the noise figure of two networks in cascade.

power has already been included in the term involving F_1.   To avoid
counting the available power $kTBK_{p2}$ twice, it must be subtracted from
the total available power at the output of network 2.   Therefore the
noise output due to the second network is $kTBF_2K_{p2} - kTBK_{p2}$.   The
over-all noise power available is

$$kTBF_{12}K_{p1}K_{p2} = kTBF_1K_{p1}K_{p2} + kTBF_2K_{p2} - kTBK_{p2}$$

from which it follows that

$$F_{12} = F_1 + \frac{F_2 - 1}{K_{p1}} \tag{7-10}$$

As anticipated, the over-all noise figure F_{12} will be very nearly equal to
F_1 if the gain of network 1 is large.   However, if K_{p1} is small, then the
over-all noise figure will depend on F_2.

In the development of Eq. (7-10) it was assumed that the bandwidths
B of both networks were equal.   Careful consideration of this matter will
show that this expression is also valid if the bandwidth of the first network is greater than and contains the bandwidth B of the second network.

The reasoning that led to Eq. (7-10) can be extended to yield expressions for the case of three or more networks in cascade.   Specifically,
for three networks in cascade, the over-all noise figure is

$$F = F_1 + \frac{F_2 - 1}{K_{p1}} + \frac{F_3 - 1}{K_{p1}K_{p2}} \tag{7-11}$$

FEEDBACK IN AMPLIFIERS*

7-5. Principles of Feedback.[6] When a part of the output signal is combined with the input signal, feedback is said to exist.   If the net effect of the feedback is to increase the effective input signal, the feedback is called *positive, direct,* or *regenerative.*   If the resultant input signal is reduced by the feedback potential, the feedback is called *negative, inverse,* or *degenerative.*

The principle of feedback is illustrated in the schematic diagram of Fig. 7-2.   For simplicity, series injection is shown at the input, but other forms of network coupling may be employed.   In the diagram shown, a potential E_1 is applied to the input terminals of the amplifier.   Suppose that the resultant potential at the output terminals is E_2.   Now suppose

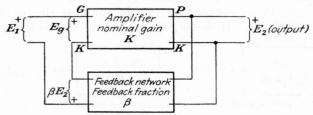

FIG. 7-2. The principles of feedback in amplifiers.

that a fraction β of this output is fed back in series with the input signal in such a way that the resultant signal that appears between the grid and cathode terminals has the form

$$E_g = E_1 + \beta E_2 \tag{7-12}$$

But the nominal gain of the amplifier is given by

$$K \equiv \frac{\text{output potential}}{\text{potential between grid and cathode}} = \frac{E_2}{E_g}$$

Then

$$E_2 = KE_g \tag{7-13}$$

Observe that the nominal gain requires the injection of a potential E_g between the grid-cathode terminals, with an evaluation of the output potential E_2, with the β network acting as part of the total output load of the circuit.

Equation (7-13) is combined with Eq. (7-12) to yield

$$E_2 = KE_1 + K\beta E_2$$

from which it follows that

$$E_2 = \frac{KE_1}{1 - K\beta} \tag{7-14}$$

---

* Part of the contents of this section was originally prepared with Dr. J. Millman for the second edition of "Electronics," McGraw-Hill Book Company, Inc., New York, 1951, although the material was not included in this text.

The resultant gain of the amplifier with feedback is defined as

$$\mathbf{K}_f \equiv \frac{\text{output potential}}{\text{input signal potential}} = \frac{\mathbf{E}_2}{\mathbf{E}_1}$$

Therefore it follows that

$$\mathbf{K}_f = \frac{\mathbf{K}}{1 - \mathbf{K}\beta} \tag{7-15}$$

This equation expresses the resultant gain of the amplifier with feedback $\mathbf{K}_f$ in terms of the nominal gain of the amplifier without feedback $\mathbf{K}$, and the feedback fraction β. It is noted that often in a practical situation the feedback path is so involved that it is not possible to isolate the β network. The discussion to follow still applies in principle, but a direct application of the mathematical expressions may not be possible.

It can be seen that if $|1 - \mathbf{K}\beta|$ is greater than unity, then $\mathbf{K}_f$ is less than $\mathbf{K}$. The feedback is then said to be negative, or degenerative. The application of negative feedback to an amplifier results in a number of characteristics that are highly desirable in the amplifier. It tends to flatten the frequency-response characteristic and to extend the range of uniform response. It materially reduces nonlinear and phase distortion. It improves the stability of the amplifier, making the gain less dependent on the operating potentials or on variations of the tube characteristics. Also, it tends to make the gain less dependent on the load, so that load variations do not seriously influence the operating characteristics of the amplifier. The use of feedback networks of special design will provide selective attenuation, thus permitting a frequency response of desired characteristic. A detailed discussion of these features will be given later.

Conversely, if $|1 - \mathbf{K}\beta|$ is less than unity, then $\mathbf{K}_f$ is greater than $\mathbf{K}$. The feedback is now termed positive, or regenerative. The application of positive feedback has effects opposite to those with negative feedback. Thus positive feedback tends to sharpen the frequency-response curve and to decrease the range of uniform response. This permits an increased gain and selectivity. Positive feedback in any amplifier is critical of adjustment. Too much regenerative feedback in any system may result in oscillation. Ordinarily, negative feedback is more common than positive feedback in amplifiers, although oscillators of the feedback variety depend for their operation on the presence of positive feedback.

Observe that, for the case when $\mathbf{K}\beta = 1 + j0$, the gain becomes infinite. In this case the amplifier becomes an oscillator, and the output potential is independent of any external signal potential.

Attention is called to the fact that the action of a feedback path depends upon the frequency of operation. That is, the feedback may remain regenerative or degenerative throughout the range of operation of the circuit, although the magnitude and phase angle of the feedback signal may vary with the frequency. It is also possible for the feedback to be positive over a certain range of frequencies and negative over another range of frequencies.

Example. The circuit of a simple triode amplifier with an impedance in the cathode lead is illustrated in Fig. 7-3. This circuit is to be analyzed by two methods. One method is a direct application of the feedback equation [Eq. (7-5)]. The second method is a direct application of electron-tube circuit principles.

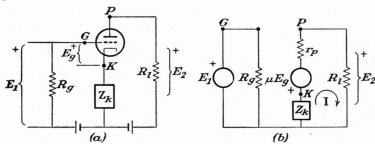

FIG. 7-3. A simple amplifier with cathode degeneration.

Solution. Refer to the equivalent circuit of the amplifier which is given in Fig. 7-3b. Observe that a part of the output is fed back into the input circuit through the impedance Z_k. It follows from the figure that

$$\mathbf{E}_g = \mathbf{E}_1 + \mathbf{I}Z_k \tag{7-16}$$

But since

$$\mathbf{I} = \frac{\mathbf{E}_2}{R_l} \tag{7-17}$$

then

$$\mathbf{E}_g = \mathbf{E}_1 + \frac{Z_k}{R_l}\mathbf{E}_2 \tag{7-18}$$

If this expression is compared with Eq. (7-12), which defines the feedback fraction, it is seen that

$$\beta = \frac{Z_k}{R_l} \tag{7-19}$$

Note also that

$$\mathbf{E}_2 = \mathbf{I}R_l = -\frac{\mu\mathbf{E}_g}{r_p + Z_k + R_l}R_l \tag{7-20}$$

and the nominal gain then becomes

$$\mathbf{K} = \frac{\mathbf{E}_2}{\mathbf{E}_g} = \frac{-\mu R_l}{r_p + Z_k + R_l} \tag{7-21}$$

The resultant gain is, by Eq. (7-15),

$$\mathbf{K}_f = \frac{\mathbf{K}}{1 - \mathbf{K}\beta} = \frac{-\mu R_l/(r_p + Z_k + R_l)}{1 - \dfrac{-\mu R_l}{r_p + Z_k + R_l}\dfrac{Z_k}{R_l}} = \frac{-\mu R_l}{r_p + (\mu + 1)Z_k + R_l} \tag{7-22}$$

These results follow of course from direct considerations of the equivalent circuit. The plate circuit yields the expression

$$\mu E_g + I(r_p + Z_k + R_l) = 0 \tag{7-23}$$

But

$$E_g = E_1 + IZ_k \tag{7-24}$$

The solution of these equations gives

$$\mu(E_1 + IZ_k) + I(r_p + Z_k + R_l) = 0$$

from which

$$I = \frac{-\mu E_1}{r_p + (\mu + 1)Z_k + R_l} \tag{7-25}$$

and the resultant gain is

$$K_f = \frac{E_2}{E_1} = \frac{-\mu R_l}{r_p + (\mu + 1)Z_k + R_l} \tag{7-26}$$

which is the same as above.

Often Z_k consists of the parallel combination of R_k and C_k, the value of R_k being so chosen that $I_b R_k$ is just equal to E_c, the quiescent d-c basis of the tube. The capacitor C_k is so chosen that its reactance is very small over the operating range of the amplifier. As a result, Z_k is very small and may be omitted in the above expression. In this case, the usual simple amplifier formula is obtained, since the feedback factor β is zero, and no feedback exists.

7-6. Feedback Amplifier Characteristics. The presence of negative feedback in an amplifier results in a number of desirable characteristics. These are discussed below.

1. *Stability of Amplification.* Suppose that the feedback is negative and that the feedback factor $K\beta$ is made large compared with unity. The resultant gain equation (7-15) becomes

$$K_f \doteq -\frac{K}{K\beta} = -\frac{1}{\beta} \tag{7-27}$$

This means that when the magnitude $K\beta \gg 1$, the actual amplification with negative feedback is a function of the characteristics of the feedback network only. In particular, if β is independent of frequency, then the over-all gain will be independent of the frequency. This permits a substantial reduction of the frequency and phase distortion of the amplifier. In fact, by the proper choice of feedback network, it is possible to achieve a wide variety of frequency characteristics.

Note that if $K\beta \gg 1$, then $K_f \doteq -K/K\beta \ll -K$, so that the over-all gain of the amplifier with inverse feedback is less than the nominal gain without feedback. This is the price that must be paid to secure the advantages of negative feedback. This is not a serious price to pay, since the loss in gain can be overcome by the use of additional tubes.

Clearly, if $K\beta$ is greater than unity, then Eq. (7-27) shows that the over-all gain will not change with tube replacements or with variations in battery potentials, since β is independent of the tube. Even if Eq. (7-27) is not completely valid, a substantial improvement results in general stability. This follows from the fact that a change in the nominal gain $d\mathbf{K}$ for whatever reason results in a change $d\mathbf{K}_f$ in the resultant gain by an amount

$$\frac{d\mathbf{K}_f}{\mathbf{K}_f} = \frac{1}{|1 - \mathbf{K}\beta|} \frac{d\mathbf{K}}{\mathbf{K}} \tag{7-28}$$

where $|1 - \mathbf{K}\beta|$ represents the magnitude of the quantity $1 - \mathbf{K}\beta$. This equation is the logarithmic derivative of Eq. (7-15). In this expression, $d\mathbf{K}_f/\mathbf{K}_f$ gives the fractional change in $\mathbf{K}_f$, and $d\mathbf{K}/\mathbf{K}$ gives the fractional change in $\mathbf{K}$. If, for example, the quantity $|1 - \mathbf{K}\beta| = 5$ in a particular feedback amplifier, then the variation in any parameter that might cause a 5 per cent change in the nominal gain will result in a change of only 1 per cent in the resultant gain of the amplifier.

2. *Reduction of Frequency and Phase Distortion.* It follows from Eqs. (7-15) and (7-27) that the over-all gain of the amplifier is almost independent of frequency, provided that β is frequency-independent. In such cases the frequency and phase distortion of an amplifier are materially reduced below the nonfeedback value.

3. *Reduction of Nonlinear Distortion.* One effect was omitted in the above considerations. It was implicitly assumed that the dynamic curve was linear and that the output potential was of the same waveshape as the input. If an appreciable nonlinear distortion exists, then the output contains harmonic components in addition to the signal of fundamental frequency. Suppose, for simplicity, that only a second-harmonic component B_2 is generated within the tube when a large signal potential is impressed on the input. Because of the feedback, the second-harmonic component B_2' that appears in the output is different from that generated within the tube. To find the relationship that exists between B_2' and B_2, the procedure parallels that for the gain considerations. Thus, for a second harmonic B_2' in the output, a fraction $\beta B_2'$ is supplied to the input. As a result, the output actually must contain two components of second-harmonic frequency, the component B_2 that is generated within the tube and the component $\mathbf{K}\beta B_2'$ that arises from the signal that is fed back to the input. This requires that

$$\mathbf{K}\beta B_2' + B_2 = B_2'$$

or

$$B_2' = \frac{B_2}{1 - \mathbf{K}\beta} \tag{7-29}$$

Note that since both $\mathbf{K}$ and β are functions of the frequency, in general, the appropriate values that appear in this equation must be evaluated at the second-harmonic frequency.

It should be pointed out that this derivation has assumed that the harmonic distortion generated within the tube depends only upon the grid swing of the fundamental signal potential. The small amount of additional distortion that might arise because a fraction of the second-harmonic component is returned to the input has been neglected. Ordinarily this procedure will lead to little error, although a more exact calculation taking these successive effects into account is readily possible.[7]

Another feature of Eq. (7-29) should be noted. According to this expression, if $|1 - K\beta| = 10$, then the second-harmonic distortion with feedback is only one-tenth its value without feedback. This is the situation when the total output-potential swing is the same in each case; otherwise the harmonic generation within the tube could not be directly compared. This requires that the signal, when feedback is applied, must be $|1 - K\beta|$ times that in the absence of feedback. As a practical consideration, since appreciable nonlinear distortion is generated only when the signal potential is large, then the full benefit of the feedback amplifier in reducing nonlinear distortion is obtained by applying negative feedback to the large-signal stages.

4. *Reduction of Noise.* Considerations such as those leading to Eq. (7-29) for the resultant nonlinear distortion in a feedback amplifier will show that the resultant noise generated in the input to an amplifier chain is reduced by the factor $1 - \beta K$, when feedback is employed. This would seem to represent a real reduction in noise. However, if the requirement is for a specified output signal, the resultant gain with feedback will have to be adjusted, by adjustment of the circuit parameters or by the addition of amplifier stages, to give the same over-all gain as the amplifier without feedback. Consequently, the noise will be amplified as well as the signal. Moreover, since the noise is independent of the signal, additional amplifier stages to compensate for the loss of gain due to feedback will introduce additional noise. In such cases, the over-all noise of the amplifier with feedback might be higher than one without feedback. If the required gain is achieved by the readjustment of the circuit parameters, a reduction in noise will result in the negative feedback amplifier. Noise generated at some intermediate point of the amplifier chain, say at a point whose gain relative to the output point is K_1, will be reduced by the factor $K_1/(1 - K\beta)$.

5. *Modification of Input and Output (Effective Internal) Impedances.* These topics will be the subject of detailed consideration in several of the following sections.

7-7. Feedback Circuits. The potential fed back from the output of the amplifier into the input may be proportional either to the potential across the load or to the current through the load. In the first case, the feedback is called *potential feedback;* in the second case, it is called *current feedback.* In either case, the feedback may be positive or negative, depending upon the connection. Often the feedback loops are so involved and interconnected that it is not possible to specify directly whether the feedback is of the potential or the current types or whether a combination of both exists.

It is possible to state rules which help to specify more uniquely the existence of potential or current feedback. Consider the circuits of Fig. 7-4, which illustrate two amplifiers employing current feedback. The first of these diagrams is identical with that of the illustrative example

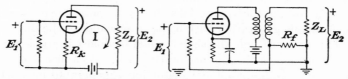

FIG. 7-4. Circuits employing current feedback.

of the foregoing section, except that the cathode impedance is now shown as a resistance R_k. As in the example, the feedback ratio is $\beta = R_k/Z_l$. Note that, for large feedback ratios, the resultant gain approaches

$$\mathbf{K}_f \doteq -\frac{1}{\beta} = -\frac{\mathbf{Z}_l}{R_k} \tag{7-30}$$

Therefore the output potential is

$$\mathbf{E}_2 = -\frac{\mathbf{Z}_l}{R_k}\,\mathbf{E}_1 \tag{7-31}$$

which is proportional to the load impedance. Also, the output current is given by

$$\mathbf{I} = \frac{\mathbf{E}_2}{\mathbf{Z}_l} = -\frac{\mathbf{E}_1}{R_k} \tag{7-32}$$

which is seen to be independent of the load impedance. These conditions are characteristic of current feedback. Hence with negative current feedback *the ratio of the feedback potential to the load current is independent of the load impedance.*

The condition that the output current should be independent of the load impedance is fulfilled when the internal impedance of the generator is high compared with the impedance of the external load. Consequently, negative current feedback has the property of increasing the internal impedance of the network. In fact, from the complete expression for the current, from Eq. (7-25), namely,

$$\mathbf{I} = \frac{-\mu\mathbf{E}_1}{r_p + (\mu + 1)R_k + Z_l}$$

it is possible to draw Fig. 7-5, which is the equivalent of Fig. 7-3a.   It
follows from this that the circuit in-
cluding feedback comprises a poten-
tial source $\mathbf{E}_{tf} = \mu\mathbf{E}_1$ with an internal impedance $\mathbf{Z}_{tf} = r_p + (\mu + 1)R_k$.
Since the internal impedance without
feedback is simply $r_p + R_k$, the effect
of the feedback is to increase the inter-

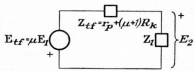

FIG. 7-5. The equivalent circuit of
Fig. 7-3a.

nal impedance by the term μR_k.   The ratio of internal impedances with
and without feedback is given by

$$\frac{Z_{tf}}{Z_t} = \frac{r_p + (\mu + 1)R_k}{r_p + R_k} = 1 + \frac{\mu R_k}{r_p + R_k} \tag{7-33}$$

A circuit which employs potential feedback is given in Fig. 7-6.   In
this circuit, the resistance combination $\beta R + (1 - \beta)R = R$ which

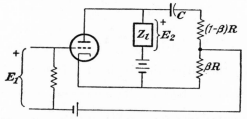

FIG. 7-6. Circuit employing potential feedback.

shunts the output is made large compared with the load impedance $\mathbf{Z}_l$.
The capacitor C has a reactance that is negligible compared with R at
the frequencies to be employed.   Its sole purpose is to block the d-c
potential from the plate circuit from appearing in the grid circuit.

The feedback ratio is shown as β in the diagram.   Also for large feedback ratios, the resultant gain approaches

$$\mathbf{K}_f = -\frac{1}{\beta}$$

The output potential is, therefore,

$$\mathbf{E}_2 = -\frac{1}{\beta}\,\mathbf{E}_1$$

which is seen to be independent of the load impedance, since β is independent of $\mathbf{Z}_l$.   Observe therefore that potential feedback is directly proportional to the output potential, and the *ratio β of the feedback potential*

to the output potential is independent of the load. A generator whose output potential is substantially independent of the load impedance must possess a very low internal impedance. Consequently negative potential feedback has the property of decreasing the internal impedance of the amplifier.

To obtain an expression for the resultant gain of the amplifier, the feedback method will be employed. By neglecting the shunting effect of the feedback resistance network on the load impedance, it follows that the nominal gain of the amplifier is given by

$$\mathbf{K} = \frac{-\mu Z_l}{r_p + Z_l} \tag{7-34}$$

Then the resultant gain with feedback is

$$\mathbf{K}_f = \frac{\mathbf{K}}{1 - \mathbf{K}\beta} = \frac{-\mu Z_l}{r_p + Z_l + \beta\mu Z_l} \tag{7-35}$$

This expression may be transformed to the form

$$\mathbf{K}_f = \frac{-\mu' Z_l}{\mathbf{r}_p' + Z_l} \tag{7-36}$$

where $\mu' = \dfrac{\mu}{1 + \mu\beta}$ $\mathbf{r}_p' = \dfrac{r_p}{1 + \mu\beta}$

But this is exactly the output that is obtained from the circuit of Fig. 7-7.

Consequently, the circuit behaves like a potential source $\mathbf{E}_{tf} = \dfrac{\mu}{1 + \mu\beta}\mathbf{E}_1$ with an internal impedance $Z_{tf} = r_p/(1 + \mu\beta)$.

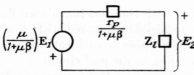

FIG. 7-7. The equivalent circuit of Fig. 7-6.

The effective internal impedance of the amplifier without feedback is simply $Z_t = r_p$. The effect of potential feedback is to reduce the internal impedance in the ratio

$$\frac{Z_{tf}}{Z_t} = \frac{1}{1 + \mu\beta} \tag{7-37}$$

From the form of Eq. (7-36), the circuit gain appears to be that obtained from a tube whose amplification factor is μ' and whose plate resistance is $\mathbf{r}_p'$. Note that the effective amplification factor is reduced in the same ratio as the plate resistance of the tube. This indicates that a tube possessing a high plate resistance can be effectively converted into a low-plate-resistance tube and thereby permit an impedance match to a low impedance load. This is accomplished, of course, at the expense of effectively converting the tube into a triode, with low μ and low r_p.

The combination of current and potential feedback in an amplifier is frequently called compound, or bridge, feedback.   The circuit of such an amplifier is given in Fig. 7-8. The feedback fraction is found to be

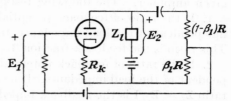

$$\beta = \beta_1 + \frac{R_k}{Z_l} = \beta_1 + \beta_2 \quad (7\text{-}38)$$

As in the analysis of Fig. 7-6, it is assumed that the resistance combination R is much greater than Z_l and that the reactance of the

FIG. 7-8. A circuit employing bridge, or compound, feedback.

capacitor is negligible over the frequency range of operation.   The resultant gain of the amplifier has the form

$$\mathbf{K}_f = \frac{-\mu Z_l}{r_p + (\mu + 1)R_k + (1 + \mu\beta_1)Z_l}$$

This may be written in the form

$$\mathbf{K}_f'' = \frac{-\mathbf{\mu}''Z_l}{\mathbf{r}_p'' + Z_l}$$

where

$$\mathbf{\mu}'' = \frac{\mu}{1 + \mu\beta_1} \quad (7\text{-}39)$$

$$r_p'' = \frac{r_p + (\mu + 1)R_k}{1 + \mu\beta_1}$$

The corresponding equivalent circuit shown in Fig. 7-9 gives rise to exactly this expression for the gain and is therefore the equivalent of Fig. 7-8.   The effect of the feedback is seen to reflect itself as a change in the effective μ and r_p of the tube.   The effective potential and internal impedance are given by the expression

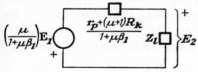

FIG. 7-9. The equivalent circuit of Fig. 7-8.

$$E_{tf} = \frac{\mu}{1 + \mu\beta_1} E_1$$

$$Z_{tf} = \frac{r_p + (\mu + 1)R_k}{1 + \mu\beta_1} \quad (7\text{-}40)$$

Owing to the form of the expression for Z_{tf}, this quantity may be made greater than, equal to, or less than its value without feedback.

Feedback can be effected over several stages and need not be limited to a stage-by-stage practice.   A two-stage RC-coupled amplifier which combines current feedback in the first stage through resistor R_1 and potential feedback between stages is illustrated in Fig. 7-10.   A careful consideration of the polarity of the potentials which are fed back will show that both types of feedback are negative.

It is not always evident what type of feedback is being employed in a given amplifier. The following tests will serve to clarify the situation:

1. If the ratio of feedback potential E_f to output potential E_2 is nearly independent of the load impedance, then potential feedback is employed. This ratio is the feedback fraction $\beta = E_f/E_2$.

2. If the ratio of feedback potential E_f to load current I is nearly independent of the load impedance, then current feedback is employed. The ratio $Z_f = E_f/I$ is the feedback impedance.

3. If the feedback potential E_f is the sum of two terms of the form

$$E_f = \beta E_2 + Z_f I$$

where *both* β and Z_f are nearly independent of the load impedance, then compound feedback is employed.

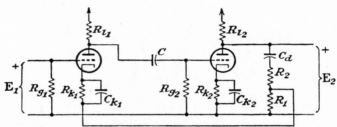

FIG. 7-10. A two-stage RC coupled amplifier with current feedback in the first stage and potential feedback between stages.

7-8. Effective Internal Impedance with Feedback. The discussion in the foregoing section has shown that the effective internal impedance of the equivalent plate circuit of an electron-tube circuit with feedback depends on the type of feedback that is employed. As shown, current feedback increases the effective internal impedance, and potential feedback decreases the effective internal impedance. These results will be generalized.

The following notation, some of which has already appeared, will apply in the following development:

β is feedback ratio

K is potential gain without feedback, with load connected

K_f is potential gain with feedback, with load connected

K_t is potential gain without feedback, with load open-circuited

E_t is effective internal potential source without feedback (this is the Helmholtz-Thévenin potential source obtained on open circuit)

E_{tf} is effective internal potential source with feedback

Z_1 is input-terminal impedance without feedback

Z_{1f} is corresponding input-terminal impedance with feedback

Z_t is effective internal impedance without feedback (this is the Thévenin impedance of the equivalent network and is the impedance
looking back into the output terminals of the amplifier, with the
load open-circuited)

Z_{tf} is corresponding effective internal impedance with feedback

Z_0 is output-terminal impedance without feedback

Z_{0f} is output-terminal impedance with feedback

E_2 is output potential

E_1 is input potential to amplifier

E_f is feedback potential

(Refer to Appendix A for a general discussion of the Helmholtz-Thévenin
theorem.)   Refer to Fig. 7-11, which shows a general feedback network

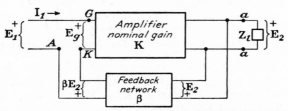

FIG. 7-11. The general potential or parallel feedback circuit.

which is provided with potential feedback.   An expression for the internal impedance Z_{tf} of this feedback network will be derived in terms of the
internal impedance Z_t without feedback.

Consider first the amplifier with the feedback potential removed.   This
is accomplished by removing lead A from the feedback network and connecting it to the cathode K.   The
Thévenin potential-source equivalent of this circuit is given in Fig.
7-12. Z_t in this diagram is the
effective internal impedance without feedback, and K_t is the gain
without feedback on open circuit
(with Z_l omitted from the diagram).

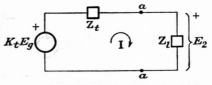

FIG. 7-12. The equivalent circuit of Fig.
7-11 with feedback removed.

To deduce the equivalent circuit of Fig. 7-11 with feedback present,
note that the effect of feedback appears in the form of the potential E_g.
Without feedback, $E_g = E_1$.   With feedback, $E_g = E_1 + \beta E_2$.   Clearly,
from this discussion, the equivalent circuit of Fig. 7-11 with feedback
present is that shown in Fig. 7-13.   It should be noted that this figure,
even though it is the equivalent circuit of Fig. 7-11 when feedback is
present, is not a Thévenin potential-source equivalent representation,
because the apparent Z_t and $K_t(E_1 + \beta E_2)$ are functions of the load.

Note from the diagram that

$$\mathbf{E}_2 = \mathbf{K}_t(\mathbf{E}_1 + \beta \mathbf{E}_2) - \mathbf{I}\mathbf{Z}_t$$

Therefore

$$\mathbf{E}_2(1 - \beta \mathbf{K}_t) = \mathbf{K}_t \mathbf{E}_1 - \mathbf{I}\mathbf{Z}_t$$

or

$$\mathbf{E}_2 = \frac{\mathbf{K}_t}{1 - \beta \mathbf{K}_t}\, \mathbf{E}_1 - \frac{\mathbf{Z}_t}{1 - \beta \mathbf{K}_t}\, \mathbf{I} \tag{7-41}$$

The Thévenin equivalent network for the circuit with feedback is, according to this expression, that shown in Fig. 7-14.

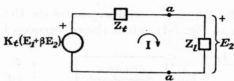

FIG. 7-13. The equivalent circuit of Fig. 7-11 with feedback present.

As a check of these results, it is noted that $\mathbf{K}_t\mathbf{E}_1/(1 - \beta \mathbf{K}_t)$ represents the open-circuit potential with feedback, $\mathbf{K}_f\mathbf{E}_1$. This agrees with the result obtained in Eq. (7-15) that $\mathbf{K}_f = \mathbf{K}/(1 - \beta \mathbf{K})$. The internal impedance with potential feedback is

$$\mathbf{Z}_{tf} = \frac{\mathbf{Z}_t}{1 - \beta \mathbf{K}_t} \tag{7-42}$$

Since, for negative feedback, $1 - \beta \mathbf{K}_t$ is greater than unity, the impedance with feedback is less than that without feedback. Note, moreover, that the effective internal impedance is reduced by the same factor as the gain, when feedback is applied.

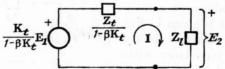

FIG. 7-14. The Thévenin equivalent network of Fig. 7-11.

It is interesting to apply these results to the potential-feedback circuit of Fig. 7-6. If the load is open-circuited, then the magnitude of the gain of the circuit is simply the μ of the tube and $\mathbf{K}_t = -\mu$. Also, the internal impedance without feedback is r_p, whence $\mathbf{Z}_t = r_p$. The results so obtained agree with those in Fig. 7-7.

It is now desired to examine the results of current or series feedback on the effective internal impedance. Refer to Fig. 7-15, which shows a general feedback circuit with current feedback. Although the impedance $\mathbf{Z}_f$ is shown isolated from the remainder of the circuit, it is a part of the feedback circuit and is not part of the external load Z_l.   The equivalent circuit will be of the form shown in Fig. 7-16.   In this dia-

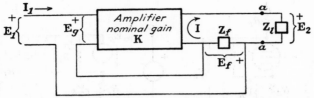

FIG. 7-15. The general current or series feedback circuit.

gram Z_t is the total internal impedance looking back from the load and includes the effect of Z_f.   From Fig. 7-16 it follows that

$$K_t(E_1 + IZ_f) = I(Z_t + Z_l)$$

from which

$$I = \frac{K_t E_1}{Z_t - Z_f K_t + Z_l}$$

But this is the current that exists in the circuit of Fig. 7-17, which is the Thévenin equivalent with current feedback.

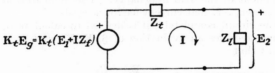

FIG. 7-16. The equivalent circuit of Fig. 7-15 with feedback present.

The effective internal impedance of the equivalent Thévenin generator with current feedback is thus seen to be

$$Z_{tf} = Z_t - K_t Z_f \qquad (7\text{-}43)$$

Note that the open-circuit potential with feedback is $K_t E_1$, which equals the open-circuit potential without feedback, in view of the significance of K_t.   This result is consistent with the observation that if Z_l is removed from Fig. 7-17, an open circuit results, and I, and so the feedback, is zero.

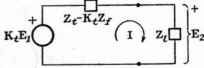

FIG. 7-17. The Thévenin equivalent of Fig. 7-15.

These results are applied to Fig. 7-4.   If the output is removed, the open-circuit gain is $K_t = -\mu$.   The internal impedance without feedback is $Z_t = r_p + R_k$.   Hence

$$Z_{tf} = r_p + R_k + \mu R_k$$

which agrees with the previous result.

Example 1. Analyze the amplifier of Fig. 7-18 by the use of feedback methods, when the output is taken across R_l.

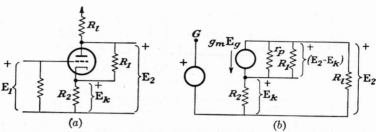

(a)   (b)

FIG. 7-18. The circuit of a specific example.

Solution. The equivalent circuit is given in Fig. 7-18b. It is first noted that the grid-cathode potential E_g is given by the expression

$$E_g = E_1 - E_k$$

But since $E_k = IR_k$, then

$$\frac{E_k}{I} = R_k$$

which is independent of the load impedance. This indicates, according to the criterion given in Sec. 7-7, that current feedback exists.

To analyze the circuit completely, it is desired to calculate both K_f and Z_{tf}. To evaluate these requires an evaluation of β, K, K_t, and Z_t. Note from the equivalent circuit that

$$\beta = -\frac{E_k}{E_2} = \frac{R_2}{R_l}$$

The nominal gain is found by noting that

$$g_m E_g + (E_2 - E_k)\left(\frac{1}{r_p} + \frac{1}{R_1}\right) = -\frac{E_2}{R_l}$$

But

$$E_k = -\frac{E_2}{R_l} R_2$$

Then

$$g_m E_g + E_2\left(1 + \frac{R_2}{R_l}\right)\left(\frac{1}{r_p} + \frac{1}{R_1}\right) + \frac{E_2}{R_l} = 0$$

or

$$g_m E_g + E_2\left[\frac{1}{R_l} + \frac{1}{R_l}\frac{(R_l + R_2)(R_1 + r_p)}{r_p R_1}\right] = 0$$

Therefore

$$K = \frac{E_2}{E_g} = \frac{-g_m}{\dfrac{1}{R_l}\dfrac{r_p R_1 + (R_l + R_2)(R_1 + r_p)}{r_p R_1}} \tag{7-44}$$

The equivalent gain on open circuit is simply

$$\mathbf{K}_t = \frac{-\mu R_1}{r_p + R_1} \tag{7-45}$$

Also the equivalent impedance $\mathbf{Z}_t$ is

$$\mathbf{Z}_t = R_2 + \frac{r_p R_1}{r_p + R_1} = \frac{(r_p + R_1)R_2 + r_p R_1}{r_p + R_1} \tag{7-46}$$

It follows from these expressions that the gain with feedback is

$$\mathbf{K}_f = \frac{-g_m R_l \dfrac{r_p R_1 + (R_l + R_2)(R_1 + r_p)}{r_p R_1}}{1 + \dfrac{R_2}{R_l} \dfrac{g_m R_l}{\dfrac{r_p R_1 + (R_l + R_2)(R_1 + r_p)}{r_p R_1}}}$$

This reduces to

$$\mathbf{K}_f = \frac{-\mu R_l R_1}{r_p(R_1 + R_2 + R_l) + (\mu + 1)R_1 R_2 + R_1 R_l} \tag{7-47}$$

Also, the effective internal impedance is

$$\mathbf{Z}_{tf} = \mathbf{Z}_t - \mathbf{K}_t \mathbf{Z}_f$$
$$= \frac{(r_p + R_1)R_2 + r_p R_1}{r_p + R_1} + \frac{\mu R_1}{r_p + R_1} R_2$$
$$\mathbf{Z}_{tf} = \frac{r_p(R_1 + R_2) + (\mu + 1)R_1 R_2}{r_p + R_1} \tag{7-48}$$

It is of some interest to examine the effects of the feedback on the gain and on the effective internal impedance. The gain ratio, given by the ratio of Eq. (7-47) to Eq. (7-44), is found to be

$$\frac{\mathbf{K}_f}{\mathbf{K}} = \frac{r_p(R_1 + R_2 + R_l) + R_1 R_l + R_1 R_2}{r_p(R_1 + R_2 + R_l) + R_1 R_l + (\mu + 1)R_1 R_2}$$

which may be written in the form

$$\frac{\mathbf{K}_f}{\mathbf{K}} = \frac{1}{1 + \dfrac{\mu R_1 R_2}{r_p(R_1 + R_2 + R_l) + R_1 R_l + R_1 R_2}}$$

This expression shows that the resultant gain with feedback is less than that without feedback, as expected.

In a somewhat similar way, the effective internal impedances may be compared, to examine the effects of the feedback. By Eqs. (7-48) and (7-46), the ratio is readily found to be

$$\frac{\mathbf{Z}_{tf}}{\mathbf{Z}_t} = 1 + \frac{\mu R_1 R_2}{r_p(R_1 + R_2) + R_1 R_2}$$

The effect of the feedback is to increase the effective internal impedance, which is characteristic of negative feedback.

Example 2. Analyze the circuit of Example 1 when the output is taken across the cathode resistor R_2.

Solution. In the present case, since $\mathbf{E}_k$ is the output potential, then since

$$\mathbf{E}_g = \mathbf{E}_1 - \mathbf{E}_k$$

it follows that

$$\beta = -1$$

But since β is independent of the load, then potential feedback now exists.

The nominal gain is obtained from a study of the equivalent circuit of Fig. 7-18*b*. It is observed that

$$g_m \mathbf{E}_g + (\mathbf{E}_2 - \mathbf{E}_k)\left(\frac{1}{r_p} + \frac{1}{R_1}\right) = \frac{\mathbf{E}_k}{R_2}$$

Also

$$\mathbf{E}_2 = -\frac{R_l}{R_2}\mathbf{E}_k$$

Then

$$g_m \mathbf{E}_g - \mathbf{E}_k\left(1 + \frac{R_l}{R_2}\right)\left(\frac{1}{r_p} + \frac{1}{R_1}\right) - \frac{\mathbf{E}_k}{R_2} = 0$$

or

$$g_m \mathbf{E}_g - \mathbf{E}_k\left[\frac{1}{R_2} + \frac{1}{R_2}\frac{(R_2 + R_l)(R_1 + r_p)}{r_p R_1}\right] = 0$$

Therefore

$$\mathbf{K} = \frac{\mathbf{E}_k}{\mathbf{E}_g} = \frac{g_m}{\dfrac{1}{R_2}\dfrac{r_p R_1 + (R_l + R_2)(R_1 + r_p)}{r_p R_1}}$$

which is

$$\mathbf{K} = \frac{\mu R_1 R_2}{r_p R_1 + (R_l + R_2)(R_1 + r_p)} \tag{7-49}$$

The equivalent gain on open circuit is

$$\mathbf{K}_t = \frac{\mu R_1}{r_p + R_1} \tag{7-50}$$

Also the equivalent impedance $\mathbf{Z}_t$ is

$$\mathbf{Z}_t = R_l + \frac{r_p R_1}{r_p + R_1} = \frac{(r_p + R_1)R_l + r_p R_1}{r_p + R_1} \tag{7-51}$$

It follows from these expressions that under feedback conditions

$$\mathbf{K}_f = \frac{\mu R_1 R_2 / [r_p R_1 + (R_l + R_2)(R_1 + r_p)]}{1 + \mu R_1 R_2 / [r_p R_1 + (R_l + R_2)(R_1 + r_p)]}$$

which reduces to

$$\mathbf{K}_f = \frac{\mu R_1 R_2}{r_p(R_1 + R_2 + R_l) + (\mu + 1)R_1 R_2 + R_1 R_l} \tag{7-52}$$

The corresponding effective internal impedance is

$$Z_{tf} = \frac{Z_t}{1 - \beta K_t} = \frac{\dfrac{(r_p + R_1)R_l + r_p R_1}{r_p + R_1}}{1 + \dfrac{\mu R_1}{r_p + R_1}}$$

or

$$Z_{tf} = \frac{(r_p + R_1)R_l + r_p R_1}{r_p + (\mu + 1)R_1} \tag{7-53}$$

While it is possible to draw certain conclusions from a comparison of the results obtained in Examples 1 and 2, the same conclusions are possible from the simplified circuit illustrated in Fig. 7-19, in which $R_l = R_2$, and R_1 is set to infinity, or an open circuit. This circuit is known as a single-tube "paraphase" amplifier and provides two equal output potentials of opposite polarity from a single excitation source. For the case when the output potential is E_2, the significant expressions deduced from Eqs. (7-47) and (7-48) are the following:

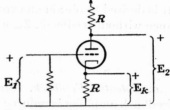

Fig. 7-19. A single-tube "paraphase" amplifier.

$$K_f = \frac{-\mu R_l}{r_p + (\mu + 2)R_l} \tag{7-54}$$

$$Z_{tf} = r_p + (\mu + 1)R_l$$

When the output potential is E_k, the appropriate expressions become, from Eqs. (7-52) and (7-53),

$$K_f = \frac{\mu R_l}{r_p + (\mu + 2)R_l}$$

$$Z_{tf} = \frac{r_p + R_l}{\mu + 1} \tag{7-55}$$

It will be observed that the gain of the amplifier with respect to each output pair of terminals is the same. However, it is also noted that the effective internal impedances looking back from these terminals are quite different, one being much higher than the other.

7-9. Effect of Feedback on the Output-terminal Impedance.

The output-terminal impedance of a circuit is the impedance looking back into the output terminals of the network when the load impedance is in place, but with the input potential reduced to zero. Clearly, the output impedance of an amplifier is the parallel combination of the effective internal impedance and the load impedance. Since the equivalent internal impedance Z_{tf} depends on the type of feedback that is incorporated in the amplifier, then the output impedance will also depend on the type of feedback. The situation is illustrated schematically in Fig. 7-20.

The output impedance Z_{0f}, which is given as the ratio of the current I_0

into the output terminals when a potential E_0 is impressed, is clearly

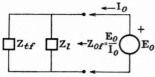

$$Z_{0f} = \frac{Z_{tf}Z_l}{Z_{tf} + Z_l} \qquad (7\text{-}56)$$

where, for the case of potential feedback, by Eq. (7-42),

Fig. 7-20. The output-terminal impedance of the general feedback amplifier.

$$Z_{tf} = \frac{Z_t}{1 - \beta K_t}$$

and for the case of current feedback, by Eq. (7-43),

$$Z_{tf} = Z_t - K_t Z_f$$

It is desired to obtain an expression for Z_{0f} in terms of the output impedance without feedback, Z_0, where

$$Z_0 = \frac{Z_t Z_l}{Z_t + Z_l} \qquad (7\text{-}57)$$

a. Potential Feedback. Suppose that the input source to the general feedback amplifier is reduced to zero and that a potential source is applied to the output terminals. The situation is illustrated in Fig. 7-21. This

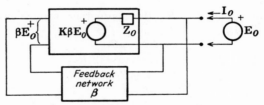

Fig. 7-21. The modifications of the general potential feedback amplifier for calculating the output-terminal impedance.

diagram is Fig. 7-2 appropriately modified for output-impedance determinations. In view of Fig. 7-14, which gives the equivalent circuit of the general amplifier with potential feedback, then Z_0 has the form of Eq. (7-57).

The current I_0 from the applied source is seen to be

$$I_0 = \frac{E_0 - K\beta E_0}{Z_0}$$

and the effective output impedance with feedback is

$$Z_{0f} = \frac{E_0}{I_0} = \frac{Z_0}{1 - K\beta} \qquad (7\text{-}58)$$

which is similar in form to Eq. (7-15). This shows that the output impedance is reduced by the same factor as the potential gain with the application of potential feedback.

b. Current Feedback. The calculation for the output impedance of an amplifier which employs current feedback follows a similar pattern. In this case, as before, the input signal is reduced to zero, and a potential source is applied to the output terminals. The current-feedback circuit for the output-terminal impedance calculation then becomes that shown in Fig. 7-22.

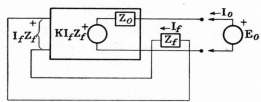

Fig. 7-22. The modifications to the general current feedback circuit for output-terminal impedance determination.

In this circuit Z_0 denotes the output impedance of the circuit without feedback and includes the effect of Z_f. K is the gain without feedback, but with Z_l in position. The potential E_g is the drop across Z_f and is $I_f Z_f$.

It follows from the diagram, by taking account of the current through the load impedance, that

$$E_0 = I_0 Z_0 - K I_f Z_f$$

But this becomes

$$E_0 = I_0 Z_0 - K Z_f \left(I_0 - \frac{E_0}{Z_l} \right)$$

This gives

$$I_0 (Z_0 - K Z_f) = E_0 \left(1 - K \frac{Z_f}{Z_l} \right)$$

from which it follows that the effective output impedance with feedback is

$$Z_{0f} = \frac{Z_0 - K Z_f}{1 - K Z_f / Z_l} = Z_0 \frac{1 - K Z_f / Z_0}{1 - K Z_f / Z_l} \tag{7-59}$$

7-10. Effect of Feedback on the Input-terminal Impedance. It is of some importance to examine how the input impedance of an amplifier is affected by the presence of feedback. It will be found that the effective input impedance increases for both potential and current feedback.

a. Potential Feedback. It follows directly from Fig. 7-11 that the input-terminal impedance with feedback is simply

$$Z_{1f} = \frac{E_1}{I_1}$$

This may be written as

$$Z_{1f} = \frac{E_g - \beta E_2}{I_1} = \frac{E_g}{I_1} (1 - K\beta)$$

But the input impedance without feedback is

$$Z_1 = \frac{E_g}{I_1}$$

Then

$$Z_{1f} = Z_1(1 - K\beta) \qquad (7\text{-}60)$$

Therefore, owing to the feedback, the input impedance with feedback is greater than the input impedance without feedback, and in the same degree as the gain and distortion decrease.

As a specific example, suppose that Z_1 is the impedance due to a capacitance between the grid-cathode terminals, and this may be the actual tube capacitance modified by the Miller effect. Since the impedance increases with feedback, this means that the effective input capacitance is decreased. Clearly, therefore,

$$C_{1f} = \frac{C_1}{1 - K} \qquad (7\text{-}61)$$

b. Current Feedback. By proceeding as in (a) for the potential feedback, but now with reference to Fig. 7-15 for the general current-feedback circuit,

$$Z_{1f} = \frac{E_1}{I_1} = \frac{E_g - IZ_f}{I_1}$$

$$= \frac{1}{I_1}\left(E_g - \frac{E_2}{Z_l} Z_f\right)$$

But

$$\beta = \frac{Z_f}{Z_l} \qquad E_2 = KE_g$$

Then it follows that

$$Z_{1f} = Z_1(1 - K\beta) \qquad (7\text{-}62)$$

Note that the input impedance with current feedback is greater than the input impedance without feedback in the same degree as for the case of potential feedback.

7-11. Feedback and Stability. A great deal of information about the stability of an amplifier can be obtained from an analysis of the factor $1 - K\beta$ that appears in the general gain expression [Eq. (7-14)]. This is best analyzed through the use of the polar plot of the expression $K\beta$. Attention is first called to the significance of the quantity $K\beta$. This is best examined by reference to the diagram of Fig. 7-23. Observe that $K\beta$ is the total open-loop gain, including the amplifier and the feedback network, but with the feedback connection open.   In network parlance, this is the open-loop transfer function of the amplifier and the feedback network.   In essence, therefore, consideration of the open-loop performance of the amplifier and feedback network is to be used to provide significant information regarding the performance of the amplifier under closed-loop operation.

$K\beta$ is a function of the frequency, and, in general, points in the complex plane are obtained for the values of $K\beta$ corresponding to all values of f from 0 to ∞.   The locus of all these points usually forms a closed curve for amplifiers.

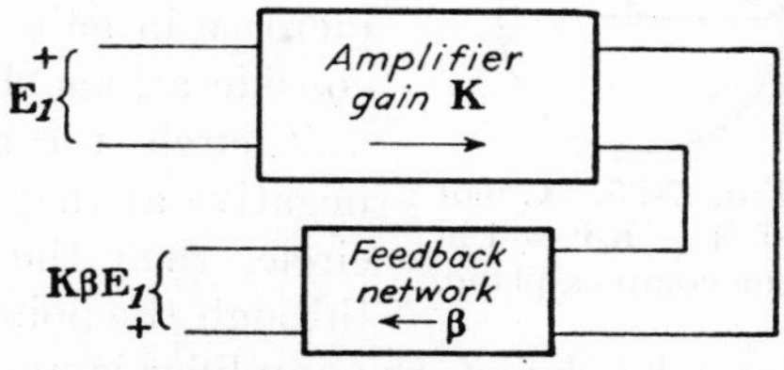

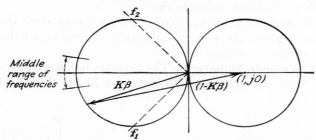

FIG. 7-23. Illustration of the significance of the factor $K\beta$.

As a particular example, suppose that the locus of $K\beta$ in the complex plane is drawn for the amplifier illustrated in Fig. 7-6.   To do this, the complete expression for the nominal gain, including the effect of the feedback circuit, must be written, rather than the simple form given in Eq. (7-34).   Also, the value of β must include the effects of the blocking capacitor C.   Certain of the features of the response of this amplifier are known.   At the mid-frequencies, the gain is substantially constant and has a phase of 180 deg.   For the low and high frequencies, the gain falls to zero, and the phase approaches ± 90 deg, respectively.   At the l-f and h-f cutoff values the phase is ± 135 deg, respectively.   It may be shown

FIG. 7-24. The locus in the complex plane of $K\beta$ for the circuit of Fig. 7-6.

that the general locus of $K\beta$ of this amplifier for all frequencies is a circle. The result is shown in Fig. 7-24.

Suppose that a phasor is drawn from the polar locus to the point $(1,j0)$. This is the quantity $1 - K\beta$, as shown.   For this particular case, its magnitude is greater than unity for all frequencies, and it has its maximum magnitude at the middle range of frequencies.   Moreover, since the resultant gain varies inversely with $1 - K\beta$, then the effect of the feedback is to cause a general flattening of the frequency-response characteristic.

The criterion for positive and negative feedback is evident on the complex plane. First note that the quantity $|1 - K\beta| = 1$ represents a circle of unit radius with its center at the point $(1,j0)$, as illustrated.

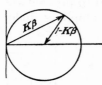

Clearly, if for a given amplifier $|1 - K\beta| > 1$, then the feedback is negative, with an over-all reduction of gain. Likewise, if $|1 - K\beta| < 1$, there is an over-all increase in gain and the feedback is positive. These considerations show that if $K\beta$ extends outside of the unit circle for any frequency, then the feedback is negative at that frequency. If $K\beta$ lies within the unit circle, then the feedback is positive. If $K\beta$ passes through the point $(1,j0)$ then $1 - K\beta = 0$, and, as will later be shown, the amplifier is unstable and oscillates. A more general analysis by Nyquist[6,8] shows that the amplifier will oscillate if the curve $K\beta$ encloses the point $(1,j0)$ and is stable if the curve does not enclose

FIG. 7-25. A plot of $|1 - K\beta| = 1$ in the complex plane.

this point. That is, if the magnitude of $K\beta$ is less than unity when its phase angle is zero, no oscillations are possible.

As a specific example for discussion, suppose that the plot of a given amplifier is that illustrated in Fig. 7-26. The feedback is negative for this amplifier in the frequency range from 0 to f_1. Positive feedback exists in the

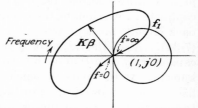

FIG. 7-26. The polar plot of an amplifier.

frequency range from f_1 to ∞. Note, however, that since the locus of $K\beta$ does not enclose the point $(1,j0)$, then, according to the Nyquist criterion, oscillations will not occur.

7-12. The Cathode Follower.[9] The cathode follower is illustrated in Fig. 7-27a, the equivalent circuit being given in Fig. 7-27b. This feed-

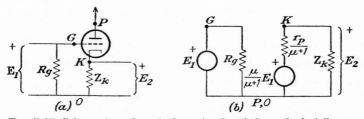

FIG. 7-27. Schematic and equivalent circuits of the cathode follower.

back circuit is singled out for detailed consideration because of its extensive use in a variety of applications. These applications stem from the fact that the cathode follower possesses a high input impedance and a low output impedance and may therefore be used as a coupling device between a high impedance source and a low impedance load.

The cathode follower is similar to the single-tube paraphase amplifier of Fig. 7-19, but with a zero plate load. The equivalent circuit is that shown in Fig. 7-27b. The grid circuit is isolated, since interelectrode capacitances are neglected, and the input impedance is R_g. The effective internal impedance is $Z_{tf} = r_p/(\mu + 1)$, which is very low. In fact, if $\mu \gg 1$, then $Z_{tf} = r_p/\mu = 1/g_m$. But since g_m for most tubes varies from 1,000 to 10,000 μmhos, then Z_{tf} is of the order of 1,000 ohms to

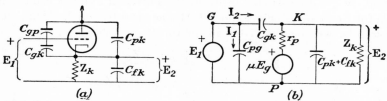

(a)   (b)

FIG. 7-28. Schematic and equivalent circuits of the cathode follower, including the interelectrode capacitances.

100 ohms. A double cathode-follower circuit has been devised which has a greatly reduced effective internal impedance.[10]

The gain is obtained from an analysis of Fig. 7-27b and is given by

$$K = \frac{\mu Z_k}{r_p + (\mu + 1)Z_k} = \frac{\mu}{\mu + 1 + r_p/Z_k} \qquad (7\text{-}63)$$

Clearly K approaches the limiting value $\mu/(\mu + 1)$ as the ratio r_p/Z_k approaches zero, or as $Z_k \gg r_p$. For tubes with large value of μ, and with $Z_k \gg r_p$, the gain approaches unity. For values of Z_k and r_p found in most normal cases, K is of the order of 0.9 or higher. In fact, it is because of this unity-gain feature that the circuit derives its name, since the output potential is almost equal to the input potential, whence the cathode and grid rise and fall together in potential by almost equal amounts (or the cathode follows the grid).

The interelectrode and wiring capacitances have been neglected in these discussions, as their effects are usually negligible for frequencies below about 1 Mc/sec. For purposes of our study, these will be taken into account. The schematic and equivalent circuits are now given in Fig. 7-28.

The expression for the gain of the amplifier is deduced by analyzing the circuit. It is noted that

$$E_2 = \frac{E_1 Y_{C_{gk}} + \mu E_g Y_p}{Y_{C_{gk}} + Y_p + Y_{C_{pk}+C_{fk}} + Y_{Z_k}} \qquad (7\text{-}64)$$

But it follows that

$$E_g = E_1 - E_2$$

and Eq. (7-64) becomes

$$E_2 = \frac{j\omega C_{gk} E_1 + \mu Y_p (E_1 - E_2)}{j\omega(C_{gk} + C_{pk} + C_{fk}) + 1/r_p + 1/Z_k} \qquad (7\text{-}65)$$

Solving for the gain K_f which is given by $K_f = E_2/E_1$, there results

$$K_f = \frac{(j\omega r_p C_{gk} + \mu)Z_k}{j\omega r_p Z_k (C_{gk} + C_{pk} + C_{fk}) + r_p + (\mu + 1)Z_k} \qquad (7\text{-}66)$$

For those values of Z_k which are normally used, the effect of the inter-electrode and wiring capacitances on the potential amplification is negligible for frequencies below about 1 Mc, as already noted. That this is so is seen by writing Eq. (7-66) in the form

$$K_f = \frac{(g_m + j\omega C_{gk})Z_k}{1 + \left(\dfrac{\mu + 1}{r_p} + j\omega C_T\right) Z_k} \qquad (7\text{-}67)$$

where $C_T = C_{gk} + C_{pk} + C_{fk}$. But the effect of the capacitances will become important only for those frequencies for which ωC_T becomes comparable with $(\mu + 1)/r_p \doteq g_m$. If C_T is taken as 30 $\mu\mu f$ and $g_m = 1,000$ $\mu mhos$, then $f \doteq g_m/2\pi C_T \doteq 5$ Mc.

To find an expression for the input capacitance of the cathode follower, refer to Fig. 7-28b. It is seen that the current flowing through the source comprises two components. One of these is the current through the capacitance C_{gp} and is

$$I_1 = j\omega C_{gp} E_1 \qquad (7\text{-}68)$$

The second is the current through the capacitance C_{gk}. This is

$$I_2 = j\omega C_{gk} E_g \qquad (7\text{-}69)$$

But as $E_g = E_1 - E_2$ and $K_f = E_2/E_1$, then

$$I_2 = j\omega C_{gk}(1 - K_f)E_1 \qquad (7\text{-}70)$$

The total current is

$$I = I_1 + I_2 = j\omega[C_{gp}E_1 + (1 - K_f)C_{gk}E_1]$$

and the effective input capacitance is

$$C_i = C_{gp} + (1 - K_f)C_{gk} \qquad (7\text{-}71)$$

Since in many circuits K_f is approximately 0.9, then C_i has the approximate value

$$C_i = C_{gp} + 0.1C_{gk} \qquad (7\text{-}72)$$

A comparison of this expression with the corresponding form given by Eq. (5-16) for the conventional amplifier stage shows a roughly similar dependence on the tube capacitances, although the numerical value for the cathode follower is considerably smaller than that for the conventional amplifier stage.

The effective internal impedance $\mathbf{Z}_{tf}$ can be determined by finding the current $\mathbf{I}_0$ as a consequence of the application of an a-c potential $\mathbf{E}_0$ to the output terminals of Fig. 7-28. The grid exciting potential is made zero. The equivalent circuit is that drawn as Fig. 7-29, if the internal impedance of the grid driving source is low. The effective internal admittance of the tube alone is found from

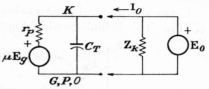

Fig. 7-29. The equivalent output circuit of the cathode follower.

$$\mathbf{I}_0 = \mathbf{E}_0 \mathbf{Y}_T + \frac{\mathbf{E}_0 - \mu \mathbf{E}_g}{r_p} \tag{7-73}$$

But under the conditions specified

$$\mathbf{E}_g = -\mathbf{E}_0$$

Then

$$\mathbf{Y}_{tf} = \frac{\mathbf{I}_0}{\mathbf{E}_0} = \mathbf{Y}_T + \mathbf{Y}_p + g_m \tag{7-74}$$

where $\mathbf{Y}_T = j\omega C_T$. It is of interest to compare this result with that which applies without capacitances being considered, viz.,

$$\mathbf{Y}_{tf} = \frac{1}{\mathbf{Z}_{tf}} = \frac{\mu + 1}{r_p} = g_m + \mathbf{Y}_p$$

The effect of the interelectrode capacitances is the addition of the term $\mathbf{Y}_T$ to the terms $\mathbf{Y}_p + g_m$. Here, as for the gain, $\mathbf{Y}_T$ does not become comparable with the other terms except at the higher video frequencies.

7-13. Graphical Analysis of the Cathode Follower. Suppose that the cathode impedance is a resistance R_k, and this is the usual situation. A graphical solution of the operation of the circuit is possible on the plate characteristics of the tube. This necessitates drawing the dynamic characteristic of the circuit from the known plate characteristics. Refer to Fig. 7-30 for notation. The controlling equations of the grid and plate circuits are

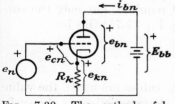

Fig. 7-30. The cathode follower with a cathode resistor.

$$e_n = e_{cn} + i_{bn} R_k \tag{7-75}$$

and

$$E_{bb} = e_{bn} + i_{bn} R_k \tag{7-76}$$

Equation (7-76) is the equation of the load line for the plate supply E_{bb} and the load resistance R_k. The procedure for constructing the dynamic characteristic follows:

1. On the plate characteristics draw the load line specified by Eq. (7-76). This is illustrated in Fig. 7-31.

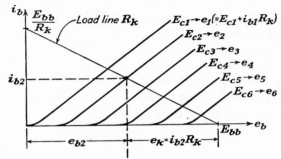

FIG. 7-31. Graphical construction for finding the dynamic characteristic of a cathode follower with cathode resistor R_k.

2. Note the plate current at each point of intersection of the load line with the plate characteristics. For example, the current at the intersection of the load line with E_{c2} is labeled i_{b2}.

3. Now relabel the plate characteristics with the appropriate symbol e, according to Eq. (7-75). Thus

$$E_{c1} \rightarrow e_1 \, (\equiv E_{c1} + i_{b1}R_k)$$
$$E_{c2} \rightarrow e_2 \, (\equiv E_{c2} + i_{b2}R_k)$$

etc.

4. The dynamic characteristic is a plot of the (i_{bn}, e_n) characteristic, where i_{bn} is the current corresponding to the input e_n. This requires calculating the value of e_n for each value of E_{cn}, and its corresponding i_{bn}.

Often the complete dynamic curve is not required, but only the current I_b for a specified value of e, say E. By Eq. (7-75) this is

$$I_b = \frac{E - E_c}{R_k}$$

For several values of e_c (and the available E_c values are used), the value of i_b is calculated, and noted on the plate characteristics, as shown in Fig. 7-32. The intersection of the load line and the line connecting the calculated points is the appropriate current I_b for the specified E.

It should be specifically noted that the value of the input signal E will be quite large before E_c, the actual grid-cathode potential, becomes positive with the consequent grid current. That is, since the cathode potential follows the grid potential rather closely (for a gain almost equal to unity), the input signal may swing considerably positive before the onset of grid current.   The larger the values of R_k, the larger will be the allowable positive swing.   When cutoff occurs, no potential difference appears across R_k.   Consequently, the applied signal required to reach cutoff is independent of R_k.

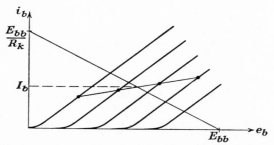

Fig. 7-32. Graphical construction for obtaining the value of I_b for a specified input potential E_1.

Example.   Consider a 6J5 tube with $E_{bb} = 300$ volts and $R_k = 10,000$ ohms. Find the maximum positive and negative input swings for positive grid-cathode potential and cutoff, respectively.

Solution.   From the plate characteristics of the 6J5 (see Appendix B-9) and the specified E_{bb} and R_k, the following data are found:

$$\text{For } E_c = 0: \quad I_b = 15.7 \text{ ma}$$
$$\text{For } E_c = -18: \quad I_b = 0$$

This shows that the cathode follower may swing from $+157$ volts to -18 volts without drawing grid current or driving the tube beyond cutoff.

Clearly, the operation of the cathode-follower circuit of Fig. 7-30 is unsymmetrical.   For small potential excursions, this causes no difficulty.

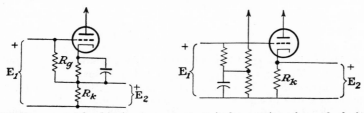

Fig. 7-33. Two ways of achieving more symmetrical operation of a cathode follower.

Also, if only positive signals are to be used, no difficulty exists.   However, if large negative signals are to be applied, it is necessary to establish the grid at a large positive potential with respect to the bottom end of R_k (ordinarily ground), although the actual tube bias E_c will still be negative.   This bias may be achieved in several ways, as illustrated in Fig. 7-33.   For symmetrical operation, the bias will be established to set the d-c level across R_k at about half of the peak-peak potential swing.

REFERENCES

1. Johnson, J. B., *Phys. Rev.*, **32**, 97 (1928).
2. Nyquist, H., *Phys. Rev.*, **32**, 110 (1928).
3. Moullin, E. B., "Spontaneous Fluctuations of Voltage," Oxford University Press, London, 1938.
4. Friis, H. T., *Proc. IRE*, **32**, 419 (1944).
5. North, D. O., and W. R. Ferris, *Proc. IRE*, **29**, 49 (1941).
6. Black, H. S., *Elec. Eng.*, **53**, 114 (1934).
   Peterson, E., J. G. Kreer, and L. A. Ware, *Bell System Tech. J.*, **13**, 680 (1934).
7. Feldkeller, R., *Teleg. fernsp. Tech.*, **25**, 217 (1936).
8. Nyquist, H., *Bell System Tech. J.*, **11**, 126 (1932).
   Bode, H. W., "Network Analysis and Feedback Amplifier Design," D. Van Nostrand Company, Inc., New York, 1945.
   Goldman, S., "Transformation Calculus and Electric Transients," Prentice-Hall, Inc., New York, 1949.
9. Reich, H. J., "Theory and Application of Electron Tubes," 2d ed., sec. 6-11, McGraw-Hill Book Company, Inc., New York, 1944.
   Reich, H. J., *Proc. IRE*, **35**, 573 (1947).
   Kraus, H. L., *Electronics*, **20**, 116 (January, 1947).
   Schlesinger, K., *Electronics*, **21**, 103 (February, 1948).
10. Hammock, C., *MIT Radiation Lab. Rept.* 469 (1943).
11. For an extensive treatment of noise, see:
    Goldman, S., "Frequency Analysis, Modulation, and Noise," McGraw-Hill Book Company, Inc., New York, 1948.
    Moullin, E. B. (see ref. 3).

PROBLEMS

7-1. *a.* Evaluate the rms thermal noise potential across the parallel network shown.

b. Comment on the results.

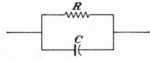

7-2. *a.* Determine the rms shot noise current in a temperature-limited diode in a 10-kc bandwidth for an average tube current of 10 ma.

b. If this current flows through a temperature-limited diode, how much noise is developed in a 10-kilohm series resistance in the diode circuit?

7-3. Consider the circuit shown, for which $r_p = 7,700$ ohms, $g_m = 2,600$ μmhos, $R_l = 25$ kilohms, and C is chosen to yield a 12-kc amplifier bandwidth.

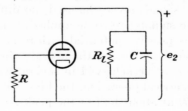

Direct-current sources have been omitted for convenience. Calculate the noise potential in the output when $R = 0$; when $R = 10$ kilohms.

7-4. Compare the value of R_{eq} of a 6AC7 when triode-connected with the value when pentode-connected. The operating potentials are those specified for normal operation.

7-5. Consider a resistor having a resistance R at room temperature. When this resistor is connected in the circuit that includes a temperature-limited diode, the d-c current I_b passes through R. Under these circumstances the effective fluctuation noise is doubled. Calculate the d-c potential across R.

7-6. Consider a simple grounded-grid amplifier stage to have fluctuation noise to be produced in the grid circuit, the cathode resistor, and both the plate resistance and the plate load resistance. Neglect transit-time effects.

a. Find an expression for the mean-square noise in the output.

b. Denote the ratio of the mean-square noise potential of (*a*) to that of an ideal tube (one with zero grid and plate noise) by the quantity N. For a specified R_l find the approximate value of R_k for which N is a minimum. *Caution:* Recall that the component potentials are random.

c. Deduce the value of $N_{\min}$ under the conditions of (*b*).

7-7. A radar receiver has an over-all bandwidth of 1.2 Mc, a noise figure of 11 db, and a gain of 110 db. Find the rms noise potential across a 500-ohm output resistance.

7-8. A type 1N21 silicon crystal diode is used in the converter of a microwave receiver. If the converter has a loss of 5.5 db and a noise figure of 9 db and is used with an i-f amplifier that has a noise figure of 3.5 db, calculate the over-all noise figure. Assume that the converter band contains the i-f band, which is the usual case in radar receivers.

7-9. An amplifier has a gain 3,000/0. When negative feedback is applied, the gain is reduced to 2,000/0. Determine the feedback network.

7-10. An amplifier without feedback gives an output of 46 volts with 8 per cent second-harmonic distortion when the input is 0.16 volt.

a. If 1 per cent of the output is fed back into the input in a degenerative circuit, what is the output potential?

b. If an output of 46 volts with 1 per cent second-harmonic distortion is permissible, what is the input potential?

7-11. Given the amplifier stage with cathode degeneration shown in the accompanying diagram,

$$E_{bb} = 250 \text{ volts} \qquad R_l = 100 \text{ kilohms}$$
$$g_m = 1,200 \ \mu\text{mhos} \qquad \mu = 70$$
$$R_g = 1 \text{ megohms}$$

a. What should be the value of R_k to give an over-all gain of 8?

b. What is the value of E_{cc}, and the largest value of e_g to yield an output without distortion?

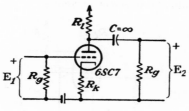

7-12. Plot the gain as a function of frequency of the simple amplifier shown in the accompanying figure. Also plot on the same sheet the gain of the stage when fixed bias is used.

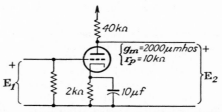

7-13. The first stage of the circuit of Fig. 7-10 uses a 6SJ7 pentode with

$$E_b = 250 \text{ volts} \qquad E_{oc1} = -3 \text{ volts} \qquad E_{cc2} = 100 \text{ volts} \qquad I_b = 3 \text{ ma}$$

The second stage is a 6C5, with $E_b = 250$ volts, $E_{cc1} = -8$ volts, $I_b = 8$ ma. The other factors are

$$R_{l1} = 100 \text{ kilohms} \qquad R_{g1} = R_{g2} = 250 \text{ kilohms} \qquad R_2 = 25 \text{ kilohms}$$
$$C = 0.04 \ \mu\text{f} \qquad C_{k1} = 10 \ \mu\text{f} \qquad C_{k2} = 2.5 \ \mu\text{f} \qquad C_d = 0.1 \ \mu\text{f} \qquad R_1 = 200 \text{ ohms}$$
$$R_2 = 150 \text{ kilohms}$$

a. Specify the values of R_{k1}, R_{k2}, E_{bb}.
b. Draw the complete mid-frequency equivalent circuit.
c. The total shunting capacitance across R_{g2} is 80 $\mu\mu$f. Calculate and plot a gain-frequency-response curve over the range from 20 to 50,000 cps.
d. Repeat (*c*) if $R_1 = 0$, $R_2 = 150$ kilohms.

7-14. Given the two-stage circuit which is provided with negative-potential feedback. The tubes have $r_p = 10^6$ ohms, $g_m = 1,200$ μmhos.
a. Calculate the output impedance.
b. Calculate the impedance between points AA.

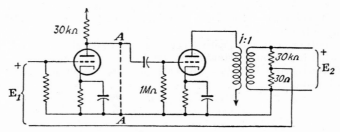

7-15. Given a simple pentode amplifier stage as illustrated, the screen by-pass capacitor being omitted. Derive an expression for the gain of the amplifier stage. Assume that I_b is independent of E_b and that μ_{sg} of the screen grid is the same relative to plate and to screen currents.

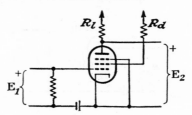

7-16. Calculate the gain of the inverse feedback pair.* Assume that the tubes are identical and that $R_g \gg R_l$.

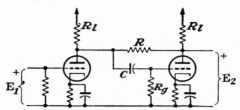

7-17. Obtain an expression for the output potentials of the cathode-coupled two-tube circuit shown in the accompanying figure.

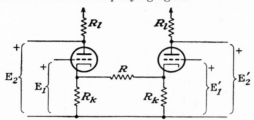

7-18. An RC coupled amplifier has a mid-frequency gain $K_0 = -27$. Potential feedback is applied, the amount of feedback being such as to reduce the lower half-power frequency to one-tenth its no-feedback value.

a. Find the feedback fraction β.

b. Find the resulting mid-frequency gain under feedback conditions.

7-19. Given a three-stage RC coupled amplifier, each stage of which has an l-f cutoff of 20 cps, and h-f cutoff of 84 kc, and a mid-frequency gain of 220. Plot the locus of the complex potential gain.

7-20. The locus of the complex potential amplification of a certain amplifier is illustrated. If 1 per cent negative feedback is applied, determine the value of the gain **K** at the following frequencies: 100 cps, 10 kc, 40 kc. Assume that β is independent of frequency and that the potential fed back is in phase with the output potential.

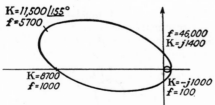

7-21. Three identical RC coupled amplifier stages are connected in cascade, inverse feedback being provided between the output and input, as indicated in the diagram at the top of page 182. The per stage constants are (see Fig. 7-4 for a typical stage)

$$R_l = 20 \text{ kilohms} \qquad C = 0.01 \ \mu\text{f}$$
$$C_g = 20 \ \mu\mu\text{f} \qquad R_g = 1 \text{ megohms}$$
$$\text{Tube: } r_p = 1 \text{ megohms} \qquad g_m = 1{,}000 \ \mu\text{mhos}$$

* G. R. Mezger, *Electronics*, **17**, 126 (April, 1944).

a. Determine the maximum value of R for which the amplifier will operate without oscillations.

b. Calculate the mid-band gain under these conditions.

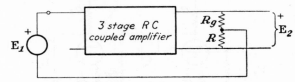

7-22. Consider the amplifier stage illustrated in the accompanying figure. Calculate the following (neglect the effects of interelectrode capacitances):

a. Input impedance Z_{1f}.   Compare this with the value R_g.

b. Effective internal impedance Z_{tf}.

c. Output-terminal impedance Z_{0f}.

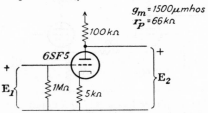

7-23. The circuit of Prob. 7-22 is rearranged by connecting the grid resistor to the cathode rather than to ground, as shown.   Repeat Prob. 7-22 for the rearranged circuit.

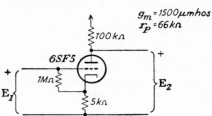

7-24. *a.* Refer to the cascode circuit illustrated.   Find expressions for the following: gain **K**, output-terminal impedance Z_{0f}.

b. Compare the results under (*a*) with the corresponding results when tube $T1$ and its cathode resistor R are replaced by a resistor R_l.

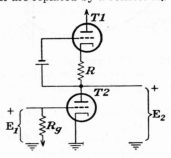

7-25. Calculate the effective input impedance at 10 kc of the circuit in the accompanying figure. Each tube has the value $g_m = 2,000$ μmhos, $r_p = 10$ kilohms. Neglect all tube and wiring capacitances.

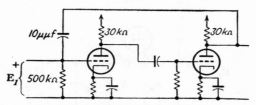

7-26. Derive an expression for the effective input impedance of the cathode-coupled amplifier shown. Under what conditions is this impedance negative?

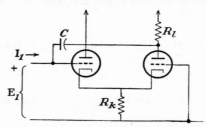

7-27. What must be the value of R_k in Fig. 7-27 if $Z_{0f} = 300$ ohms at 1,000 cps? A 6J5 tube is used.

7-28. Given the cathode-follower circuit with the grid resistor R_g tied from grid to cathode, as shown in the accompanying figure. Derive expressions for the effective input impedance $\mathbf{Z}_{1f}$ and the output-terminal impedance $\mathbf{Z}_{0f}$. Neglect tube capacitances. Show that $\mathbf{Z}_{1f}$ can be written in the form $\mathbf{Z}_{1f} = R_g/(1 - \mathbf{K})$. Find an expression for $\mathbf{K}$.

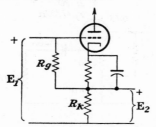

7-29. Compare the values of gain, effective input impedance, effective internal impedance of the two cathode-follower stages illustrated.

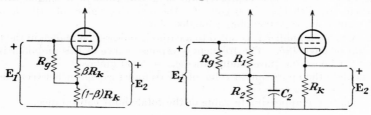

7-30. Calculate and plot as a function of frequency on semilog paper the gain, output impedance, and input impedance of the cathode-follower amplifier shown

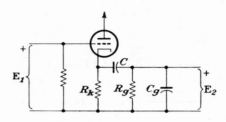

at the following values of ω: 250; 2,500; 250,000; 2.5×10^6; 5×10^6 rad/sec. Choose a 6J5 tube for which

$$r_p = 7,700 \text{ ohms} \qquad \mu = 20 \qquad C_{gp} = 3.4 \,\mu\mu\text{f} \qquad C_{gk} = 3.4 \,\mu\mu\text{f} \qquad C_{pk} = 3.6 \,\mu\mu\text{f}$$

Also choose

$$R_k = 10 \text{ kilohms} \qquad R_g = 200 \text{ kilohms} \qquad C = 0.01 \,\mu\text{f} \qquad C_g = 40 \,\mu\mu\text{f}$$

7-31. Consider the circuit shown in the accompanying diagram. Determine:
a. The positive signal that will drive e_c to zero.
b. The negative signal to drive the tube to cutoff.
c. The mid-frequency gain.
d. The input admittance when $C_{gp} = 3.4 \,\mu\mu\text{f}$, $C_{gk} = 4 \,\mu\mu\text{f}$.

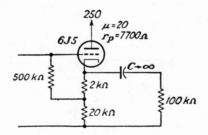

7-32. Repeat Prob. 7-31 when the tube is changed to a 6AC7 pentode. The tube operates in its linear region, with $g_m = 9,000 \,\mu\text{mhos}$, $r_p = 1$ megohm.

7-33. Plot the dynamic characteristic of a 6J5 tube in a simple cathode-follower circuit, with $E_{bb} = 250$ volts, for the following values of cathode resistance R_k: 5,000 ohms; 25,000 ohms; 100,000 ohms.

7-34. A video amplifier is coupled to a cathode follower, as shown in the figure at the top of page 185. The frequency-response curve of this amplifier is also sketched. Choose the transconductance $g_m = 9,000 \,\mu\text{mhos}$.

a. Calculate the approximate value of the coupling capacitor between the two stages.

b. Calculate the approximate value of the total shunt capacitance.

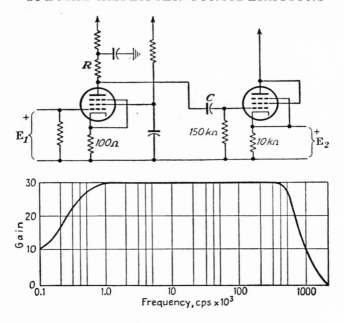

7-35. The essentials of a double cathode follower[10] are illustrated.
a. Show that the expression for the gain is

$$K_f = \frac{\mu^2 + \mu r_p/R_l}{\mu^2 + \mu + 1 + (\mu + 2)r_p/R_l}$$

b. Show that the output admittance is

$$\mathbf{Y}_{0f} = \frac{\mu + 1}{r_p + R_l} + \frac{1 + \dfrac{\mu(\mu + 1)}{1 + r_p/R_l}}{r_p} \doteq \mu g_m$$

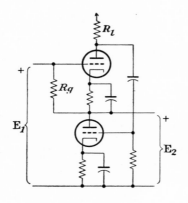

7-36. Consider the double cathode follower shown in the diagram. Calculate the gain and effective output-terminal impedance of this amplifier.

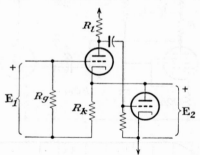

CHAPTER 8

UNTUNED POWER AMPLIFIERS

The potential amplifiers discussed in Chap. 6 are designed to increase a potential signal from a low level to one which is adequate for operating some low-power circuit. Such amplifiers are generally operated in class A since the amplification is to be accomplished without distortion.

A power amplifier serves to supply an appreciable amount of power to some power-absorbing circuit, although in general it must be accomplished under very low grid-driving-power demands. Power amplifiers may be operated as class A, B, or C or at any point between these limits, the choice of operating conditions being determined by the ultimate purpose of the amplifier. If the amplifier is to reproduce the audio spectrum without distortion, then the amplifier must be operated in class A if a single tube is used. If two tubes are used in a push-pull circuit, then the amplifier may also be operated in class AB or class B. If the amplifier is to reproduce the input waveshape over a very narrow range of frequencies, tuned class B or tuned class C amplifiers may be used. Only a-f amplifiers will be considered in this chapter.

8-1. Class A Triode Power Amplifiers. The basic schematic diagram of a typical series-fed power amplifier and its equivalent circuit is given

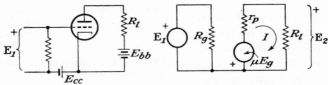

FIG. 8-1. The schematic and equivalent circuits of a simple series-fed power amplifier.

in Fig. 8-1. It is observed that this circuit is identical with that of Fig. 6-1 for the simple potential amplifier.

If it is assumed that the dynamic curve is linear over the entire range of operation, then the plate current is given by

$$I = \frac{-\mu E_1}{R_l + r_p} \qquad (8\text{-}1)$$

187

since $E_g = E_1$, and the power supplied to the load is

$$P = I^2 R_l = \frac{\mu^2 E_1^2}{4r_p} \frac{4}{(1 + R_l/r_p)^2} \frac{R_l}{r_p} \tag{8-2}$$

A sketch showing the variation of the output power as a function of R_l/r_p is given in Fig. 8-2. It can be seen that the power curve reaches a maximum at the point at which $R_l/r_p = 1$, although this maximum is quite

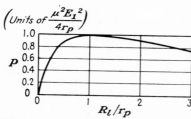

broad. P is a slowly varying function of R_l in the neighborhood of the maximum, and the power is at least 88 per cent of its maximum value for values of R_l/r_p ranging from 0.5 to 2.0. This condition shows that the power loss is less than 2.25 db for all values of R between $0.5r_p$ and $2r_p$.

Fig. 8-2. Variation of power output as a function of resistance ratio R_l/r_p.

Since the maximum power transfer occurs when the load resistance equals the internal plate resistance of the tube, it is necessary to use tubes with low values of r_p in order to obtain reasonable amounts of power with nominal values of plate supply potential. Since the g_m of a tube cannot be designed over very wide limits, then tubes with low r_p also possess low values of μ. As a result, large grid excitation potentials are required for appreciable amounts of power output. Note from Eq. (8-2) for a given value of E_g that tubes which possess large values of

$$\frac{\mu^2}{r_p} = g_m \mu$$

possess high output-power output. In fact, the power sensitivity which was defined by Eq. (3-4) becomes, under the conditions of maximum power transfer, simply $\mu g_m/4$.

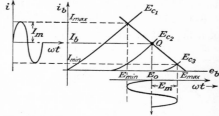

Fig. 8-3. The output current and potential waveforms in a triode power amplifier.

To determine the power output directly from the static plate characteristic of the tube, it is necessary only to draw the appropriate load line on these characteristics and read the significant information from the diagram. Thus, by referring to Fig. 8-3, it follows that

$$I = \frac{I_m}{\sqrt{2}} = \frac{I_{\max} - I_{\min}}{2\sqrt{2}}$$

and

$$E = \frac{E_m}{\sqrt{2}} = \frac{E_{\max} - E_{\min}}{2\sqrt{2}} \tag{8-3}$$

The power output is

$$P = \frac{E_m I_m}{2} = \frac{I_m^2 R_l}{2}$$

which may be written in the form

$$P = \frac{(E_{\max} - E_{\min})(I_{\max} - I_{\min})}{8} \tag{8-4}$$

If distortion is not negligible, the harmonic components must be evaluated according to Eqs. (4-32). The total power output is then

$$P = (B_1^2 + B_2^2 + B_3^2 + \cdots) \frac{R_l}{2}$$

This may be written as

$$P = \left[1 + \left(\frac{B_2}{B_1} \right)^2 + \left(\frac{B_3}{B_1} \right)^2 + \cdots \right] \frac{B_1^2}{2} R_l$$

which becomes, by Eq. (4-33),

$$P = (1 + D_2^2 + D_3^2 + \cdots)P_1$$

or

$$P = (1 + D^2)P_1 \tag{8-5}$$

where D is the total distortion. Notice, however, that if the total distortion is high, say 10 per cent, then $P = 1.01P_1$. That is, a 10 per cent distortion represents a power of only 1 per cent of the fundamental. Thus, with little error, the output power is approximately that of the fundamental-frequency component only.

8-2. Output Circuits. It is not always feasible, nor is it generally desirable, to connect the load directly in the plate lead, as shown in Fig. 8-1. Among the reasons for this are: that the quiescent current through the load resistor represents a considerable waste of power, as it does not contribute to the a-c component of power; and that the quiescent current may cause a serious polarization of the output. For example, it is inadvisable to pass a large d-c current through the voice coil of a loud-speaker. For these reasons, the transformer-coupled load is used extensively, although the parallel-feed system may be used.

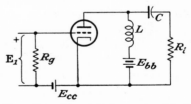

Fig. 8-4. A parallel or shunt-fed power amplifier.

The circuit of the parallel-feed system is illustrated in Fig. 8-4. It is clear that this is just the impedance-capacitance coupled system discussed in Chap. 5. In this system the plate supply is connected to the plate of the tube through a high inductance L, the load resistor being connected across the output through a blocking capacitor C. The inductor L must be so chosen that $\omega L \gg R_l$, and C must be so chosen that $1/\omega C \ll R_l$ over the operating range of frequencies.

The potential and current relations for the parallel-feed system are illustrated in Fig. 8-5. Observe that the quiescent current through the tube is determined by R_L, the resistance of the inductor, although the "dynamic" resistance into which the tube is working is R_l. Since the static resistance of the choke or the transformer winding is usually small, the static load line is almost vertical.

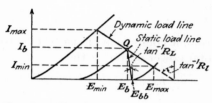

FIG. 8-5. The dynamic and static load lines of a shunt-fed or transformer-coupled amplifier.

Suppose that the load resistance into which the tube works is small; for example, the resistance of the voice coil of a dynamic loud-speaker usually ranges from about 5 to 15 ohms. If such a low resistance load were used in either the series- or the shunt-feed circuits, only a very small power output would be possible, most of the power being lost within the tube resistance. In this case, and in fact in any case in which the load resistance does not properly match the tube resistance, the use of a transformer as an impedance-matching device will permit optimum power transfer. Such a system is illustrated in Fig. 8-6.

The impedance-transforming property of an ideal transformer follows from the simple transformer relations

$$\mathbf{E}_2' = \frac{N_1}{N_2} \mathbf{E}_2$$

and

$$\mathbf{I}_2' = \frac{N_2}{N_1} \mathbf{I}_2$$

(8-6)

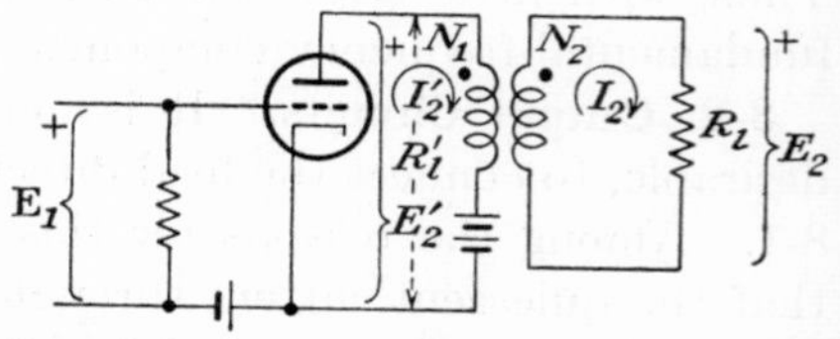

where $\mathbf{E}_2'$ and $\mathbf{E}_2$ are the primary and secondary potentials, respectively, and $\mathbf{I}_2'$ and $\mathbf{I}_2$ are the primary and secondary currents. The ratio of the above yields

FIG. 8-6. A simple transformer-coupled load in a power amplifier.

$$\frac{\mathbf{E}_2'}{\mathbf{I}_2'} = \left(\frac{N_1}{N_2}\right)^2 \frac{\mathbf{E}_2}{\mathbf{I}_2}$$

which may be written as

$$R_l' = \left(\frac{N_1}{N_2}\right)^2 R_l = \frac{1}{n^2} R_l$$

(8-7)

since $\mathbf{E}_2'/\mathbf{I}_2'$ and $\mathbf{E}_2/\mathbf{I}_2$ represent the effective input and output impedances, which are resistances. When the turns ratio N_1/N_2 is greater than unity, the transformer is called a *step-down* transformer; with the ratio N_1/N_2 less than unity, it is a *step-up* transformer.

Equation (8-7) is true for an ideal transformer. In general, however, the coupling is not perfect, the primary and secondary resistances are not negligible, and the core losses cannot be neglected. By taking these factors into account, the input impedance is given by

$$Z_l' = R_1 + \frac{R_2}{n^2} + j\omega\left(L_1' + \frac{L_2'}{n^2}\right) + \frac{Z_l}{n^2} \qquad (8\text{-}8)$$

where R_1 and R_2 are the primary and secondary winding resistances, L_1' and L_2' are the primary and secondary leakage inductances, and Z_l is the load impedance.

The same distinction between the static and dynamic load lines must be made for transformer-coupled loads as for the shunt-feed circuit, and, as noted, Fig. 8-5 applies for both circuits. But for the reasons discussed in Sec. 6-10 the frequency response of the transformer is not flat for all frequencies. However, the effects are less severe than for a transformer interstage coupling, since over the audio range the transformer capacitances, tube capacitances, and stray capacitances appear across a relatively low plate-resistance tube or across the low-output load resistance.

8-3. Maximum Undistorted Power. The foregoing analyses, which are based on the linear equivalent plate circuit, are not completely valid owing to the curvature of the dynamic characteristic, particularly in the region of small plate currents. In order to obtain the maximum possible power output without making the instantaneous plate current too small during the most negative part of the applied signal, and without driving the grid positive at the positive peak of the applied signal, it is necessary to maintain a careful balance among the grid bias, load impedance, plate supply potential, and plate resistance.

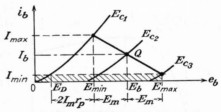

FIG. 8-7. Graphical construction for determining the operation conditions and maximum undistorted power output from an amplifier.

To find the expression for the output power under these conditions, and also to determine the appropriate conditions in order to achieve the present results, refer to the graphical construction of Fig. 8-7. Since the distortion that results at small plate currents arises from the curvature of the static characteristics, this region is eliminated by setting I_{min} at an appropriate value. This specifies the crosshatched area of the diagram. Thus the grid is allowed to swing from any point Q, corresponding to the potential E_b (which would be E_{bb} if an ideal shunt-fed or transformer-coupled load were used) between zero grid bias and that bias which corresponds to I_{min}. It will be assumed that the distortion is negligible in this region. The characteristics are essentially linear in the operating region, with a slope corresponding to r_p.

To find the value of load resistance for which the power will be a maximum, refer to Fig. 8-7. It is noted that

$$E_b = E_D + 2I_m r_p + E_m$$

But since

$$E_m = R_l I_m$$

then it follows that

$$E_b = E_D + 2I_m r_p + I_m R_l$$
$$= E_D + I_m(R_l + 2r_p)$$

Solving this expression for I_m, there results

$$I_m = \frac{E_b - E_D}{R_l + 2r_p} \tag{8-9}$$

The power to the load is then given by the expression

$$P = \frac{I_m^2 R_l}{2} = \frac{(E_b - E_D)^2}{16r_p} \frac{4R_l/2r_p}{(1 + R_l/2r_p)^2} . \tag{8-10}$$

A sketch showing the variation of the output power as a function of R_l/r_p

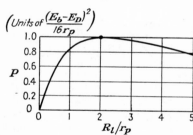

FIG. 8-8. Variation of output power as a function of load R_l.

is given in Fig. 8-8. This curve, like that of Fig. 8-2, reaches a maximum, but in this case at the point at which $R_l = 2r_p$, although the variation is not rapid in the region of the maximum. The power remains at least 88 per cent of its maximum value for load resistances R_l ranging from r_p to $4r_p$.

To find the appropriate bias for these conditions, combine Eq. (8-9) with the fact that the current changes from I_b to I_m when the signal potential E_g is equal to E_c. Thus

$$I_m = \frac{\mu E_c}{R_l + r_p} \tag{8-11}$$

The result, by equating Eq. (8-9) to (8-11), yields

$$E_c = \frac{3}{4\mu} (E_b - E_D) \tag{8-12}$$

in which R_l has been set equal to $2r_p$. The value of E_D is obtained directly from the curves.

The maximum undistorted power output becomes, from Eqs. (8-10) and (8-12),

$$P_{\max} = \frac{\mu^2 E_c^2}{9r_p}$$

Further, since $E_c = E_{gm}$, this becomes

$$P_{\max} = \frac{\mu^2 E_{gm}^2}{9r_p} = \frac{2}{9}\mu g_m E_g^2 \tag{8-13}$$

and the power sensitivity at optimum power output is

$$\text{Power sensitivity} = \frac{P}{E_g^2} = \frac{2}{9}\mu g_m \qquad \text{mhos} \tag{8-14}$$

which is slightly less than that for the conditions of Sec. 8-1.

The results showing the power output and second-harmonic distortion as a function of R_l of a type 6A3 triode are illustrated in Fig. 8-9.   Optimum output is obtained at about $R_l = 2,500$ ohms, which is approximately three times the plate resistance r_p of the tube. Although the second-harmonic distortion is not negligible at this point, a 5 per cent distortion is usually tolerable.

The above analysis is based on the use of a plate-supply source of so-called nominal value (about 300 volts). If it is assumed that a plate source of any potential is available, then with increases in the value of E_{bb} the ultimate limitation will be imposed by the allowable plate dissipation. Under these circumstances, it is found that the circuit should be operated with a value of R_l that greatly exceeds $2r_p$.[1]

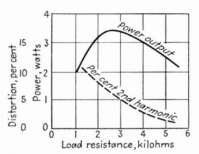

FIG. 8-9. Power output and second-harmonic distortion of a type 6A3 triode as a function of load resistance.

8-4. Plate-circuit Efficiency.   The foregoing discussion gives the methods for calculating the output power of a power amplifier.   The a-c power so obtained is converted from the d-c plate supply by the vacuum tube. The ratio of these quantities is called the *plate-circuit efficiency* of the amplifier.   Thus

$$\eta_p = \frac{\text{a-c power output to the load}}{\text{d-c power input to the plate circuit}} \times 100\% \tag{8-15}$$

Suppose that P_p denotes the average power dissipated by the plate. Then by the principle of the conservation of energy

$$E_{bb}I_b = I_b^2 R_1 + E_p I_p + P_p$$

where R_1 is the static load resistance. By solving for P_p, there obtains

$$P_p = E_{bb}I_b - I_b^2 R_1 - E_p I_p$$

But as

$$E_{bb} = E_b + I_b R_1$$

then P_p has the form

$$P_p = E_b I_b - E_p I_p \qquad (8\text{-}16)$$

This equation expresses the amount of power that must be dissipated by the plate and represents the kinetic energy of the electrons that is converted into heat at the plate. Notice in particular that the heating of the anode is reduced by the amount of the a-c power that the tube supplies to the load. Hence, a tube is cooler when delivering power to a load

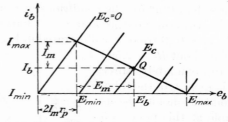

Fig. 8-10. The plate characteristics of an ideal triode.

than when there is no such a-c power transfer. This is a very important factor in the operation of high-power r-f transmitting tubes, since such tubes are ordinarily operated close to the rated allowed plate dissipation. If for any reason the output circuit becomes slightly detuned, with a consequent decrease in output power, the plate power may become dangerously high.

The plate-circuit efficiency may be written in several different forms. From Eq. (8-15),

$$\eta_p = \frac{E_p I_p}{E_{bb} I_b} \times 100\% \qquad (8\text{-}17)$$

This may also be written as

$$\eta_p = \frac{P_0}{P_0 + P_p + I_b^2 R_1} \times 100\% \qquad (8\text{-}18)$$

Clearly, a large value of η_p means a small value of P_p for a given output. This means that a smaller tube with a smaller plate-supply source may be used.

It is possible to obtain an approximate expression for the theoretical value of η_p for the series-fed and the shunt-fed circuits. Consider that an ideal tube is used in an amplifier circuit. The plate characteristics of such a tube would have the form illustrated in Fig. 8-10. Suppose that the grid does not swing beyond $E_c = 0$ and may swing to give zero current.   Then, by the proper choice of E_c,

$$I_b = I_m$$

and

$$\eta_p = \frac{E_p I_p}{E_{bb} I_b} = \frac{E_m I_m}{2 E_{bb} I_m} = 50 \frac{E_m}{E_{bb}} \qquad \% \qquad (8\text{-}19)$$

For the series-fed circuit, the point marked $E_{max} = E_{bb}$, and from the diagram,

$$E_{max} = E_{bb} = 2E_m + 2I_m r_p$$

Hence Eq. (8-19) becomes

$$\eta_p = 50 \frac{E_m}{2(E_m + I_m r_p)} = \frac{25}{1 + I_m r_p/E_m} \qquad \%$$

from which, since

$$E_m = I_m R_l$$

then

$$\eta_p = \frac{25}{1 + r_p/R_l} \qquad \% \qquad (8\text{-}20)$$

The theoretical maximum plate-circuit efficiency for the series-fed amplifier is 25 per cent.   For the conditions of maximum power output, when $R_l = r_p$, $\eta_p = 12.5$ per cent.   Actually, owing to the limited range of operation without distortion, η_p seldom exceeds 10 per cent in practice. Evidently, the linear vacuum-tube amplifier is an inefficient device for converting d-c into a-c power.

In the shunt-fed system a means has been devised for eliminating the d-c power loss in the load.   This results in an improved plate efficiency. If the static resistance is assumed negligible, then

$$E_{bb} = E_b = E_m + 2I_m r_p$$

and

$$\eta_p = 50 \frac{E_m}{E_{bb}} = 50 \frac{E_m}{E_m + 2I_m r_p} \qquad \%$$

This reduces to the form

$$\eta_p = \frac{50}{1 + 2r_p/R_l} \qquad \% \qquad (8\text{-}21)$$

The theoretical maximum plate-circuit efficiency of the shunt-fed or transformer-fed amplifier is 50 per cent.   Thus the elimination of the static power loss in the load reflects itself as an improved plate efficiency. For the conditions of maximum output power, when $R_l = 2r_p$, $\eta_p = 25$ per cent.   However, since the static resistance is not negligible and since the current I_{min} cannot be taken as zero if distortion is to be avoided, the actual plate-circuit efficiency will be less than the 25 per cent figure.

8-5. Power Pentodes and Beam Power Tubes. The plate characteristics of the power pentode are markedly different from those of a triode, and the graphical analyses given above are not valid for pentodes. Since the characteristics of the beam power tubes are similar to those of the power pentode, the discussion to follow applies for both the power pentode and the beam power tube.

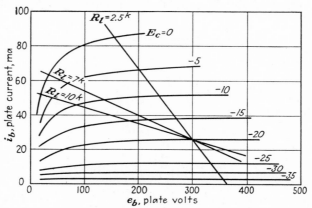

FIG. 8-11. Plate characteristics of a 6F6 power pentode.

Power pentodes differ from triodes principally in the character of the dynamic curve with increasing load resistances. In the triode, the distortion decreases as the magnitude of the load resistance increases. This follows from the fact that the dynamic curve becomes increasingly linear as the load resistance becomes higher. In the power pentode, the dynamic characteristic is critically dependent on the load resistance, with excessive curvature at both the high and the low values of load resistance. Moreover, the critical load resistance to be used cannot be related analytically with the plate resistance of the tube. This resistance is always less than the plate resistance of the tube. It might appear therefore that the output-power capacity of the tube would be too low to make the tube feasible. Actually, owing to the large μg_m product, even with the appropriate R_l the power output is usually higher than with the tube connected as a triode, and this with a smaller grid driving-potential amplitude.

To examine the matter in somewhat greater detail, refer to Fig. 8-11,

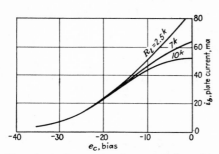

FIG. 8-12. Dynamic characteristics of a 6F6 for three values of plate load resistance.

which gives the plate characteristics of a 6F6 power pentode. It will be supposed that the load is transformer-coupled to the tube and that the plate potential is maintained at 300 volts. Three load lines are shown, 2,500, 7,000, and 10,000 ohms. The corresponding dynamic curves are given in Fig. 8-12. The following example will help clarify the situation:

Example. Calculate the output power, the plate-circuit efficiency, and the second, third, and fourth harmonics for the 6F6 that supplies power to a loudspeaker, the effective resistance of which is changed to have values of 2.5 kilohms, 7 kilohms, and 10 kilohms. A 300-volt source is available, and the tube is biased at -20 volts.

Solution. The important data from Figs. 8-11 and 8-12 are included in the tabulation. The general character of the results is given graphically in Fig. 8-13.

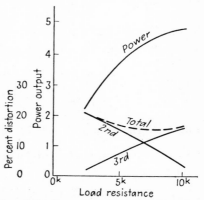

FIG. 8-13. Operating characteristics of a 6F6 pentode as a function of load resistance.

Notice that optimum power transfer occurs somewhat above 10 kilohms, which is very small compared with the tube resistance of 78,000 ohms.

R_l / I	2.5 kilohms	7 kilohms	10 kilohms
I_{max}	86	64	53
$I_{1/2}$	52	49	46
I_b	25	25	25
$I_{-1/2}$	6	6	6
I_{min}	1	1	1

R_l / B	2.5 kilohms	7 kilohms	10 kilohms
B_0	9	4	1
B_1	44	35	31
B_2	9	4	1
B_3	-1	-4	-5
B_4	$+1/2$	$-1/2$	

R_l / D	2.5 kilohms	7 kilohms	10 kilohms
D_2	20.5	11.5	3.2
D_3	-2.3	-11.5	-16
D_4	$+1$	-1.4	

R_l	2.5 kilohms	7 kilohms	10 kilohms
I_{a-c}	45.0	35.5	31
P_{a-c}	2.5	4.4	4.8
I_{d-c}	34	29	26
P_{d-c}	10.2	8.7	7.8
η_p	24.5	50.6	61.6

8-6. Push-Pull Amplifiers. The use of two tubes in parallel provides the possibility of obtaining twice the output power of a single tube with the same distortion. A push-pull amplifier circuit is a much more desirable connection for two tubes. In this circuit, the two tubes are arranged as shown in Fig. 8-14. The excitation potentials to the grids of the two tubes must be of equal magnitude, but of opposite phase. In the circuit shown, a center-tapped transformer is used to provide these two equal potentials that differ by 180 deg. A number of vacuum-tube circuits are possible for achieving these results, and several of these will be examined below.

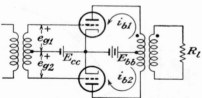

FIG. 8-14. The basic push-pull circuit.

To examine certain of the features of such an amplifier, suppose that the input grid potential to one tube is of the form

$$e_{g1} = E_{gm} \cos \omega t$$

The plate current of this tube will be represented in general by the expression (see Sec. 4-8)

$$i_{b1} = B_0 + B_1 \cos \omega t + B_2 \cos 2\omega t + B_3 \cos 3\omega t + \cdots \quad (8\text{-}22)$$

The corresponding signal to the second tube is

$$e_{g2} = -E_{gm} \cos \omega t = E_{gm} \cos (\omega t + \pi)$$

and the output plate current is

$$i_{b2} = B_0 + B_1 \cos (\omega t + \pi) + B_2 \cos 2(\omega t + \pi) + B_3 \cos 3(\omega t + \pi) + \cdots$$

which has the form

$$i_{b2} = B_0 - B_1 \cos \omega t + B_2 \cos 2\omega t - B_3 \cos 3\omega t + \cdots \quad (8\text{-}23)$$

But, from Fig. 8-14, the currents are in opposite directions through the output-transformer windings. The total output is then proportional to the difference between the plate currents in the two tubes. This is

$$i = k(i_{b1} - i_{b2}) = 2k(B_1 \cos \omega t + B_3 \cos 3\omega t + \cdots) \quad (8\text{-}24)$$

This expression shows that the push-pull circuit balances out all even harmonics in the output and leaves the third-harmonic term as the principal source of distortion.

Another feature of importance in the push-pull system is evident from the circuit of Fig. 8-14. It is observed that the steady components of the plate currents flow in opposite directions in the windings, thus opposing each other magnetically in the transformer core. This eliminates any tendency toward core saturation and the resulting distortion that might arise from the magnetization of the transformer core.

The effects of ripple potentials that may be contained in the power supply due to inadequate filtering will be balanced out in the push-pull circuit. This is so because the currents that are produced by this ripple potential are in opposition in the output transformer and hence will not appear in the load. Of course, the effects of the ripple potential that appear on the grids of the tubes will not be balanced out and will be noticeable with the signal.

Another feature of this amplifier is that under self-biased conditions there is no need for a by-pass capacitor across the cathode resistor. This follows from the fact that the potential which appears across the self-bias resistor R_k is $(i_{b1} + i_{b2})R_k$. But this is, from Eqs. (8-22) and (8-23),

$$(i_{b1} + i_{b2})R_k = 2R_k(I_b + B_0 + B_2 \cos 2\omega t + B_4 \cos 4\omega t + \cdots)$$

But for tubes operating in class A the harmonic amplitudes are very small and are therefore not significant.

One of the particularly significant features of the push-pull amplifier is that the output power possible with the two tubes for a given total distortion is higher than twice that of the single tube. This results from the fact that with the automatic cancellation of even harmonics in the output the tubes may be driven harder until the third harmonic terms become significant.

Note also that, with the increased grid drive, the rectification component $2B_0R_k$ becomes significant and adds to the bias $2I_bR_k$, if self-bias is used. As a result, the effective bias increases, with consequent reduction of output power. This means that the output power of a push-pull amplifier under otherwise similar conditions will be higher with fixed bias than with self-bias.

8-7. Equivalent Circuit of a Class A Push-Pull Amplifier. Suppose that both tubes of the push-pull amplifier are identical and that μ and r_p

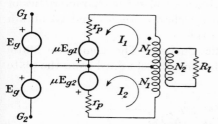

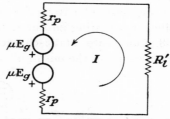

FIG. 8-15. Equivalent circuit of the class A push-pull amplifier of Fig. 8-14.

FIG. 8-16. The simplified equivalent circuit of the class A push-pull amplifier.

are constant over the range of operation. The equivalent circuit of the system then has the form given in Fig. 8-15. Observe that the connection between the cathode terminals and the mid-point of the output transformer does not carry a fundamental-frequency component of current, owing to the cancellation that occurs. This connection may be omitted from the diagram without influencing the operation. The resulting circuit then has the form given in Fig. 8-16.   In this diagram

$$R_l' = \left(\frac{2N_1}{N_2}\right)^2 R_l \qquad (8\text{-}25)$$

The resultant current is given by

$$\mathbf{I} = \frac{2\mu \mathbf{E}_g}{2r_p + R_l'} \qquad (8\text{-}26)$$

which may be written in the form

$$\mathbf{I} = \frac{\mu \mathbf{E}_g}{r_p + R_l'/2} \qquad (8\text{-}27)$$

The total power delivered to the load is then

$$P = I^2 R_l' = 2\left(\frac{\mu \mathbf{E}_g}{r_p + R_l'/2}\right)^2 \frac{R_l'}{2} \qquad (8\text{-}28)$$

This expression may be interpreted to mean that the total output power is twice the power of each tube considered to be working into the equivalent load resistance $R_l'/2$.

A more significant expression results by writing Eq. (8-28) in the form

$$P = \left(\frac{\mu \mathbf{E}_g}{r_p/2 + R_l'/4}\right)^2 \frac{R_l'}{4} \qquad (8\text{-}29)$$

This may be interpreted to show that the class A push-pull amplifier may be represented by a single composite generator which has emf $\mu \mathbf{E}_g$, with an internal resistance $r_p/2$, and which works into a load resistance equal to $R_l'/4$.   It is possible, in fact, to derive a set of static characteristics of the composite tube from the tube plate characteristics and to obtain significant operating information from this.

8-8. Composite Static-characteristic Curves.   The composite static characteristics of the push-pull amplifier may be obtained from the plate

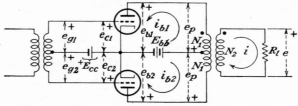

FIG. 8-17. The potentials in the push-pull amplifier.

characteristics of the individual tube by a graphical construction.[2]   It is assumed that the output transformer is ideal, whence the potentials across each half of the transformer are equal.   The situation is illustrated in

Fig. 8-17. The load potential is given by

$$e = \frac{N_2}{N_1} e_p \qquad (8\text{-}30)$$

Also, in the ideal transformer, the total primary ampere-turns are equal to the secondary ampere-turns, from which

$$N_1 i_{b1} - N_1 i_{b2} = N_2 i \qquad (8\text{-}31)$$

Thus the load potential is

$$e = iR_l = (i_{b1} - i_{b2}) \frac{N_1}{N_2} R_l \qquad (8\text{-}32)$$

By combining Eqs. (8-30) and (8-32) there results

$$e_p = (i_{b1} - i_{b2}) \left(\frac{N_1}{N_2}\right)^2 R_l \quad (8\text{-}33)$$

which may be written in the form

$$e_p = (i_{b1} - i_{b2}) \frac{R'_l}{4} \quad (8\text{-}34)$$

where R'_l is the plate-plate resistance.

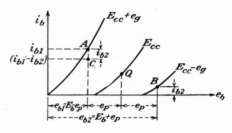

The following relationships are evident from an inspection of the diagram of Fig. 8-17:

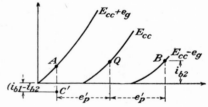

$$\begin{aligned} e_{b1} &= E_b - e_p \\ e_{b2} &= E_b + e_p \\ e_{c1} &= E_{cc} + e_g \\ e_{c2} &= E_{cc} - e_g \end{aligned} \qquad (8\text{-}35)$$

It follows from these equations that when the plate-cathode potential e_{b1} of tube $T1$ decreases from the quiescent-point value E_b by an amount e_p, then the corresponding potential e_{b2} of tube $T2$ increases beyond E_b by a like amount. Also, when the grid-cathode potential e_{c1} increases

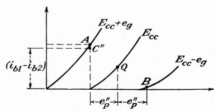

FIG. 8-18. To construct the composite static characteristics of a push-pull amplifier from the plate characteristic.

beyond E_{cc} by the signal potential e_g, the corresponding value of e_{c2} decreases below E_{cc} by e_g. These conditions are shown in Fig. 8-18 for three different values of e_p. In these diagrams point A corresponds to conditions $e_{b1} = E_b - e_p$, $e_{c1} = E_{cc} + e_g$, the tube current being i_{b1}.

Point B is that for $e_{b2} = E_b + e_p$, $e_{c2} = E_{cc} - e_g$, and the tube current is i_{b2}.   Point C has the ordinate $i_{b1} - i_{b2}$ for the chosen value of e_p.

The composite static characteristics are the family curves of $i_{b1}-i_{b2}$ vs. e_b, with grid signal potential as a parameter.   Clearly, point C is one point on the composite static curve for the signal potential e_g.   Other points

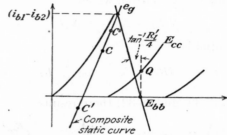

Fig. 8-19. The composite static curve derived from the constructions of Fig. 8-18.

on this characteristic are found by maintaining e_g constant and by varying e_p.   The construction for two other values e_p' and e_p'' are given in Fig. 8-18b and 8-18c.   These locate two other points C' and C'' on the composite static characteristic.   The complete composite static is given in Fig. 8-19.

Several significant features are evident from Fig. 8-19.   The composite static characteristic extends above and below the zero-current axis.

Also, the composite static curve is much more linear than the plate characteristics of the individual tube.

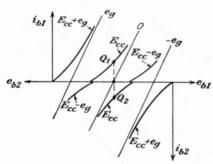

Fig. 8-20. The Thompson method of obtaining the composite static characteristics of a push-pull amplifier.

An alternative method for obtaining the composite static characteristics was described by Thompson.[3]   According to this method, the plate characteristics of the tube are plotted in the usual way.   The curves are also plotted in an inverted manner, with the potential scale shifted so that the potentials E_b of both sets of curves are aligned with each other.   This construction is shown in Fig. 8-20.   The inverted curves represent the plate family of tube $T2$.   The two methods are essentially equivalent.

The foregoing discussion of the graphical construction is general and applies to any type of tube under class A, AB, or B conditions of operation.   Although the illustrations are for triodes, the curves for other tube types are obtained in the same way.   In fact, owing to their shape, the composite static characteristics for pentode-type tubes are more easily obtained than the triode curves.   The simplification results because the current i_{b2} remains substantially constant for large variations in e_b.   The composite static characteristics for the 6F6 pentode are shown in Fig. 8-21.

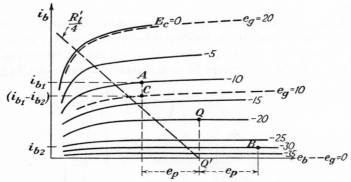

FIG. 8-21. Composite static characteristics of a 6F6 pentode push-pull amplifier.

8-9. Composite Dynamic Characteristic.   The composite dynamic characteristic of a push-pull amplifier is obtained from the composite static characteristics in precisely the same way that the dynamic curve is obtained from the plate characteristics of a single-tube amplifier.   This requires drawing the effective composite load line on the composite static curves and noting the points of intersection of the two, which are points on the composite dynamic curve.   This construction also permits obtaining the load line into which each tube is working and hence also the dynamic characteristic of the individual tubes.   The construction is shown in Fig. 8-22. Clearly, the intersection of the push-pull load line with the composite plate characteristics gives

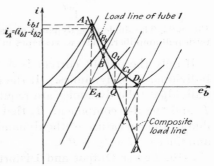

FIG. 8-22. The load line of the composite circuit, and the load line of one tube of the push-pull amplifier.

points on the composite dynamic characteristic.   That is, points A, B, C, D are points on the composite dynamic curve.   These points are replotted in Fig. 8-23 to give the composite dynamic curve.

To find the dynamic characteristic of each tube, the procedure is essentially the reverse of that of Sec. 8-8.   In particular, consider the point B in Fig. 8-22.   This point is a representation of $i_{b1}-i_{b2}$ corresponding to the appropriately chosen value of e_p. But the point i_{b1} lies vertically above this point, by an amount i_{b2}, and must lie on the plate characteristic of the tube. This defines the point A_1. The other points are obtained in a similar way, and the results are shown in Fig. 8-22. These points are plotted also in Fig. 8-23. The points A_2, B_2, C_2, D_2 for tube $T2$ are obtained by symmetry from the corresponding points of tube $T1$.

It is interesting to note that the composite dynamic curve is practically a straight line, although the individual tube dynamic curves are markedly curved. Thus, for a sinusoidal input, the total output current is closely sinusoidal, although the current in each tube is not sinusoidal, in general.

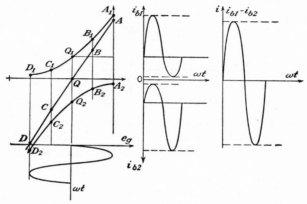

FIG. 8-23. The single-tube dynamic characteristics and the composite dynamic of the push-pull amplifier. The waveshapes in each tube and in the output are also shown.

If only the output current is desired, there is no requirement for the individual tube dynamics. If the plate-circuit efficiency is required, the individual tube dynamics are required in order to calculate the value of I_b and the d-c component B_0 that results from the partial rectification due to the curvature of the dynamic. The total d-c power input to the amplifier is $2E_{bb}(I_b + B_0)$.

8-10. Power Output and Distortion in Push-Pull Amplifiers. Owing to the fact that the dynamic curve must be an odd function, by virtue of the manner of its construction, then for the composite circuit

$$I_b = 0$$
$$I_{max} = -I_{min} \tag{8-36}$$
$$I_{1/2} = -I_{-1/2}$$

Under these circumstances the five-point schedule of Eq. (4-30) reduces to

$$B_0 = B_2 = B_4 = 0$$
$$B_1 = \tfrac{2}{3}(I_{max} + I_{1/2}) \tag{8-37}$$
$$B_3 = \tfrac{1}{3}(I_{max} - 2I_{1/2})$$

The fundamental power output is given by the expression

$$P_1 = \left(\frac{B_1}{\sqrt{2}}\right)^2 \frac{R_l'}{4} = \frac{B_1^2 R_l'}{8} \tag{8-38}$$

By neglecting the harmonic components of power, the total power is given by

$$P_1 = \frac{E_m I_m}{2} \tag{8-39}$$

where E_m and I_m denote the peak values of the a-c output voltage and current, respectively. These values are obtained directly from the curves of Fig. 8-22, since $I_m = I_A$ and $E_m = E_b - E_A$, whence

$$P = \frac{(E_b - E_A) I_A}{2} \tag{8-40}$$

To find the maximum output power in the push-pull class A system utilizing triodes, use is made of the fact that the load resistance should equal the internal resistance of the equivalent or composite generator. This follows from Eq. (8-29) for the class A amplifier and requires that $R_l'/4 = r_p/2$. This requires that the slope of the effective load line must be equal to the reciprocal of the composite static characteristic, which has a value of $r_p/2$.

Suppose that the tubes are operated in push-pull class B. Now, since the tubes are biased to cutoff, then either one or the other of the two tubes will be supplying current to the circuit and each contributes power for one-half of each cycle. Consequently, the equivalent generator will be one with an internal resistance equal to r_p of the tube. The maximum power under these conditions will be obtained for $R_l'/4 = r_p$. It is reasonable to expect that the internal resistance of the equivalent source of a push-pull class AB amplifier will lie between the value for the class A circuit $r_p/2$ and that for a class B circuit r_p. In all cases, however, recourse should be had to the composite static characteristics, and then $R_l'/4$ should be set equal to the reciprocal of the slope of these lines.

The situation for pentodes is different from that discussed above for triodes and follows roughly the reasoning of Sec. 8-5. The optimum load is that which yields the maximum power with low distortion. The optimum load line is drawn through the point Q' so that it intersects the peak composite grid-voltage curve in the neighborhood of the knee of the curve. This is illustrated in Fig. 8-21 for the 6F6 tube.

8-11. Driver Stages for Push-Pull Amplifiers. The driver may be considered to comprise the circuit that supplies the two potentials of equal magnitude but in phase opposition to the grids of the push-pull power amplifier. A variety of suitable circuits exist, the most direct of which is illustrated in Fig. 8-24. This circuit consists of a simple amplifier with a transformer in the output, the secondary of which is center-tapped. The characteristics of this stage are determined by the grid driving-power requirements of the power amplifier. If the push-pull circuit requires substantially no driving power, then there are no serious requirements imposed on the driver stage. If the driver stage is called upon to supply power, and this would seldom exceed 15 per cent of the output of the push-pull stage, although it is ordinarily less than this amount, the driver stage must have a relatively low internal resistance if no distortion is to be introduced into the grid circuit of the push-pull amplifier. It is advisable in such cases that a step-down transformer be used to couple the driver stage to the push-pull input in order to reduce the effective resistance in the grid circuit.

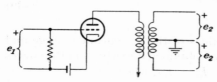

FIG. 8-24. A simple driver circuit for a push-pull amplifier.

If the power requirements are low, then any one of a wide variety of "paraphase" circuits may be used. A paraphase circuit is one which provides two equal output potentials which are 180 deg apart in phase from a single signal source.

Single-tube Paraphase Amplifier. A single-tube amplifier in which the load resistor is divided equally between the plate and cathode circuits is the simplest form of paraphase amplifier. The circuit, redrawn for convenience in Fig. 8-25, is discussed at some length in Sec. 7-8. The resistors R_l and R_k have the same value, whence the amplitude of the potential developed across each is the same, since the same current flows through each. The polarity is opposite because the cathode output is taken from the more positive end of R_k and the

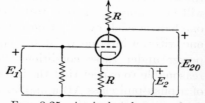

FIG. 8-25. A single-tube paraphase amplifier.

plate output is taken from the less positive end of R_l. The analysis of this circuit in Sec. 7-8 shows that the gain of the stage is less than unity and is given by the expression

$$\mathbf{K}_f = \frac{\pm \mu R}{(\mu + 2)R + r_p} \doteq \pm \frac{\mu}{\mu + 2} \tag{8-41}$$

Two-tube Paraphase Amplifiers. In the two-tube paraphase amplifier, one tube is used as a conventional amplifier, and a second tube is used as a phase-inverter amplifier. Figure 8-26 illustrates such a circuit. The resistors R_1 and R_2 comprise a potential divider across the output of a conventional amplifier, the ratio of the resistances being chosen so that the output of $T1$ is equal to the output of $T2$. Also, the operating conditions of the tubes are carefully chosen to allow the curvature of the characteristic of $T2$ to compensate for the curvature of $T1$. Thus the output potentials relative to ground are both slightly distorted to provide a comparatively undistorted potential difference between the output terminals. This method is difficult to apply in practice because the adjustments necessary to reduce distortion to a minimum are critical.

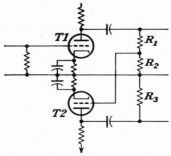

A second form of two-tube paraphase amplifier employs the differential potential between the outputs of two tubes as the input signal to the phase-inverter section. This circuit, which is also referred to as the *floating paraphase* amplifier, is illustrated in two versions in Fig. 8-27.

FIG. 8-26. A two-tube paraphase amplifier.

In the circuit of Fig. 8-27a tube $T1$ is an amplifier to increase the amplitude of the applied waveform. The cathode resistors R_k, if not by-passed, will provide some degeneration, which will help to reduce distortion. The output from $T1$ is coupled through C_1 to R_1 and R_3, both of which have the same value as R_2. The potential which appears across R_3 is applied to the grid of $T2$. The output of $T2$ is passed through C_2 and is applied across R_2 and R_3. Thus half the output of both $T1$ and $T2$ appears

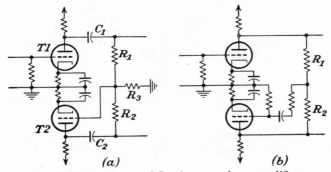

FIG. 8-27. Two forms of floating paraphase amplifiers.

across R_3. Since these potentials are of opposite polarity, the resultant potential across R_3 is the difference between these two. The output of $T1$ is larger than the output of $T2$, and in order that this difference should be kept as small as possible, pentodes are used, so as to take advantage of their high amplification.

The feature of the circuit of Fig. 8-27b is that the difference between the output potentials is taken care of in the choice of the resistors R_1 and R_2 so that the output potentials have the same amplitude. To do this requires that the following condition be satisfied:

$$\frac{K - 1}{K + 1} \doteq \frac{R_2}{R_1} \tag{8-42}$$

where K is the gain of the stage.

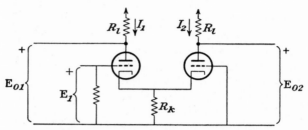

FIG. 8-28. A cathode-coupled paraphase amplifier.

The cathode-coupled paraphase amplifier, which is closely related to the cathode-coupled amplifier which was discussed in Sec. 6-8, is illustrated graphically in Fig. 8-28. This circuit is used extensively to provide push-pull deflection potentials for the plates of a cathode-ray tube, and also as the driver of a push-pull amplifier.

An analysis of this amplifier circuit is readily effected in terms of the Thévenin equivalent circuit as viewed from the cathode-ground terminals.

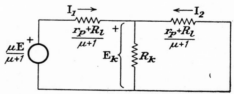

FIG. 8-29. The equivalent circuit of Fig. 8-28 as viewed from the cathode-ground terminals.

The resulting equivalent circuit is given in Fig. 8-29. It follows directly from this figure that the potential drop across R_k is given by

$$\mathbf{E}_k = -\mathbf{I}_2 \frac{r_p + R_l}{\mu + 1} = \frac{\mathbf{I}_1 R_k \dfrac{r_p + R_l}{\mu + 1}}{R_k + \dfrac{r_p + R_l}{\mu + 1}}$$

From this

$$-\frac{\mathbf{I}_1}{\mathbf{I}_2} = 1 + \frac{r_p + R_l}{R_k(\mu + 1)} \tag{8-43}$$

Notice from this expression that the current I_1 is always greater than I_2. For example, for a typical triode with, say, $r_p = 10,000$ ohms and $\mu = 19$, and with $R_l = R_k = 10,000$ ohms, $I_1/I_2 = 1.10$. In general, if the magnitude of I_1 is not to exceed the magnitude of I_2 by more than, say, 10 per cent (this requires than $-I_1/I_2 \leqq 1.1$), then

$$R_k \geqq 10 \frac{r_p + R_l}{\mu + 1}$$

It should be observed that the more nearly I_1 and I_2 are to be the same, the larger must R_k be. In fact, the two currents are equal only if $R_k = \infty$, an impractical condition. As a result, this circuit can never give exactly equal outputs, although by making R_k large compared with $(r_p + R_l)/(\mu + 1)$ almost equal outputs are possible.

To determine the output potentials, it is noted from the diagram that

$$\frac{\mu}{\mu + 1} E + I_1 \frac{r_p + R_l}{\mu + 1} - I_2 \frac{r_p + R_l}{\mu + 1} = 0$$

from which

$$I_1 - I_2 = \frac{\mu E}{r_p + R_l}$$

If it is assumed that $I_1 = -I_2$ approximately, as discussed above, then

$$I_1 = -I_2 = \frac{\mu E}{2(r_p + R_l)}$$

whence

$$E_{01} = -E_{02} = \frac{\mu E}{2(r_p + R_l)} \tag{8-44}$$

REFERENCES

1. Nottingham, W. B., *Proc. IRE*, **29**, 620 (1941).
2. Millman, J., and S. Seely, "Electronics," 1st ed., chap. XX, McGraw-Hill Book Company, Inc., New York, 1941.
3. Thompson, B. J., *Proc. IRE*, **21**, 591 (1933).

PROBLEMS

8-1. A 6F6 tube is operated as a triode and supplies power to a 4,000-ohm load. With $E_{bb} = 300$, $E_{cc} = -25$ volts and with a peak signal of 25 volts, calculate the following:

    a. Output power.   *b.* Plate-circuit efficiency.

    c. Per cent second-harmonic distortion.   *d.* Plate dissipation.

8-2. Repeat Prob. 8-1 when the load is transformer-coupled to the tube.

8-3. It is supposed that the plate dissipation at the operating point is kept constant. Prove that for class A operation the plate load is made larger with increasing values of E_{bb} and the plate efficiency increases.

8-4. A 6V6 is operated with $E_{bb} = E_{c2} = 250$ volts and with $E_{cc} = -12.5$ volts. The grid signal is sinusoidal, with a peak value of 12.5 volts. Calculate the following for a shunt-fed load of 5,000 ohms:

    a. Output power.   *b.* Total distortion.

    c. Plate dissipation.   *d.* Plate-circuit efficiency.

8-5. Repeat Prob. 8-4 if the load is 2,000 ohms; 8,000 ohms.

8-6. Two 6F6 tubes are connected as triodes and are operated in push-pull class A from a 350-volt plate source, with a grid bias of -30 volts. A 30-volt peak signal is used.

    a. Draw the composite static characteristics.

    b. From this, determine the plate-plate resistance for maximum output power.

    c. Calculate the power output, third-harmonic distortion, and plate-circuit efficiency.

8-7. Two 6F6 tubes are connected as pentodes and are operated in push-pull class AB from a 350-volt plate source, with a grid bias of -25 volts. The screen potentials are maintained at 250 volts.

    a. Draw the composite static characteristics.

    b. Plot the composite dynamic and the dynamic characteristic of each tube.

    c. Calculate the output power, third-harmonic distortion, and plate-circuit efficiency for a plate-plate resistance of 10,000 ohms. The peak grid signal is 40 volts.

8-8. Two 2A3 triodes are operated in push-pull with $E_{bb} = 300$, $E_{cc} = -60$ volts.

    a. Draw the composite static characteristic.

    b. From this, determine the plate-plate resistance for maximum power output.

    c. Calculate the power output under these conditions.

    d. Repeat *c* for $\frac{1}{2}$ and 2 times the optimum value.

    e. Construct the paths of operation for the individual tubes.

8-9. A 6N7 zero-bias tube is connected as a class B push-pull audio amplifier and is to furnish 10 watts into a dynamic loud-speaker, the voice coil of which has a resistance of 8 ohms. A 35:1 step-down transformer is used. The plate supply is 325 volts. Determine the following:

    a. D-c plate current.   *b.* Grid driving potential.

8-10. The typical operating characteristics of a 6L6 beam power tube when used in push-pull class A are shown below. Values shown are for two-tube unless otherwise specified.

Plate supply	270 volts
Screen supply	270 volts
Cathode resistor	125 ohms
Zero-signal plate current	134 ma
Maximum-signal plate current	145 ma
Zero-signal plate current	11 ma
Maximum-signal screen current	17 ma
Plate resistance	23,500 ohms
Transconductance	5,700 μmhos
Effective load resistance (plate to plate)	5,000 ohms
Maximum-signal power output	18.5 watts

The 6L6 tubes are to supply the 18.5 watts to the grids of a pair of 806 triodes which are operating in class B push-pull. The required peak grid driving potential is 660 volts.

a. Calculate the turns ratio of the output transformer.
b. What is the peak a-c plate potential on each tube?
c. What is the peak a-c grid-potential swing on each tube?
d. Does grid current flow during any part of the input cycle?
e. Calculate the plate-circuit efficiency.

8-11. The diagram gives the basic circuit of what has been called a single-ended push-pull amplifier.*

a. Prove qualitatively that push-pull operation is achieved with this amplifier.
b. Choose $E_{g1} = -E_{g2}$. What is the output potential E_2? From this find an expression for the power output, and show that it is the same as Eq. (8-29).

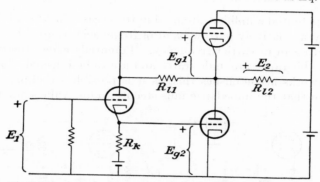

8-12. Verify the conditions (8-42) imposed on the floating paraphase amplifier for balanced output potentials. What conditions are imposed on R_3?

8-13. It is suggested that the paraphase principle be combined with a push-pull amplifier to yield push-pull operation without a separate driving source. The push-pull amplifier feeds a dynamic speaker. Discuss the suggested operation from the point of view of class of operation possible; of distortion.

* A. Peterson, and D. B. Sinclair, *Proc. IRE*, **40**, 7 (1952).

CHAPTER 9

TUNED POTENTIAL AMPLIFIERS

Tuned potential amplifiers are used in those cases in which it is desired to amplify a relatively narrow band of frequencies centered about some designated mean or carrier frequency. Potentials whose frequencies lie outside of this range are undesirable and are to be rejected. The use of tuned networks accomplishes this, as it is possible to adjust the tuned network so that the impedance falls steeply to low values outside of the

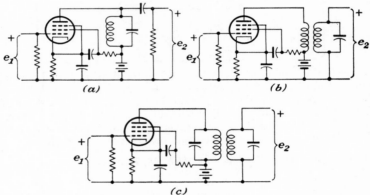

Fig. 9-1. The three basic tuned amplifier circuits: (a) single-tuned, direct coupling; (b) single-tuned, transformer coupling; (c) double-tuned.

desired frequency band, with the consequent reduction in amplifier gain to negligibly low values. The resulting nonlinear distortion that is produced in these amplifiers is very small, both because the stage is operated under class A conditions and because the tuned plate-circuit impedance may be very low for any harmonic frequencies that might be generated within the tube.

There are three basic amplifier circuits, and these are illustrated in Fig. 9-1. Pentodes are ordinarily used in such amplifiers, and the circuits are drawn showing such tubes. In two of these types, a single resonant circuit is used, which may be included directly in the plate circuit (direct-coupled) or which may be inductively coupled to the plate circuit (transformer-coupled). In the third type, a double-tuned band-

212

pass arrangement is used, both the primary and secondary circuits being tuned.   An analysis of the operation of each of these amplifier circuits will be given.

9-1. Single-tuned Direct-coupled Amplifier.   The equivalent circuit of a typical single-tuned direct-coupled stage is given in Fig. 9-2.   Included in this diagram are the output tube capacitances [see Eq. (5-23)] and the input and wiring capacitances to the following stage.   The coupling capacitance may be neglected, as this is presumed to be large.

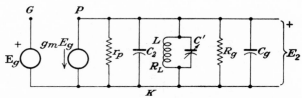

FIG. 9-2. The equivalent circuit of a single-tuned direct-coupled class A amplifier

In accordance with the discussion of Sec. 5-7, the gain of the amplifier can be written directly as

$$\mathbf{K} = -g_m\mathbf{Z} \tag{9-1}$$

where $\mathbf{Z}$ is the total load impedance.   This impedance has the complex form given by

$$\frac{1}{\mathbf{Z}} = \frac{1}{r_p} + \frac{1}{R_g} + \frac{1}{\mathbf{Z}_t} \tag{9-2}$$

where $\mathbf{Z}_t$ is the impedance of the antiresonant circuit and comprises the inductance L and the sum of the various capacitances $C_t = C_2 + C_g + C'$,. where C_2 is defined as in Eq. (3-23).

The impedance $\mathbf{Z}_t$ has the form

$$\mathbf{Z}_t = \frac{-j\dfrac{1}{\omega C}\,(R_L + j\omega L)}{R_L + j\left(\omega L - \dfrac{1}{\omega C}\right)} \tag{9-3}$$

which may be written in the form

$$\mathbf{Z}_t = \frac{\dfrac{L}{C}\left(1 - j\dfrac{R_L}{\omega L}\right)}{R_L\left[1 + j\dfrac{\omega L}{R_L}\left(1 - \dfrac{1}{\omega^2 LC}\right)\right]} \tag{9-4}$$

By writing

$$\omega_0 = \frac{1}{\sqrt{LC}}$$

$$\delta = \frac{\omega}{\omega_0} - 1 \tag{9-5}$$

$$Q = \frac{\omega_0 L}{R_L} = \frac{1}{\omega_0 C R_L} = \frac{1}{R_L}\sqrt{\frac{L}{C}}$$

the impedance function becomes

$$Z_t = \frac{R_L Q^2 \left(1 - j\frac{1}{Q}\frac{\omega_0}{\omega}\right)}{1 + jQ\left(\frac{\omega}{\omega_0} - \frac{\omega_0}{\omega}\right)}$$

$$Z_t = \frac{R_L Q^2 \left[1 + \delta - j\frac{1}{Q}\right]}{1 + \delta + jQ\delta(2 + \delta)} \tag{9-6}$$

At resonance $\omega = \omega_0$, and $\delta = 0$. Then

$$Z_t = R_L Q^2 \left(1 - j\frac{1}{Q}\right) \tag{9-7}$$

Since Q for the circuit used is usually high, with $Q \geqq 10$, then with good approximation

$$Z_t = R_0 \doteq R_L Q^2 \tag{9-8}$$

This result shows that the shunt impedance R_0 of the antiresonant circuit for circuits with $Q > 10$ is essentially resistive at the resonant frequency.

By combining Eq. (9-8) with Eq. (9-2), the gain at resonance becomes

$$K_{res} = \frac{-g_m}{\dfrac{1}{r_p} + \dfrac{1}{R_g} + \dfrac{1}{R_L Q^2}} = \frac{-g_m \omega_0 L Q}{1 + \dfrac{\omega_0 L Q}{r_p} + \dfrac{\omega_0 L Q}{R_g}} \tag{9-9}$$

This expression may be written in the form

$$K_{res} = -g_m \omega_0 L Q_e \tag{9-10}$$

where Q_e, the effective Q of the amplifier, is

$$Q_e = \frac{Q}{1 + \omega_0 L Q/r_p + \omega_0 L Q/R_g} \tag{9-11}$$

This is the equivalent Q of the resonance curve of the tuned amplifier and is the Q of the actual resonant circuit as modified by the shunting resistances R_g and r_p.

To find the gain of the amplifier when the input frequency and the resonant frequency of the tuned circuit are slightly different from each

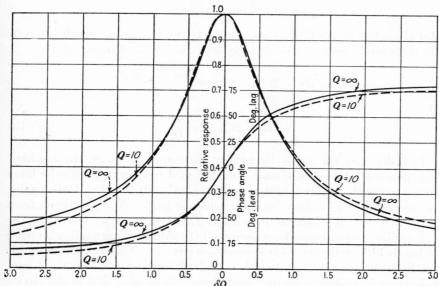

FIG. 9-3. Plots showing the amplitude K/K_{res} and phase of the output of a single-tuned direct-coupled amplifier.   (*From F. E. Terman, "Radio Engineering," 3d ed., McGraw-Hill Book Company, Inc., New York*, 1947.)

other, it is supposed that $\omega \doteq \omega_0$, whence δ is small.   From Eq. (9-6), it follows that

$$\mathbf{Z}_t = R_L Q^2 \frac{1 - j(1/Q)}{1 + 2j\delta Q} \doteq \frac{R_L Q^2}{1 + 2j\delta Q} \qquad (9\text{-}12)$$

The corresponding value of the gain, given by Eq. (9-9), is

$$\mathbf{K} = - \frac{g_m}{\dfrac{1}{r_p} + \dfrac{1}{R_g} + \dfrac{1 + 2j\delta Q}{R_L Q^2}} \qquad (9\text{-}13)$$

The gain ratio $\mathbf{K}/\mathbf{K}_{res}$ is then

$$\frac{\mathbf{K}}{\mathbf{K}_{res}} = \frac{1}{1 + j2\delta Q_e} \qquad (9\text{-}14)$$

from which the amplitude ratio is

$$\frac{K}{K_{res}} = \frac{1}{\sqrt{1 + (2\delta Q_e)^2}} \qquad (9\text{-}15)$$

A plot of these results is given in Fig. 9-3.   This is essentially the "universal resonance" curve.   Note from Eq. (9-15) that when

$$2\delta Q_e = 1$$

then

$$\frac{K}{K_{res}} = \frac{1}{\sqrt{2}}$$

But since the bandwidth of the circuit is the frequency width between the 3-db power points, then for a symmetrical gain characteristic

$$B = 2(f_{3db} - f_0) = \frac{2(f_{3db} - f_0)f_0}{f_0}$$

or

$$B = 2\delta_{3db}f_0 = \frac{f_0}{Q_e} \tag{9-16}$$

In order that the potential gain at resonance be large, the resonant impedance of the tuned circuit, and the grid resistor R_g, must be large compared with r_p. It might appear from Eq. (9-10) that higher gains are accomplished by choosing large values of L/C. Note, however, from Eqs. (9-5) and (9-8) that an increase of Z_t at resonance by increasing the L/C ratio is accompanied by a decreased Q_e, with a corresponding increase of bandwidth or decreased frequency selectivity. This is an undesirable condition if a narrow bandwidth is desired, but it is an important consideration in wide-band tuned amplifiers. Note also that if the circuit Q of the tuned circuit is increased at fixed values of ω_0 and L/C ratio, then the effective Q_e of the amplifier is increased, with a corresponding increase of frequency selectivity or decreased bandwidth.

9-2. Single-tuned Transformer-coupled Amplifier. The general behavior of the single-tuned transformer-coupled amplifier is quite similar to that of the direct-coupled circuit.

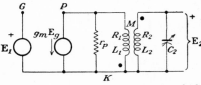

To examine the operation of the circuit in some detail, refer to Fig. 9-4, which gives the equivalent circuit of this amplifier. An approximate expression for the potential gain of the amplifier is readily obtained. If it is noted that r_p is usually large compared with R_1 and

Fig. 9-4. The equivalent circuit of the single-tuned transformer-coupled potential amplifier.

ωL_1, then the potential induced in the secondary of the transformer is given by

$$\mathbf{E}_{ind} \doteq j\omega M(g_m\mathbf{E}_g) = j\omega M(g_m\mathbf{E}_1) \tag{9-17}$$

since in this circuit $\mathbf{E}_g = \mathbf{E}_1$. The output potential, which is the potential across the capacitor C_2, is then

$$\mathbf{E}_2 = \frac{j\omega M(g_m\mathbf{E}_1)}{R_2 + j(\omega L_2 - 1/\omega C_2) + \omega^2 M^2/r_p}\frac{1}{j\omega C_2} \tag{9-18}$$

where $\omega^2 M^2/r_p$ is the reflected impedance of the primary into the secondary circuit. The expression for the gain then becomes

$$\mathbf{K} = \frac{\mathbf{E}_2}{\mathbf{E}_1} = \frac{\mu M/C_2}{r_p[R_2 + j(\omega L_2 - 1/\omega C_2)] + \omega^2 M^2} \tag{9-19}$$

The corresponding expression for the potential gain at resonance is

$$\mathbf{K}_{res} = \frac{\mu M/C_2}{r_p R_2 + \omega_0^2 M^2} \tag{9-20}$$

This result may also be expressed in terms of $Q_2 = \omega_0 L_2/R_2 = 1/\omega_0 C_2 R_2$ and is

$$\mathbf{K}_{res} = g_m \frac{\omega_0 M Q_2}{1 + \omega_0^2 M^2/r_p R_2} \tag{9-21}$$

which may be written as

$$\mathbf{K}_{res} = g_m \omega_0 M Q_e \tag{9-22}$$

where the effective value Q_e is

$$Q_e = \frac{Q_2}{1 + \omega_0^2 M^2/r_p R_2} \tag{9-23}$$

A comparison of this expression with Eq. (9-10) shows that transformer coupling modifies the amplification by the ratio M/L. This provides a means for controlling the gain of the stage and still retaining the high Q required for selectivity. It might appear that there are no limits on the gain and that it continued to increase with increasing values of M. This is not so, owing to the appearance of M in the denominator of Eq. (9-20). An optimum value of gain exists, and this occurs when M has the value required to make $\partial K_{res}/\partial M = 0$. This yields, for the optimum value of M,

$$\frac{\partial K_{res}}{\partial M} = \frac{\mu/C_2}{r_p R_2 + \omega_0^2 M^2} - \frac{(\mu M/C_2)2\omega_0^2 M}{(r_p R_2 + \omega_0^2 M^2)^2} = 0$$

or

$$M_{opt} = \frac{\sqrt{r_p R_2}}{\omega_0} \tag{9-24}$$

Equation (9-21) becomes

$$\mathbf{K}_{res,opt} = g_m \frac{\sqrt{r_p R_2}\, Q_2}{2}$$

$$= \frac{\mu Q_2}{2} \sqrt{\frac{R_2}{r_p}} \tag{9-25}$$

To find the bandwidth of the amplifier, consider the general expression for the gain given by Eq. (9-19). By writing, as before,

$$\omega_0 = \frac{1}{\sqrt{LC}},$$

$$\delta = \frac{\omega}{\omega_0} - 1 \qquad (9\text{-}26)$$

$$Q_2 = \frac{\omega_0 L_2}{R_2} = \frac{1}{\omega_0 C_2 R_2} = \frac{1}{R_2}\sqrt{\frac{L_2}{C_2}}$$

and noting that in the neighborhood of resonance

$$\omega L_2 - \frac{1}{\omega C_2} = \sqrt{\frac{L_2}{C_2}}\left(\frac{\omega}{\omega_0} - \frac{\omega_0}{\omega}\right)$$

$$\doteq 2\delta\sqrt{\frac{L_2}{C_2}} = 2\delta R_2 Q_2 \qquad (9\text{-}27)$$

Eq. (9-19) becomes

$$\mathbf{K} = \frac{\mu M/C_2}{r_p R_2\left(1 + j\,\dfrac{1}{R_2}\,2\delta\,\sqrt{\dfrac{L_2}{C_2}}\right) + \omega^2 M^2} \qquad (9\text{-}28)$$

The gain ratio [Eqs. (9-28) to (9-20)] then becomes

$$\frac{\mathbf{K}}{\mathbf{K}_{res}} = \frac{1}{1 + j2\delta Q_e} \qquad (9\text{-}29)$$

which has the same form as for the direct-coupled connection [Eq. (9-14)]. The bandwidth of this amplifier is, following the same reasoning as that which led to Eq. (9-16),

$$B = \frac{f_0}{Q_e} \qquad (9\text{-}30)$$

The optimum value of M is not of much importance, owing to practical limitations. This follows from Eq. (9-24), which shows that for pentodes, with the corresponding large values of r_p, the value of M would be large. In fact, to achieve these values of M, the distributed capacitances of the windings may become excessive, and the self-resonant frequency may be so low as to make the coils useless. Owing to this, the mutual inductance is usually chosen far below the optimum value in the pentode amplifier.

9-3. The Double-tuned Amplifier. Both the single-tuned direct-coupled amplifier and the double-tuned amplifier are extensively used in radar, television, and communication receivers. For the i-f amplifiers of both a-m and f-m types, the double-tuned amplifier is commonly used. This is so because such an amplifier can provide substantially constant amplification over a band of frequencies and the gain falls more sharply outside of this band than does the single-tuned stage.

To examine the operation of the circuit, refer to the equivalent circuit of the amplifier given in Fig. 9-5. This circuit can be further simplified by applying Thévenin's theorem to the portion of the circuit to the left of the points *aa*. The equivalent generator has the potential

$$\mathbf{E} = \frac{\mu \mathbf{E}_1(1/j\omega C_1)}{r_p + 1/j\omega C_1} \tag{9-31}$$

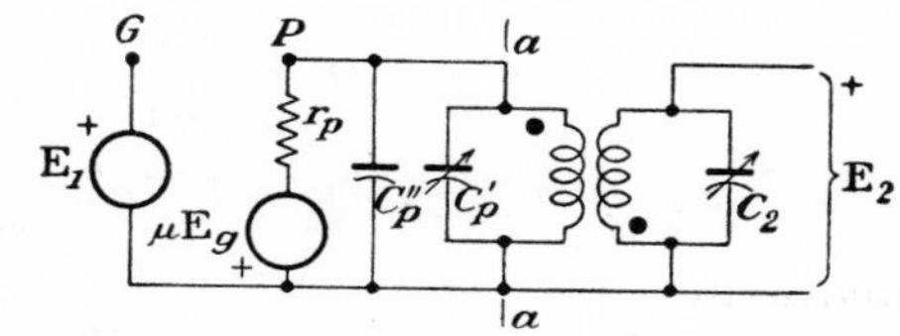

FIG. 9-5. The equivalent circuit of a double-tuned amplifier.

where $C_1 = C_p' + C_p''$. But since $r_p > 1/\omega C_1$ for the pentode, then with good approximation

$$\mathbf{E} \doteq \frac{\mu \mathbf{E}_1}{j\omega r_p C_1} = \frac{g_m \mathbf{E}_1}{j\omega C_1} \tag{9-32}$$

The internal impedance of the equivalent generator will have the value

$$\mathbf{Z} = \frac{r_p(1/j\omega C_1)}{r_p + 1/j\omega C_1}$$

which is, to the same approximation as above,

$$\mathbf{Z} \doteq \frac{1}{j\omega C_1} \tag{9-33}$$

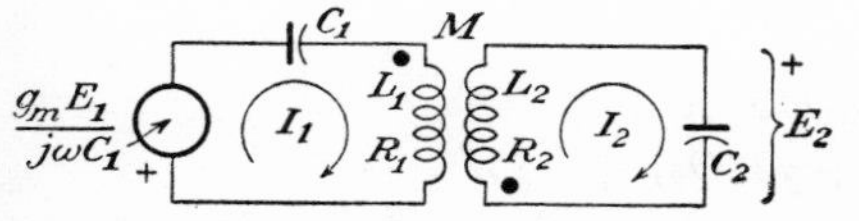

FIG. 9-6. The equivalent series form of Fig. 9-5.

Then the equivalent circuit of Fig. 9-5 reduces to the form of Fig. 9-6.

This circuit is analyzed by the standard methods of network analysis. Accordingly, if one writes

$$\begin{aligned} \mathbf{E} &= \varrho_{11}\mathbf{I}_1 + \varrho_{12}\mathbf{I}_2 \\ 0 &= \varrho_{12}\mathbf{I}_1 + \varrho_{22}\mathbf{I}_2 \end{aligned} \tag{9-34}$$

then the current in the secondary is

$$\mathbf{I}_2 = -\frac{\mathbf{E}\varrho_{12}}{\varrho_{11}\varrho_{22} - \varrho_{12}^2} \tag{9-35}$$

where

$$\begin{aligned} \varrho_{11} &= R_1 + j\left(\omega L_1 - \frac{1}{\omega C_1}\right) \\ \varrho_{12} &= j\omega M \\ \varrho_{22} &= R_2 + j\left(\omega L_2 - \frac{1}{\omega C_2}\right) \end{aligned} \tag{9-36}$$

The gain of the amplifier becomes

$$\mathbf{K} = \frac{\mathbf{E}_2}{\mathbf{E}_1} = \frac{(g_m/j\omega C_1)(1/j\omega C_2)j\omega M}{\varrho_{11}\varrho_{22} - \varrho_{12}^2} \tag{9-37}$$

But it must be noted that both circuits are tuned to the same resonant frequency. Thus

$$\omega_0 = \frac{1}{\sqrt{L_1 C_1}} = \frac{1}{\sqrt{L_2 C_2}}$$

Also define*

$$Q_1 = \frac{\omega_0 L_1}{R_1} = \frac{1}{\omega_0 C_1 R_1}$$

$$Q_2 = \frac{\omega_0 L_2}{R_2} = \frac{1}{\omega_0 C_2 R_2} \tag{9-38}$$

and write

$$a = \frac{\omega_0 M}{\sqrt{R_1 R_2}} = k \sqrt{Q_1 Q_2}$$

Then, by Eq. (9-27),

$$\varrho_{11} = R_1 + j\left(\omega L_1 - \frac{1}{\omega C_1}\right) = R_1(1 + j2\delta Q_1)$$

Similarly $\quad \varrho_{22} = R_2(1 + j2\delta Q_2) \tag{9-39}$

and $\quad \varrho_{12} = j\omega M$

The expression for the gain [Eq. (9-37)] then becomes for frequencies near resonance

$$\mathbf{K} = \frac{-jg_m(M/\omega_0 C_1 C_2)}{R_1 R_2(1 + j2\delta Q_1)(1 + j2\delta Q_2) + \omega_0^2 M^2}$$

$$\mathbf{K} = \frac{-jg_m \dfrac{\omega_0 M}{\sqrt{R_1 R_2}} Q_1 Q_2 \sqrt{R_1 R_2}}{1 + \omega_0^2 M^2/R_1 R_2 + 2j\delta(Q_1 + Q_2) - 4\delta^2 Q_1 Q_2}$$

or finally

$$\mathbf{K} = \frac{-jag_m Q_1 Q_2 \sqrt{R_1 R_2}}{1 + a^2 + j2\delta(Q_1 + Q_2) - 4\delta^2 Q_1 Q_2} \tag{9-40}$$

The gain at resonance is obtained by setting $\delta = 0$ in this expression. There results

$$\mathbf{K}_{res} = \frac{-jag_m Q_1 Q_2 \sqrt{R_1 R_2}}{1 + a^2} \tag{9-41}$$

The gain ratio at frequencies slightly different from resonance is given by

$$\frac{\mathbf{K}}{\mathbf{K}_{res}} = \frac{1}{\left(1 - \dfrac{4\delta^2 Q_1 Q_2}{1 + a^2}\right) + j\dfrac{2\delta(Q_1 + Q_2)}{1 + a^2}} \tag{9-42}$$

The exact shape of the response curve of the double-tuned system depends upon the parameter a, or, correspondingly, on k, the coefficient of coupling between the primary and secondary coils. The resonant gain

* If the amplifier is one of a chain, the loading effect of the following stage should be included in Q_2.

is a maximum when $a = 1$, as may be verified by examining $d\mathbf{K}/da = 0$. Moreover, if the primary and secondary Q values are the same and $a = 1$, the response curve has the maximum possible single-peak flatness in the vicinity of resonance. This is the condition for critical coupling k_c. A value of a greater than unity (overcoupling) results in double peaks, whereas a value of a less than unity (undercoupling) causes the response to be rounded on the top. If the circuit is considerably undercoupled, then the gain may be less than that at resonance. The situation discussed is illustrated graphically in Fig. 9-7.

An analytic expression for the positions of the peaks in the output of the overcoupled circuit is readily possible. These are given, of course, by the values of frequency at which Eq. (9-40) is a maximum. To find these

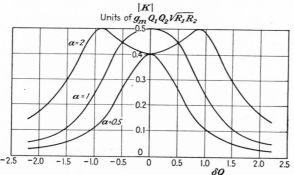

FIG. 9-7. The response characteristics of a double-tuned amplifier for various values of coupling.

values, it is noted that the gain is a maximum without regard to the phase. Thus the square of the absolute value of Eq. (9-40) is differentiated with respect to δ and maximized. The results are

$$|K|^2 = (g_m Q_1 Q_2 \sqrt{R_1 R_2})^2 \frac{a^2}{(1 + a^2 - 4\delta^2 Q_1 Q_2)^2 + [2\delta(Q_1 + Q_2)]^2} \qquad (9\text{-}43)$$

and the derivative $\partial|K|^2/\partial\delta = 0$ yields

$$1 + a^2 - 4\delta^2 Q_1 Q_2 = \frac{(Q_1 + Q_2)^2}{2Q_1 Q_2}$$

from which

$$\delta = \pm \frac{1}{2} \sqrt{k^2 + \frac{1}{Q_1 Q_2} - \frac{1}{2}\left(\frac{Q_1 + Q_2}{Q_1 Q_2}\right)^2} \qquad (9\text{-}44)$$

Frequently the circuits are designed with $Q_1 = Q_2$. Even if this condition is not true, ordinarily Q_1 does not differ too markedly from Q_2, and it is possible to assume that

$$\sqrt{Q_1 Q_2} \doteq \frac{Q_1 + Q_2}{2}$$

Subject to this approximation, Eq. (9-44) becomes

$$\delta = \pm \frac{1}{2}\sqrt{k^2 - \frac{1}{Q_1 Q_2}} \qquad (9\text{-}45)$$

which becomes, in the manner of representation of Fig. 9-7, simply

$$\delta \sqrt{Q_1 Q_2} = \pm \tfrac{1}{2}\sqrt{a^2 - 1} \qquad (9\text{-}46)$$

The value of the gain at either peak K_{max} is obtained by combining Eq. (9-46) with (9-40). The result is

$$\mathbf{K}_{max} = -j(g_m Q_1 Q_2 \sqrt{R_1 R_2}) \frac{a}{2(1 + j\sqrt{a^2 - 1})}$$

or

$$K_{max} = \tfrac{1}{2}(g_m Q_1 Q_2 \sqrt{R_1 R_2}) \qquad (9\text{-}47)$$

This shows that for the overcoupled case the maximum gain is the same as that for critical coupling $a = 1$, and at resonance $\delta = 0$.

The gain at the dip, at the frequency ω_0, can be found readily by setting $\delta = 0$ in Eq. (9-40). The result is

$$\mathbf{K}_{min} = -j(g_m Q_1 Q_2 \sqrt{R_1 R_2}) \frac{a}{1 + a^2}$$

or

$$K_{min} = g_m Q_1 Q_2 \sqrt{R_1 R_2} \frac{a}{1 + a^2} \qquad (9\text{-}48)$$

It follows from Eqs. (9-46) and (9-47) that increased coupling increases the frequency separation of two peaks but does not change their amplitudes. If the coupling is very large, then the approximation made in Eq. (9-40) is no longer valid. The effect of the factor ω/ω_0 in this equation is to increase the lower frequency maximum and decrease the higher frequency maximum.

The corresponding dependence of the current in the primary winding on the frequency is of some interest. It is obtained directly by solving Eq. (9-34) for I_1. The results are illustrated in Fig. 9-8. For the case when the coefficient of coupling k is small, the secondary circuit has little effect in the primary, and the resulting response is essentially that of the simple resonant circuit. When $k = k_c$, the reflected resistance from the secondary decreases the current at resonance. On each side of resonance, the reflected reactance is either inductive (below resonance) or capacitive (above resonance). A point is reached on each side of resonance when the reflected reactances cancel the primary reactances, which are capacitive below resonance and inductive above resonance. As a result, the current shows peaks. For values $k > k_c$, the double peak in the primary circuit becomes more pronounced.

For the case where the primary and secondary Q values are not the same, Aiken[1] has shown that a somewhat higher value of k is needed to produce double peaks in the secondary. The flattest selectivity curve may be shown to occur when

$$a^2 = \frac{1}{2}\left(\frac{Q_1}{Q_2} + \frac{Q_2}{Q_1}\right) \tag{9-49}$$

although the mid-band gain is not a maximum under these conditions. When Eq. (9-49) is satisfied, the circuit is said to be *transitionally* coupled. The transitional value of coupling coefficient is, by Eqs. (9-49) and (9-38),

$$k_t = \sqrt{\frac{1}{2}\left(\frac{1}{Q_1^2} + \frac{1}{Q_2^2}\right)} \tag{9-50}$$

For a coupling coefficient larger than this value, the selectivity curve divides into two peaks. For values less than this, the curve has a single peak.

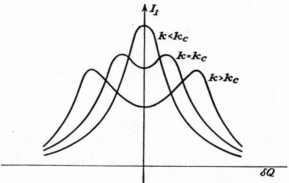

FIG. 9-8. The primary current of a double-tuned amplifier, corresponding to the conditions of Fig. 9-7.

For different primary and secondary Q values, but with $L_1 = L_2 = L$, and for k greater than the transitional coupling coefficient k_t, Aiken has shown that the frequency spread between peaks is

$$\Delta\omega = \frac{1}{L}\sqrt{(\omega_0 M)^2 - \frac{R_1^2 + R_2^2}{2}} \tag{9-51}$$

If $R_1 = R_2 = R$, this becomes

$$\Delta\omega = \frac{1}{L}\sqrt{(\omega_0 M)^2 - R^2}$$

from which it follows that

$$\frac{\Delta\omega}{\omega_0} = \frac{1}{\omega_0 L}\sqrt{(\omega_0 M)^2 - R^2} = \sqrt{k^2 - k_c^2} \tag{9-52}$$

The dip at resonance when k exceeds k_t is a function of the ratio k/k_c. Aiken shows this relation to have the form illustrated in Fig. 9-9. The bandwidth over which the response remains above the center value is $\sqrt{2}\,\Delta f$.

It is interesting to compare the gain of the double-tuned circuit with a single-tuned circuit having the same Q. The gains of the two circuits at resonance are given by Eqs. (9-10), and (9-41) for optimum value of a, and are

Single-tuned direct-coupled: $\mathbf{K}_{res} = -g_m\omega_0 L Q_e$
Double tuned (with $a = 1$ and identical coils):

$$\mathbf{K}_{res} = -j0.5 g_m Q^2 R = -j0.5 g_m \omega_0 L Q$$

It is observed that for critical coupling the gains at resonance of the two amplifiers are identical if it is assumed that the tuning capacitance of the

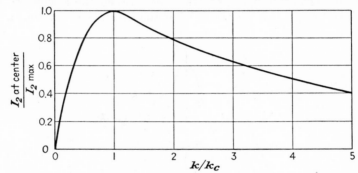

FIG. 9-9. The effect of the ratio of actual to critical coupling in a double-tuned circuit.

individual tuned circuit in the double-tuned circuit is one-half the tuning capacitance for the single-tuned case.

Despite the fact that the response characteristics are optimum under critical coupling conditions, the transformers in narrow-band double-tuned amplifiers are usually undercoupled slightly. This is done in order that the frequency alignment of the tuned circuits may be made easier, since, with undercoupled stages, each stage can be adjusted separately to give maximum response at the specified frequency. If over-coupled circuits exist, owing to the interactions between coils and the resulting double peak, this alignment is more critical. The critical coupling case is likewise difficult to align.

The bandwidth of the amplifier, under optimum conditions $a = 1$ and with equal primary and secondary values of Q, is readily calculated. Under these conditions Eq. (9-42) becomes

$$\frac{\mathbf{K}}{\mathbf{K}_{res}} = \frac{1}{1 - 2\delta^2 Q^2 + j2\delta Q} \tag{9-53}$$

and the magnitude becomes

$$\frac{K}{K_{res}} = \frac{1}{\sqrt{1 + 4\delta^4 Q^4}} \qquad (9\text{-}54)$$

Since, by definition, the bandwidth gives a measure of the frequency spread over which the gain remains within 3 db of the maximum value, then

$$4\delta^4 Q^4 = 1$$

from which it follows that the bandwidth is

$$B = 2\delta f_0 = \sqrt{2}\frac{f_0}{Q} \qquad (9\text{-}55)$$

A comparison of this result with Eq. (9-16) for the single-tuned stage shows that the 3-db band width of the double-tuned circuit is 1.414 times that of the single-tuned stage.

9-4. Cascaded Tuned Amplifiers. It is frequently necessary to incorporate more than one stage of amplification in a given amplifier. Although such a practice provides a higher gain, this higher gain is accompanied by a narrower bandwidth than for the single stage. The situation here is sensibly the same as that which was considered in Sec. 6-6. Analytic expressions for the effect of cascading identical amplifiers are readily possible, following the previous method of analysis.

Consider first n single-tuned stages in cascade. The gain of such an n-stage amplifier becomes, from Eq. (9-15),

$$\left(\frac{K}{K_{res}}\right)^n = \frac{1}{[1 + (2\delta Q_e)^2]^{n/2}} \qquad (9\text{-}56)$$

To find the corresponding bandwidth, it is noted that

$$[1 + (2\delta Q_e)^2]^{n/2} = \sqrt{2}$$

from which

$$1 + (2\delta Q_e)^2 = 2^{1/n}$$

so that

$$2\delta Q_e = \sqrt{2^{1/n} - 1}$$

But the bandwidth is given by

$$B_{1n} = 2\delta f_0 = \frac{\sqrt{2^{1/n} - 1}}{Q_e/f_0} \qquad (9\text{-}57)$$

This may be expressed in terms of the bandwidth of the single stage B_1, in the form

$$B_{1n} = B_1 \sqrt{2^{1/n} - 1} \qquad (9\text{-}58)$$

Table 6-1 gives the bandwidth reduction function $\sqrt{2^{1/n} - 1}$. It is seen, for example, that two stages in cascade have a bandwidth that is only 0.64 times that of a single stage. To maintain a given bandwidth, it is accordingly necessary that the Q of the individual stages be decreased as the number of stages is increased.

A corresponding expression is possible for the double-tuned amplifier. For such an n-stage amplifier, with critical coupling $a = 1$ and equal primary and secondary values of Q, the relative gain becomes, from Eq. (9-54),

$$\left(\frac{K}{K_{res}}\right)^n = \frac{1}{(1 + 4\delta^4 Q^4)^{n/2}}$$

It follows from this that

$$\delta Q = \sqrt[4]{\frac{2^{1/n} - 1}{4}}$$

The bandwidth of the n-stage amplifier then has the form

$$B_{2n} = 2\delta f_0 = 2\sqrt[4]{\frac{2^{1/n} - 1}{4}}\frac{f_0}{Q}$$

which may be written in terms of one-stage bandwidth as

$$B_{2n} = B_2 \sqrt[4]{2^{1/n} - 1} \tag{9-59}$$

The band-width reduction factor is tabulated in Table 9-1. For a two-stage double-tuned amplifier with the coils critically coupled, the bandwidth is 0.802 times that of the single-stage amplifier. Note that

TABLE 9-1

THE DOUBLE-TUNED-AMPLIFIER BANDWIDTH REDUCTION
FACTOR FOR $a = 1$

n	$\sqrt[4]{2^{1/n} - 1}$
1	1.00
2	0.802
3	0.713
4	0.659
5	0.622
6	0.592
7	0.568
8	0.548

this reduction is considerably less than the corresponding reduction of the two-stage single-tuned amplifier. This arises from the fact that the amplification or selectivity curve of the double-tuned amplifier has steeper sides than that of the single-tuned circuit and with successive stages drops away less rapidly than for the single-tuned case. In particular, an ideal amplifier with a rectangular response curve would show no bandwidth reduction with the addition of successive stages.

9-5. Gain-Bandwidth Product.[*]   It is of interest to tabulate the gain at resonance of the three amplifier circuits that have been studied.   These follow:

Single-tuned direct-coupled: $\mathbf{K}_{res} = -g_m\omega_0 L Q_e$
Single-tuned transformer-coupled: $\mathbf{K}_{res} = g_m\omega_0 M Q_e$
Double-tuned: $\mathbf{K}_{res} = -j0.5 g_m Q_1 Q_2 \sqrt{R_1 R_2}$

These expressions may be interpreted as showing that the gain in each case has the form

$$\mathbf{K}_{res} = g_m \mathbf{Z} \tag{9-60}$$

where g_m is the transconductance of the tube and $\mathbf{Z}$ is the effective impedance of the load.   Moreover, the foregoing analyses for these amplifiers show that the bandwidth in each case varies inversely with the effective Q of the tuned circuit.   Clearly, therefore, the higher gains are accompanied by a decreasing bandwidth.

The gain-bandwidth product of the single-tuned direct-coupled amplifier is obtained by combining Eq. (9-10) with Eq. (9-16).   There results

$$K_{res}B = g_m\omega_0 L Q_e \frac{f_0}{Q_e} = g_m \frac{\omega_0^2 L}{2\pi}$$

which may be written in the form

$$K_{res}B = \frac{g_m}{2\pi C}$$

In the limit where the capacitance C is due only to interelectrode capacitances, the limiting gain-bandwidth product is

$$K_{res}B = \frac{g_m}{2\pi(C_{\text{in}} + C_{\text{out}})} \tag{9-61}$$

and is the same value as found in Sec. 6-5 for the RC amplifier.

The gain-bandwidth product of the double-tuned amplifier is found by combining Eq. (9-41) with Eq. (9-55) and is

$$K_{res}B = \frac{g_m}{2} Q_1 Q_2 \sqrt{R_1 R_2} \sqrt{2} \frac{f_0}{\sqrt{Q_1 Q_2}}$$

$$= \frac{1}{\sqrt{2}} g_m \sqrt{Q_1 Q_2 R_1 R_2} \frac{\omega_0}{2\pi}$$

$$= \frac{g_m}{2\pi} \frac{1}{\sqrt{2} \sqrt{C_{\text{out}} C_{\text{in}}}} \tag{9-62}$$

This expression shows that the gain-bandwidth product of the double-tuned amplifier is $\sqrt{2}$ as great as that for the single-tuned circuit.   That

[*] Refer to Sec. 6-5.

is, by splitting the tube input and output capacitances by the use of the double-tuned circuit, there is an increase in the gain-bandwidth product.

9-6. Stagger Tuning.[2] If it is desired to build a wide-band high-gain amplifier, one procedure is to use either single-tuned or double-tuned circuits which have been heavily loaded so as to increase the bandwidth. The gain per stage is correspondingly reduced, by virtue of the constant gain-bandwidth product. The use of a cascaded chain of stages will provide for the desired gain. For example, a particular amplifier comprising nine cascaded single-tuned stages each having a 6 Mc bandwidth has an over-all bandwidth of 1.7 Mc. A nine cascaded chain of double-tuned amplifiers, each also of 6 Mc bandwidth, yields an over-all bandwidth of 3.2 Mc. Generally, for a specified gain and bandwidth the double-tuned cascaded amplifier is preferred, since fewer tubes are often

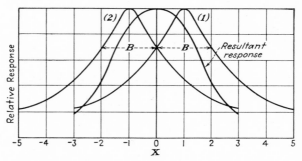

FIG. 9-10. The adjustments of frequency of a stagger-tuned pair.

possible, and also since the pass-band characteristics of the double-tuned cascaded chain are more favorable, falling more rapidly outside the pass band. From practical considerations, the double-tuned stages are more difficult to align, and they also are more sensitive to variations in tube capacitance and coil inductance than the single-tuned circuits.

A means is available for achieving the large bandwidth and other characteristics of double-tuned circuits by using single-tuned circuits. This consists in taking two single-tuned circuits of a certain bandwidth, and displacing, or "staggering," their resonance peaks by an amount equal to their bandwidth. The resultant staggered pair will have a bandwidth that is $\sqrt{2}$ times as great as that of each of the individual single-tuned circuits making up the pair; the over-all selectivity function will be identical in form with that of a single-stage double-tuned system. The general situation is illustrated in Fig. 9-10.

An analytic expression is readily obtained for the over-all characteristics of the stagger-tuned pair. If it is noted that the general selectivity function of the single-tuned direct-coupled circuit is, from Eq. (9-14),

$$\frac{\mathbf{K}}{\mathbf{K}_{res}} = \frac{1}{1 + j2\delta Q_e} = \frac{1}{1 + jx}$$

and the bandwidth between the 3-db points is, from Eq. (9-16),

$$B = 2\delta f_0 = \frac{f_0}{Q_e}$$

then the corresponding selectivity functions of the two circuits are, respectively,

$$\left(\frac{\mathbf{K}}{\mathbf{K}_{res}}\right)_1 = \frac{1}{1 + j(x + 1)}$$

and

$$\left(\frac{\mathbf{K}}{\mathbf{K}_{res}}\right)_2 = \frac{1}{1 + j(x - 1)}$$

By multiplying the selectivity functions together, there results

$$\left(\frac{\mathbf{K}}{\mathbf{K}_{res}}\right)_1 \left(\frac{\mathbf{K}}{\mathbf{K}_{res}}\right)_2 = \frac{1}{2 - x^2 + 2jx}$$

The magnitude of the resulting function is

$$\left(\frac{K}{K_{res}}\right)_1 \left(\frac{K}{K_{res}}\right)_2 = \frac{1}{\sqrt{4 + x^4}} = \frac{1}{2} \frac{1}{\sqrt{1 + 4\delta_0^4 Q^4}} \qquad (9\text{-}63)$$

where δ_0 is the value of δ referred to the new frequency ω_0 and where Q is the value of Q_e for each circuit referred to ω_0. A comparison of this expression with Eq. (9-54) for the double-tuned circuit shows that the forms of the variation are identical.

It is of some interest to compare the gain-bandwidth products of the following: two synchronously tuned stages, a stagger-tuned pair, two synchronously tuned double-tuned stages. The results are found to be, respectively, $0.643K^2B_1$, $0.707K^2B_1$, $1.13K^2B_1$. Thus, not only are the resultant gain-bandwidth products higher for the more complicated coupling systems, but the selectivity is also better.

The advantage of stagger-tuned amplifiers, and the principle may be extended to stagger triples (and to stagger n-uples in general), lies in the fact that simple single-tuned circuits are used throughout. This makes the alignment of the stages relatively easy, especially if stagger triples or higher were to be used, since no interaction exists among tuning elements of the several stages. To attempt a triple-tuned single-stage coupling network proves an almost impossible practical tuning task. A practical disadvantage of the stagger-tuned circuit exists which makes the double-tuned circuit preferable and often almost necessary for 60 Mc and above. The input impedance of an amplifier stage at these high frequencies is low and may be no more than several thousand ohms.

This input loading of the tuned circuit of the previous stage may make it almost impossible to effect stagger tuning for a prescribed over-all bandwidth, whereas this loading affects the double-tuned response characteristics to a lesser degree, with a consequent less stringent restriction on the operation.

As noted, the principle of stagger tuning can be extended, and staggered triples have been used in radar receivers. In this case a centered single-tuned circuit of relative bandwidth 2 and relative resonant gain $\frac{1}{2}$ is combined with two single-tuned circuits, each of relative bandwidth 1 and relative gain 1, staggered so that their resonance peaks are $\pm \sqrt{3}/2$ from the band center. The resulting sensitivity function is of the form

$$\frac{K}{K_{res}} = \frac{1}{\sqrt{1 + x^6}} \tag{9-64}$$

This selectivity function has the same form as that for an optimally flat triple-tuned circuit.

9-7. The Parallel- or Twin-T Circuit.[3]

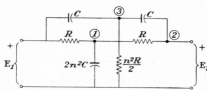

FIG. 9-11. The parallel-T circuit.

The use of RLC resonant networks for achieving band-pass amplifiers with high selectivity has been considered in some detail in the foregoing sections. Such amplifiers are not suitable for use at the low frequencies, since it is difficult to obtain high-Q coils at the low frequencies, and moreover the circuits become rather bulky at these lower frequencies. In fact, a tuned circuit which has a high Q at, say, 30 cps would be extremely difficult to build. Fortunately, a number of RC networks possess frequency-selective properties like those of resonant and band-pass filter sections. They have, as a result, found widespread application. The parallel-, or twin-T, circuit is one of this type and will be examined in some detail.

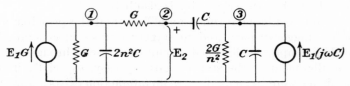

FIG. 9-12. The parallel-T circuit drawn for a junction analysis.

The form of the parallel-T circuit to be analyzed is illustrated in Fig. 9-11. While this is not the most general choice of parameter, it is a form which has received widespread use. To analyze this network, the current-source form of the network is used, and the circuit is rearranged as in Fig. 9-12. The output potential can be written in determinantal form by inspection.   It is

$$
E_2 = \frac{\begin{vmatrix} 2(G + j\omega n^2 C) & GE_1 & 0 \\ -G & 0 & -j\omega C \\ 0 & j\omega C E_1 & 2\left(\dfrac{G}{n^2} + j\omega C\right) \end{vmatrix}}{\begin{vmatrix} 2(G + j\omega n^2 C) & -G & 0 \\ -G & G + j\omega C & -j\omega C \\ 0 & -j\omega C & 2\left(\dfrac{G}{n^2} + j\omega C\right) \end{vmatrix}}
$$

(9-65)

The expansion of these determinants yields

$$
\frac{E_2}{E_1} = \frac{1 - \omega^2 n^2 R^2 C^2}{1 - \omega^2 n^2 R^2 C^2 + j2(n^2 + 1)\omega RC},
$$

(9-66)

Now define the quantity

$$
\omega_0 \equiv \frac{1}{nRC}
$$

(9-67)

and combine with the above.   This gives

$$
\frac{E_2}{E_1} = \frac{1 - (\omega/\omega_0)^2}{1 - \left(\dfrac{\omega}{\omega_0}\right)^2 + j\,\dfrac{2(n^2 + 1)}{n}\,\dfrac{\omega}{\omega_0}}
$$

which assumes the form

$$
\beta = \frac{E_2}{E_1}
$$
$$
= \frac{1}{1 + j\,\dfrac{\omega/\omega_0}{1 - (\omega/\omega_0)^2}\,\dfrac{2(n^2 + 1)}{n}}
$$

(9-68)

A plot showing the variation of β as a function of ω/ω_0 for $n = 1$ is given in Fig. 9-13.   Note that the ratios E_2/E_1 are the same for equal values ω/ω_0 and ω_0/ω.

It should be observed that at resonance $E_2 = 0$, and the network may

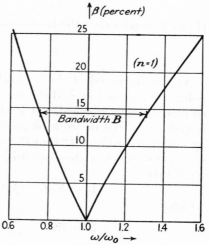

FIG. 9-13. The relation between E_2/E_1 and ω/ω_0 for the parallel-T circuit.

be terminated in any impedance Z across the terminals without any effect. However, a finite terminating Z will greatly affect the frequency-response characteristics of the network, except at the resonant value, although the general characteristics remain substantially unchanged.   For example, if the load is comparable with the network parameters, the off-resonance response is seriously affected, the selectivity is poor, and the curve is no longer symmetrical about the resonant point.

To find the bandwidth of the network, write

$$\Omega \equiv \frac{\omega}{\omega_0} - \frac{\omega}{\omega_0} \tag{9-69}$$

Equation (9-68) then becomes

$$\beta = \frac{E_2}{E_1} = \frac{1}{1 - j\frac{2}{\Omega}\frac{n^2 + 1}{n}} \tag{9-70}$$

But the bandwidth is defined by the requirement that the amplitude ratio fall by 3 db over the frequency range. This occurs when

$$\frac{2}{\Omega_b}\frac{n^2 + 1}{n} = 1$$

or

$$\Omega_b = 2\frac{n^2 + 1}{n} \tag{9-71}$$

But for $\omega \doteq \omega_0$

$$\Omega = \frac{\omega^2 - \omega_0^2}{\omega\omega_0} \doteq \frac{(\omega + \omega_0)(\omega - \omega_0)}{\omega_0^2} = 2\frac{\Delta\omega}{\omega_0}$$

Hence it is seen that the bandwidth is given by

$$B = 2\Delta\omega \doteq \frac{f_0}{Q} = \frac{\omega_0}{2\pi}\Omega_b \tag{9-72}$$

As already noted, if the network is loaded, the sharpness of the null point will be affected, and the bandwidth or the Q of the network will be correspondingly changed.   It is of importance therefore that the input impedance of the network be ascertained.   This is readily accomplished by noting from Fig. 9-12 that the total current from source E_1 is made up of two components, that toward junction 1 and that toward junction 3. Evidently

$$I_1 = E_1(G + j\omega C) \tag{9-73}$$

which is

$$I_1 = E_1\frac{1 + j\omega CR}{R}$$

so that

$$Z_1 = \frac{E_1}{I_1} = \frac{R}{1 + j\omega CR} = \frac{R}{1 + j\frac{n\omega CR}{n}} \tag{9-74}$$

At the resonant frequency $n\omega CR = 1$, and for $n = 1$

$$Z_1 = \frac{R}{1 + j1} = \frac{R}{2}(1 - j1) \tag{9-75}$$

In fact, Z_1 does not vary rapidly in the neighborhood of resonance, and this expression may be used for Z_1 for ordinary calculations. Attention is also called to fact that the network is symmetrical, so that $Z_2 = Z_1$.

For the normal circuit parameters used, the output impedance is fairly large. Consequently a load of several megohms might still constitute an appreciable load on the network. This fact will dictate both the location of the grid resistor when such a network is used in an amplifier and also the form of the amplifier circuit. Moreover, the network is inherently a rejection device, and its use in a cascade circuit with the network in either the input or the output of an amplifier will provide a rejection, or "notch," type of device. By combining the network in appropriately chosen feedback circuits, a frequency-selective band-pass amplifier may be achieved. The simplest form is sketched in Fig. 9-14. Loading of the

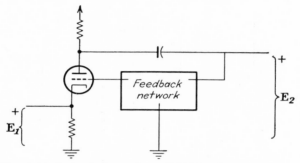

FIG. 9-14. A simple form of parallel-T band-pass amplifier.

output of the network is avoided by injecting the signal in the cathode circuit. To avoid loading of the input, more elaborate circuits must be used.

Three circuits incorporating such parallel-T networks in negative feedback amplifiers are given in Fig. 9-15.

The output response characteristics of such amplifiers are of considerable interest. Observe that in these circuits $\beta = 0$ at the resonant frequency and $\beta \neq 0$ for all other frequencies. Consequently feedback occurs at all frequencies except at the frequency ω_0 at which $\beta = 0$. Thus the circuits have maximum gain at ω_0, and, owing to the feedback, the gain falls at all other frequencies. This means that the circuit attenuates all frequencies except ω_0, so that a "band-pass" amplifier does exist.

If the nominal gain of the amplifier is K, then with feedback the form will be

$$K_f = \frac{K}{1 - \beta K} \qquad (9\text{-}76)$$

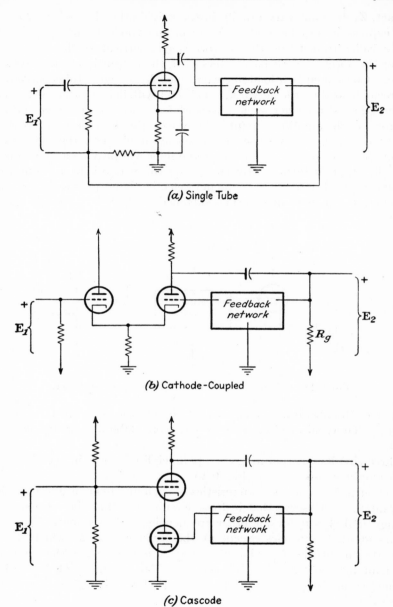

(a) Single Tube

(b) Cathode-Coupled

(c) Cascode

Fig. 9-15. Practical parallel-**T** feedback band-pass amplifiers.

Now combine this expression with Eq. (9-70).   The result is

$$K_f = \cfrac{K}{1 - K \cfrac{1}{1 - j\dfrac{2}{\Omega}\dfrac{n^2 + 1}{n}}}$$

Then

$$K_f = \frac{K\left(1 - j\dfrac{2}{\Omega}\dfrac{n^2 + 1}{n}\right)}{1 - K - j\dfrac{2}{\Omega}\dfrac{n^2 + 1}{n}} \tag{9-77}$$

from which it follows that

$$\frac{K_f}{K} = \sqrt{\frac{1 + \left(\dfrac{2}{\Omega}\dfrac{n^2 + 1}{n}\right)^2}{|1 - K|^2 + \left(\dfrac{2}{\Omega}\dfrac{n^2 + 1}{n}\right)^2}} \tag{9-78}$$

It is of interest to define the effective Q of this circuit, as a basis of comparison with an RLC circuit.   At the half-power points the gain ratio must be $1/\sqrt{2}$, whence

$$\frac{1 + \left(\dfrac{2}{\Omega_b}\dfrac{n^2 + 1}{n}\right)^2}{|1 - K|^2 + \left(\dfrac{2}{\Omega_b}\dfrac{n^2 + 1}{n}\right)^2} = \frac{1}{2}$$

Upon solving for Ω_b from this expression, there results

$$\frac{4\left(\dfrac{n^2 + 1}{n}\right)^2}{|1 - K|^2 - 2} = \Omega_b^2 \tag{9-79}$$

Ordinarily K is negative and greater than 1.   Then when $|1 - K|^2 \gg 2$,

$$\Omega_b \doteq \frac{2(n^2 + 1)/n}{|1 - K|}$$

Also, when $-K \gg 1$, which is the usual case,

$$\Omega_b \doteq \frac{2(n^2 + 1)/n}{K} \tag{9-80}$$

But by Eq. (9-72)

$$\Omega_b = \frac{1}{Q}$$

Then

$$Q = \frac{K}{2(n^2 + 1)/n} \tag{9-81}$$

The use of a pentode in a single-tube parallel-T feedback circuit will ordinarily have a nominal gain of 100 or more at audio frequencies. Consequently such an amplifier with a parallel-T loop becomes equivalent to a resonant circuit with a Q of the order of 25 or more, for $n = 1$. A triode amplifier will, because of the lower gain, give a lower effective Q. However, this may be ample for many applications. Of course the cascode circuit of Fig. 9-15c has a high gain with triodes and will yield appreciable Q values.

9-8. The Bridged-T and Wien-bridge Circuits. The parallel-T circuit discussed in the foregoing section is only one of a number of different

TABLE 9-2

FREQUENCY-SELECTIVE RC NETWORKS

1. Bridged T

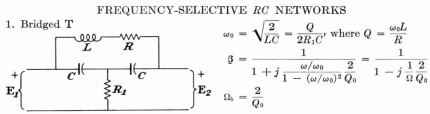

$$\omega_0 = \sqrt{\frac{2}{LC}} = \frac{Q}{2R_1C}, \text{ where } Q = \frac{\omega_0 L}{R}$$

$$\beta = \frac{1}{1 + j\dfrac{\omega/\omega_0}{1 - (\omega/\omega_0)^2}\dfrac{2}{Q_0}} = \frac{1}{1 - j\dfrac{1}{\Omega}\dfrac{2}{Q_0}}$$

$$\Omega_b = \frac{2}{Q_0}$$

2. Bridged T

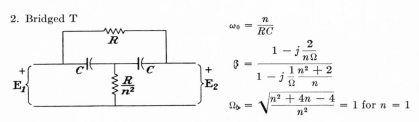

$$\omega_0 = \frac{n}{RC}$$

$$\beta = \frac{1 - j\dfrac{2}{n\Omega}}{1 - j\dfrac{1}{\Omega}\dfrac{n^2 + 2}{n}}$$

$$\Omega_b = \sqrt{\frac{n^2 + 4n - 4}{n^2}} = 1 \text{ for } n = 1$$

3. Wien bridge

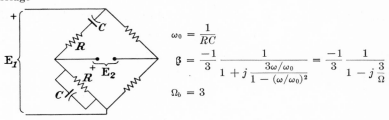

$$\omega_0 = \frac{1}{RC}$$

$$\beta = \frac{-1}{3}\frac{1}{1 + j\dfrac{3\omega/\omega_0}{1 - (\omega/\omega_0)^2}} = \frac{-1}{3}\frac{1}{1 - j\dfrac{3}{\Omega}}$$

$$\Omega_b = 3$$

RC frequency-selective networks which may be used to yield band-pass characteristics somewhat like the RLC tuned resonant circuits. Among others,[4] the bridged-T (in several forms) and the Wien-bridge networks also have the desired characteristics. The final results are tabulated without proof in Table 9-2 (see Probs. 9-24 to 9-26).

REFERENCES

1. Aiken, C. B., *Proc. IRE*, **25**, 230 (February), 672 (June) (1937).
2. Wallman, H., *MIT Radiation Lab. Rept.* 524 (Feb. 23, 1944).
   Wallman, H., *Electronics*, **21**, 100 (May, 1948).
3. Stanton, L., *Proc. IRE*, **34**, 447 (1946).
4. Massachusetts Institute of Technology, Radiation Laboratory Series, vol. 18, McGraw-Hill Book Company, Inc., New York, 1948.
5. As a general reference, consult:
   Sturley, K. R., "Radio Receiver Design," pt. I, John Wiley & Sons, Inc., New York, 1943.

PROBLEMS

9-1. A 6SJ7 pentode is used in a certain class A r-f amplifier, with $E_{bb} = 250$ volts, $E_{cc2} = 100$ volts, and $E_{cc1} = -3$ volts. At these conditions the tube parameters are approximately $g_m = 1,600$ μmhos, $r_p = 1.2 \times 10^6$ ohms. A single-tuned load consists of a 1-mh coil in parallel with a 100-$\mu\mu$f capacitor. The resonant Q of the load is 200.

a. Determine the potential gain of the stage at the resonant frequency.

b. Determine the potential gain of the stage 10 kc above and below resonance.

9-2. In a single-tuned direct-coupled amplifier stage using a 6SJ7 tube that is tuned to 1,100 kc, it is found that the bandwidth is 18 kc. Determine the Q of the circuit.

9-3. It is discussed in the text that the response of the single-tuned direct-coupled or transformer-coupled amplifier for small deviation δ and high Q is given by either Eq. (9-14) or Eq. (9-29).

a. Calculate the error in each case for $Q = 3$, δ very small.

b. Repeat for Q large, $\delta = 0.1$.

9-4. A single-tuned circuit employing a 6SK7 tube feeds a diode detector. The equivalent output circuit is illustrated. The tank is tuned to $f_0 = 1$ Mc, $L = 0.5$ mh, $Q = 60$. Assume for the 6SK7 that $r_p = 10^6$ ohms, $g_m = 2,000$ μmhos. Determine:

a. Gain at resonance.

b. Gain at resonance if detector is removed.

c. Bandwidth with and without the detector circuit.

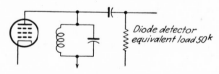

*Diode detector equivalent load 50*k

9-5. A direct-coupled single-tuned amplifier has a band width of 150 kc and a resonant shunt impedance of 50 kilohms. What must be the value of the shunting resistance across the tank if the gain is to be constant within 10 per cent over the 150-kc band?

9-6. A direct-coupled single-tuned amplifier has a bandwidth of 50 kc, when $C = 25$ $\mu\mu$f. Calculate the bandwidth if C is increased to 100 $\mu\mu$f, and:

a. If the resonant frequency is kept constant.

b. If L is maintained constant.

9-7. A single-tuned direct-coupled stage has a $Q = 100$ when tuned to 800 kc. Two equal signals are fed to the grid, one of which is 50 cps off resonance and the other of which is 5,000 cps off resonance. What will the amplitude ratio be in the output of the amplifier?

9-8. A direct-coupled single-tuned amplifier is to have a bandwidth of 200 kc at 4.7 Mc. If the total capacitance is 25 $\mu\mu f$:

a. Calculate the maximum impedance and the value of L.

b. Over what frequency band is the total phase shift through this amplifier less than 30 deg?

9-9. The circuit of a cascode band-pass amplifier (often called the Wallman circuit) is shown in the accompanying diagram. Z_1 and Z_2 are parallel resonant circuits tuned to the same resonant frequency.

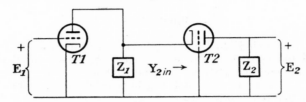

a. Find an expression for $Y_{2,\text{in}}$, assuming that g_{m2} is much larger than G_1, G_2, and $1/r_{p2}$, where G_1 and G_2 are the shunt conductances of the tuned circuits at resonance.

b. Subject to these same conditions, find an expression for the over-all gain of the amplifier, and show that it is the same as that of a single grounded-cathode stage with a parallel resonant interstage network [Eq. (9-13)].

The advantage of such a cascode amplifier over that of a single-stage circuit utilizing a pentode is that it provides the low noise level of a triode with the operating characteristics of a pentode. Triodes may be used because the Miller effects are negligible owing to the very low potential gain of the first stage. Also, the cathode lead inductance in the second tube is unimportant because of the low impedance level.

9-10. Repeat Prob. 9-8 for the transformer-coupled single-tuned amplifier, for optimum coupling.

9-11. A double-tuned circuit with $C = 12$ $\mu\mu f$ has a bandwidth of 1 Mc at 10 Mc for the critically coupled stage. Determine the value of L and Q if both primary and secondary windings are identical.

9-12. A single-stage double-tuned amplifier using a 6SK7 tube is critically coupled. It operates at 455 kc and has a bandwidth of 12 kc. The total primary C and total secondary C are each 26 $\mu\mu f$. The coils and loading are the same.

a. Calculate the values of shunt resistance of each circuit, L and M.

b. Calculate the mid-frequency gain. Choose $g_m = 1,500$ μmhos.

c. If the resonant frequency and the bandwidth are maintained constant, calculate the mid-frequency gain as C is varied from 10 to 100 $\mu\mu f$.

9-13. A 6SK7 double-tuned circuit comprises two identical 200-μh coils, with $Q = 80$, which are tuned to 500 kc.

a. Calculate the critical coefficient of coupling.

b. Calculate and plot the gain of the stage as the mutual inductance is varied from zero to twice the critical value.

9-14. Determine the proper design for the winding of an i-f transformer with $L_1 = L_2$ and each winding tuned to resonance by a capacitance of 100 $\mu\mu f$. The secondary potential is not to fall below 0.88 of the peak value in a 10-kc band, centered at 465 kc. Find k, L_1, L_2, Q_1, Q_2 and the secondary potential, with 1 volt, 465 kc to the primary. Assume critical coupling.

9-15. A 6SJ7 is used in a double-tuned circuit which feeds a diode detector and automatic-gain-control circuit. The significant portion of the circuit is shown. The rms potential across the secondary feeding the detector–automatic-gain-control circuits must be 10 volts.

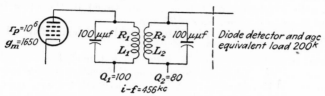

a. What is the coefficient of coupling?

b. What is the value of e_g to give the required output?

9-16. The i-f amplifier section in a radar receiver consists of four identical stages, each of the form illustrated. The maximum over-all gain of the four stages is 10,000, and the gain at 28.5 and 31.5 Mc is 7,070. 6AC7 tubes are used, with $g_m = 9,000$ μmhos, $C_i = 11$ $\mu\mu$f, $C_o = 5$ $\mu\mu$f.

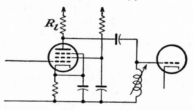

a. Calculate the value of the plate-load resistance.

b. Calculate the wiring capacitance.

c. Calculate the value of the inductance of the coil.

9-17. A six-stage single-tuned i-f amplifier using 6AC7 tubes has a maximum over-all gain of 4,100 and an over-all bandwidth of 6.0 Mc. If the over-all gain had to be obtained from four stages instead of six stages, what would have been the bandwidth?

9-18. A six-stage single-tuned amplifier using 6AC7 tubes has a maximum over-all gain of 530,000 and an over-all bandwidth of 2 Mc.

a. If it is found that the over-all bandwidth need not be greater than 1.5 Mc, what would be the corresponding over-all gain by an appropriate change in the value of the effective shunt resistance of each stage?

b. If the original over-all gain of 530,000 had been obtained from four stages instead of six, calculate the over-all bandwidth that would result.

9-19. Suppose that three identical stages having the characteristics of Prob. 9-2 are connected in cascade. Calculate and plot a curve of relative gain in decibels vs. frequency. Carry out the calculations to frequencies at which the gain is down at least 75 db below the optimum value.

9-20. A three-stage direct-coupled single-tuned amplifier is used in a broadcast receiver. A three-ganged 165-$\mu\mu$f capacitor is used to tune the receiver over the range from 550 to 1,650 kc. The loading is chosen to give a minimum bandwidth of 10 kc.

a. Determine the variation of bandwidth as the receiver is tuned over the entire range, assuming that Q remains constant.

b. Repeat for the case where C is fixed at 100 $\mu\mu f$ and L is varied.

9-21. Refer to a tube manual, and prepare a table of the *merit* of the following tubes: 6AB7, 6AC7, 6AG7, 6AK5, 6C5, 6K7, 6L6, 6SF5, 6SJ7, 6SK7, 6V6, 6Y6.

9-22. A two-stage direct-coupled single-tuned amplifier using 6AC7 tubes operates at 60 Mc and is to have a 2-Mc bandwidth.

a. What gain is possible if both stages are tuned to the same frequency? Assume that the shunt capacitance is 25 $\mu\mu f$.

b. If the stages are to be stagger-tuned to be critically flat, what gain is possible?

9-23. Show that, by choosing the three single-tuned stages in the manner discussed in the text to yield a staggered triple, the relative response function has the form given by Eq. (9-62). Sketch the individual response characteristics and that of the resultant staggered triple.

9-24. Analyze the bridged-T network, given as circuit 1 in Table 9-2, in the manner of Sec. 9-7. Verify the data given in Table 9-2 for this network.

9-25. Repeat Prob. 9-24 for the bridged-T network, given as circuit 2 in Table 9-2.

9-26. Repeat Prob. 9-24 for the Wien-bridge network, given as circuit 3 in Table 9-2.

9-27. The network shown is used in a simple potential-feedback circuit.

a. Calculate the transfer function β of the network, when $R_1C_1 = R_2C_2$.

b. Calculate and plot on a decibels vs. log f scale the relative gain of the amplifier.

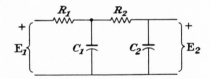

9-28. Repeat Prob. 9-27 for the network shown.

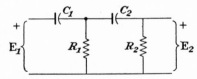

9-29. The two amplifiers of Probs. 9-27 and 9-28 are connected in cascade. Calculate and plot the gain of the resulting two-stage band-pass amplifier.

CHAPTER 10

TUNED POWER AMPLIFIERS

10-1. Introduction. In common with the operation of the classes of tube circuits being studied, it is the function of an r-f power amplifier to convert d-c power from the power supply into r-f power. Owing to the amounts of power that may be involved, it is essential that this conversion be effected at the highest possible efficiency. Essentially, therefore, the power amplifier may be regarded as a power converter, as contrasted with the r-f and i-f potential amplifiers that are used to raise a potential level. The settings of the r-f power amplifier are chosen to ensure a high conversion efficiency.

The basic circuit of a tuned power amplifier is substantially that of the single-tuned direct-coupled type discussed in Sec. 9-1. The essential differences are in the magnitude of the grid-bias supply potential E_{cc}, the corresponding value of the grid input signal e_g, and the amount of power involved. A schematic diagram of a tuned power amplifier is given in Fig. 10-1.

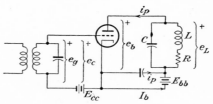

Fig. 10-1. Schematic diagram of a tuned power amplifier.

Owing to the negative bias on the tube, which is adjusted approximately to plate-current cutoff in the class B amplifier and which is adjusted beyond plate-current cutoff in the class C amplifier, harmonic currents are generated in the plate which are comparable in amplitude with the fundamental component. However, if the Q of the tuned plate circuit has a value of 10 or more, the impedance of the tank circuit to the second or higher harmonics will be very low. As a result, the higher-harmonic potentials across the tank will be very small compared with the fundamental potential. That is, the effect of the harmonic generation in the tube plate current is largely suppressed by the tuned plate load.

But the requirement that the Q of the tank circuit must be high in order to suppress harmonics in the output imposes a limitation on the frequency-response characteristics of the amplifier, since then the gain is constant only over a very narrow band of frequencies. Consequently such amplifiers are confined in their operation to narrow frequency bands.

241

In fact, as will be discussed in some detail, the class B amplifier may be used to amplify a narrow band of frequencies of differing amplitudes, whereas the class C amplifier is confined to a narrow band of frequencies of constant amplitudes. Despite these severe restrictions, both classes of amplifier are extensively used in restricted applications, the class B amplifier to amplify an a-m r-f carrier wave, the class C amplifier as a frequency multiplier or as a source for the production of an a-m carrier wave.

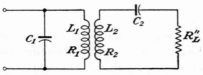

FIG. 10-2. A typical tuned-amplifier tank circuit.

10-2. Properties of the Tank Circuit. The tuned plate load in the diagram of Fig. 10-1 is drawn as a simple parallel resonant circuit. Ordinarily the load is coupled inductively to the plate tank, and a more typical coupling network is that shown in Fig. 10-2. The capacitor C_2 is assumed to be so adjusted that $1/2\pi \sqrt{L_2 C_2}$, the resonant frequency of the secondary circuit, is equal to the operating frequency of the amplifier. Because of the resonance in the secondary circuit, only a resistive component $R'_L = \omega M^2/(R''_L + R_2)$ is reflected into the primary of the tuned circuit. The equivalent circuit then becomes that shown in Fig. 10-3.

If the characteristics of the tank circuit were ideal, the impedance at resonance would be resistive and equal to the shunt resistance R_0 of

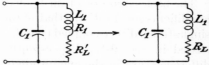

FIG. 10-3. The equivalent circuits of Fig. 10-2.

the resulting network. The impedance would be zero at any of the harmonic frequencies. That is, the impedance would be

$$\begin{aligned} \mathbf{Z}(\omega_0) &= R_0 \\ \mathbf{Z}(n\omega_0) &= 0 \qquad n = 2, 3, 4, \ldots \end{aligned} \qquad (10\text{-}1)$$

These ideal conditions do not prevail in practice, although it is possible to achieve relatively low impedance for $Z(n\omega_0)$. To examine this, refer to Eq. (9-6) for the impedance function of the simple tuned circuit,

$$\mathbf{Z} = R_L Q^2 \frac{1 + \delta - j(1/Q)}{1 + \delta + jQ\delta(2 + \delta)} \qquad (10\text{-}2)$$

At resonance $\omega = \omega_0$, and $\delta = 0$. Equation (10-2) reduces to

$$\mathbf{Z}(\omega_0) = R_L Q^2 \left(1 - j\frac{1}{Q}\right) = R_L Q^2 \sqrt{1 + \frac{1}{Q^2}} \big/\tan^{-1}\frac{1}{Q}$$

Note, however, that if $Q = 10$, then

$$\mathbf{Z}(\omega_0) = R_L Q^2 \times 1.005 /\underline{-5.7°}$$

which shows that the impedance of the tank circuit is essentially resistive and is given by

$$\mathbf{Z}(\omega_0) = R_0 \doteq R_L Q^2 \tag{10-3}$$

Under these conditions it follows that

$$R_0 = R_L Q^2 = \omega_0 L_1 Q = \frac{L_1}{R_L C_1} = Q \sqrt{\frac{L_1}{C_1}} \tag{10-4}$$

Now consider the situation at the second-harmonic frequency. When $\omega = 2\omega_0$, $\delta = 1$ and Eq. (10-2) reduces to

$$\mathbf{Z}(2\omega_0) = R_L Q^2 \frac{1 - j\dfrac{1}{2Q}}{1 + j1.5Q} = R_L Q^2 \frac{0.25 - j\left(\dfrac{1}{2Q} + 1.5Q\right)}{1 + 2.25Q^2} \tag{10-5}$$

For $Q = 10$ this reduces to

$$\mathbf{Z}(2\omega_0) \doteq R_L Q^2 \frac{1}{j1.5Q} = -j\frac{1}{1.5}\sqrt{\frac{L_1}{C_1}} \tag{10-6}$$

The ratio of the second harmonic to the fundamental-frequency impedance is then

$$\frac{Z(2\omega_0)}{Z(\omega_0)} = \frac{R_L Q^2(1/1.5Q)}{R_L Q^2} = \frac{1}{1.5Q}$$

In fact, under the extreme conditions when $I_{p2} = I_{p1}$, the relative power ratio is

$$\frac{P_{L1}}{P_{L2}} = \frac{I_{p1}^2 \text{ Re } Z(\omega_0)}{I_{p2}^2 \text{ Re } Z(2\omega_0)} = \frac{R_L Q^2 I_{p1}^2}{R_L Q^2 I_{p2}^2/4(1 + 2.25Q^2)} = 4(1 + 2.25Q^2)$$

where Re denotes "the real part of." With $Q = 10$, this reduces to

$$\frac{P_{L1}}{P_{L2}} = 900$$

Clearly, therefore, the second-harmonic power is negligible under these conditions.

Obviously, there will be losses in the tank circuit owing to the resistive component of the coils, and perhaps the capacitor. The power delivered to the load is

$$P_L'' = (QI_{p1})^2 \frac{\omega^2 M^2}{R_L'' + R_2} \frac{R_L''}{R_L'' + R_2} \tag{10-7}$$

and the power lost in the tank circuit is

$$P_L = (QI_{p1})^2 \left(R_1 + \frac{\omega^2 M^2}{R_L'' + R_2} \frac{R_2}{R_L'' + R_2}\right) \tag{10-8}$$

The circuit transfer efficiency, which is defined as the ratio of the power delivered to the load to that supplied to the tank circuit, is given by

$$\eta = \frac{P_L''}{P_L'' + P_T} \times 100\% = \frac{P_L' - P_T}{P_L'} \times 100\% \quad (10\text{-}9)$$

An interesting and informative form for the circuit transfer efficiency is possible by writing it as follows:

$$\eta = \eta_1 \eta_2 = \frac{\text{power delivered to secondary}}{\text{power delivered to primary}} \times \frac{\text{power delivered to load}}{\text{power delivered to secondary}}$$

where η_1 is associated with the first ratio and η_2 is associated with the second ratio. These may be written as

$$\eta_1 = \frac{I_1^2 R_L'}{I_1^2 (R_1 + R_L')} = \frac{R_L'}{R_1 + R_L'}$$

Similarly

$$\eta_2 = \frac{I_2^2 R_L''}{I_2^2 (R_2 + R_L'')} = \frac{R_L''}{R_2 + R_L''}$$

The expression for η_1 may be written in the following forms:

$$\eta_1 = \frac{\omega_0 L_1 / R_1 - \omega_0 L_1 / (R_L' + R_1)}{\omega_0 L_1 / R_1} = \frac{Q_{01} - Q_{01L}}{Q_{01}} = 1 - \frac{Q_{01L}}{Q_{01}} \quad (10\text{-}10a)$$

where $Q_{01} = \omega_0 L_1 / R_1$ is the unloaded Q of the primary coil at resonance
$Q_{01L} = \omega_0 L_1 / (R_L' + R_1)$ is the loaded Q of the primary circuit at resonance, including the reflected resistance of the secondary in the primary circuit

In an entirely similar way, the expression for η_2 may be written in the form

$$\eta_2 = 1 - \frac{Q_{02L}}{Q_{02}} \quad (10\text{-}10b)$$

where $Q_{02} = \omega_0 L_2 / R_2$ is the unloaded Q of the secondary coil at resonance
$Q_{02L} = \omega_0 L_2 / (R_2 + R_L'')$ is the loaded Q of the secondary coil at resonance but without any effect of the primary circuit on the secondary

The complete expression for the circuit transfer efficiency becomes

$$\eta = \left(1 - \frac{Q_{01L}}{Q_{01}} \right) \left(1 - \frac{Q_{02L}}{Q_{02}} \right) \quad (10\text{-}11)$$

For high circuit transfer efficiency, the loaded values Q_{01L} and Q_{02L} must be low, and the unloaded values Q_{01} and Q_{02} should be high. Ordinarily the loaded Q's must be 10 or greater in order to provide for a low harmonic content in the output. The unloaded Q's are subject to purely practical limitations; the possible values depend on the power output, the character of construction of the coil, and the frequency of operation.

Typical values for coils of conventional design vary somewhat as follows for frequencies in the range from 500 to 1,500 kc:

Unloaded $Q \sim 100$–200 for low-power coils

~ 500–800 for high-power coils

10-3. Choice of Q_L. It is of some interest to examine the factors which influence the choice of Q_L. Several of the factors have already been considered, but for completeness these will also be included in the tabulation below. The following conditions prevail for *low* Q_L:

1. High circuit transfer efficiency η.
2. Broader bandwidth.
3. Higher harmonic components.
4. Greater L/C ratio.

Factor 1 has been considered in considerable detail in Sec. 10-2. Factor 2 relates to the width of the pass band. This must be adequate to pass the desired frequency band but must attenuate the frequencies outside the specified band. A measure of the response is obtained from Eq. (10-2), which becomes, for frequencies near resonance

$$\frac{Z(\omega)}{Z(\omega_0)} = \frac{1}{(\omega Q/\omega_0)[1 - (\omega_0/\omega)^2]} \tag{10-12}$$

Factor 3 was discussed in some detail in Sec. 10-2, where it was shown that the harmonic output is small if Q_L is fairly high. When Q_L is low, the harmonic output is not negligible and might result in troublesome harmonic potentials in the circuit.

Factor 4 is examined through Eq. (10-4) for the lowest Q_L for a specified R_0; this demands that the L/C ratio must be high. The highest L/C ratio exists when C is a minimum, which, in the extreme, is the tube plus stray wiring capacitances. If a capacitor is used, it should be relatively small, in parallel with a large inductor. In any design considerations Q_L is established by the allowable harmonic content and by power considerations. Normally, as already discussed, Q_L will range from 10 to 20. The unloaded Q_u is determined by requiring that the circuit transfer efficiency should be high, perhaps 90 per cent, at the lower powers and should be higher for high powers. With Q_L and Q_u known, the circuit constants can be determined.

Example. Evaluate the approximate circuit constants of a tank circuit which is to deliver 500 watts to a 72-ohm load at 2 Mc from an a-c supply of 2,000 volts.

Solution. Choose $Q_L = 12$; $\eta = 90$ per cent. Also given, $R_L'' = 72$ ohms, $P_L'' = 500$ watts.

a. Power input

$$P_1 = \frac{500}{0.9} = 556 \text{ watts}$$

b. From expression (10-11)

$$Q_u = \frac{Q_L}{0.1} = 120$$

c. Since

$$Q_L = \frac{\omega_0 L_1}{R_L} = \frac{\omega_0 L_1 I_1 I_1}{I_1^2 R_L} = \frac{E I_1}{I_1^2 R_L}$$

then

$$I_1 = \frac{12 \times 556}{2,000} = 3.33 \text{ amp}$$

Also

$$L \doteq \frac{E}{\omega I_1} = \frac{2,000}{2 \times 2 \times 10^6 \times 3.33} = 47.8 \times 10^{-6} \text{ henry}$$

$$C = \frac{I_1}{\omega E} = \frac{3.33}{2 \times 2 \times 10^6 \times 2,000} = 132.4 \times 10^{-12} \text{ farad}$$

d. To find M, note that

$$M I_1 \doteq I_2 R_L'' \qquad P = I_2^2 R_L''$$

Hence

$$M \doteq \frac{I_2 R_L''}{I_1 \omega} = \frac{\sqrt{P R_L''}}{I_1 \omega}$$

$$= \frac{\sqrt{500 \times 72}}{3.33 \times 2 \times 2 \times 10^6} = 4.53 \times 10^{-6} \text{ henry}$$

e. Current I_{p1}

$$I_{p1} = \frac{556}{2,000} = 0.277 \text{ amp}$$

f. Loaded R_0

$$\text{Loaded } R_0 = \frac{2,000}{0.277} = 7,220 \text{ ohms}$$

g. Unloaded R_0

$$\text{Unloaded } R_0 = {}^{120}\!/_{12} \times 7,220 = 72,200 \text{ ohms}$$

10-4. Class B Tuned Amplifiers. Considerations regarding the actual choice of tube will be given in Sec. 10-16. Transmitters may employ high- or low-impedance triodes, tetrodes, or pentodes. It will be found that the plate-circuit efficiency, i.e., the ability of the tube to convert d-c power from the supply into a-c power, is not particularly dependent on the type of tube that is used. This fact will become clearer in the light of subsequent discussions.

Under class B operation, the grid-bias supply potential E_{cc} in Fig. 10-1 is made negative by an amount sufficient to reduce the plate current to zero for zero signal potential e_g. If the dynamic characteristic of the amplifier is linear over the range of operation, then for sinusoidal input signal potential the current will consist of half-wave rectified pulses.

The construction for deducing the output waveshape is sketched in Fig. 10-4.

It is important that it be recognized that Fig. 10-4 represents an idealized picture which depends upon a linear dynamic curve. This is not completely true, although, in the analysis to follow, it will be assumed that the linear relation does apply. If the dynamic curve is not linear, then a graphical solution must be used in order to determine the shape of the plate-current curve and the linear class B analysis is not valid.

To find the operating path of an amplifier with a tuned load, a special construction is required, since the conditions are different from those of an amplifier with a pure resistance load. This is so because of the interrelation of a number of factors and the different manner of operation of the circuit. Among the important factors that must be considered are

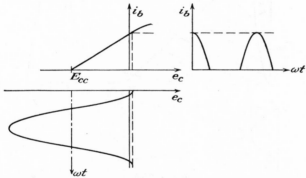

FIG. 10-4. The output waveshape from a class B stage, with a linear dynamic curve.

the allowable plate dissipation of the tube, the Q of the circuit, the effective shunt resistance of the tank circuit, the grid driving potential, the shape of the plate-current wave, and the corresponding harmonic components in the plate current. Ordinarily a method of successive approximations is necessary in which a given set of conditions is assumed and a calculation is made. If a consistent solution is not found, a second trial must be made. This procedure must be continued until a consistent solution is found.

Although the determination of the operating path is not essential for the linear analytical solution to follow, the method will be discussed here, since it will permit a check on the validity of the linear assumptions. Moreover, it is a general method and will also be used later in the discussion of the tuned class C amplifier. The details of the construction are illustrated in Fig. 10-5.

To find the operating path, it is assumed that the plate-potential swing is sinusoidal when the grid input signal is sinusoidal. Also, as a starting point, it is assumed that $e_{b,\,min}$ is approximately 10 per cent of E_{bb}. The value of $e_{c,\,max}$ must not be allowed to reach an instantaneous positive potential that is higher than the plate potential $e_{b,\,min}$; otherwise the current to the grid will increase very rapidly. This may cause serious damage to the tube. Even if no damage results, the increasing grid current is accompanied by a decreasing plate current, and in consequence the analysis will no longer be valid owing to the resulting nonlinearity of the dynamic curve. With the indicated choice of conditions, the analysis can be completed, and a calculation can be made of the following: the d-c power from the plate-supply source, the a-c power output to the load,

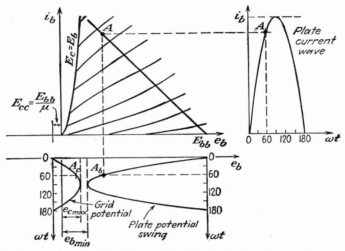

Fig. 10-5. The construction for determining the plate-current waveshape graphically from the plate characteristics.

and the plate dissipation. If the plate dissipation is within the rating of the tube, then the resulting calculations will indicate the adjustments of the circuit parameters that are necessary to achieve the indicated results.

The specific procedure is the following (refer to Fig. 10-5): Select any particular instantaneous grid potential e_c, such as that corresponding to the point A_c. Determine the corresponding instantaneous plate potential e_b by locating the point A_b at the same phase angle in the operating cycle. By projecting A_b up to its intersection with the curve for the selected grid potential, the point A on the operating path will be located. Other points are determined in a similar manner. For class B operation, the operating path should be approximately linear and should intersect the plate-potential axis at E_{bb}, approximately.

To determine the shape of the plate-current pulse as a function of the phase angle, the current corresponding to each point A on the operating path is plotted as a function of the appropriate phase angle.　The corresponding plate-current pulse is plotted in Fig. 10-5 as $(i_b, \omega t)$.　The curves of Fig. 10-6 illustrate the important waveshapes of the amplifier.

10-5. Analytic Solution of Tuned Class B Amplifier.[1]　An analytic solution of the tuned class B amplifier is based on finding an analytic form for the tube characteristics. From Eq. (2-14), the general relationship between the plate current and the plate and grid potentials is of the form

$$i_b = k \left(e_c + \frac{e_b}{\mu} \right)^\alpha \qquad e_c + \frac{e_b}{\mu} > 0$$

Actually, it is found that for power triodes over a wide range of parameters the plate current is of the form

$$i_b = k \left(e_c + \frac{e_b}{\mu} \right)$$

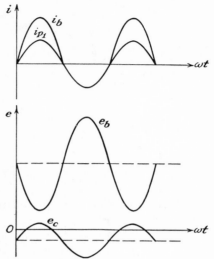

FIG. 10-6. The important waveshapes in a class B tuned amplifier.

which may be written in the more complete form

$$i_b = g_m \left(e_c + \frac{e_b}{\mu} \right) \tag{10-13}$$

This is, of course, simply the first term in the Taylor expansion for the current.

The instantaneous potentials are of the form

$$\begin{aligned} e_c &= E_{cc} + E_{gm} \cos \omega t \\ e_b &= E_{bb} - E_{p1m} \cos \omega t \end{aligned} \tag{10-14}$$

But since the current is zero when the grid signal is zero, then, for $i_b = 0$,

$$e_c + \frac{e_b}{\mu} = 0$$

which requires that

$$E_{cc} + \frac{E_{bb}}{\mu} = 0$$

or, for cutoff,

$$E_{cc} = - \frac{E_{bb}}{\mu} \tag{10-15}$$

By combining Eqs. (10-13) and (10-14), the expression for plate current becomes

$$i_b = g_m \left(E_{cc} + E_{gm} \cos \omega t + \frac{E_{bb}}{\mu} - \frac{E_{p1m}}{\mu} \cos \omega t \right)$$

$$= g_m \left(E_{gm} \cos \omega t - \frac{E_{p1m}}{\mu} \cos \omega t \right)$$

$$= g_m \left(E_{gm} - \frac{E_{p1m}}{\mu} \right) \cos \omega t \qquad (10\text{-}16)$$

which is written in the form

$$i_b = I_{bm} \cos \omega t \qquad -\frac{\pi}{2} < \omega t < \frac{\pi}{2}$$

$$i_b = 0 \qquad \frac{\pi}{2} < \omega t < \frac{3\pi}{2} \qquad (10\text{-}17)$$

where

$$I_{bm} = g_m \left(E_{gm} - \frac{E_{p1m}}{\mu} \right)$$

The average value of the plate current is

$$I_b = \frac{1}{2\pi} \int_0^{2\pi} i_b \, d(\omega t) \qquad (10\text{-}18)$$

or

$$I_b = \frac{2}{2\pi} \int_0^{\pi/2} I_{bm} \cos \omega t \, d(\omega t) = \frac{I_{bm}}{\pi} \qquad (10\text{-}19)$$

Also, by Fourier analysis, the amplitude of the fundamental component of the plate current is

$$I_{p1m} = \frac{1}{\pi} \int_0^{2\pi} i_b \cos \omega t \, d(\omega t) \qquad (10\text{-}20)$$

or

$$I_{p1m} = \frac{2}{\pi} \int_0^{\pi/2} I_{bm} \cos^2 \omega t \, d(\omega t) = \frac{I_{bm}}{2} \qquad (10\text{-}21)$$

But at resonance $\mathbf{Z}(\omega_0) = R_0$ is resistive, and the fundamental-frequency potential difference across the load is

$$E_{p1m} = I_{p1m} R_0 \qquad (10\text{-}22)$$

Combining Eq. (10-22) with (10-21) and (10-17),

$$E_{p1m} = \frac{R_0 I_{bm}}{2} = \frac{R_0}{2} g_m \left(E_{gm} - \frac{E_{p1m}}{\mu} \right)$$

It follows from this that

$$E_{p1m} + \frac{R_0}{2} g_m \frac{E_{p1m}}{\mu} = \frac{R_0}{2} g_m E_{gm}$$

or

$$E_{p1m} = R_0 \frac{\mu E_{gm}}{R_0 + 2r_p} \tag{10-23}$$

which yields, for the rms value of the fundamental-frequency component of current, the expression

$$\mathbf{I}_{p1} = \frac{\mu \mathbf{E}_g}{2r_p + R_0} \tag{10-24}$$

Also, from Eqs. (10-21) and (10-24),

$$I_b = \frac{I_{bm}}{\pi} = \frac{2\sqrt{2}\, I_{p1}}{\pi} = \frac{2\sqrt{2}}{\pi} \frac{\mu E_g}{2r_p + R_0} \tag{10-25}$$

The gain of the amplifier is given in Eq. (10-23) and is

$$\mathbf{K} = -\frac{\mu R_0}{2r_p + R_0} \tag{10-26}$$

The d-c power input to the plate circuit, which is equal to the average power furnished by the plate supply when the d-c power dissipated in the plate load resistance is negligible, is given by

$$P_{bb} = \frac{1}{2\pi} \int_0^{2\pi} E_{bb} i_b \, d(\omega t)$$

This becomes

$$P_{bb} = E_{bb} \frac{1}{2\pi} \int_0^{2\pi} i_b \, d(\omega t) = E_{bb} I_b \tag{10-27}$$

The a-c power output of importance is that at the fundamental frequency and is given by

$$P_L = \frac{1}{2\pi} \int_0^{2\pi} e_L i_p \, d(\omega t)$$

which becomes

$$P_L = \frac{1}{2\pi} \int_0^{2\pi} E_{p1m} \cos \omega t \, I_{p1m} \cos \omega t \, d(\omega t)$$
$$P_L = E_{p1} I_{p1} = I_{p1}^2 R_0 \tag{10-28}$$

The plate-circuit efficiency, which is the ratio of P_{ac} to P_{bb}, is

$$\eta_p = \frac{P_L}{P_{bb}} \times 100\% = \frac{E_{p1} I_{p1}}{E_{bb} I_b} \times 100\%$$
$$\eta_p = \frac{E_{p1} I_{p1}}{E_{bb}(2\sqrt{2}/\pi) I_{p1}} = \frac{\pi}{2\sqrt{2}} \frac{E_{p1}}{E_{bb}} = \frac{\pi}{4} \frac{E_{p1m}}{E_{bb}}$$
$$\eta_p = 78.5 \times \frac{E_{p1m}}{E_{bb}} \quad \% \tag{10-29}$$

The plate dissipation is given by

$$P_p = \frac{1}{2\pi} \int_0^{2\pi} e_b i_b \, d(\omega t)$$

or

$$P_p = \frac{1}{2\pi} \int_0^{2\pi} (E_{bb} - e_L) i_b \, d(\omega t) = E_{bb} I_b - P_L \qquad (10\text{-}30)$$

which becomes, by virtue of Eqs. (10-27) to (10-29),

$$P_p = (1 - \eta_p) P_{bb} \qquad (10\text{-}31)$$

It is of some interest to calculate the results corresponding to the optimum conditions $e_{c,\max} = e_{b,\min}$. For this condition

$$\begin{aligned} e_{c,\max} &= E_{cc} + E_{gm} \\ e_{b,\min} &= E_{bb} - E_{p1m} \end{aligned} \qquad (10\text{-}32)$$

from which

$$E_{gm} + E_{p1m} = E_{bb} - E_{cc}$$

By Eqs. (10-14) and (10-23), this yields

$$E_{gm} + E_{gm} \frac{\mu R_0}{2r_p + R_0} = E_{bb} + \frac{E_{bb}}{\mu}$$

or

$$E_{gm} = E_{bb} \frac{\mu + 1}{\mu} \frac{2r_p + R_0}{2r_p + (\mu + 1)R_0} \qquad (10\text{-}33)$$

The corresponding expressions for the fundamental-frequency component and the d-c components of current are, respectively,

$$I_{p1} = \frac{E_{bb}(\mu + 1)}{\sqrt{2}} \frac{1}{2r_p + (\mu + 1)R_0} \qquad (10\text{-}34)$$

and

$$I_b = \frac{2}{\pi} E_{bb}(\mu + 1) \frac{1}{2r_p + (\mu + 1)R_0} \qquad (10\text{-}35)$$

The corresponding values of the optimum P_{bb}, P_{ac}, and η_p are readily calculated from these expressions for I_{p1} and I_b. The expression for the plate-circuit efficiency is found to be

$$\eta_p = \frac{I_{p1}^2 R_0}{E_{bb} I_b} = \frac{\left[\dfrac{E_{bb}(\mu + 1)}{\sqrt{2}} \dfrac{1}{2r_p + (\mu + 1)R_0} \right]^2 R_0}{\dfrac{2}{\pi} E_{bb}^2 (\mu + 1) \dfrac{1}{2r_p + (\mu + 1)R_0}}$$

which reduces to

$$\eta_p = 78.5 \times \frac{R_0(\mu + 1)}{2r_p + R_0(\mu + 1)} \qquad \% \qquad (10\text{-}36)$$

Ordinarily the plate dissipation will be a fixed rating of the amplifier and is the limiting factor on the output power. The appropriate value of R_0 is then specified, since all aspects of the circuit may be expressed in terms of it. To examine this, note that

$$P_p = E_{bb}I_b - I_{p1}^2 R_0$$

which may be written as

$$P_p = E_{bb}^2 \frac{2}{\pi} (\mu + 1) \frac{1}{2r_p + (\mu + 1)R_0} - R_0 \left[\frac{E_{bb}}{\sqrt{2}} (\mu + 1) \frac{1}{2r_p + (\mu + 1)R_0} \right]^2$$

This expression may be rearranged and yields the following quadratic expression for R_0, from which R_0 may be evaluated:

$$R_0^2 + \left[\frac{4r_p}{\mu + 1} - \frac{E_{bb}^2}{P_p} \left(\frac{2}{\pi} - \frac{1}{2} \right) \right] R_0 + \left[\frac{4r_p^2}{(\mu + 1)^2} - \frac{E_{bb}^2}{P_p} \frac{4r_p}{(\mu + 1)\pi} \right] = 0 \quad (10\text{-}37)$$

10-6. Analysis of Class C Amplifiers. An analysis of the operation of the tuned class C amplifier can be made on the basis of the assumption of a linear tube characteristic, essentially as an extension of the method of Sec. 10-4.[2] This analysis is considerably complicated by the fact that E_{cc} is no longer the single value chosen to yield a zero current for zero excitation but is now a parameter. Moreover, it is no longer valid to assume that the operating characteristic is linear. Hence, although such a linear-tube-characteristic analysis is possible, it is a poor approximation. It does have the advantage over other methods of giving an explicit solution for the optimum operating conditions. Owing to its approximate nature, other methods are preferred.

To see that the operating path is not linear, the construction of Fig. 10-5 is again employed. The only differences that exist arise because the grid bias E_{cc} is adjusted beyond the cutoff value. With such values of E_{cc} and with the appropriately increased value of grid driving potential, the results have the form illustrated in Fig. 10-7. The curves of Fig. 10-8 illustrate the important waveshapes in such an amplifier.

A comparison of these curves with those of Fig. 10-6 indicates that in the class C amplifier the plate current consists of pulses the duration of which is less than 180 deg of the cycle. Also, it is not possible, in general, to derive easily an analytic expression for the shape of the plate-current pulse.

Some progress can be made in finding an approximate analytical solution if the curves of Fig. 10-7 are idealized. The idealization made is in the assumption of linear curves, as illustrated in Fig. 10-9. This approximation permits the operating path to be represented by two straight-line segments. It is now possible to write an expression for the plate-current

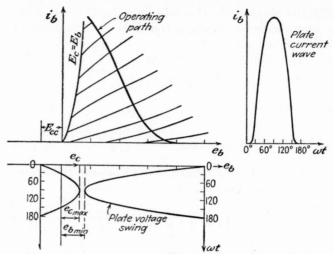

FIG. 10-7. The construction for determining the plate-current pulses in a class C amplifier.

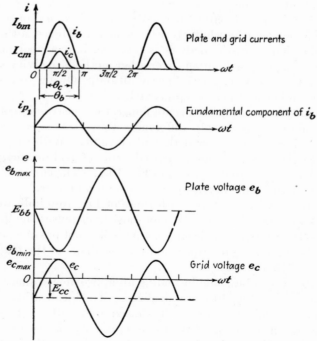

FIG. 10-8. The waveshapes at various points in the tuned amplifier.

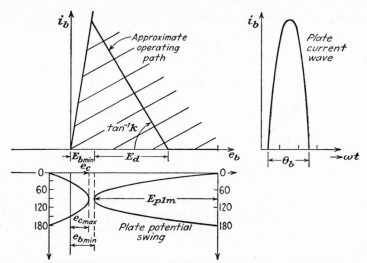

FIG. 10-9. The conditions in an idealized class C amplifier.

pulse.   This is given by the relation

$$i_b = k[E_{p1m} \cos \omega t - (E_{p1m} - E_d)] \qquad \text{for } i_b > 0 \qquad (10\text{-}38)$$

where, by definition, for the condition of zero current

$$\frac{\theta_b}{2} = \omega t_b = \cos^{-1} \frac{E_{p1m} - E_d}{E_{p1m}} = \cos^{-1}\left(1 - \frac{E_d}{E_{p1m}}\right) \qquad (10\text{-}39)$$

Note that the maximum tube current is given by

$$I_{b,\max} = kE_d \qquad (10\text{-}40)$$

With the shape of the current pulse known, it is possible to compute plate-circuit information.   The average value of the plate-current pulse is

$$I_b = \frac{1}{2\pi} \int_0^{2\pi} i_b \, d(\omega t)$$

which is given by the relation

$$I_b = \frac{k}{\pi} \int_0^{\theta_b/2} [E_{p1m} \cos \omega t - (E_{p1m} - E_d)] \, d(\omega t)$$

This integrates to the value

$$I_b = \frac{k}{\pi}\left[E_{p1m} \sin \frac{\theta_b}{2} - (E_{p1m} - E_d) \frac{\theta_b}{2} \right] \qquad (10\text{-}41)$$

Similarly, the amplitude of the fundamental component is given by the integral

$$I_{p1m} = \frac{1}{\pi} \int_0^{2\pi} i_b \cos \omega t \, d(\omega t)$$

which may be written in the form

$$I_{p1m} = \frac{2k}{\pi} \int_0^{\theta_b/2} [E_{p1m} \cos \omega t - (E_{p1m} - E_d)] \cos \omega t \, d(\omega t)$$

This integrates to the value

$$I_{p1m} = \frac{2k}{\pi} \left[\frac{E_{p1m}}{4} (\theta_b + \sin \theta_b) - (E_{p1m} - E_d) \sin \frac{\theta_b}{2} \right] \quad (10\text{-}42)$$

It is quite possible to continue with this analysis and obtain expressions for the power transferred to the load, the plate dissipation in the tube, the power supplied by the plate power supply, and the plate-circuit efficiency, in a manner analogous to that for the class B amplifier. However, it is noted that the construction of Fig. 10-9 is necessary in order to deduce the operating path before the approximate operating path may be obtained. The results will be in error consequently, owing to the approximations. Moreover, once the construction of Fig. 10-9 is available, a semigraphical solution may be effected directly without the approximations involved in the foregoing. Because of this, the above method of analysis will not be continued, but the semigraphical method will be discussed in detail.

Attention is called to the fact that, with the class C amplifier, there will be no output for small grid signals, since the plate current is zero Consequently, the output potential is not proportional to the input potential, and these amplifiers cannot be used where such a linear relation must be maintained. They are used extensively for amplifying a signal of fixed amplitude. They are also used extensively in radio communications as either low-level or high-level modulation stages. This latter application will be examined in detail in Chap. 12. When the amplifier is biased to class B operation, a linear relation between the output and input potentials does exist and such amplifiers find extensive use in those applications requiring this characteristic. The most important application is to increase the power level of a modulated carrier wave.

10-7. Semigraphical Analysis of Class C Amplifiers. Before carrying out the details of the analysis, attention is called to a second method of obtaining the operating path of a tuned power amplifier. This makes use of the fact that the operating line appears as a straight line on the constant-current (e_b, e_c) characteristics of the tube. These constant-current tube characteristics are available for transmitting-type tubes and are provided for this particular purpose.

To verify that the dynamic characteristic is a straight line on the constant-current characteristics, use is made of Eqs. (10-13) for the grid and plate potentials, viz.,

$$e_c = E_{cc} + E_{gm} \cos \omega t$$
$$e_b = E_{bb} - E_{p1m} \cos \omega t \qquad (10\text{-}43)$$

This latter expression is valid when the Q of the tank circuit is 10 or greater. Now combine these expressions by writing

$$\frac{e_c}{E_{gm}} = \frac{|E_{cc}}{E_{gm}} + \cos \omega t$$

$$\frac{e_b}{E_{p1m}^2} = \frac{E_{bb}}{E_{p1m}} - \cos \omega t$$

Adding these expressions gives

$$\frac{e_c}{E_{gm}} + \frac{e_b}{E_{p1m}} = \frac{'E_{cc}}{E_{gm}} + \frac{E_{bb}}{E_{p1m}}$$

This may be written in the form

$$e_c = -\frac{E_{gm}}{E_{p1m}} e_b + E_{cc} + \frac{E_{gm}}{E_{p1m}} E_{bb} \qquad (10\text{-}44)$$

which is the slope-intercept form of the equation of a straight line.   The results are illustrated in Fig. 10-10.

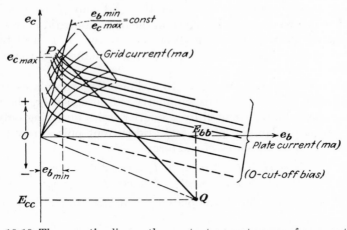

Fig. 10-10. The operating line on the constant-current curves of a power tube.

In order to establish the range of operation, it is necessary to specify the end points of the region of operation.   Ordinarily this is done by specifying E_{bb}, $e_{b,\,min}$, $e_{c,\,max}$, quantities which are determined from considerations of economy, power output desired, efficiency, and tube ratings.   The manner of this dependence will be investigated below.

With these factors specified, the operating characteristics of the amplifier are obtained from the curves in the manner illustrated in Fig. 10-11.

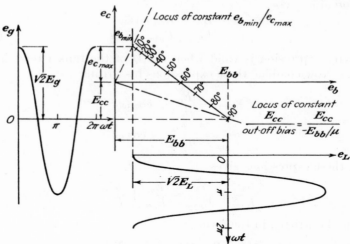

Fig. 10-11. The operating characteristics of a class C amplifier.

10-8. Grid and Plate Currents in Class C Amplifiers.[3]   In order to obtain a numerical solution of the operational features of the amplifier, such as power output, efficiency, grid driving power, and plate dissipation, the average and rms values of the grid and plate currents are required.   These must be deduced from the plate- and grid-current pulses as obtained from the curves, as discussed above.   It is well to examine this matter before considering a detailed analysis of the amplifier operation.

An inspection of Figs. 10-7 and 10-8 shows that the plate- and grid-current pulses possess zero-axis symmetry.   Consequently, these recurring waves may be represented by a Fourier series involving only cosine terms.   In particular, the plate- and grid-current pulses may be represented analytically by series of the form

$$i_b = I_b + I_{p1m} \cos \omega t + I_{p2m} \cos 2\omega t + \cdot \cdot \cdot$$
$$i_c = I_c + I_{g1m} \cos \omega t + I_{g2m} \cos 2\omega t + \cdot \cdot \cdot$$

$$(10\text{-}45)$$

The average or d-c value of the plate current is given by the integral

$$I_b = \frac{1}{2\pi} \int_0^{2\pi} i_b \, d(\omega t)$$

which becomes, by virtue of the zero-axis symmetry and the fact that conduction proceeds over the angle θ_b,

$$I_b = \frac{1}{\pi} \int_0^{\theta_b/2} i_b \, d(\omega t)$$

$$(10\text{-}46)$$

This integral expresses the area under the plate-current pulse. Since, however, an analytic expression for the current pulse is not available, recourse is had to any of the available methods of numerical integration, e.g., through the use of a planimeter; by dividing the base of the wave into equal parts, approximating the mean ordinates of the resulting rectangles, and then summing the areas of these rectangles; or through the use of other methods devised for numerical integration.

The details of the second method are given. Suppose that Fig. 10-12 is the current waveform, certain features of which are to be examined. Suppose that the half recurrence period is divided into n equal parts; hence each division is $\pi/n = 180/n$ deg long. Since the

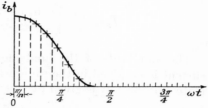

FIG. 10-12. Current waveform and its approximate representation.

current flow will proceed for less than 90 deg in each half period, and taking account of the symmetry, the integral for I_b is then given with good approximation by the expression

$$I_b \doteq \frac{1}{n}\left[\frac{i_b(0)}{2} + \sum_{k=1,2,3,\dots} i_b\left(\frac{k\pi}{n}\right)\right] \tag{10-47}$$

where $i_b(k\pi/n)$ denotes the value of the current at the angle $k\pi/n$.

The average value of the grid current is found in a similar manner from the graph of the grid-current pulse. It is

$$I_c = \frac{1}{2\pi}\int_0^{2\pi} i_c\, d(\omega t)$$

which has the form

$$I_c = \frac{1}{\pi}\int_0^{\theta_c/2} i_c\, d(\omega t) \tag{10-48}$$

where θ_c denotes the grid-current conduction angle. In terms of the approximate calculation, this becomes

$$I_c \doteq \frac{1}{n}\left[\frac{i_c(0)}{2} + \sum_{k=1,2,3,\dots} i_c\left(\frac{k\pi}{n}\right)\right] \tag{10-49}$$

The amplitude of the fundamental-harmonic component of the plate current is obtained from considerations of the general Fourier series representation of the current. This leads to the form

$$I_{p1m} = \frac{1}{\pi}\int_0^{2\pi} i_b \cos \omega t\, d(\omega t)$$

which may be written, in view of the existing symmetry, in the form

$$I_{p1m} = \frac{2}{\pi} \int_0^{\theta_b/2} i_b \cos \omega t \, d(\omega t) \tag{10-50}$$

This integral may be expressed as a summation by the approximate methods that have been employed above. This becomes

$$I_{p1m} \doteq \frac{2}{n} \left[\frac{i_b(0) \cos 0}{2} + \sum_k i_b \left(\frac{k\pi}{n} \right) \cos \frac{k\pi}{n} \right] \tag{10-51}$$

The amplitude of the fundamental-harmonic component of the grid current is obtained in the same way as the corresponding component of plate current. It is given by

$$I_{g1m} = \frac{1}{\pi} \int_0^{2\pi} i_c \cos \omega t \, d(\omega t)$$

which reduces to the form

$$I_{g1m} = \frac{2}{\pi} \int_0^{\theta_c/2} i_c \cos \omega t \, d(\omega t) \tag{10-52}$$

In general, the grid current flows for a relatively small portion of the cycle in the neighborhood of $\theta_c = 0$. But the value of $\cos \omega t$ does not appreciably differ from unity during this interval. Then approximately

$$I_{g1m} \doteq \frac{2}{\pi} \int_0^{\theta_c/2} i_c \, d(\omega t)$$

from which it follows that

$$I_{g1m} \doteq 2I_c \tag{10-53}$$

In general, it is not necessary to plot the grid- and plate-current waveforms, since the information may be taken directly from the curve of Fig. 10-11 and combined in a table like Table 10-1 to yield the desired results.

10-9. Power Considerations in Class C Amplifiers. A number of the results are the same as those considered in Sec. 10-3 for the class B amplifier. Here too the d-c power input to the plate circuit, which is equal to the average power furnished by the plate supply when the d-c power dissipated in the plate load resistance is negligible, is given by

$$P_{bb} = \frac{1}{2\pi} \int_0^{2\pi} E_{bb} i_b \, d(\omega t) = E_{bb} I_b \tag{10-54}$$

The a-c power output of importance is that at the fundamental frequency and is given by

$$P_L = \frac{1}{2\pi} \int_0^{2\pi} e_L i_p \, d(\omega t) = \frac{1}{2\pi} \int_0^{2\pi} E_{p1m} \cos \omega t I_{p1m} \cos \omega t \, d(\omega t)$$

which is

$$P_L = \frac{E_{p1m}I_{p1m}}{2} = E_{p1}I_{p1} \tag{10-55}$$

The plate-circuit efficiency is

$$\eta_p = \frac{P_L}{P_{bb}} \times 100\% = \frac{E_{p1}I_{p1}}{E_{bb}I_b} \times 100\% \tag{10-56}$$

The plate-circuit efficiency depends, of course, on the value of $e_{b,\min}$, since, for a specified E_{bb}, E_{p1m} is dictated by $e_{b,\min}$. A calculation of this dependence may be accomplished, using the results of Sec. 10-6. The

TABLE 10-1

ANALYSIS OF CLASS B AND CLASS C TUNED AMPLIFIER

Tube_____

| E_{bb}_____ | E_{cc}_____ | E_{gm}_____ | $e_{c,\max}$_____ |

$e_{b,\min}$_____

$e_{c,\max}$_____ $e_{b,\min}$_____ E_{p1m}_____ $i_{b,\max}$_____

$i_{c,\max}$_____ n_____ k_____ θ_b_____

$i_b = l = $ length of line PQ_____

1	k	0	1	2	3	4	5	6	7	8	9
2	θ_k										
3	$\cos \theta_k$										
4	$l \cos \theta_k$										
5	$i_b(\theta_k)$										
6	$i_c(\theta_k)$										
7	$i_b(\theta_k) \cos \theta_k$										

$$I_b = \frac{1}{n}\left[\frac{i_b(0)}{2} + \sum i_b\left(\frac{k\pi}{n}\right)\right]$$

$$I_c = \frac{1}{n}\left[\frac{i_c(0)}{2} + \sum i_c\left(\frac{k\pi}{n}\right)\right]$$

$$I_{p1m} = \frac{2}{n}\left[\frac{i_b(0)\cos 0}{2} + \sum i_b\left(\frac{k\pi}{n}\right)\cos\left(\frac{k\pi}{n}\right)\right]$$

general form of the relationship is best presented graphically, as in Fig. 10-13, which shows the plate-circuit efficiency vs. the plate-current conduction angle θ_b, with E_{p1m}/E_{bb} as a parameter. It might be noted that typical values for class C operation are θ_b in the range 120 to 150 deg, with corresponding plate-circuit efficiencies approximately from $\eta_p \sim 80$ to 60 per cent.

The power dissipated in the plate of the tube is given by

$$P_p = \frac{1}{2\pi} \int_0^{2\pi} e_b i_b \, d(\omega t) = \frac{1}{2\pi} \int_0^{2\pi} (E_{bb} - e_L) i_b \, d(\omega t)$$

which reduces to

$$P_p = E_{bb} I_b - E_{p1} I_{p1} = P_{bb} - P_L \tag{10-57}$$

By combining this with Eq. (10-56), there results

$$P_p = (1 - \eta_p) P_{bb} \tag{10-58}$$

This expression shows that the plate dissipation decreases as the output power increases, for a given plate power input.

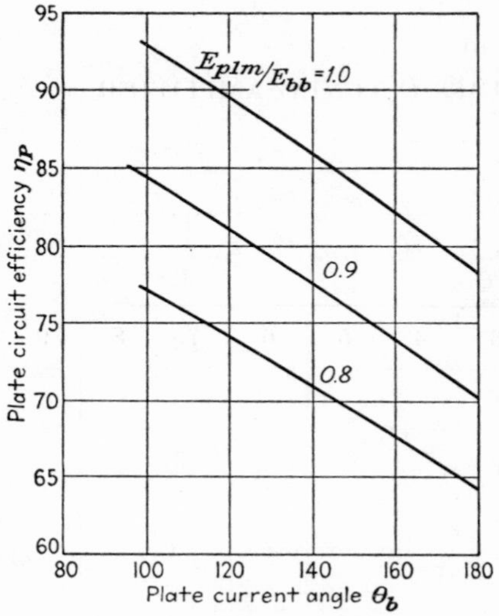

The average grid power supplied by the driving source is given by

$$P_g = \frac{1}{2\pi} \int_0^{2\pi} e_g i_c \, d(\omega t)$$

This reduces, under the assumption that the grid potential is at its maximum value when the grid current flows and does not vary appreciably during this interval, to

$$P_g \doteq E_{gm} \frac{1}{2\pi} \int_0^{2\pi} i_c \, d(\omega t)$$

which is

$$P_g \doteq E_{gm} I_c \tag{10-59}$$

The results of Thomas[4] have shown that the grid driving power is given more accurately by the expression

$$P_g = 0.9 E_{gm} I_c \tag{10-60}$$

FIG. 10-13. Approximate plate-circuit efficiency for different angles of current flow. (*After A. W. Ladner and C. R. Stoner, "Short Wave Wireless Communication," chap. 10, John Wiley & Sons, Inc., New York, 1950.*)

A somewhat better approximation is given by Maling,[5]

$$P_g = E_{gm} I_c \left(0.85 + 0.16 \cos \frac{\theta_c}{2} \right) \qquad \text{for triodes}$$

$$P_g = E_{gm} I_c \left(0.81 - 0.20 \cos \frac{\theta_c}{2} \right) \qquad \text{for tetrodes and pentodes}$$

$$\tag{10-61}$$

The average grid dissipation is given by the expression

$$P_c = \frac{1}{2\pi} \int_0^{2\pi} e_c i_c \, d(\omega t)$$

This may be written as

$$P_c = \frac{1}{2\pi} \int_0^{2\pi} (E_{cc} + e_g) i_c \, d(\omega t)$$
$$= E_{cc} I_c + E_{gm} I_c \qquad (10\text{-}62)$$

But the first term gives a measure of the amount of power that the grid battery is absorbing from the input driving source, since

$$P_{cc} = \frac{1}{2\pi} \int_0^{2\pi} E_{cc} i_c \, d(\omega t) = E_{cc} I_c \qquad (10\text{-}63)$$

and E_{cc} is inherently negative. Hence the power dissipated in the grid circuit is

$$P_c = P_g - |P_{cc}| \qquad (10\text{-}64)$$

Example.   In order to illustrate the calculations for a typical transmitting tube, consider the following specific problem: A type 806 triode having the constant-

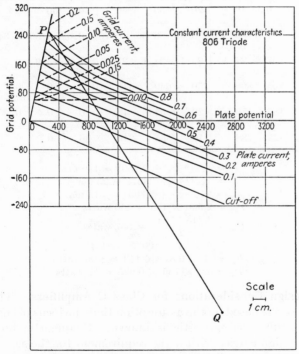

Fig. 10-14. Constant-current characteristics of an 806 triode.

current characteristics shown in Fig. 10-14 is used as a class C amplifier, under the following conditions:

$$E_{bb} = 2{,}500 \text{ volts} \qquad E_{cc} = -500 \text{ volts}$$
$$\frac{e_{b,\,min}}{e_{c,\,max}} = 1.0 \qquad E_{gm} = 755 \text{ volts}$$

Determine the following:
- *a.* Power supplied by the plate power supply.
- *b.* A-c power output.   *c.* Plate-circuit efficiency.
- *d.* Plate dissipation.   *e.* Grid driving power.

(Note: The details of the solution are given in Table 10-2.)

TABLE 10-2

ANALYSIS OF CLASS C AMPLIFIER

Tube—806

$E_{bb} = 2,500$ $E_{cc} = -500$ $E_{gm} = 755$ $e_{c,\max} = 255$

$\dfrac{e_{b,\min}}{e_{c,\max}} = 1.0$ $e_{b,\min} = 255$ $E_{p1m} = 2,245$ $I_{b,\max} = 825$ ma

$I_{c,\max} = 185$ ma $n = 18$ $k = 9$ $\theta_b = 120°$

Length of line $PQ = 27.8$ cm

1	k	0	1	2	3	4	5	6	7	8	9
2	θ_k, deg	0	10	20	30	40	50	60	70	80	90
3	$\cos \theta_k$	1.0	0.985	0.94	0.86	0.76	0.64	0.50	0.34	0.17	0.00
4	$l \cos \theta_k$	27.8	27.4	26.1	24.1	21.3	17.9	13.9	9.5	4.8	0.0
5	$i_b(\theta_k)$	825	800	750	640	410	150	0	0	0	0
6	$i_c(\theta_k)$	185	170	120	55	12	0	0	0	0	0
7	$i_b(\theta_k) \cos \theta_k$	825	788	710	555	314	96	0	0	0	0

$$I_b = \tfrac{1}{18}(^{825}\!/_2 + 2,750) = 176 \text{ ma}$$
$$I_c = \tfrac{1}{18}(^{185}\!/_2 + 357) = 25 \text{ ma}$$
$$I_{p1m} = \tfrac{1}{9}(^{825}\!/_2 + 2,463) = 319 \text{ ma}$$
$$P_{bb} = 2,500 \times 176 = 440 \text{ watts}$$
$$P_L = \frac{2,245 \times 319}{2} = 357 \text{ watts}$$
$$\eta = {^{357}\!/_{440}} \times 100\% = 81\%$$
$$P_p = (1 - 0.81) \times 440 = 83.5 \text{ watts}$$
$$P_g = 0.9 \times 755 \times 0.025 = 17 \text{ watts}$$

10-10. Design Considerations for Class C Amplifiers. The analysis presented above is based on the assumption that the locus of the operating point of the tube characteristic is known. Frequently, however, the engineering design carries with it the requirement for the selection of the tube and the selection of the operating conditions that govern the locus to give a high plate-circuit efficiency, and other specified results. A number of factors are important in such a design, and it is desirable to examine the influence of these.

The important factors that are involved in the engineering design of a class C amplifier are the following:

1. The peak space current that should be demanded of a given tube. This is usually controlled by the values of $e_{b,\,min}$ and $e_{c,\,max}$, since the total peak-space-current demand is given by

$$I_{s,max} = I_{b,max} + I_{c,max}$$
$$= f(e_{b,min}, e_{c,max})$$

2. The minimum potential to which the plate falls, $e_{b,min}$.
3. The maximum value of the instantaneous grid potential, $e_{c,max}$.
4. The angle of plate-current flow, θ_b.
5. The angle of grid-current flow, θ_c.
6. The plate supply potential, E_{bb}.

The influence of each of these factors is considered in some detail.

Item 1. In so far as the total space current that may be safely drawn in a vacuum tube is concerned, it is limited by the allowable emission from the cathode, if saturation current may be drawn from the tube. Although it might not be too unreasonable to draw emission saturation current on the current peaks in a tube that is provided with a pure-tungsten filament, it is unwise to drive a tube with either a thoriated-tungsten or an oxide-coated cathode to such extremes. Reasonable figures for the average emitter are:

Tungsten filament—$I_{s,max}$ approximately 100 per cent of total emission current.

Thoriated-tungsten—$I_{s,max}$ from 15 to 35 per cent of the total emission current.

Oxide-coated cathode—$I_{s,max}$ from 10 to 20 per cent of the total emission current.

Items 2 *and* 3. The optimum values of $e_{b,min}$ and $e_{c,max}$ will be such that the total allowable peak space current will not be exceeded. Moreover, their relative values must be so chosen that the maximum plate current occurs at $\omega t = 0$. This requires that the tube must not be driven so hard that it operates in the region of rapidly falling plate current. Such a condition is avoided by keeping $e_{b,min} > e_{c,max}$. However, high plate-circuit efficiency results when $e_{b,min} = e_{c,max}$, although for low grid driving power it is required that $e_{b,min} > e_{c,max}$. Typical values of the ratio $e_{b,min}/e_{c,max}$ usually range from 1 to 2.

Item 4. The range over which plate conduction occurs, i.e., the conduction angle θ_b, influences both the average current I_b and the first-harmonic current amplitude I_{p1m}. For a large value of the first-harmonic current amplitude, it is desirable that θ_b be made large. However, in order to provide a high value of plate-circuit efficiency, small values of θ_b are indicated. Consequently, it is necessary to compromise between plate efficiency and power output. Typical values for class C operation, as already discussed, are θ_b in the range from 120 to 150 deg, with corresponding plate efficiencies η from about 80 to 60 per cent (see Fig. 10-13).

With the choice of I_s, $e_{b,\text{min}}$, $e_{c,\text{max}}$, and θ_b specified, the other operating conditions are established. It is desired, therefore, to examine the relation that expresses the grid bias, E_{cc}, and also the grid conduction angle θ_c, in terms of the fixed parameters. To find an expression for E_{cc}, it is noted that the plate current becomes zero when $\omega t = \theta_b/2$. At this point, the grid signal is given by

$$e_g = E_{gm} \cos \omega t = E_{gm} \cos \frac{\theta_b}{2} \qquad (10\text{-}65)$$

But at this point it is necessary that $e_c + e_b/\mu = 0$. This follows from the fact that the plate current may be written by an expression of the form $i_b = f(e_c + e_b/\mu)$ and, for i_b to be zero, $e_c + e_b/\mu$ must be zero. By virtue of this

$$E_{gm} \cos \frac{\theta_b}{2} + E_{cc} + \frac{1}{\mu} \left(E_{bb} - E_{p1m} \cos \frac{\theta_b}{2} \right) = 0$$

But since

$$e_{c,\text{max}} = E_{gm} + E_{cc}$$
$$e_{b,\text{min}} = E_{bb} - E_{p1m}$$

it follows that

$$(e_{c,\text{max}} - E_{cc}) \cos \frac{\theta_b}{2} + E_{cc} + \frac{1}{\mu} \left[E_{bb} - (E_{bb} - e_{b,\text{min}}) \cos \frac{\theta_b}{2} \right] = 0$$

from which

$$E_{cc} = \frac{-E_{bb}}{\mu} + \left(e_{c,\text{max}} + \frac{e_{b,\text{min}}}{\mu} \right) \frac{\cos (\theta_b/2)}{\cos (\theta_b/2) - 1} \qquad (10\text{-}66)$$

The angle of grid flow is readily determined, since the grid current becomes zero when $\omega t = \theta_c/2$. At this point

$$e_c = E_{gm} \cos \frac{\theta_c}{2} + E_{cc} = 0$$

from which it follows that

$$\cos \frac{\theta_c}{2} = - \frac{E_{cc}}{E_{gm}} \qquad (10\text{-}67)$$

where E_{cc} is obtained from Eq. (10-66).

10-11. Grid Bias. The foregoing mathematical discussion assumed that the grid bias potential E_{cc} was constant in magnitude. Often, however, the bias potential is obtained by means of a resistor-capacitor combination in the grid line, in the manner illustrated in Fig. 10-15. The choice of grid resistance R_g is dictated by the required bias potential and the average grid current I_c. This is frequently referred to as grid-leak bias.

It might be thought that I_c would be a definite value for a given peak driving potential E_{gm}, with the result that the grid resistance would be firmly established. As a practical fact, variations of R_g are accompanied by an almost inverse variation of I_c, with the result that, for fixed E_{gm}, the potential E_{cc} remains sensibly constant. It is desirable, therefore, that the largest R_g possible be used, with stable amplifier operation. This follows from the fact that the loss in the grid resistor is due to the heating, or $I_c^2 R_g$, loss. But for a given negative bias, $I_c R_g$ is constant, and I_c varies inversely with R_g. Consequently, by increasing R_g, I_c is reduced, and the corresponding loss is reduced.

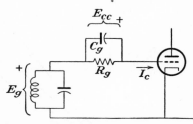

The grid driving power P_g is usually of the order of 5 to 10 per cent of the a-c power output of the amplifier P_L, when the tube is operated within its designed frequency limits. When operated above the normal frequency limits of the tube, the grid driving power increases rapidly, owing in some measure to increased dielectric losses,

Fig. 10-15. The use of a grid resistor and grid capacitor for biasing the amplifier.

but principally because of transit-time loading. This latter factor is discussed at some length in Sec. 5-8. A limit is thereby set to the h-f limit of the tube.

10-12. Grid Potential and Amplifier Linearity. It has been noted on several occasions that the plate-circuit efficiency η_p depends upon the plate-current conduction angle θ_b. Moreover, the plate-current conduction angle depends upon the grid bias and the magnitude of the grid driving potential, more negative values of E_{cc} and higher E_{gm} being accompanied by smaller values of θ_b. The general character of the variation of output current and plate-circuit efficiency as a function of input grid potential is shown in Fig. 10-16.

These curves show that the a-c component of current I_{p1}, and the efficiency η_p, increase with increasing values of E_g over a wide range of E_g. A saturation value is reached beyond which there is no essential change, except that the grid current, and so the grid driving power, continue to increase. An interesting fact is that the situation remains roughly the same whether fixed bias or grid-leak bias is used. With grid-leak bias, however, the input power rises to larger values than with fixed bias. This is so because an increased E_g tends to result in a higher I_c; but this in turn causes an increase in E_{cc}. Hence, for a given output power, a larger E_{gm} is required, with a corresponding less linear relationship between E_g and I_{p1}. Clearly, overdriving the amplifier merely results in a high power dissipation in the grid circuit. Underdriving leads to a reduced amplifier output and efficiency.

The question of a linear relation between I_{p1} and E_g is of considerable importance when the tube is used for grid-circuit amplitude modulation. This matter will be discussed in Chap. 12.

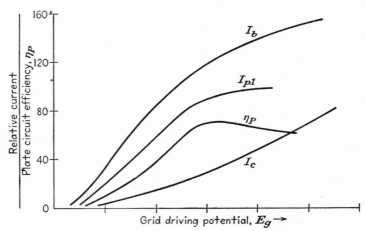

Fig. 10-16. The effect of varying the input grid potential on several of the important amplifier factors.

10-13. Approximate Analytic Solution.[6] The semigraphical method discussed in the foregoing sections permits a relatively accurate analysis of the performance of a class C amplifier. This analysis requires that the instantaneous plate and grid potentials and currents should be obtained and plotted and then from these curves should be derived such information as the plate loss, the power output, and the grid driving power. This method, while it possesses the virtue of yielding a relatively accurate solution, does have the disadvantage of being fairly laborious.

An approximate calculation of the performance can be obtained without recourse to the point-by-point analysis. This approximate calculation takes advantage of the fact that the total space current can be expressed quite accurately by an expression of the form

$$i_s = i_b + i_c = k \left(e_c + \frac{e_b}{\mu} \right)^\alpha \qquad \text{for } e_c + \frac{e_b}{\mu} > 0 \qquad (10\text{-}68)$$

The constant α ordinarily lies in the range from 1 to $\frac{3}{2}$. The value of α is found to be 1.0 for the 889A triode, the characteristics of which are shown in Figs. 2-18 and 2-19. The accuracy of the results that follow under this approximation will probably be well within the accuracy with which tube circuit conditions are known and within the reasonable variations of individual tubes from the average of the group.

Evidently, when the current is specified by this relationship, the pulses of current have a form that may be analytically expressed. However, the current pulses so specified are for the space current, and not for the plate current. Consequently the method yields information regarding the space-current pulses. By making reasonable assumptions, information is also obtained regarding the grid-current pulses. The difference between these two must then be the plate current. Since the grid current is ordinarily a small fraction of the total space current, then an error in the choice of the grid-current pulse will not introduce a very large error in the resulting plate current.

To examine the situation in some detail, use is made of the known relations for the grid and plate potentials [see Eqs. (10-14)], viz.,

$$e_c = E_{cc} + E_{gm} \cos \omega t$$
$$e_b = E_{bb} - E_{p1m} \cos \omega t$$

with

$$E_{gm} = e_{c,\max} - E_{cc}$$
$$E_{p1m} = E_{bb} - e_{b,\min}$$

Now within the limits of current flow, i.e., within the limits from $-\theta_b/2$ to $\theta_b/2$, the space current may be written in the form

$$i_s = k \left[(e_{c,\max} - E_{cc}) \cos \omega t + E_{cc} + \frac{E_{bb}}{\mu} - \frac{E_{bb} - e_{b,\min}}{\mu} \cos \omega t \right]^\alpha$$

which is

$$i_s = k \left[\left(e_{c,\max} + \frac{e_{b,\min}}{\mu} \right) \cos \omega t + \left(E_{cc} + \frac{E_{bb}}{\mu} \right) (1 - \cos \omega t) \right]^\alpha \qquad (10\text{-}69)$$

But the maximum value of this expression, which occurs when $\cos \omega t = 1$, is

$$I_{s,\max} = k \left(e_{c,\max} + \frac{e_{b,\min}}{\mu} \right)^\alpha \qquad (10\text{-}70)$$

Hence the ratio of the current at any instant to the maximum value is given by

$$\frac{i_s}{I_{s,\max}} = \left[\cos \omega t + \frac{E_{cc} + E_{bb}/\mu}{e_{c,\max} + e_{b,\min}/\mu} (1 - \cos \omega t) \right]^\alpha \qquad (10\text{-}71)$$

But the value of the bias potential to provide for a conduction angle θ_b is given by Eq. (10-66). By combining Eqs. (10-66) and (10-71), the current ratio becomes

$$\frac{i_s}{I_{s,\max}} = \left[\cos \omega t + \frac{\cos (\theta_b/2)}{\cos (\theta_b/2) - 1} (1 - \cos \omega t) \right]^\alpha$$

which reduces to the form

$$\frac{i_s}{I_{s,\max}} = \left[\frac{\cos (\theta_b/2) - \cos \omega t}{\cos (\theta_b/2) - 1} \right]^\alpha \qquad (10\text{-}72)$$

This expression may be used to provide the fractional average or d-c component of the space current and any of the fractional harmonic-component values. In particular, the fractional average or d-c component of the space current is given by the expression

$$\frac{I_s}{I_{s,max}} = \frac{1}{2\pi} \int_0^{2\pi} \frac{i_s}{I_{s,max}} \, d(\omega t)$$

which reduces to the form

$$\frac{I_s}{I_{s,max}} = \frac{1}{\pi} \int_0^{\theta_b/2} \left[\frac{\cos(\theta_b/2) - \cos \omega t}{\cos(\theta_b/2) - 1} \right]^\alpha d(\omega t) \qquad (10\text{-}73)$$

In a similar way, the fundamental component has the form

$$\frac{I_{s1m}}{I_{s,max}} = \frac{1}{\pi} \int_0^{2\pi} \frac{i_s}{I_{s,max}} \cos \omega t \, d(\omega t)$$

which may be written as

$$\frac{I_{s1m}}{I_{s,max}} = \frac{2}{\pi} \int_0^{\theta_b/2} \left[\frac{\cos(\theta_b/2) - \cos \omega t}{\cos(\theta_b/2) - 1} \right]^\alpha \cos \omega t \, d(\omega t) \qquad (10\text{-}74)$$

These expressions, for given values of α, are functions of θ_b, and they may be conveniently expressed in graphical form. The curves of Fig. 10-17

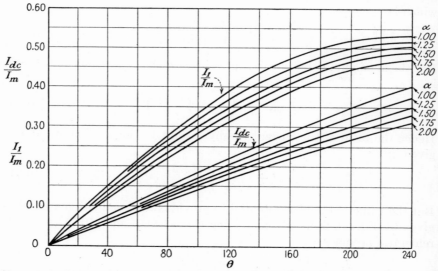

FIG. 10-17. Curves giving the relation of d-c and peak fundamental-frequency component of current as a function of the angle of current flow and the peak amplitude.

give the relation of the d-c and fundamental-frequency components of the space-current pulse as a function of the angle of flow θ_b, and the peak amplitude $I_{s,max}$, with α as a parameter.

To find the corresponding values of the plate current, the grid current is approximated by assuming an analytic form for the equation of the grid current.   As the grid current is usually a small part of the total space current, a reasonable choice for the grid current will provide good results for the plate current.   An expression that represents the grid current with good approximation is*

$$i_c = k' \left(e_c + \frac{e_b}{\mu} \right)^\alpha \qquad \text{for } e_c > 0 \qquad (10\text{-}75)$$

Consequently, by following a parallel development to that above, there results

$$\frac{i_c}{I_{c,\max}} = \left[\frac{\cos (\theta_c/2) - \cos \omega t}{\cos (\theta_c/2) - 1} \right]^\alpha \qquad (10\text{-}76)$$

from which the d-c and fundamental-frequency components become

$$\frac{I_c}{I_{c,\max}} = \frac{1}{\pi} \int_0^{\theta_c/2} \left[\frac{\cos (\theta_c/2) - \cos \omega t}{\cos (\theta_c/2) - 1} \right]^\alpha d(\omega t) \qquad (10\text{-}77)$$

and

$$\frac{I_{c1m}}{I_{c,\max}} = \frac{2}{\pi} \int_0^{\theta_c/2} \left[\frac{\cos (\theta_c/2) - \cos \omega t}{\cos (\theta_c/2) - 1} \right]^\alpha \cos \omega t \, d(\omega t) \qquad (10\text{-}78)$$

These expressions are functions of θ_c and have the same graphical form as the space-current components.   Consequently the curves of Fig. 10-17 are also a valid representation of the grid-current components.

Example.   To illustrate the methods of Sec. 10-13, the example in Sec. 10-9 is repeated according to the methods of Sec. 10-13, and the corresponding results will be compared.

Peak space current: $I_{sm} = I_{b,\max} + I_{c,\max} = 825 + 185 = 1{,}010$ ma

To find the grid current, choose $\alpha = 2$; then

$$\frac{\theta_c}{2} = \cos^{-1} \frac{500}{755} = 48° \qquad \theta_c = 96°$$

and from Fig. 10-17

$$\frac{I_c}{I_{c,\max}} = 0.14 \qquad \frac{I_{c1m}}{I_{c,\max}} = 0.26$$

Hence the currents of importance are

$$I_c = 0.14 \times 185 = 26 \text{ ma}$$
$$I_{c1m} = 0.26 \times 185 = 48 \text{ ma}$$

To find the plate current, the space current must be calculated.   To do this,

* Maling finds that the exponent 2 is suitable for most triodes, and a value 1.4 seems suitable for most tetrodes and pentodes.

choose $\alpha = \frac{3}{2}$, and

$$\frac{\theta_b}{2} = \cos^{-1}\frac{378}{755} = 60° \qquad \theta_b = 120°$$

Then, from Fig. 10-17,

$$\frac{I_s}{I_{s,\max}} = 0.19 \qquad \frac{I_{s1m}}{I_{s,\max}} = 0.35$$

from which it follows that

$$I_s = 0.19 \times 1,010 = 192 \text{ ma}$$
$$I_{s1m} = 0.35 \times 1,010 = 353 \text{ ma}$$

The plate-current components are then

$$I_b = I_s - I_c = 192 - 26 = 166 \text{ ma}$$
$$I_{p1m} = 353 - 48 = 305 \text{ ma}$$

The significant quantities are

$$P_{bb} = 2,500 \times 166 \times 10^{-3} = 415 \text{ watts}$$
$$P_L = \frac{1}{2} \times 305 \times 10^{-3}(2,500 - 255) = 342 \text{ watts}$$
$$P_p = 415 - 342 = 73 \text{ watts}$$
$$P_g = 755 \times 0.26 \times 0.9 = 17.6 \text{ watts}$$
$$\eta_p = \frac{342}{415} \times 100 = 82.3\%$$

A more accurate calculation would require a logarithmic plot of Eq. (10-68) for the particular tube and a determination from this of the exponent α. However, the use of the approximate methods would not be justified under these circumstances in general since the effort involved would be comparable with that in applying the methods of Sec. 10-8.

10-14. Push-Pull Tuned Amplifiers. The push-pull tuned amplifier is illustrated in Fig. 10-18. It will be observed that this circuit possesses

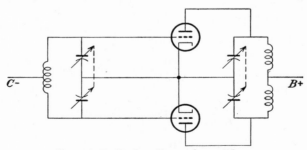

FIG. 10-18. Push-pull tuned amplifier.

the expected form, with the tuned circuits in the input and output. The plate and grid tanks are excited by current pulses which have the waveforms illustrated in Fig. 10-8, except that current pulses occur each half cycle instead of the alternate half cycle shown, alternate pulses being inverted.

The main differences between single-tube and push-pull operation are of interest. For this, assume that each tube, relative to the mid-point or d-c level, has its associated L and C tank circuit. When connected in push-pull, the tank elements are then essentially in series, with the total L being doubled (assuming no magnetic coupling exists between these coils), and the total C being halved. This reasoning is not generally correct, since mutual coupling between the coils does exist. But it does make plausible the fact that the tank circuit Q is roughly doubled. The circuit might involve some readjustment if a given Q is desired, but this is generally easy to achieve.

Relative to the harmonic content, the situation here is no different from that which exists in the untuned push-pull amplifier. The correctly adjusted push-pull amplifier automatically eliminates all even harmonics, and the second harmonic, which would normally be the most troublesome, disappears. This condition is true quite independently of the value of Q. The third-harmonic component is still present. If the analysis of Sec. 10-9 or 10-13 is extended to an evaluation of the third-harmonic components, it is found that, for $\theta_b = 120$ deg and $Q_L = 10$, the ratio of third harmonic to fundamental is less than 0.01. In fact, with a push-pull circuit, satisfactory operation with Q_L as low as 5 is feasible.

10-15. Neutralization. When a triode is used as a power amplifier in the circuit of Fig. 10-1, some feedback between the grid circuit and the plate circuit exists through the interelectrode capacitance C_{gp}. This feedback is usually positive and tends to cause the stage to oscillate. It may be balanced out by one of several methods of *neutralization*. Tetrodes and pentodes usually do not require neutralization, as the capacitance C_{gp} is usually small enough in these tubes so that the amount of feedback is very small. The principle of neutralization is very simple and consists in providing feedback through external circuits in an amount equal to that through C_{gp}, but in opposite phase.

Two common methods of neutralization are illustrated in Fig. 10-19. The first is called *grid* neutralization, and the second is called *plate* neutralization. In Fig. 10-19a the plate is connected through the adjustable neutralizing capacitance C_N to a point in the grid circuit which has a potential of phase opposite to that of the grid. In Fig. 10-19b the grid is connected to a point in the plate circuit at which the potential is of opposite phase to that of the plate. In these circuits the feedback through C_{gp} has been neutralized, although a degree of dissymmetry relative to ground exists. This fact is important, since C_{gp} is not the only capacitance through which feedback may occur, and these methods of neutralization will not generally overcome such other capacitance effects.

A symmetrical circuit with ground as datum provides the best possible arrangement for complete neutralization, since it is possible to balance capacitance effects to ground. Such a neutralizing method was developed by C. S. Franklin and has the form shown in Fig. 10-20.

The diagrams of Fig. 10-21 show the neutralized push-pull tuned amplifier, together with the balancing circuit. Observe that the balancing circuit is symmetrical with respect to ground.

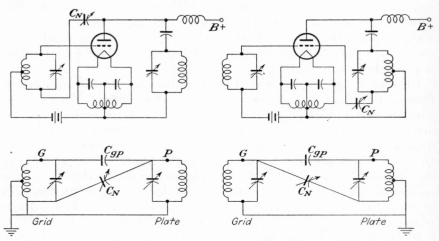

(a) Grid neutralization   (b) Plate neutralization

Fig. 10-19. Diagrammatic and schematic sketches of grid and plate neutralization.

10-16. Tubes as Tuned Class C Amplifiers. It is of some interest to compare the triode as a tuned class C amplifier with the tetrode and pentode. According to Eq. (10-61) the grid driving power of the triode is higher than that of the tetrode and pentode under the same conditions

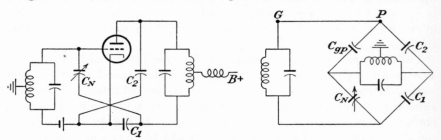

Fig. 10-20. The Franklin symmetrical neutralization method.

of grid driving potential, average current, and grid conduction angle. However, such a comparison is inconclusive in itself, since ordinarily these factors are not the same.

Consider first, therefore, the influence of changing the amplification factor μ of the tube. This comparison is best accomplished by direct reference to the operation of two similar triodes with different values of μ.

The actual operating conditions for two groups of similar triodes of different μ are contained in Table 10-3.

It might appear initially that the low-μ tube, owing to the lower cutoff value, and so a lower operating bias, might be accompanied by a

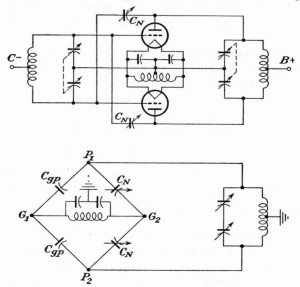

FIG. 10-21. The neutralized push-pull amplifier, and the neutralizing circuit.

low excitation power. But the low-μ triode requires a larger E_{gm} and a higher $e_{c,\max}$. As a result of the higher $e_{c,\max}$ and the lower μ, there is a slight decrease in the conduction angle θ_c. When all factors are taken

TABLE 10-3

COMPARISON OF LOW- AND HIGH-μ POWER TRIODES*

	250TL	250TH	304TL	304TH
μ of tube	14	37	12	20
D-c plate potential, volts	3,000	3,000	2,000	2,000
D-c grid potential, volts	−350	−150	−300	−200
D-c plate current, ma	335	333	600	600
D-c grid current, ma	45	90	85	125
Peak r-f grid input potential	720	395	480	325
Driving power, watts	29	32	36	39
Grid dissipation, watts	15	19	11	
Plate power input, watts	1,000	1,000	1,200	1,200
Plate dissipation, watts	250	250	300	300
Plate power output, watts	750	750	900	900

* Courtesy of Eitel-McCullough, Inc., San Bruno, Calif.

into account, the average grid current I_c is lower for the lower-μ tube. Although E_{gm} is higher for the low-μ tube, owing to the lower average grid current, the grid driving power is approximately the same for both the low-μ and the high-μ tubes. As a result, therefore, triodes of the high-μ type are to be preferred, since lower excitation potentials are required. In fact, the tendency in the design of transmitting triodes is toward the higher values of μ.

Consider now a tetrode as a tuned class C amplifier. Owing to the screening of the plate by the screen grid, the control-grid current is not dependent on the changing plate potential e_b, as it is in the triode. As a consequence, full plate potential may be used without excessive excitation power; that is, $e_{c,max}$ may exceed $e_{b,min}$ without excessive grid driving power. This applies also for the pentode and represents one of the advantages of the tetrode and pentode over the triode.

A second advantage of the tetrode and pentode results from the smaller grid-plate capacitance than in the triode, with the great advantage that neutralization is unnecessary. The double screening effect of the screen and suppressor grids gives the pentode preference over the tetrode in most cases.

10-17. Parasitic Oscillations. As discussed in Sec. 10-15, the use of some neutralization scheme will prevent a power amplifier from oscillating, since the effect of the feedback through the grid-plate capacitance is largely canceled. While this overcomes the tendency of the amplifier to oscillate at the fundamental frequency, the possibility remains for the system to oscillate at a variety of frequencies, the tank circuits comprising wiring or fixed inductances, with stray or wiring capacitances. These frequencies bear no relation to the fundamental or any of the harmonics of the amplifier and are known as *parasitic* oscillations. Parasitic oscillations are more likely to occur in amplifiers which incorporate tubes in parallel, and in such cases it is common to include "suppressor" resistors in the plate leads (and also in the screen leads, if pentodes are used).

Parasitic oscillations may be suspected in an amplifier under a number of different conditions. Among these are a high plate current, grid currents which appear unusual, general instability, and peculiar transient behavior. If the parasitic oscillation occurs in the a-f range, or if these oscillations cause blocking at an audio rate, transformers and iron-core chokes may "sing." Of course, in this latter case, if a receiver is tuned to the parasitic frequency, any audio variation will appear as an audio signal.

The suppression of parasitic oscillations, whether these be of a low frequency or of a very high frequency, is often a difficult problem, since it is not easy to ascertain the circuit elements which cause the parasitic tank circuit. Often a rearrangement of circuit elements will eliminate the oscillations. Often appropriately connected resistors or shunting capacitors will be sufficient.

10-18. Grounded-grid Amplifier. A triode may be connected in a grounded-grid circuit, in the manner illustrated in Fig. 10-22. It is

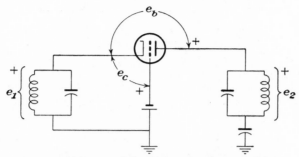

FIG. 10-22. A grounded-grid tuned power amplifier.

observed that the grounded grid forms a screen between the input and the output circuits, quite like the screen grid in a tetrode or a pentode. As a result, the tendency to oscillate is considerably reduced. If oscillations do occur, the necessary neutralizing capacitors are considerably smaller than in the conventional grounded-cathode circuit.

The curves of Fig. 10-23 show the approximate waveforms which appear in a class B grounded-grid tuned amplifier. Note that the input excitation potential and the output plate potential are in phase, although, as usual, the grid potential and the plate potential are 180 deg out of phase. Observe also that the input and output circuits are in series, and therefore the excitation source supplies some power to the output. As a result, the exciter must have a somewhat higher power capacity than that required for the more conventional circuit. Some of this added power is transferred to the plate circuit.

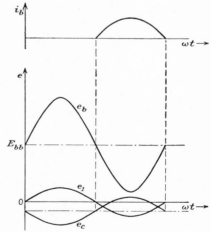

FIG. 10-23. The important waveforms in the grounded-grid tuned class B amplifier.

When a grounded-grid circuit is to be modulated, it is necessary to modulate both the exciter and the output circuit. This follows because some of the exciter power appears in the output.

10-19. Frequency Multiplication. There is frequently need for a system to provide frequency multiplication, in order to furnish a frequency which is some multiple of a given driving frequency. Such a system as this often permits high frequencies with less difficulty than in attempting to generate and amplify the high frequencies directly. This is particularly the case when crystal-controlled systems are used, since crystals for the high frequencies become extremely thin and consequently are fragile both mechanically and electrically. By using a crystal of low frequency and then employing frequency multipliers, effective crystal-controlled h-f systems are possible.

The use of tuned amplifiers for frequency multiplication follows from the fact that the current pulses in the class C amplifier, with a sinusoidal

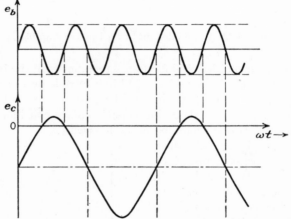

FIG. 10-24. The waveshapes at important points in a tuned class C frequency multiplier.

driving potential, are nonsinusoidal in character and so contain harmonic components of the fundamental frequency. This fact was made use of in evaluating the output characteristics of the tuned amplifier [see Eq. (10-50)] and was illustrated in Fig. 10-8. In addition to the fundamental component, which is of importance in the tuned amplifier, the second-, third-, or higher-harmonic components are of importance in frequency multipliers. In this latter case, the output tank is tuned to the desired-harmonic component, depending on the order of frequency multiplication desired.

The output from a given amplifier at the various harmonics will depend on the bias used on the amplifier. The higher the harmonic required, the greater must be the negative bias, and correspondingly the higher must be the grid drive that is used. For best results, the tank circuit is energized for one-half cycle of the harmonic output for each primary cycle.

Thus if a third harmonic is required, the output circuit is energized once every third half cycle, and the bias should be so adjusted that the plate-current conduction angle is nearly $\frac{360}{6}$ = 60 deg. The situation is somewhat as illustrated in Fig. 10-24. Clearly, of course, the higher the harmonic, the narrower will be the tube current pulse. Since the available drive is usually limited, this means that, with increasing harmonic multiplication, the smaller will be the output. Because of this, frequency multiplication higher than the fourth harmonic with a single stage is usually impractical. Higher values of multiplication will use two or more stages in cascade.

Harmonic amplifiers may incorporate triodes, tetrodes, or pentodes, although triodes are more often used in the higher-power stages. When triodes are used, neutralization is necessary.

Frequency multiplication is very common through the use of multi-vibrator circuits, as it is possible to synchronize the input of one multi-vibrator with the output of the previous stage. Such multivibrator circuits permit stable multiplication as high as 9 or 10. If a sinusoidal output is desired from a multivibrator multiplying chain, it is necessary only to incorporate a tuned circuit in the output to act as a filter and thereby extract the desired sinusoidal component. For the low-power applications, the use of multivibrator multiplying chains has largely supplanted the tuned-circuit frequency multipliers.

REFERENCES

1. Everitt, W. L., "Communication Engineering," 2d ed., pp. 582–590, McGraw-Hill Book Company, Inc., New York, 1937.
2. Everitt, W. L., "Communication Engineering," 2d ed., pp. 565–594, McGraw-Hill Book Company, Inc., New York, 1937.
3. Massachusetts Institute of Technology Staff, "Applied Electronics," chap. X, John Wiley & Sons, Inc., New York, 1943.
   Cruft Laboratory, War Training Staff, "Electronic Circuits and Tubes," chap. XIV, McGraw-Hill Book Company, Inc., New York, 1947.
   Mouromtseff, I. E., and H. N. Kozanowski, *Proc. IRE*, **23**, 752 (1935).
4. Thomas, H. P., *Proc. IRE*, **21**, 1134 (1933).
5. Maling, H. F., private communication.
6. Terman, F. E., and J. H. Ferns, *Proc. IRE*, **22**, 359 (1934).
   Terman, F. E., and W. C. Roake, *Proc. IRE*, **24**, 620 (1936).

PROBLEMS

10-1. A type 800 tube is to be used in a tuned power amplifier. Find the operating curves for E_{bb} = 1,000 and the following three conditions of grid characteristics:

$$
\begin{array}{ll}
E_{cc} = -55 \text{ volts} & E_{gm} = 170 \text{ volts peak} \\
\phantom{E_{cc}} = -95 & \phantom{E_{gm}} = 210 \\
\phantom{E_{cc}} = -135 & \phantom{E_{gm}} = 250
\end{array}
$$

Would any of the indicated operating conditions yield class B operation? Choose $e_{b,\min} = e_{c,\max}$.

10-2. The type 800 tube is operated as an r-f power amplifier under class B conditions under the following conditions:

D-c plate potential..................................	1,000 volts
D-c grid potential..................................	−55 volts
Peak r-f grid potential..............................	170 volts
μ..	15
r_p..	5,700 ohms

Calculate the following for $e_{b,\min} = 1.5e_{c,\max}$:
a. Power output.
b. Plate dissipation.
c. Plate-circuit efficiency.
d. The impedance of the tuned circuit at resonance.

10-3. A type 833A triode has the following maximum ratings for operation as a class B r-f amplifier.

D-c plate potential..................................	4,000 volts
D-c grid potential..................................	−120 volts
Peak r-f grid potential..............................	180 volts
Plate dissipation....................................	400 watts
μ..	35
g_m..	15,800 μmhos

It is planned to use this tube as a class B amplifier with a grid-signal frequency of 16.0 Mc, a plate supply of 4,000 volts, and a value of $e_{b,\min}/e_{c,\max}$ equal to 2.0. Find the following:
a. A-c power output.
b. Current by the plate power supply.
c. Plate dissipation.
d. Plate efficiency.
e. Impedance of tuned circuit at resonance.
f. The values of L and C in the tuned circuit if the loaded resonant Q is 12.
g. What value of R_0 should be used if the maximum allowable plate dissipation is 400 watts and $e_{b,\min} = e_{c,\max}$?

10-4. A class C amplifier uses an 851 tube and operates under the following conditions:

D-c plate potential..................................	2,500 volts
D-c grid potential..................................	−250 volts
Peak r-f grid potential..............................	450 volts
Plate dissipation....................................	550 watts
Shunt resistance of tank circuit.....................	1,550 ohms
D-c grid current....................................	0.10 amp

Calculate the following:
a. A-c plate potential.
c. D-c plate current.
e. Grid driving power.
b. Output power.
d. Plate-circuit efficiency.
f. Grid dissipation
Assume that $e_{b,\min} = e_{c,\max}$.

10-5. A class C amplifier uses an 852 tube and operates under the following conditions:

D-c plate potential	3,000 volts
D-c grid bias	−600 volts
Peak r-f signal	850 volts
D-c plate current	85 ma
D-c grid current	15 ma
Fundamental component of plate current	120 ma peak

Calculate the following, assuming $e_{b,min} = e_{c,max}$:
a. Output power.
b. Plate-circuit efficiency.
c. Grid driving power.
d. The amplifier is to operate at 1,500 kc. Specify the elements of the plate tank. Choose $Q = 23$.

10-6. The typical operating conditions for the type 893 A-R transmitting triode when used as a class C r-f power amplifier or oscillator are

D-c plate potential	18,000 volts
D-c grid bias	−1,000 volts
Peak r-f grid signal	1,630 volts
D-c plate current	3.6 amp
D-c grid current	0.21 amp approx.
Grid driving power	340 watts approx.
Fundamental component of plate current	6.25 amp peak
Minimum value of plate potential $e_{b,min}$	1,000 volts

Calculate the following:
a. Power output.
b. The inductance required in the tank circuit. Assume that the effective Q of the tank circuit = 5, resonant frequency = 1 Mc.
c. The required capacitance to tune to 1 Mc.
d. The circulating current in the tank circuit.
e. The grid driving power. Compare this result with that shown in the tabulation above. Explain any discrepancy.
f. The power input to the plate circuit.
g. The plate-circuit efficiency.

10-7. A type 851 triode is used as a class C amplifier. The operating conditions are to be

D-c plate potential	2,500 volts
D-c grid potential	−250 volts
Peak r-f grid potential	450
Ratio $e_{b,min}/e_{c,max}$	1

Determine the following:
a. D-c plate supply power. *b.* A-c output power.
c. Plate-circuit efficiency. *d.* Plate dissipation.
e. Grid driving power.

10-8. Repeat Prob. 10-7 using the method of Sec. 10-13.

10-9. A class C amplifier is operated under the following conditions:

D-c plate potential..................................	3,000 volts
D-c grid bias......................................	−200 volts
Peak r-f grid......................................	360 volts
$e_{b,min}/e_{c,max}$..	2
Peak space current.................................	2.2 amp
Conduction angle...................................	120 deg
Ratio:	
D-c grid current to peak space current...............	0.15
D-c plate current to peak space current..............	0.21
Peak plate a-c current to peak space current..........	0.37
Frequency...	2 Mc
Loaded Q..	12

Calculate the following:

a. D-c plate current.   b. Plate-circuit power input.
c. Plate dissipation.   d. Plate efficiency.
e. Grid driving power.   f. Load impedance.
g. Tank-circuit inductance.   y. Tank-circuit capacitance.

10-10. Refer to the illustrative example in Sec. 10-9. Plot the appropriate data to determine the idealized class C amplifier characteristic illustrated in Fig. 10-9. Compare the values of I_b and I_{p1m} deduced from Eqs. (10-41) and (10-42) with those given in Table 10-2.

10-11. Show the general character of the construction (like Fig. 10-7) for determining the operating features of a class C frequency tripler. In this circuit the output tank is tuned to a frequency that is three times the frequency of the grid driving source. What can be said about the plate conduction angle?

CHAPTER 11

OSCILLATORS

11-1. Introduction. The effects of feedback in amplifiers were examined in Chap. 7. It is there shown that positive feedback is to be avoided in an amplifier if stability is to be achieved. On the other hand, if the circuit is provided with a sufficient amount of regenerative feedback, the vacuum-tube circuit will serve as a generator of periodically varying waves. This output may be sinusoidal, with a high degree of purity of waveform; it may be an essentially square wave, hence being of high harmonic content; or it may be a periodically recurring nonsinusoidal waveshape.

A large variety of feedback circuits which differ considerably in detail are available for the production of self-sustained oscillations. These possess certain features which are common to all. In each case a circuit exists through which is fed back into the input circuit a certain fraction of the output and in such a phase and of such an amplitude that self-excitation results. In the usual class of tube, the feedback from the output to the input circuit is accomplished externally to the tube itself by means of coupling networks. In certain special types of tubes, e.g., a klystron of the reflex type and a magnetron of the running-wave type, the feedback is accomplished through the electron beam itself. Nevertheless even these can be represented by equivalent circuits which have features that are common to all feedback oscillators.

Conventional self-excited oscillators ordinarily operate as class C devices, although class A oscillators are possible and will be discussed below. It is desirable to consider the class C oscillator first. It is important to keep clearly in mind the fact that the theory of class C oscillators is of necessity only an approximate one owing to the nonlinear character of the region of operation of such devices. Therefore, this theory, while contributing materially to an understanding of the operation of the device, must be recognized as a limited solution of the oscillator problem. But by supplementing the theory with practical design and operating data a generally satisfactory understanding is possible.

Oscillators may assume a variety of forms, depending upon the application. The application will dictate the frequency range, the necessary

283

frequency stability, the output power, the character of the tuning controls, and other items. For example, relatively l-f power oscillators are often used for induction heating, and such units in excess of 50 kw are available commercially. The question of frequency stability is of relatively minor importance in this application. Similarly, the higher frequency dielectric heaters are also relatively simple power oscillators, with little real need for frequency stability.

The oscillator which is part of the superheterodyne receiver has a different set of requirements. Such an oscillator must be simple in design but at the same time must be quite stable. It must also be of low power and small size and must be capable of tuning over a relatively wide frequency range.

The oscillator which is to be amplified to serve as the carrier of a radio transmitter must be extremely stable, of low power, and of a single fixed frequency. In this case temperature-controlled crystal oscillators are used, with multipliers and amplifiers to set the desired frequency and power level.

11-2. Conditions for Self-excitation.[1] To ascertain the conditions that must be fulfilled for oscillations to be sustained in a vacuum-tube circuit, refer to Fig. 11-1. In Fig. 11-1a, the circuit is supposed to be open at

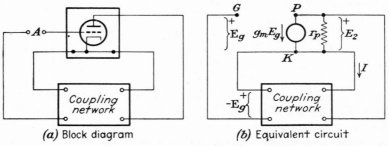

(a) Block diagram   (b) Equivalent circuit

Fig. 11-1. A vacuum-tube circuit with coupling between the output and input circuit.

point A, as shown. Suppose that a potential $\mathbf{E}_g$ is impressed on the grid of the tube, without regard to the source of this potential. The output current is given by $g_m\mathbf{E}_g$, for an assumed linear operation of the circuit. Now because of the current $\mathbf{I}$ to the input of the coupling network, a certain potential will appear across the output terminals of this coupling network. If this return potential is equal in magnitude and phase to the original potential $\mathbf{E}_g$, the circuit may be connected at point A and the system will continue to operate.

On the basis of this discussion the criterion for oscillation may be given in terms of the total gain, both amplitude and phase, around the loop consisting of the input through the amplifier, and then through the coupling network. Oscillations will occur if this total loop gain is unity and the phase change through the loop is either zero or an integral multiple of 2π.

To examine the criterion for oscillation analytically, consider first the transfer impedance of the coupling network, which is denoted by $\mathbf{Z}_T$, and which is defined as the ratio of the output potential to the input current. From the diagram of Fig. 11-1b, this is seen to be $\mathbf{Z}_T = -\mathbf{E}_g/\mathbf{I}$. Consequently, for oscillations to occur, it is necessary that

$$\left(g_m\mathbf{E}_g + \frac{\mathbf{E}_2}{r_p}\right)\mathbf{Z}_T = -\mathbf{E}_g$$

or

$$g_m\mathbf{Z}_T\left(\mathbf{E}_g + \frac{\mathbf{E}_2}{\mu}\right) = -\mathbf{E}_g$$

But since the output potential of the vacuum-tube amplifier is related to the input potential by the gain, then

$$\mathbf{E}_2 = \mathbf{K}\mathbf{E}_g$$

and so, combining with the above,

$$g_m\mathbf{Z}_T\mathbf{E}_g\left(1 + \frac{\mathbf{K}}{\mu}\right) = -\mathbf{E}_g$$

Therefore, for oscillations to be sustained, it is necessary that

$$g_m\mathbf{Z}_T\left(1 + \frac{\mathbf{K}}{\mu}\right) = -1 \tag{11-1}$$

It should be noted that both the transfer impedance $\mathbf{Z}_T$ and the driving-point impedance of the coupling network $\mathbf{Z}$ (defined as $-\mathbf{E}_2/\mathbf{I}$) are involved in this expression, the latter appearing in the expression for the gain. Equation (11-1) is one form of the Barkhausen criterion for oscillations.

A parallel expression for the conditions for sustained oscillations involving only the impedance $\mathbf{Z}$ is readily possible. Thus noting that the potential $-\mathbf{E}_2$ is given by $\mathbf{I}\mathbf{Z}$,

$$\left(g_m\mathbf{E}_g + \frac{\mathbf{E}_2}{r_p}\right)\mathbf{Z} = -\mathbf{E}_2$$

This becomes

$$\left(g_m\mathbf{E}_g + \frac{\mathbf{K}\mathbf{E}_g g_m}{\mu}\right)\mathbf{Z} = -\mathbf{K}\mathbf{E}_g$$

which reduces to

$$g_m\mathbf{Z}\left(\frac{1}{\mathbf{K}} + \frac{1}{\mu}\right) = -1 \tag{11-2}$$

This may also be written in the form

$$\frac{1}{g_m Z} + \frac{1}{\mu} = -\frac{1}{K} \qquad (11\text{-}3)$$

This is another form of the Barkhausen criterion for oscillations.

It should be noted that the ratio E_g/E_2 is a measure of the fraction of the output potential that is fed back into the input circuit through the coupling network. This ratio is denoted as β, and

$$\frac{1}{g_m Z} + \frac{1}{\mu} = -\beta \qquad (11\text{-}4)$$

Note, by combining Eqs. (11-3) and (11-4), that the feedback ratio of the network is related to the gain of the amplifier circuit by the simple relation

$$\beta K = 1 \qquad (11\text{-}5)$$

which shows that the total loop gain is unity. This condition for oscillation was discussed in Sec. 7-5.

The condition $K\beta = 1$ is the minimum case for oscillation and provides no margin for changes which might occur either in the tube or in the circuit components of the oscillator. Ordinarily practical considerations dictate that $K\beta$ be slightly greater than unity in order to allow for incidental variations in the tube and circuit parameters. A factor of safety of 5 per cent is usually adequate under most circumstances to ensure oscillation, although often the factor actually used is much higher than this.

11-3. Influence of Transconductance g_m. The criteria for oscillation given in Eqs. (11-1), (11-3), and (11-4) are valid only for the linear region of the tube characteristics, since it is only for this region that the current-source equivalent circuit is valid. Despite this limitation, the expressions may be extended with significant results over the nonlinear portion of the tube characteristics.

Refer first to Eq. (11-1). As a first approximation, K/μ, for constant μ, depends directly on g_m. Factors other than g_m are external to the tube and are independent of the potential and current magnitudes. Clearly, g_m is the only factor in the expression that will depend on the portion of the tube characteristics that is used. Likewise, in Eqs. (11-3) and (11-4), if it is assumed that μ remains substantially constant over wide excursions of signal amplitude, and this is a reasonable assumption, and since K involves μ and r_p, or g_m, then here, too, g_m is the only factor that may vary during operations.

The transconductance g_m, which is the slope of the e_c-i_b curve, is not constant for large changes of input grid potential. In fact, it is precisely this variable character of g_m which accounts for the successful operation of oscillators.   For a given set of circuit parameters, the oscillations will build up until the value assumed by g_m is such that the conditional equations [Eqs. (11-1), (11-3), and (11-4)] are satisfied, when sustained oscillations will result.   If g_m cannot assume a sufficiently large value for these equations to be satisfied, then the potential fed back from the output to the input circuit is insufficient for maintaining the oscillations and they will die out.   If g_m were too large, the potential fed back would be greater than that required for the oscillations just to be sustained and the amplitude would continue to increase.

If the average transconductance $\overline{g_m}$ is defined as the slope of the line connecting the two extreme points on the transfer characteristic appropriate to the input signal, as illustrated in Fig. 11-2,

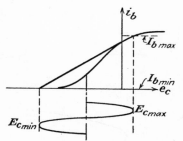

$$\overline{g_m} = \frac{I_{b,\max} - I_{b,\min}}{E_{c,\max} - E_{c,\min}} \quad (11\text{-}6)$$

FIG. 11-2. Sketch for defining the average transconductance $\overline{g_m}$.

The Barkhausen criteria for sustained oscillations in modified form become

$$\left. \begin{array}{c} -\overline{g_m}\mathbf{Z}_T\left(1 + \dfrac{\mathbf{K}}{\mu}\right) \\[2mm] -\dfrac{1}{\beta}\left(\dfrac{1}{\overline{g_m}\mathbf{Z}} + \dfrac{1}{\mu}\right) \\[2mm] -\mathbf{K}\left(\dfrac{1}{\overline{g_m}\mathbf{Z}} + \dfrac{1}{\mu}\right) \end{array} \right\} \quad \begin{array}{l} < 1 \qquad \text{decaying oscillations} \\[2mm] = 1 \qquad \text{sustained oscillations} \qquad (11\text{-}7) \\[2mm] > 1 \qquad \text{growing oscillations} \end{array}$$

An approximate relation between the average transconductance $\overline{g_m}$ as defined in Eq. (11-6) and the mutual conductance of the tube g_m is possible.   This is done by assuming that the transfer curve is linear, as illustrated in Fig. 11-3.   It follows for the usual class C condition which is illustrated that

$$\overline{g_m} = \frac{I_{b,\max}}{2E_{gm}} \quad (11\text{-}8)$$

and also that

$$g_m = \frac{I_{b,\max}}{-E_{g0} + E_{c,\max}} \quad (11\text{-}9)$$

The ratio of these expressions gives

$$\frac{\overline{g_m}}{g_m} = \frac{-E_{g0} + E_{c,\max}}{2E_{gm}} \quad (11\text{-}10)$$

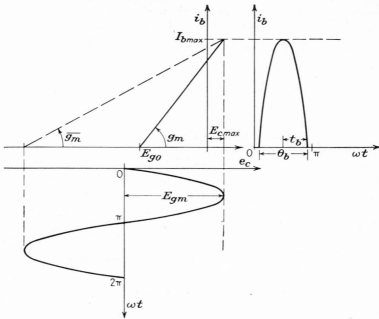

Fig. 11-3. Idealized linear transfer characteristic of a vacuum tube in an oscillator circuit.

This expression may be written in terms of the plate conduction angle θ_b. To do this requires the expression for the plate-current pulses, which is seen to be

$$i_b = g_m(-E_{g0} + E_{c,\max} - E_{gm} + E_{gm} \cos \omega t) \qquad \text{for } i_b \geqq 0 \quad (11\text{-}11)$$

But the plate current $i_b = 0$ when $t = t_b$. This leads directly to

$$-E_{g0} + E_{c,\max} = E_{gm}(1 - \cos \omega t_b) \qquad (11\text{-}12)$$

from which

$$\frac{-E_{g0} + E_{c,\max}}{2E_{gm}} = \sin^2 \frac{\omega t_b}{2} = \sin^2 \frac{\theta_b}{4} \qquad (11\text{-}13)$$

By combining this expression with Eq. (11-10), there results

$$\frac{\overline{g_m}}{g_m} = \sin^2 \frac{\theta_b}{4} \qquad (11\text{-}14)$$

It follows from this that $\overline{g_m}$ is proportional to g_m but otherwise depends only on the ratio $(-E_{g0} + E_{c,\max})/E_{gm}$. If, for example, $\theta_b = 120$ deg, then from the expression $\overline{g_m}/g_m = 0.25$.

11-4. Alternative Expression for Average Transconductance.[2] A slightly different expression for the transconductance to be used in the

Barkhausen criterion is possible. In this case the procedure assumes, as in the foregoing, that the system operates as a class C device. Also, it is based on the fact that oscillation is sustained when the loop gain at the *fundamental* frequency is unity. That is, the assumed condition for oscillation is that

$$\beta K = 1 \qquad \text{at fundamental frequency} \qquad (11\text{-}15)$$

where, as before, β is the network feedback factor, and K is the amplifier gain, at the fundamental frequency.

The assumption is now made that it is possible to define an effective transconductance $\overline{g_m}$ such that the gain of the amplifier K at the fundamental frequency is given by a relation of the usual type, namely,

$$K = \overline{g_m}Z \qquad (11\text{-}16)$$

despite the fact that the system is operating under class C conditions.

An approximate expression for $\overline{g_m}$ in terms of the g_m of the tube is possible for a transfer characteristic of specified shape. Suppose that the transfer curve is linear, as illustrated in Fig. 11-3. It is desired to find a relation between the transconductance of the tube, and $\overline{g_m}$, which is defined by the relation

$$\overline{g_m} = \frac{I_{p1m}}{E_{gm}} \qquad (11\text{-}17)$$

For the linear curve illustrated, g_m is given by Eq. (11-9). To find the desired relation, it is necessary to evaluate the fundamental component of current, I_{p1m}. This is given by the Fourier expression

$$I_{p1m} = \frac{2}{T} \int_0^T i_b \cos \omega t \, dt$$

But the plate-current pulse has the known form given by Eq. (11-11). Therefore the required expression is

$$I_{p1m} = \frac{2}{T} \int_{t_b}^{t_b} g_m[-E_{g0} + E_{c,\text{max}} - E_{gm} + E_{gm} \cos \omega t] \cos \omega t \, dt \qquad (11\text{-}18)$$

This expression integrates to

$$I_{p1m} = \frac{2}{T} g_m \frac{E_{gm}}{2} \left(t - \frac{\sin 2\omega t}{2\omega} \right) \Big|_{-t_b}^{t_b}$$

which becomes

$$I_{p1m} = \frac{g_m E_{gm}}{\pi} \omega t_b - \frac{g_m E_{gm}}{2\pi} \sin 2\omega t_b \qquad (11\text{-}19)$$

Therefore by Eq. (11-17)

$$\frac{\overline{g_m}}{g_m} = \frac{\omega t_b}{\pi} - \frac{\sin 2\omega t_b}{2\pi} \qquad (11\text{-}20)$$

In terms of the conduction angle θ_b

$$\frac{\overline{g_m}}{g_m} = \frac{\theta_b}{2\pi} - \frac{\sin \theta_b}{2\pi} \tag{11-21}$$

But for the transfer curve as defined, the plate conduction angle is defined through Eq. (11-12), namely,

$$\frac{\theta_b}{2} = \omega t_b = \cos^{-1} \frac{-E_{g0} + E_{c,\max} - E_{gm}}{E_{gm}} \tag{11-22}$$

Equation (11-21) shows that the effective slope $\overline{g_m}$ is proportional to the normal slope g_m but otherwise depends only on the ratio

$$\frac{-E_{g0} + E_{c,\max}}{E_{gm}}$$

The dependence in this case is on the same factors as in the prior calculation in Sec. 11-3, but in a somewhat different manner.

As a comparison with Eq. (11-14), again assume that $\theta_b = 120$ deg. For the present case $\overline{g_m}/g_m = 0.195$, a value slightly less than that given before. However, since both forms (11-14) and (11-21) are only approximations, either may be used with roughly comparable results.

11-5. Amplitude and Frequency Conditions. Since in Eqs. (11-7) the quantities $\mathbf{K}$, $\mathbf{Z}$, and $\mathbf{Z}_T$ are complex in general, the conditions for self-sustained oscillations require that both the real and the imaginary parts of the expressions separately and simultaneously satisfy the appropriate conditions. Refer specifically to the third equation of (11-7). Here the conditions to be satisfied are

$$\operatorname{Re}\left(\frac{1}{\overline{g_m}\mathbf{Z}} + \frac{1}{\mu}\right) = \operatorname{Re}\left(-\frac{1}{\mathbf{K}}\right)$$
$$\operatorname{Im}\left(\frac{1}{\overline{g_m}\mathbf{Z}} + \frac{1}{\mu}\right) = \operatorname{Im}\left(-\frac{1}{\mathbf{K}}\right) \tag{11-23}$$

where Re and Im denote the real and imaginary parts, respectively. The equivalent pair of expressions are

$$\left|\frac{1}{\overline{g_m}\mathbf{Z}} + \frac{1}{\mu}\right| = \left|\frac{1}{K}\right|$$
$$\angle\left(\frac{1}{\overline{g_m}\mathbf{Z}} + \frac{1}{\mu}\right) = \angle\frac{1}{\mathbf{K}} \tag{11-24}$$

The first of the two sets of conditions contains a great deal of information concerning the amplitude of the oscillations and specifies, in fact, a value of $\overline{g_m}$ or $\overline{g_m}$ and in consequence determines the amplitude of the oscillations. The second of the two sets of conditions contains information about the frequency of oscillation.

An examination of the first of Eqs. (11-24) reveals the following general information: Since μ appears in the denominator, then for large μ there is an almost $1:1$ correspondence between $\overline{g_m}$ and $\mathbf{K}$. Since, however, g_m will vary over a range from zero to some finite value, then any condition that makes $\mathbf{Z}$ large (and $\mathbf{K}$ therefore reaches a constant value) would permit most easily the production of sustained oscillations. That is, sustained oscillations are favored by circuits for which $\mathbf{Z} > r_p$. An antiresonant circuit possesses a high impedance at the resonant frequency, and the impedance drops rapidly as the frequency moves off resonance. Such a circuit is suitable to provide sustained oscillations and also provides good frequency stability. However, certain nonresonant frequency-selective circuits are also used satisfactorily in oscillator circuits. Circuits of both the resonant and nonresonant frequency-selective network types will be studied in detail.

11-6. Fixed Bias and Starting Characteristics. Before examining particular types of oscillator circuits, it is well to examine the effect of the

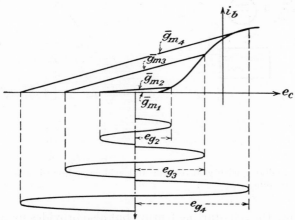

Fig. 11-4. A feedback oscillator biased to the left of cutoff, and the corresponding secants for determining the average transconductance.

grid bias on the operating features of the feedback circuit. In particular, suppose that the bias of the circuit, as indicated in Fig. 11-2, is set to a value beyond the cutoff of the tube. A number of possible operating conditions are illustrated in Fig. 11-4. Evidently the initial value of $\overline{g_m} = \overline{g_{m1}}$ is zero, and Eqs. (11-7) show that oscillations cannot build up since the circuit conditions correspond to decaying oscillations.

Suppose that a potential e_{g2} is applied, whether from an external source or produced by a transient phenomenon. If the mean value of $\overline{g_{m2}}$ is small, the conditions required by Eqs. (11-7) for sustained oscillations may still not be satisfied and the oscillations may die out. If the signal, say e_{g3}, appears on the grid and if this is sufficiently large for oscillations to grow, the amplitude of e_{g3} will increase until the conditions for sustained oscillations are fulfilled.

Clearly, for an oscillator biased near to or beyond cutoff, the circuit will not be self-starting. However, as is evident by comparing the results illustrated in Fig. 11-4 with those in Fig. 11-2, the amplitude of the oscillations is larger in the heavily biased oscillator. This results in an increased efficiency, a feature that may be very desirable in a power oscillator although it is usually of small consequence in low-power sources. Also, since it is quite easy to induce oscillations, the overbiased condition is not objectionable from this point of view.

11-7. Grid-resistor–Grid-capacitor Biasing Circuits. The use of a grid-resistor and grid-capacitor combination, as illustrated in Fig. 11-5,

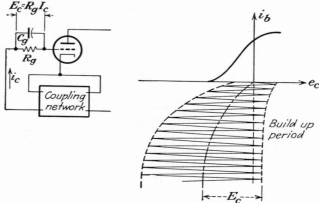

Fig. 11-5. An oscillator with grid-resistor and grid-capacitor biasing. The build-up conditions are sketched.

not only allows the self-starting feature but also provides for an operating bias at or beyond cutoff. The operation of the circuit is illustrated in Fig. 11-5 and is essentially the following: When the circuit is first placed in operation, the grid bias is zero and the operating point is high on the characteristic, where the value of g_m is large. The third of the criteria [Eqs. (11-7)] applies, and growing oscillations occur and continue to increase in amplitude. On the positive portion of the swing, the grid potential becomes positive, thus charging the capacitor. The time constant of the grid resistor and capacitor is such that a substantially steady bias is maintained. This bias displaces the operating point to the left, as illustrated, with consequent increasing amplitude of oscillations. The amplitude of the oscillations continues to increase until an equilibrium condition is reached between this amplitude and the consequent bias E_c.

The magnitude of the bias may be controlled to some extent by the proper choice of R_g and C_g, although, as discussed in Sec. 10-9, the values of R_g and C_g are not critical. They are generally determined experimentally.

As illustrated, the amplitude of oscillation will be such as to allow a small grid current to flow during the positive peaks of the cycle. It is this small grid current which serves to charge the grid capacitor. In fact, the variation in grid current can be used as an indication that oscillations have been established and also as a rough indication of the amplitude.

If the time constant $R_g C_g$ is too large, the bias potential across C_g adjusts itself slowly to sudden changes in the amplitude of oscillation. If this rate of adjustment is so slow that the oscillations can die out before the bias potential can change appreciably, then with sudden changes in the amplitude the action is very much as though fixed bias were used. As a result, it is possible that the oscillations will die out. Hence a possible condition is one in which the oscillations first build up in amplitude to the equilibrium value. Any slight irregularity that tends to reduce the amplitude of the oscillations will cause the oscillations to die out owing to the substantially steady bias that exists. Once the grid capacitor discharges through the grid resistor and the bias reduces sufficiently, the oscillations will again build up, until the above process repeats itself. This intermittent operation can be overcome by decreasing the time constant $R_g C_g$. For stability to exist, it is necessary that the bias reduce as the amplitude of oscillations decreases.

11-8. Tuned-plate Oscillator. The tuned-plate oscillator is one in which an antiresonant circuit is connected directly in the plate circuit of the vacuum tube, the grid excitation being supplied by inductive coupling to this plate circuit. The complete circuit has the form illustrated in Fig. 11-6. It should be specifically noted that this is just the circuit of a tuned class C amplifier, but with the circuit providing its own grid excitation. Consequently the analyses of Chap. 10 of the tuned class C

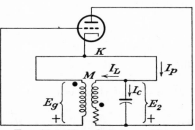

Fig. 11-6. Tuned-plate oscillator.

amplifier apply for the tuned-plate oscillator except that the grid driving power reduces the total available power output. Owing to this slight difference, power tubes carry a single manufacturer's rating as an r-f power amplifier and oscillator.

In order to examine certain of the properties of the oscillator the conditional equation for sustained oscillations [Eqs. (11-7)] will be examined. For simplicity, it will be assumed that the grid current may be neglected.

The grid excitation is then simply

$$\mathbf{E}_g = j\omega M\mathbf{I}_L \equiv \mathbf{Z}_M\mathbf{I}_L$$

The transfer impedance is given by the relation

$$\mathbf{Z}_T = \frac{-\mathbf{E}_g}{\mathbf{I}_p} = -\frac{\mathbf{Z}_M\mathbf{I}_L}{\mathbf{I}_L + \mathbf{I}_c} \tag{11-25}$$

But since $\mathbf{I}_L\mathbf{Z}_L = \mathbf{I}_c\mathbf{Z}_c$,

$$\mathbf{Z}_T = -\frac{\mathbf{Z}_M\mathbf{I}_L}{\mathbf{I}_L + \mathbf{I}_L(\mathbf{Z}_L/\mathbf{Z}_c)} = -\frac{\mathbf{Z}_M\mathbf{Z}_c}{\mathbf{Z}_L + \mathbf{Z}_c} \tag{11-26}$$

Also, the quantity

$$1 + \frac{\mathbf{K}}{\mu} = 1 - \frac{\mathbf{Z}}{r_p + \mathbf{Z}} = \frac{r_p}{r_p + \mathbf{Z}} \tag{11-27}$$

where

$$\mathbf{Z} = \frac{\mathbf{Z}_L\mathbf{Z}_c}{\mathbf{Z}_L + \mathbf{Z}_c} \tag{11-28}$$

The conditional equation for sustained oscillations may then be written in the form

$$\overline{g_m} \frac{\mathbf{Z}_M\mathbf{Z}_c}{\mathbf{Z}_L + \mathbf{Z}_c} \frac{r_p}{r_p + (\mathbf{Z}_L\mathbf{Z}_c/\mathbf{Z}_L + \mathbf{Z}_c)} = 1 \tag{11-29}$$

which is

$$\overline{g_m}\mathbf{Z}_M\mathbf{Z}_c = (\mathbf{Z}_L + \mathbf{Z}_c) + \frac{\mathbf{Z}_L\mathbf{Z}_c}{r_p}$$

or

$$\overline{g_m}\frac{M}{C} = R + j\left(\omega L - \frac{1}{\omega C}\right) - j\frac{R}{\omega Cr_p} + \frac{L}{Cr_p} \tag{11-30}$$

By equating the real and the imaginary terms, there results

$$\overline{g_m}\frac{M}{C} = R + \frac{L}{Cr_p} \qquad \text{amplitude condition}$$

$$\tag{11-31}$$

and $\qquad \omega L - \frac{1}{\omega C} - \frac{R}{\omega Cr_p} = 0 \qquad \text{phase condition}$

The first of these equations may be written in the form

$$\overline{g_m} = \frac{\mu RC}{\mu M - L} \tag{11-32}$$

which specifies the average of $\overline{g_m}$ (or $\overline{\overline{g_m}}$) and which, through Eq. (11-14) or (11-21), specifies the plate conduction angle θ_b. This expression provides information, at least in principle, concerning the amplitude of the oscillations.

The second equation becomes

$$\omega^2 = \frac{1}{LC}\left(1 + \frac{R}{r_p}\right) \tag{11-33}$$

If the quantity ω_0 is defined by the relation

$$\omega_0 = \frac{1}{\sqrt{LC}}$$

Eq. (11-33) becomes

$$\omega = \omega_0 \sqrt{1 + \frac{R}{r_p}} \qquad (11\text{-}34)$$

This equation shows that the frequency of oscillation will be approximately the resonant frequency of the circuit, the factor involving the ratio R/r_p being small. However, the frequency of oscillation will always be slightly higher than the resonant value. Clearly, the tube plays only a minor part in determining the frequency of oscillation, the external circuit elements exercising the main control. In fact, the influence of the tube on the frequency becomes less as the shunt resistance of the antiresonant circuit increases or, correspondingly, as the series resistance in the tank decreases.

If circuits of very low dissipation are provided, the oscillator has a very high degree of stability.

A sinor diagram of the circuit in its steady oscillating state may be drawn; this applies for the fundamental frequency. In the diagram (Fig. 11-7), the sinors are not drawn to scale owing to the different orders of magnitude that usually exist

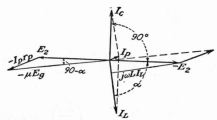

Fig. 11-7. The sinor diagram of a tuned-plate oscillator.

among the currents and potentials. Also, angles are exaggerated for clarity.

Under most circumstances the angle $\alpha = \tan^{-1}(\omega L/R) = \tan^{-1} Q$ will be very nearly equal to 90 deg, and the feedback angle $(90 - \alpha)$, that is, the angle between $-\mathbf{E}_2$ and $\mathbf{E}_g$, will be very small. This means that the feedback occurs substantially with 180 deg phase displacement, so that a decreasing plate potential reflects itself as an increasing potential on the grid. Since there is also a phase shift of 180 deg through the tube, the phase shift around the complete loop is zero or 2π, as already discussed.

11-9. Other Oscillator Circuits. A variety of vacuum-tube feedback oscillator circuits exist, each of which possesses some special characteristics. The basic circuits and the coupling networks of the more important types of oscillators (see Prob. 11-1 for the amplitude and frequency equations) are contained in Fig. 11-8. In each of these circuits operation is essentially class C, the essential difference among them being in the coupling network.

Each of these circuits provides an antiresonant circuit of some type, with either inductive or conductive coupling between the output and input circuits. This does not imply that only circuits which possess an antiresonant circuit will operate successfully as an oscillator. In fact, circuits in which the feedback is accomplished through resistance

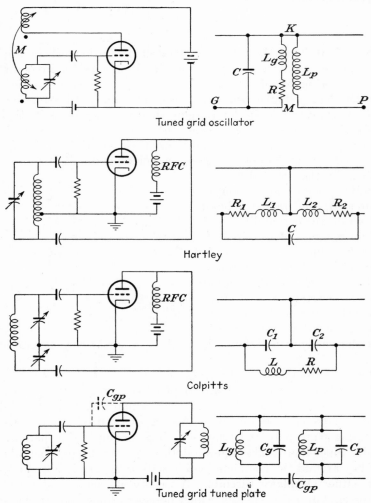

FIG. 11-8. The circuits and coupling networks of the more important oscillators.

and capacitance networks will be examined in some detail. However, the above networks do possess a feature that is common to all feedback oscillator circuits; they all provide a 180-deg phase shift between the output and input circuit so as to satisfy the necessary condition for regenerative feedback to exist.

A special word is desirable about the tuned-grid–tuned-plate oscillator. This oscillator depends for its operation on the feedback that will be possible through the grid-plate capacitance C_{gp}. In this circuit the plate tank resonant frequency is slightly higher than the resonant frequency of the grid tank. This causes the plate circuit to be inductive, and a negative input resistance results which overcomes the grid-circuit losses and thus allows oscillations to occur.

11-10. Stabilization of Feedback Oscillators.[3] Vacuum-tube oscillators will suffer changes in frequency with variations in any operating characteristic that involves either the tube or the circuit parameters. For example, a change in temperature may cause a change in the inductance and capacitance of the tank elements and may also cause a change in the grid-cathode and the plate-cathode interelectrode capacitances. Also, a change in plate potential will result in changes in the interelectrode capacitances. A change in the coupled load causes a change in the shunt resistance, with a consequent change in frequency. Although these factors have been neglected in the explicit discussion given above of the various oscillator circuits, they do play a part in determining the frequency, since they will contribute to a variation of the tube or circuit constants of the coupling network.

A relationship can be obtained which serves as a guide in estimating the relative frequency stability of an oscillator, the comparative frequency stability of several oscillators, or the influence of factors which have only a slight effect on the frequency of the oscillator.

The desired relationship may be found from Eq. (11-5), viz., $\mathbf{K\beta} = 1$, which is the condition for oscillation. When oscillations exist, the amplitude $|\mathbf{K\beta}|$ and the total circuit phase shift must have such values as to satisfy the basic condition for oscillation. Suppose that the phase shift through the tube does not vary appreciably with frequency, for very small changes in frequency. This is generally a valid assumption. Any variation in frequency must be accompanied by a change in the phase of the β network which is such that the total phase of the circuit remains substantially constant; otherwise oscillations will cease. The rate of variation of phase with frequency $d\theta/d\omega$ is evidently related to the frequency stability of the system. In fact, the frequency stability S_f is defined by the relation

$$S_f = \omega_0 \frac{d\theta}{d\omega} = \frac{d\theta}{d\omega/\omega_0} \tag{11-35}$$

where ω_0 is the mean frequency of the oscillator. Clearly, the larger the value of S_f, the more stable is the system. In the limit as S_f becomes infinite, the oscillator is completely frequency-stable.

As an indication of the significance of this stability criterion, suppose that a variation occurs in some element of the circuit, other than the β network, which is supposed to control the frequency of the system. If the requisite phase condition implied by Eq. (11-5) were initially satisfied at the particular frequency of oscillation, then when the change in the element occurs, the circuital phase condition will, in general, no longer be satisfied. As a result, the frequency of the oscillator will shift until the circuital phase condition is satisfied once again. If the β network produces a very large phase shift for a small frequency change, i.e., if S_f is large, then the required frequency shift to restore the circuital phase condition will be very small.

A number of corrective measures may be taken in order to improve the stability of an oscillator. This would include the careful choice of the inductor and capacitor, either with negligible temperature coefficients or with such temperature variation that a change in one is counteracted by an opposite change in the other. Any changes that might result

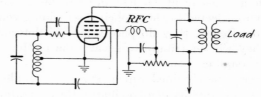

Fig. 11-9. Electron-coupled oscillator.

from changes in the plate potential can be overcome by the use of adequately regulated sources.

The effect of changes in the load impedance on the frequency may be eliminated by using an amplifier to separate the load from the oscillator. This system is called a *master-oscillator power-amplifier arrangement* and is usually abbreviated MOPA.

The oscillator and power amplifier can be combined into a single tube by using a tetrode or a pentode. Such an oscillator is called an *electron-coupled* oscillator. A typical electron-coupled oscillator circuit employing a pentode is illustrated in Fig. 11-9. Here the cathode, grid 1, and grid 2 are operated as a conventional Hartley oscillator, grid 2 acting as the ordinary anode in a triode. The current to grid 2 is small, but it is sufficient to maintain the oscillations. The main part of the space current serves to produce the power in the load impedance. The plate current is controlled by the oscillator portion of the tube, but since the plate current is substantially independent of the plate potential, except at the very low plate potentials, there is a very little reaction between the output circuit and the oscillator section of the tube.

In such electron-coupled oscillators it is found that increasing the plate potential causes the frequency to decrease slightly, whereas increasing the screen potential causes the frequency to increase slightly.   Hence, by obtaining the screen potential from a potential divider, as shown in Fig. 11-9, and by locating the screen tap at the proper point (and this is determined experimentally), it is possible to make the frequency substantially independent of the plate supply potential.

The effects of a varying plate resistance r_p on the frequency can be materially reduced through the use of *resistance stabilization*.   In this, a resistance R_s is added between the plate of the tube and the tank circuit. This added resistance serves to make the total effective resistance in the plate circuit so high that changes in the plate resistance of the tube have very little effect on the frequency.   The resistance also serves as a convenient means of controlling the feedback and hence the amplitude of the oscillations.   It is ordinarily desirable that the resistance be made so high that the oscillations will just barely start.

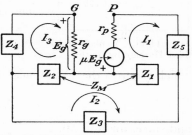

FIG. 11-10. The basic circuit of impedance stabilization.

Llewellyn[3] has shown that the frequency of oscillation can be made to approach the resonant frequency of the tuned circuit by inserting suitable reactances in series with the grid or with the plate, or both.   This might be called *impedance stabilization*.   It follows from the equivalent circuit of an oscillator shown in Fig. 11-10 that

$$- \mu E_g = \varrho_{11}I_1 + \varrho_{12}I_2 + \varrho_{13}I_3$$
$$0 = \varrho_{21}I_1 + \varrho_{22}I_2 + \varrho_{23}I_3 \qquad (11\text{-}36)$$
$$0 = \varrho_{31}I_1 + \varrho_{32}I_2 + \varrho_{33}I_3$$

where

$$\varrho_{11} = r_p + Z_1 + Z_5 \qquad \qquad \varrho_{22} \equiv Z_0 = Z_1 + Z_2 + Z_3 + 2Z_M$$
$$\varrho_{12} = \varrho_{21} = -Z_1 + Z_M \qquad \varrho_{23} = \varrho_{32} = -(Z_2 + Z_M) \qquad (11\text{-}37)$$
$$\varrho_{13} = -Z_M \qquad \qquad \qquad \varrho_{33} = r_g + Z_2 + Z_4$$

and

$$E_g = I_3 r_g \qquad (11\text{-}38)$$

The expressions that result by equating the real and the imaginary terms are

$$X_0[r_p(X_2 + X_4) + r_g(X_1 + X_5)] + \mu r_g(X_1 + X_M)(X_2 + X_M)$$
$$= X_0 X_M \mu r_g - (X_1 + X_M)^2 r_g + (X_2 + X_M)^2 r_p \qquad (11\text{-}39)$$

from the reals and

$$X_0[r_p r_g - (X_1 + X_5)(X_2 + X_4)] - 2X_M(X_1 + X_M)(X_2 + X_M)$$
$$= -X_0 X_M^2 - (X_1 + X_M)^2(X_2 + X_4) - (X_2 + X_M)^2(X_1 + X_5) \qquad (11\text{-}40)$$

from the imaginaries. If in Eq. (11-40) X_4 and X_5 have such values as to satisfy the condition

$$2X_M(X_1 + X_M)(X_2 + X_M)$$
$$= (X_1 + X_M)^2(X_2 + X_4) + (X_2 + X_M)^2(X_1 + X_5)$$

which contains all terms not containing Z_0, then the resonant frequency is exactly that to cause X_0 to become zero and to remain so independently of r_p, r_g, and μ. That is, the frequency of oscillation is exactly the series-resonant frequency of the tuned circuit.

As a particular example, consider a plate-stabilized Hartley oscillator, as shown in Fig. 11-11. The condition for stabilization becomes, by writing $X_4 = 0$,

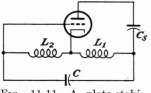

Fig. 11-11. A plate-stabilized Hartley oscillator.

$$X_5 = 2\omega M \frac{L_1 - M}{L_2 + M} - \omega L_2 \left(\frac{L_1 + M}{L_2 + M}\right)^2 - \omega L_1$$

which requires that X_5 be negative. By setting

$$X_5 = -\frac{1}{\omega C_5}$$

and since, for $X_0 = 0$,

$$\omega^2 = \frac{1}{C(L_1 + L_2 + 2M)}$$

then

$$C_5 = C \frac{L_1 + L_2 + 2M}{L_1 + L_2 \left(\dfrac{L_1 + M}{L_2 + M}\right)^2 - 2M \dfrac{L_1 + M}{L_2 + M}}$$

For the ideal case in which the effective tank circuit Q is extremely high, the compensation is perfect, and the frequency is independent of the tube potentials. In the actual case, the compensating reactances must be adjusted experimentally, and the compensation, although not perfect, represents a substantial improvement in independence of frequency from tube variations.

Several other cases, with all power sources omitted, are illustrated in Fig. 11-12.

11-11. Crystal Oscillators.[4] The frequency stability of an oscillator can be made very high by utilizing piezoelectric crystals as antiresonant circuits. Such crystals, which are sections cut from a quartz crystal in such a way that the flat sides are perpendicular to an electrical axis, when stressed or compressed along this axis, are accompanied by the appearance of electric charges on the surface of the crystal. Conversely, when such crystals are placed in an alternating electric field, they are set into mechanical vibration. If the applied electrical frequency is very near to that which produces mechanical resonance, the amplitude of the vibrations will be very large.

A vibrating crystal can be replaced by an equivalent electrical circuit, as shown in Fig. 11-13. In this circuit, C_m represents the capacitance of the crystal and its mounting when it is not oscillating; the series combination L, C, and R represents the electrical equivalent of the vibrational characteristics of the material. L is the electrical equivalent of the crystal mass that is effective in vibration, C is the electrical equivalent of

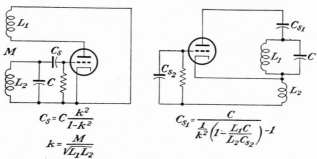

$$C_S = C \frac{k^2}{1-k^2}$$

$$k = \frac{M}{\sqrt{L_1 L_2}}$$

$$C_{S_1} = \frac{C}{\frac{1}{k^2}\left(1 - \frac{L_1 C}{L_2 C_{S_2}}\right) - 1}$$

FIG. 11-12. Impedance-stabilized oscillators.

the crystal compliance, and R is the electrical equivalent of the coefficient of friction. The values of L and C are in series resonance at the frequency of mechanical resonance.

One of the most common types of crystal-controlled oscillators is illustrated in Fig. 11-14. When the crystal is replaced by its equivalent circuit, it is seen that the oscillator is essentially of the tuned-plate tuned-grid type, the crystal making up the tuned-grid circuit. Owing to the

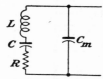

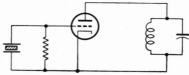

FIG. 11-13. The equivalent electrical network of a vibrating quartz crystal.

FIG. 11-14. A crystal-controlled oscillator.

extremely high Q of the equivalent circuit of the crystal, which may be 100 times as high as that of a conventional electrical circuit, the crystal can oscillate only over a very narrow frequency range. As a result, the frequency stability of such an oscillator is very high. When the temperature of the crystal is maintained constant, the frequency drift can be made less than 1 part in 10^6.

11-12. Class A Oscillator.[5] Considerable stabilization is made possible by operating an oscillator as a class A instead of a class C device, for this eliminates the grid current and any nonlinear effects resulting from it. Moreover, the output waveshape from a class A oscillator will be sinusoidal, with a high degree of purity of waveform. Owing to the manner of its operation, the oscillating frequency is determined by the resonant elements. However, since the self-regulating amplitude-control feature of the nonlinear tube characteristic is no longer being employed, other methods must be provided in order to stabilize the amplitude of the

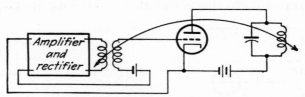

FIG. 11-15. A linear-stabilized oscillator.

output. One way for providing for linear stabilized operation is illustrated in Fig. 11-15. In this circuit, the output is coupled to a rectifier, the output of which is used to control the d-c bias of the oscillator. If the gain of the amplifier before rectification is large, thus yielding a large d-c output, the oscillator will operate as a linear amplifier. A circuit showing the details of such an amplitude-stabilized oscillator is given in Fig. 11-16.

Amplitude stabilization may be effected by providing an amplitude-sensitive network to control the output of the oscillator. Such a method

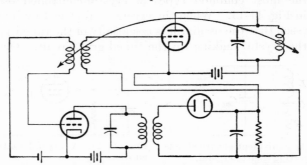

FIG. 11-16. The circuit of a linear-stabilized oscillator.

is employed in the Wien-bridge oscillator, which is described in the next section.

11-13. Resistance-Capacitance Oscillators. A form of coupling network that has been used extensively in relatively l-f oscillators is given in Fig. 11-17. The phase shift through such a network as this is a fairly sensitive function of the frequency, and such RC oscillators possess good frequency stability. However, such a simple network will not provide a large phase shift between the input and output terminals, and it is necessary to incorporate a second vacuum tube in the circuit in order to provide an additional 180-deg phase shift.   The circuit, when drawn in the manner of the previous circuits, is shown in Fig. 11-18.

This circuit may be analyzed in a direct manner by an application of Eqs. (11-7). Refer to Fig. 11-19, which shows the com-

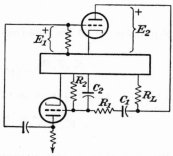

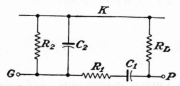

Fig. 11-17. An RC coupling network for an oscillator.

Fig. 11-18. An RC coupled oscillator.

plete coupling network, in which the amplifier is replaced by a "black box" which provides a gain K and a phase shift of 180 deg.   An inspection of this diagram shows that

$$E_1 = K_N E_2'$$

This may be written in the form

$$E_1 = K_N I Z_g$$

if it is assumed that the input impedance to the amplifier is very high.

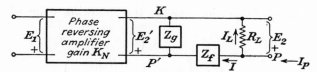

Fig. 11-19. The complete coupling circuit of the RC oscillator.

The transfer impedance of the network becomes

$$Z_T = \frac{E_1}{I_p} = \frac{K_N I Z_g}{I_L + I}$$

But as

$$I(Z_g + Z_f) = I_L R_L$$

then

$$Z_T = \frac{K_N I Z_g}{I \dfrac{Z_g + Z_f}{R_L} + I} = \frac{K_N Z_g R_L}{Z_g + Z_f + R_L} \tag{11-41}$$

Also, it is noted that the impedance looking into the feedback network is

$$Z = \frac{R_L(Z_g + Z_f)}{R_L + Z_g + Z_f} \tag{11-42}$$

The term $1 + \mathbf{K}_a/\mu$ which appears in Eqs. (11-7) becomes

$$1 + \frac{\mathbf{K}_a}{\mu} = \frac{r_p}{r_p + \dfrac{R_L(\mathbf{Z}_g + \mathbf{Z}_f)}{R_L + \mathbf{Z}_g + \mathbf{Z}_f}} \tag{11-43}$$

Equation (11-7) for sustained oscillations becomes

$$-\overline{g_m}\mathbf{K}_N\mathbf{Z}_gR_L \frac{r_p}{r_p(R_L + \mathbf{Z}_g + \mathbf{Z}_f) + R_L(\mathbf{Z}_g + \mathbf{Z}_f)} = 1 \tag{11-44}$$

This may be written in the form

$$-\overline{g_m}\mathbf{K}_N R_L r_p = \frac{r_p(R_L + \mathbf{Z}_g + \mathbf{Z}_f) + R_L(\mathbf{Z}_g + \mathbf{Z}_f)}{\mathbf{Z}_g} \tag{11-45}$$

By including in this expression the known expressions of $\mathbf{Z}_g$ and $\mathbf{Z}_f$, namely,

$$\mathbf{Z}_g = \frac{-j(R_2/\omega C_2)}{R_2 - j(1/\omega C_2)} \qquad \mathbf{Z}_f = R_1 - j\frac{1}{\omega C_1}$$

and equating real and imaginary terms, two expressions result.   They are

$$r_p R_L R_2 + (r_p + R_L)\left(R_1 R_2 - \frac{1}{\omega^2 C_1 C_2}\right) = 0$$

$$-\overline{g_m}\mathbf{K}_N R_L r_p R_2 = r_p R_L + (r_p + R_L)\left(R_1 + R_2 + \frac{R_2 C_2}{C_1}\right) \tag{11-46}$$

The first of these expressions yields the following expression for the frequency:

$$\omega^2 = \frac{1}{C_1 C_2\left(R_1 R_2 + \dfrac{R_2 R_L}{1 + R_L/r_p}\right)} \tag{11-47}$$

The second expression yields

$$\overline{g_m} = \frac{1}{\mathbf{K}_N R_L r_p R_2}\left[r_p R_L + (r_p + R_L)\left(R_1 + R_2 + \frac{R_2 C_2}{C_1}\right)\right] \tag{11-48}$$

Ordinarily the circuit constants are chosen: $R_1 = R_2 = R; C_1 = C_2 = C;$ $R \gg R_L;$

$$\omega^2 = \frac{1}{C^2\left(R^2 + \dfrac{R R_L}{1 + R_L/r_p}\right)} \doteq \frac{1}{C^2 R^2} \tag{11-49}$$

and

$$\overline{g_m} = -\frac{1}{\mathbf{K}_N R_L r_p R}[r_p R_L + 3R(r_p + R_L)] = -\frac{3}{\mathbf{K}_N}\left(\frac{1}{r_p} + \frac{1}{R_L}\right) \tag{11-50}$$

It will be observed from Eq. (11-50) that the coupling amplifier $\mathbf{K}_N$ which is part of the β network must indeed provide phase reversal, as indicated in Fig. 11-19. Moreover, for the values of r_p and R_L which might ordinarily be used, the magnitude of the gain of this coupling amplifier might be of the order of unity or less. What is implied by this expression, therefore, is that the phase shift through the passive elements of the coupling network, composed of C_1R_1 in series with the parallel combination of C_2 and R_2, is 0 deg, a fact that is readily verified by simple network considerations, and that the amplifier circuit is required in order to provide the necessary 180 deg. From purely practical considerations since the amplifier $\mathbf{K}_N$ would normally provide a gain considerably in excess of that required, negative feedback is ordinarily

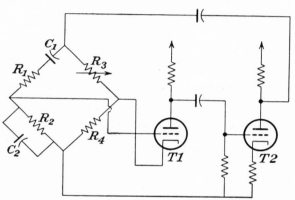

FIG. 11-20. The Wien-bridge oscillator.

included in both vacuum-tube circuits, both to reduce the gain and to improve the waveform. The manner of achieving feedback is illustrated in Fig. 11-20. Because of the form of the network, this RC oscillator is known as a Wien-bridge oscillator.

The modification shown introduces certain significant consequences into the operation of the circuit. In particular, for a given R_4 and tube $T1$, if R_3 is adjusted so that the bridge is balanced, the grid-cathode potential is zero. That is, the Wien-bridge output (in this case, chosen as the grid-cathode potential) is zero at the balance point but is different from zero for all frequencies in the neighborhood of balance. Clearly, there will be no feedback at the balance point, and the system will not oscillate. Note that, for the bridge itself (neglecting the loading of R_4 by tube $T1$), the conditions for balance and the frequency at balance are

$$\frac{R_3}{R_4} = \frac{R_1}{R_2} + \frac{C_2}{C_1} \qquad \omega_0^2 = \frac{1}{R_1R_2C_1C_2}$$

which become, for $R_1 = R_2 = R$, $C_1 = C_2 = C$, as chosen above

$$\frac{R_3}{R_4} = 2 \qquad \omega_0 = \frac{1}{RC}$$

Thus, for these conditions, the circuit is a frequency-selective feedback rejection amplifier (see Sec. 9-8). For the circuit to act as an oscillator, the ratio R_3/R_4 must be chosen greater than 2.

Continuous variation of frequency of this oscillator is accomplished by varying simultaneously the two capacitors C_1 and C_2, these being variable air capacitors. Changes in frequency range are accomplished by switching into the circuit different values for the two resistors R_1 and R_2. Variable resistors could, in principle, be used for the continuous control, but it is more difficult to build resistors which track with the same precision possible with variable air capacitors.

Owing to the limitations imposed on variable air capacitors, to attain low frequencies requires that large resistances be used. A practical limit exists to the size of R, in one instance because of blocking that might occur in $T1$ (note that one R is the grid resistance of this stage) and second because of the increasing problem of shielding the grid against stray 60-cps potentials from the power supply. A practical limit to the size of R is perhaps 10 megohms, so that low frequencies of the order of

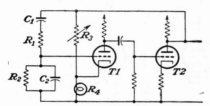

FIG. 11-21. The Wien-bridge oscillator with amplitude stabilization.

10 cps may readily be achieved. At the high frequencies, with the consequent reduction of R, the loading of the phase-inverting amplifier increases. Even if the loading does not stop the oscillations, it will affect the stability of the amplitude of the oscillations with changes of frequency range.

A very ingenious modification of this circuit,[6] which serves to stabilize the amplitude against range switching and against aging of tubes, replaces R_4 by a tungsten-filament lamp, ordinarily a 115-volt 3-watt lamp. The revised circuit is given in Fig. 11-21. The effect of providing the tungsten-filament lamp, which possesses a positive temperature coefficient of resistance, is to provide a system which automatically changes the feedback factor of the coupling network in such a direction as to keep the total gain more nearly constant as the gain of $T1$ and $T2$ varies because of loading or other variations in the circuit. Suppose that there were, for whatever reason, an increase of current through the lamp. The lamp resistance will increase, thereby increasing the feedback factor and reducing the gain. The gain change will be such as to maintain the current through the lamp almost unchanged.

The current through the tungsten lamp R_4 consists of three components; (1) the d-c component through $T1$, which for class A operation is essentially constant; (2) the a-c component through $T1$ due to the a-c potential on the grid; (3) the a-c component of opposite phase through R_3 to the cathode. The resultant a-c current through R_4 is comparable with, and perhaps larger than, the d-c component, with the result that the value of the resistance of R_4 will be controlled to a very large extent by the amplitude of the oscillations. Note, of course, that for adequate control of the amplitude the thermal time constant of the tungsten lamp

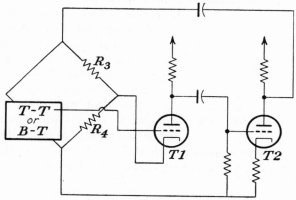

Fig. 11-22. The bridged-T or twin-T oscillator.

must be large compared with the period of the oscillations; otherwise an amplitude drift may occur.

The parallel-T and the bridged-T networks which were examined in Chap. 9 together with the Wien-bridge as coupling networks for frequency-selective amplifiers may also be used in oscillator circuits,[7] in much the same way as the Wien bridge. However, as noted in Chap. 9 these networks are essentially rejection circuits at the balance frequency. To effect the necessary inversion and the proper freedom from loading, the circuit of Fig. 11-22 may be used. In this circuit, the inversion is derived from the resistor combination R_3R_4, tube $T2$ serving principally to provide a low-impedance driving source. That is, the cathode of tube $T1$ is always at a higher a-c potential than the grid. In these circuits R_4 must be larger than R_3.

It is possible to view the foregoing circuits as well as the Wien-bridge circuit as providing two potentials to the input of tube $T1$, one of which is of such phase as to constitute regenerative feedback and thereby increases the gain over that in the absence of feedback, while the other introduces degenerative feedback. The resultant magnitudes of the two feedback potentials as a function of frequency are such that degeneration occurs at all frequencies except for a small range in the neighborhood of the frequency of oscillation. It is only at these frequencies that oscillation will occur.

From practical considerations, the Wien-bridge oscillator is preferred to the other circuits, because of the ease of frequency control and variation, and because fewer variable circuit elements are required for control.

A simple one-tube *phase-shift*[8] oscillator is possible which incorporates RC networks alone to provide the requisite 180-deg phase difference between input and output potentials. The circuit is illustrated in Fig. 11-23. The operation may best be understood by considering that each L section, which consists of a C and R combination, shifts the phase by 60 deg at the frequency ω. This explanation assumes that there is no loading by- one RC combination on the others and that there is no loading by the coupling networks on the plate load resistance. The use of three such sections will shift the phase of the output by a total of 180 deg relative to

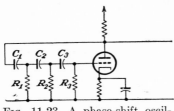

Fig. 11-23. A phase-shift oscillator.

the input, and this, together with the 180-deg shift by the tube, will provide the 2π shift for successful operation. Under these assumptions, it follows that

$$\tan \theta = \sqrt{3} = \frac{1}{\omega RC}$$

or

$$\omega = \frac{1}{\sqrt{3}\ RC} \qquad (11\text{-}51)$$

A more exact calculation, under the assumption that the amplifier loading by the phase-shifting network may be neglected, yields the relation

$$\omega = \frac{1}{\sqrt{6}\ RC} \qquad (11\text{-}52)$$

It would be possible, of course, to obtain the required 180-deg phase shift with more than three sections, but there is no particular advantage in doing so.

As might be surmised, there is an appreciable attenuation in potential in progressing through the network. At the frequency of oscillation, it is found that $\beta = \frac{1}{29}$. For oscillations to be possible, i.e., to fulfill the condition $|\beta K| = 1$, the amplifier gain must be at least 29. Consequently, either a high-μ triode or a pentode must be employed in such a circuit.

The frequency of the oscillator may be varied by changing the value of any of the elements in the feedback network. However, care in the change of the element is important; otherwise the impedance looking into the phase-shifting network, and its phase, may change to such an extent that the $K\beta = 1$ relation may no longer be satisfied, and oscillations will cease. For small variations in frequency, a single element may be changed. For wide variations in frequency, the three capacitors should be varied simultaneously. The three resistors could also be varied simultaneously, but this would cause a serious change in impedance, with a consequent effect on the amplifier gain and the possibility of discontinued oscillation. It is quite possible, of course, to remove the restriction that the values of all R and of all C be equal. Such a change will complicate the matter of securing variable frequency operation.

11-14. Negative-resistance Oscillators. One may consider the foregoing analyses of feedback oscillators as a demonstration of the fact that

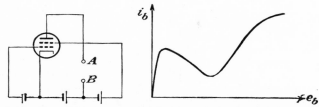

Fig. 11-24. A negative-resistance tetrode circuit, and the plate characteristics, showing the region of negative plate resistance.

it is possible to devise circuits containing vacuum tubes in which the power generated is sufficient to overcome the losses of the circuit and also to provide the power that is transferred to an external circuit. If the total loading or dissipation within the circuit is represented by a certain equivalent resistance in the plate circuit, then one might consider the tube as representing a negative resistance of such a magnitude as just to overcome the total dissipative terms. The oscillations in the circuit will then be sustained at the stable level required by the variations of the negative-resistance properties of the circuit.

If one is able to find a device that possesses a negative resistance, i.e., a device in which a positive increment of current through it is accompanied by a negative potential increment across it, then this can be used to neutralize the positive resistance representing the total dissipation.

Such negative-resistance devices do exist, the simple tetrode operating with a plate potential below that of the screen being a common example. The connections of such a device and the plate characteristics which show the region of negative plate resistance are shown in Fig. 11-24.

A circuit that exhibits an effective negative resistance and at the same time avoids the objectionable features of secondary emission is illustrated in Fig. 11-25. A pentode is operated with a plate potential that is lower than the screen potential, and the suppressor grid is maintained slightly negative relative to the cathode. Since the plate is at a low positive potential, it does not exert much force on the electrons and under these conditions the suppressor grid repels most of the electrons that manage to get past the screen grid, with a resulting higher screen current.

If the suppressor potential is increased slightly, i.e., is made less negative, then there will be less repelling action by the suppressor and more plate current will flow at the expense of the screen current. The electrons that were previously being repelled by the suppressor and returned to the screen will now pass to the plate, with a consequent reduced screen current. Note that even if the screen potential is increased by the same potential as that applied to the suppressor grid the net effect is still a reduction of the screen-grid current.

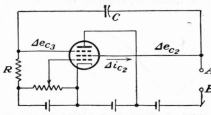

That is, if the screen current were to increase somewhat with the increase of screen potential, the decrease in screen current owing to the action of the suppressor grid is so much greater that the net effect is a reduction of the screen current. Therefore, with the circuit shown, there is a decrease of current through

FIG. 11-25. A pentode circuit that exhibits a negative output resistance.

the terminals AB with an increase in potential across these terminals, with a consequent negative resistance.

To analyze the circuit,[9] it is assumed that the change in screen current is a linear function of the changes in the suppressor-grid and screen-grid potentials and also that the suppressor-grid current is negligible. That is, it is assumed that

$$\Delta i_{c2} = g_{32} \, \Delta e_{c3} - \frac{\Delta e_{c2}}{r_{g2}}$$

The factor g_{32} has the dimensions of a conductance and is such that $g_{32} \, \Delta e_{c3}$ gives a measure of the influence of a change in current i_{c2} due to a change in potential of the suppressor grid. Note from the foregoing discussion that g_{32} is inherently negative since a positive Δe_{c3} is accompanied by a negative Δi_{c2}. The factor r_{g2} is a measure of the change in i_{c2} due to a change in e_{c2}.

If it is assumed that g_{32} and r_{g2} remain constant over the range of operation, and by noting that with a large C and R a change in potential Δe_{c2} appears on the suppressor as a change Δe_{c3}, then

$$\Delta i_{c2} = \left(g_{32} + \frac{1}{r_{g2}} \right) \Delta e_{c2}$$

The input resistance between points A and B is then

$$r \equiv \frac{\Delta e_{c2}}{\Delta i_{c2}} = \frac{r_{g2}}{1 + g_{32}r_{g2}}$$

which is negative when

$$-g_{32}r_{g2} > 1$$

To examine the operation of the circuit of such negative resistances as part of an oscillator, suppose that a tank circuit is coupled to the terminals AB of the two circuits shown in Fig. 11-26.   These circuits may be drawn

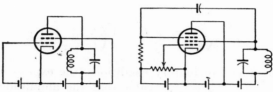

FIG. 11-26. A negative-resistance, or dynatron, and a negative-transconductance, or transitron, oscillator.

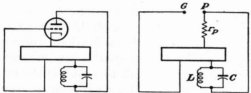

FIG. 11-27. The equivalent and simplified circuit of the negative-resistance oscillator

in the manner of Fig. 11-1.   Since the feedback potential is zero, the circuit simplifies to that shown in Fig. 11-27.   This may be drawn as a simple coupled circuit, in the form illustrated in Fig. 11-28.

To evaluate the characteristics of the circuit, apply Kirchhoff's law to the two-loop network.   This yields

$$\left(r_p + \frac{1}{Cp}\right) i_1 - \frac{1}{Cp} i_2 = 0$$

$$-\frac{1}{Cp} i_1 + \left(R + Lp + \frac{1}{Cp}\right) i_2 = 0$$

(11-53)

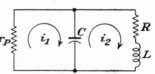

FIG. 11-28. The basic equivalent circuit of a negative-resistance oscillator.

To solve for i_2, the current through the inductance and load, the following differential equation must be evaluated:

$$\frac{d^2 i_2}{dt^2} + \left(\frac{R}{L} + \frac{1}{r_p C}\right) \frac{di_2}{dt} + \left(\frac{R + r_p}{r_p CL}\right) i_2 = 0 \qquad (11\text{-}54)$$

If it is assumed that r_p, which is inherently negative, remains substantially constant over the range of operation, this equation may be solved directly to give, for the oscillatory case,

$$i_2 = Ae^{-\frac{1}{2}\left(\frac{R}{L}+\frac{1}{r_pC}\right)t} \sin(\omega t + \theta) \tag{11-55}$$

where A and θ are constants. The expression for i_1 has exactly the same form, although with different values for A and θ. The angular frequency of oscillation is

$$\omega = \sqrt{\frac{R + r_p}{r_p LC} - \frac{1}{4}\left(\frac{R}{L} + \frac{1}{r_pC}\right)^2}$$

or

$$\omega = \sqrt{\frac{1}{LC}\frac{r_p + R}{r_p} - \frac{1}{4}\left(\frac{R}{L} + \frac{1}{r_pC}\right)^2} \tag{11-56}$$

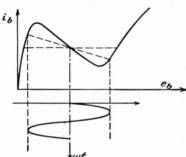

FIG. 11-29. The amplitude of oscillation increases until the value of r_p assumes the critical value L/CR.

Under the assumed oscillatory conditions, the expression for i_2 indicates that the amplitude of the oscillations may decrease, remain constant, or increase, depending upon the exponential term in the expression. If the term $(R/L) + (1/r_pC)$ is positive, then the oscillations which might have been started in any manner will ultimately fall to zero. If the quantity $(R/L) + (1/r_pC)$ is negative, the oscillations will tend to increase in amplitude with time. For the critical case for which the quantity $(R/L) + (1/r_pC)$ equals zero, the exponential factor is unity and the amplitude of the oscillations remains constant. For this condition,

$$r_p = -\frac{L}{RC} \tag{11-57}$$

and the corresponding frequency is

$$\omega = \sqrt{\frac{1}{LC}\left(1 + \frac{R}{r_p}\right)} = \sqrt{\frac{1}{LC}\left(1 - \frac{R^2C}{L}\right)} \tag{11-58}$$

Such negative-resistance oscillators are self-regulating in much the same manner as the normal feedback oscillators. Thus, owing to the variation of the negative-resistance characteristic of the tube circuit that is used, if the quantity $(R/L) + (1/r_pC)$ were negative, thus allowing for continually increasing amplitude of oscillations, these oscillations would increase until the region of operation extended to the point where

$r_p = -L/RC$, when the build-up condition would cease. These conditions are illustrated in Fig. 11-29. It should be noted from the diagram that even with an assumed sinusoidal output potential, and this is not a required condition, the output current will be nonsinusoidal.

REFERENCES

1. Barkhausen, H., "Lehrbuch der Elektronenrohren," vol. III, S. Hirzel Verlag, Leipzig, 1935.
   Massachusetts Institute of Technology Staff, "Applied Electronics," chap. XI, John Wiley & Sons, Inc., New York, 1943.
2. Dammers, B. G., J. Haantjes, J. Otte, and H. vanSuchtelen, "Application of the Electronic Valve in Radio Receivers and Amplifiers," N. V. Phillips Gloelampenfabriken, Eindhoven, Netherlands, 1950.
3. Terman, F. E., *Electronics,* **6,** 190 (1933).
   Llewellyn, F. B., *Proc. IRE,* **19,** 2063 (1931).
   Jefferson, H., *Wireless Eng.,* **22,** 384 (1945).
4. For further details, see:
   Terman, F. E., "Radio Engineering," 3d ed., Sec. 8-3, McGraw-Hill Book Company, Inc., New York, 1947.
5. Arguimbau, L. B., "Vacuum Tube Circuits," p. 320, John Wiley & Sons, Inc., New York, 1948.
6. Terman, F. E., R. R. Buss, W. R. Hewlett, and F. C. Cahill, *Proc. IRE,* **24,** 649 (1939).
7. Sulzer, P. G., *Electronics,* **23,** 88 (September, 1950).
8. Ginzton, E. L., and L. M. Hollingsworth, *Proc. IRE,* **29,** 43 (1941).
9. Herold, E. W., *Proc. IRE,* **23,** 1201 (1935).
10. As a general reference, see:
    Edson, W. A., "Vacuum Tube Oscillators," John Wiley & Sons, Inc., New York, 1953.

PROBLEMS

11-1. Show that the amplitude and frequency of the oscillators illustrated in Fig. 11-8 are the following

Tuned grid:

$$\omega = \frac{1}{\sqrt{L_g C \left(1 + \dfrac{RL_p}{r_p L_g}\right)}} \qquad \overline{g_m} \doteq \frac{\mu R L_g C}{M(\mu L - M)}$$

Hartley:

$$\omega = \sqrt{\frac{1 + R_2/r_p}{C(L_1 + L_2 + 2M)}} \qquad \overline{g_m} \doteq \frac{C(R_1 + R_2)(L_1 + L_2 + 2M)}{(L_1 + M)(L_2 + M)}$$

Colpitts:

$$\omega = \sqrt{\frac{1}{L}\left(\frac{1}{C_1} + \frac{1}{C_2} + \frac{R}{r_p C_2}\right)} \qquad \overline{g_m} \doteq \frac{\mu R(C_1 + C_2)}{L(\mu - C_1/C_2)}$$

11-2. Two identical triodes are connected in a Franklin oscillator. Determine, in terms of the circuit parameters:

a. The expression for the critical value of the resistance R_{l2} at which oscillations will just begin.

b. The frequency of oscillation.

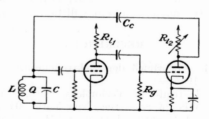

Assume that the power absorbed in the tuned circuit, which determines its Q, may be represented by an equivalent resistance in shunt with the inductance and capacitance.

11-3. Two identical triodes are connected in the oscillator circuit shown. Determine:

a. The resonant frequency ω_0.

b. The minimum values of g_m, assuming that the tubes are being operated under identical conditions, for oscillations to be maintained.

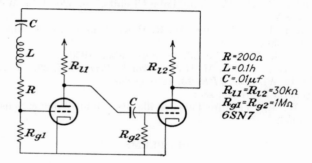

$R = 200\Omega$
$L = 0.1h$
$C = .01\mu f$
$R_{l1} = R_{l2} = 30k\Omega$
$R_{g1} = R_{g2} = 1M\Omega$
$6SN7$

11-4. Obtain an expression for the operating frequency of the cathode-coupled oscillator shown in the diagram.*

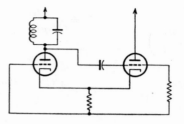

11-5. Using the 806 tube whose constant-current characteristics are given in Chap. 10, calculate the performance when it is used in the oscillator circuit illustrated on page 315.

* M. G. Crosby, *Electronics*, **19**, 136 (May, 1946).

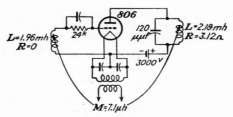

11-6. A type 852 triode has the following ratings as an r-f power amplifier and oscillator (key down conditions without modulation per tube):

D-c plate potential..........................	3,000 volts
D-c grid potential...........................	−600 volts
Peak r-f grid potential.......................	850 volts
D-c plate current............................	85 ma
D-c grid current.............................	15 ma approx.
Driving power...............................	12 watts approx.
Power output................................	165 watts approx.

The tube is operated under rated conditions in a tuned-plate oscillator, operating at a frequency of 1 Mc. Determine the following:
a. Grid dissipation. b. Plate dissipation.
c. Power output. d. Oscillator efficiency.
e. Resonant impedance of tank circuit.
f. Grid leak required.
g. Mutual inductance between grid and plate coils.

Assume that the maximum grid potential is equal to the minimum plate potential. Neglect the leakage inductances and resistances of the grid and plate coils, and assume that the tank circuit has $Q = 20$.

11-7. A type 806 triode when used as an r-f power amplifier has the following ratings:

D-c plate potential.................................	2,500 volts
D-c grid potential..................................	−500 volts
D-c plate current...................................	195 ma
D-c grid current....................................	25 ma
Driving power......................................	17 watts
Grid resistor.......................................	20,000 ohms
Power output.......................................	370 watts

This tube is connected as a Hartley oscillator and is operated under the conditions specified. The tank tuning capacitor is 250 $\mu\mu f$; the resonant frequency is 2 Mc; the loaded Q is 23.5. Determine the following:
a. The inductance, and resistance of the tank circuit.
b. The power output.
c. How far from the bottom of the tank coil is the cathode connection?
d. The oscillator efficiency.

Assume $e_{c,\max} = e_{b,\min}$.

11-8. An 833A transmitting tube has characteristics that may be represented approximately by the equations

$$i_b = 4 \times 10^{-4}\,(25e_c + e_b) \qquad \text{amp} \qquad \text{for } (25e_c + e_b) > 0$$
$$i_b = 0 \qquad\qquad\qquad\qquad\qquad \text{for } (25e_c + e_b) < 0$$

This tube is to be operated as a power oscillator in the circuit shown in the accompanying figure. Assume that $e_{b,\text{min}} = e_{c,\text{max}}$. Calculate the following:

    a. Power input to the plate circuit.   *b.* A-c power output.

When calculating the grid signal potential, neglect the grid driving power.

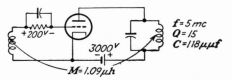

11-9. Typical constants of a crystal are

$$R = 1,500 \text{ ohms} \qquad L = 250 \text{ henrys} \qquad C = 0.04 \ \mu\mu\text{f} \qquad C_m = 8 \ \mu\mu\text{f}$$

    a. Calculate the Q of the crystal.

    b. Calculate the series- and parallel-resonant frequencies.

    c. What is the percentage change in the series and parallel frequencies if C_m is doubled?

11-10. Crystals may be used in what are called series-resonant crystal-controlled oscillators.* Discuss the operating features of the accompanying figures.

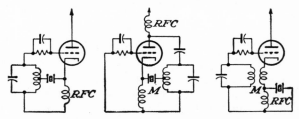

11-11. Discuss the operation of the Pierce oscillator illustrated. Observe that the crystal is the only resonant element in the circuit, the crystal in this case operating as a parallel-resonant circuit.

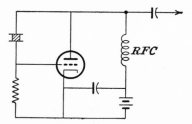

11-12. An amplitude-controlled oscillator uses a 6J5 tube. It operates at 5 Mc. A measurement of the network and rectifier when the oscillator tube is

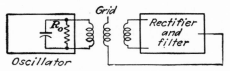

* F. Butler, *Wireless Eng.*, **23**, 157 (1946).

removed indicates that, with an input of $E_p = 8$ volts rms, the potentials are $E_g = 0.4$ rms, $E_{cc} = 11.4$ volts d-c. What is the value of R_0 for the bias to adjust itself to -7.5 volts?

11-13. Refer to the tuned-plate oscillator of Sec. 11-8. Neglect grid loading, and evaluate the frequency stability S_f at the value of ω_0 where $\theta = \pi/2$. Express the final results to show the dependence on the Q of the resonant circuit.

11-14. Deduce an expression for the frequency stability of the phase-shift oscillator discussed in Sec. 11-13.

11-15. Evaluate S_f at the resonant value of a twin-T oscillator. Neglect grid loading.

11-16. Consider the coupling network illustrated, which is for use in a phase-shift oscillator.

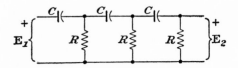

a. Derive an expression for the transfer function β of this network.

b. Determine the frequency ω_0 at which the total phase shift through the network is π.

c. Evaluate the expression for β at ω_0.

d. Determine the input impedance at $\omega = \omega_0$.

11-17. a. Find an expression for the frequency stability S_f of the circuit of Prob. 11-16.

b. Suppose that the loading of one RC combination on the previous one is negligible, so that the total phase shift is three times that of each section. Compute S_f for this. Compare with the results under (a).

11-18. Consider the phase-shift oscillator shown.

a. Evaluate the frequency of oscillation of this circuit.

b. Find the relationship among parameters for which the amplitude is independent of the frequency of oscillation.

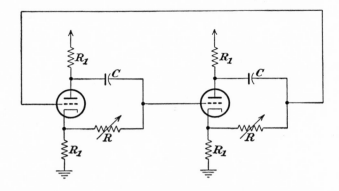

11-19. A cathode-coupled Wien-bridge oscillator is shown in the diagram on page 318. Determine the critical value of R_l at which oscillations will just start.

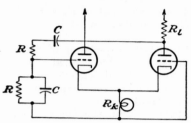

11-20. The Meacham bridge-stabilized oscillator* is illustrated.   Here R_4 is a resistor, the resistance of which varies with the amplitude of oscillation, although the thermal capacity is sufficiently large so that the temperature remains substantially constant over the cycle of oscillation.

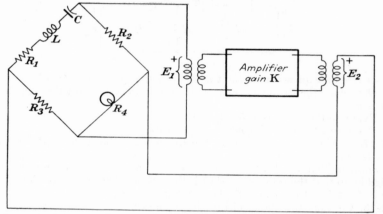

a. Suppose that the gain of the amplifier has the form $K = K_0(1 + j\delta)$ in the immediate neighborhood of ω_0.   Derive an expression for S_f.

b. If $Q = 10^5$ of the resonant circuit (this is possible with a crystal), $K_0 = 100$, $\delta = 0.1$, calculate S_f.

c. Calculate the frequency shift $\Delta f/f_0$ due to a 0.1-rad variation in the phase angle of the amplifier.

11-21. The plate characteristic of a type 24A tube connected as a tetrode is given in the figure.   The d-c potential E_{bb} is adjusted to 45 volts.   A parallel-resonant circuit tuned to 1 Mc is used, with $C = 250\ \mu\mu f$.

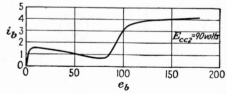

a. Determine the minimum value of R for which oscillations will be sustained.

b. Plot the oscillation amplitude as a function of R.

c. Plot the current waveshape for maximum oscillation amplitude.

* L. A. Meacham, *Proc. IRE,* **26,** 1278 (1938).

11-22. Discuss the operation of the negative-differential-transconductance crystal-controlled oscillators* illustrated. Note that here, as for the Pierce oscillator (see Prob. 11-11), the crystal is the only resonant element in the circuit.

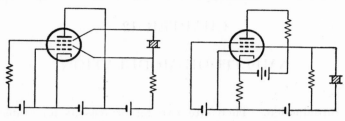

11-23. Discuss the operation of the transitron oscillators illustrated.

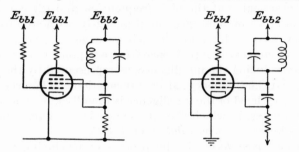

11-24. Consider the two-tube oscillator circuit shown. Show that for $R_l > r_p$ and $R_c + R_g > R_l$ the apparent resistance between terminals AB may be negative. The circuit is supposed to operate under class A conditions.

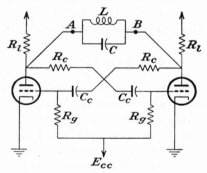

* S. Bernstein, *Electronics*, **26**, 198 (February, 1953).

CHAPTER 12

AMPLITUDE MODULATION

12-1. Introduction. There are two major reasons for transmitting intelligence at a relatively high frequency level: (1) transmission by radiation is practicable at the high frequencies, and (2) it is possible to transmit a number of messages simultaneously without interference if the frequency level is different for each message. Of course, any complete system of conveying intelligence from one point to another must be capable of reproducing the intelligence, as represented by the amplitude, or loudness, and the frequency, after transmission. The process of altering the frequency level of the intelligence is broadly known as *modulation*. The inverse process, in which the intelligence is extracted from the radiated wave, is known as *demodulation* or *detection*.

By definition[1] *modulation* is the process of producing a wave some characteristic of which varies as a function of the instantaneous value of another wave called the *modulating wave*. The modulating wave is usually the signal, the modulated wave being the h-f *carrier wave*, which has been altered in a manner to carry the intelligence.

Consider a wave which may be represented analytically by the expression

$$e = A \cos (\omega t + \theta) \tag{12-1}$$

where t is the time. If either A, ω, or θ is varied according to some function of the instantaneous value of a modulating wave, then this expression will represent the modulated wave. It is possible, in fact, to produce a wave in which all three parameters vary simultaneously. However, in each of the modulating methods that are important practically, only one of these parameters is varied, and in commercial transmitters great care is taken to avoid the use of more than one type of modulation.

In *amplitude modulation*, the amplitude A is varied in accordance with the modulating wave, while ω and θ remain constant. In *frequency modulation*, the frequency ω is varied, and both A and θ remain constant. In *phase modulation*, the phase θ is varied, while A and ω remain constant. It should perhaps be mentioned that phase modulation is not of much practical importance in itself, but as will be shown later, it may be used as an intermediate step in achieving frequency modulation.

12-2. Characteristics of Amplitude Modulation. As indicated, amplitude modulation is produced by varying the magnitude of the carrier in accordance with the amplitude and frequency of the modulating source. Let the signal potential be designated as

$$e_m = E_m \cos \omega_m t \tag{12-2}$$

and let the unmodulated carrier be written as

$$e_c = E_c \cos (\omega_c t + \theta) \tag{12-3}$$

The carrier frequency ω_c is usually much greater than the signal frequency ω_m and is chosen at the designated frequency level desired for the transmission. The resulting modulated wave has the form

$$e = (E_c + k_a E_m \cos \omega_m t) \cos \omega_c t \tag{12-4}$$

The amplitude factor $E_c + k_a E_m \cos \omega_m t$ expresses the sinusoidal variation of the amplitude of the wave, where the proportionality factor k_a determines the maximum variation in amplitude for a given modulating signal E_m. In this expression the arbitrary constant phase θ has been chosen as zero, since it plays no part in the modulating process.

In examining this wave in detail, the expression is written in the form

$$e = E_c(1 + m_a \cos \omega_m t) \cos \omega_c t \tag{12-5}$$

which is then expanded to the form

$$e = E_c \cos \omega_c t + \frac{m_a E_c}{2} \cos (\omega_c + \omega_m)t + \frac{m_a E_c}{2} \cos (\omega_c - \omega_m)t \tag{12-6}$$

The factor m_a is known as the *modulation index*,

$$m_a = \frac{k_a E_m}{E_c} \tag{12-7}$$

and $100m_a$ is the *percentage modulation*. A sketch of Eq. (12-5) has the form shown in Fig. 12-1.

The expanded expression of Eq. (12-6) indicates the frequency spectrum of the modulated wave. The first term is of carrier frequency ω_c;

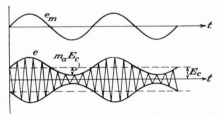

FIG. 12-1. The modulating signal and a modulated carrier.

the second has the frequency $\omega_c + \omega_m$ and is called the *upper sideband*. Its frequency is equal to the sum of the carrier and the signal frequencies. The third term has the frequency $\omega_c - \omega_m$, which is equal to the difference between the carrier and the signal frequency. This component is known as the *lower sideband*. A plot of the frequency spectrum of the modulated wave is illustrated in Fig. 12-2. Modulation may therefore be viewed as the process in which signal information, which is specified relative to a zero-frequency reference, is shifted on the frequency scale so that it is specified with respect to the carrier level ω_c. At the same time, the intelligence appears symmetrically disposed relative to ω_c.

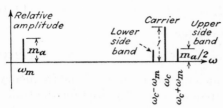

FIG. 12-2. Frequency spectrum of a sinusoidally modulated wave.

It should be emphasized that the foregoing is not a mathematical fiction, as it is possible by means of appropriate filters to extract the frequencies in the spectrum. In fact, the features of transmission of intelligence with one or more of the frequencies in the spectrum suppressed will be examined below.

A simple sinor representation of Eq. (12-6) by means of a pair of rotating conjugate sinors in the complex plane is readily possible. A little thought will convince the reader that the three sinors in Fig. 12-3 represent the three terms of the equation and that the resultant sinor does exhibit the properties of the a-m wave.

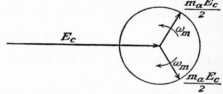

In general, the modulating signal is not sinusoidal but is a complex wave. Since, however, this complex wave may be represented by a Fourier series if the wave is periodic or by a Fourier integral if it is nonperiodic, the modulated

FIG. 12-3. The sinor representation of an a-m wave.

carrier wave possesses a frequency spectrum which is more complex than that illustrated. But each frequency in the modulating signal produces a pair of side frequencies in the frequency spectrum. Then

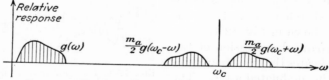

FIG. 12-4. The frequency spectrum of a complex wave.

a signal with frequencies in the band $g(\omega)$ will yield a frequency spectrum with a band of sidebands

$$\frac{m_a}{2} g(\omega_c + \omega) \qquad \text{and} \qquad \frac{m_a}{2} g(\omega_c - \omega)$$

symmetrically disposed about the carrier ω_c. Such a spectrum would have the form illustrated in Fig. 12-4.

The frequency-shifting property of modulation is not limited to shifting an audio-frequency to a higher position in the frequency spectrum. It is possible to shift an h-f signal up or down in the frequency scale, and both processes are important. Since such frequency shifting or frequency changing does not involve directly the intelligence to be transmitted, frequency changing is classed, not as a modulation process, but rather as a detection process.

12-3. Circuits for Amplitude Modulation. In the ideal case the amplitude A in Eq. (12-1), which in general will actually be the signal waveshape rather than a single constant amplitude, must be faithfully imposed as the amplitude envelope of the carrier frequency, over the full range of amplitude variations. Moreover, the signal waveshape must be maintained over the entire frequency band involved in the intelligence, from the rather narrow band required for carrier telegraphy, to the broader band required for commercial broadcasting, to the very broad band required for television.

The degree of linearity, i.e., the degree to which the signal waveshape and the envelope of the modulated carrier must be the same, is determined by the character of the transmission. For commercial broadcasting, it is required that the intelligence be transmitted with a minimum of distortion over the specified audio spectrum, and over a wide degree of modulation. While some consideration is given to the matter of efficiency of a modulated transmitter, ordinarily the principal consideration is linearity rather than efficiency. It is possible to design highly efficient transmitters in which the power is varied with the modulation requirements, although in most cases the transmitters operate rather inefficiently, and at an average modulation of less than 50 per cent.

For commercial telephony, the requirements imposed are quite different from those for broadcasting. The frequency band is narrower, and the frequency response need not be strictly linear. Power efficiency is important, and it is essential that a high modulation index be maintained in order that the signal/noise ratio at the receiver be optimum for the available carrier power. Many small transmitters operate in much this same way.

It might appear reasonable to modulate the oscillator, and certain of the circuits to be considered could be used in such an application. However, the discussion of the problem of frequency stability of an oscillator in Chap. 11 showed that the frequency does depend on the load, and a varying load would in most cases be accompanied by a varying frequency. The amount of frequency modulation so introduced is greater than can be tolerated, although the modulation can be so introduced as to have no adverse effect on the oscillating circuit. Because of this, oscillators are never modulated in regular broadcast practice.

Amplitude modulation is ordinarily accomplished in the power-amplifier chain and may be carried out at low level or at high level.   In low-level modulation, the modulation is accomplished at relatively low power level, and the power level is then raised until the desired level is reached. Since the carrier is modulated, the amplifier stages must maintain a linear relationship between input and output over the entire signal-frequency range, to avoid what is called *sideband clipping*, and over the entire range of modulation.   Class B tuned power amplifiers are used in this application, as discussed in Chap. 10.   A system of this type for high-power applications therefore comprises a low-power modulator and a chain of class B tuned-power-amplifier stages.   The modulator has relatively little effect on the over-all efficiency of the chain of relatively low-efficiency class B amplifier stages.

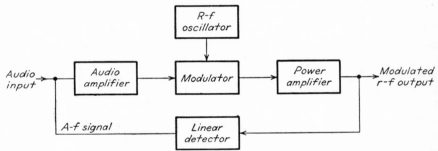

Fig. 12-5. A feedback scheme for improving the linearity of a modulating system.

In the case of high-level modulators, the unmodulated carrier is amplified by means of relatively high-efficiency class C amplifiers, and linearity is unimportant, owing to the constant signal level.   The modulator, which is simply an audio amplifier, must now provide the full audio power component of the transmitter, since the modulating signal must be made available at high power.   This requires considerable power amplification of the modulating signal.   This system comprises, therefore, highly efficient class C amplifiers, but a large and inefficient modulator. as regards over-all efficiency, there is little to choose between the low-level and the high-level methods for a given power output, and both systems are widely used.

As will be discussed, an amplifier can be modulated by applying the modulating signal in the grid, plate, or cathode circuits, and in the case of pentodes either of the available grids may be used.   The point of application of the modulating signal often determines the name or type of the modulation.

The linearity of modulation can be improved by the application of inverse feedback.   This is accomplished by means of a system such as that illustrated in block form in Fig. 12-5.   In this circuit the output of the linear detector (see Chap. 13 for a discussion of the linear detector), which is assumed to be a faithful reproduction of the output from the modulation system, is an audio-frequency signal which, in the ideal case, is identical with the audio input. Any difference between them serves as a correction to reduce the difference, thereby improving the resulting linearity. It is important, of course, that audio-frequency or r-f envelope phase shifts be minimized through the feedback loop, as well as that proper amplitude relationships be maintained around the loop.

12-4. Square-law or Small-signal Modulation. Amplitude modulation may be produced by impressing two sinusoidal potentials of different frequencies in a nonlinear circuit. The van der Bijl modulator is one of the earliest devices embodying methods of this type, but it is seldom used at present. This modulator depends for its operation on the curvature of the transfer characteristic of the tube. A circuit of this modulator is

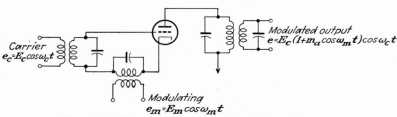

FIG. 12-6. The circuit of the van der Bijl modulator.

given in Fig. 12-6. The carrier- and modulation-frequency potentials are both applied in the grid circuit of a triode or multigrid tube, and the modulated wave appears across the tank circuit in the plate circuit of the tube. The tank is tuned to the carrier frequency and must be sufficiently broad to include all the important sidebands, usually about ± 10 kc for normal broadcast purposes; otherwise *sideband clipping* occurs. The operation of the modulator is made clear in the sketches of Fig. 12-7.

To examine the modulation process analytically, it is supposed that the transfer curve is parabolic over the range of operation, so that the a-c plate current may be related to the input grid potential by the first two terms of the series expansion

$$i_p = a_1 e_g + a_2 e_g^2 \qquad (12\text{-}8)$$

where a_1 and a_2 are constants. The excitation potential e_g is of the form

$$e_g = E_m \cos \omega_m t + E_c \cos \omega_c t \qquad (12\text{-}9)$$

and it follows, by combining this expression with Eq. (12-8), that the

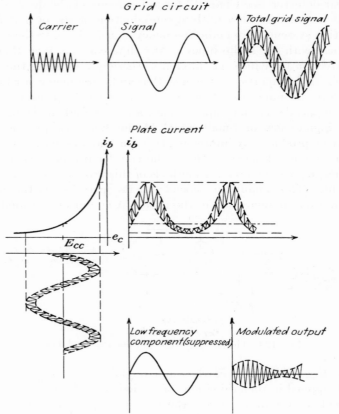

FIG. 12-7. The waveshapes at various points in the van der Bijl modulator.

plate current is

$$i_p = a_1E_m \cos \omega_m t + a_1E_c \cos \omega_c t + a_2E_m^2 \cos^2 \omega_m t + a_2E_c^2 \cos^2 \omega_c t \\ + a_2E_c E_m \cos \omega_m t \cos \omega_c t$$

This may be written as

$$i_p = a_1E_c \cos \omega_c t + a_2E_m E_c \cos (\omega_c + \omega_m)t + a_2E_m E_c \cos (\omega_c - \omega_m)t \\ + a_1E_m \cos \omega_m t + \frac{a_2E_m^2}{2} + \frac{a_2E_m^2}{2} \cos 2\omega_m t + \frac{a_2E_c^2}{2} + \frac{a_2E_c^2}{2} \cos 2\omega_c t \quad (12\text{-}10)$$

Assuming that $\omega_c \gg \omega_m$ and also that those frequencies which are not in the neighborhood of ω_c are eliminated by the use of tuned circuits, the only potentials which appear across the output are produced by

$$i_p = a_1E_c \cos \omega_c t + a_2E_m E_c \cos (\omega_c + \omega_m)t \\ + a_2E_m E_c \cos (\omega_c - \omega_m)t \quad (12\text{-}11)$$

This may be written in the form

$$i_p = a_1E_c\left(1 + \frac{2a_2E_m}{a_1}\cos\omega_m t\right)\cos\omega_c t \tag{12-12}$$

from which it is seen that the modulation index is given by

$$m = \frac{2a_2E_m}{a_1} \tag{12-13}$$

The amount of modulated output available without appreciable distortion in such a modulator as here considered is not great, and the efficiency is low.

Owing to the fact that the plate circuit contains a parallel tuned rather than a pure resistance load, the foregoing analysis is not completely correct—this despite the fact that the load is purely resistive at or near resonance. By taking this matter into account, Carson[2] has shown that a substantial increase in output occurs with the substitution of the resonant load. However, other methods provide better modulation characteristics and have displaced the low-level method here discussed.

12-5. Balanced Modulators. The use of a balanced modulator,[3] which possesses an appearance somewhat like the push-pull amplifier, automatically eliminates either the carrier or the modulating frequency, as well as many of the intermodulation frequencies. The circuit of the balanced modulator is given in Fig. 12-8.

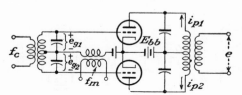

Fig. 12-8. A balanced modulator.

It is assumed that the two tubes are identical and that the circuit is symmetrical. The tube characteristics may be expressed by equations of the form

$$\begin{aligned}
i_{p1} &= a_1e_{g1} + a_2e_{g1}^2 \\
i_{p2} &= a_1e_{g2} + a_2e_{g2}^2
\end{aligned} \tag{12-14}$$

But the input potentials have the form

$$\begin{aligned}
e_{g1} &= E_c\cos\omega_c t + E_m\cos\omega_m t \\
e_{g2} &= -E_c\cos\omega_c t + E_m\cos\omega_m t
\end{aligned} \tag{12-15}$$

Then the currents in the plate circuits become

$$i_{p1} = a_1 E_c \cos \omega_c t + a_1 E_m \cos \omega_m t + a_2 E_c^2 \cos^2 \omega_c t$$
$$+ a_2 E_m^2 \cos^2 \omega_m t + a_2 E_c E_m \cos (\omega_c + \omega_m)t$$
$$+ a_2 E_c E_m \cos (\omega_c - \omega_m)t$$
$$i_{p2} = -a_1 E_c \cos \omega_c t + a_1 E_m \cos \omega_m t + a_2 E_c^2 \cos^2 \omega_c t$$
$$+ a_2 E_m^2 \cos^2 \omega_m t - a_2 E_c E_m \cos (\omega_c + \omega_m)t$$
$$- a_2 E_c E_m \cos (\omega_c - \omega_m)t$$

$$(12\text{-}16)$$

But the potential induced in the secondary of the coupling network is given approximately by

$$e \doteq M \frac{d(i_{p1} - i_{p2})}{dt} \tag{12-17}$$

Then the output is of the form

$$e \doteq 2\omega_c M a_1 E_c \cos \left(\omega_c t + \frac{\pi}{2} \right)$$
$$+ 2\omega_c M a_2 E_c E_m \left\{ \cos \left[(\omega_c + \omega_m)t + \frac{\pi}{2} \right] + \cos \left[(\omega_c - \omega_m)t + \frac{\pi}{2} \right] \right\}$$

which may be written as

$$e \doteq 2\omega_c M a_1 E_c \left(1 + E_m \frac{a_2}{a_1} \sin \omega_m t \right) \sin \omega_c t \tag{12-18}$$

In certain applications it is found advantageous to use a balanced modulator in such a manner as to eliminate the carrier. This is readily accomplished by interchanging the sources f_m and f_c in the diagram.

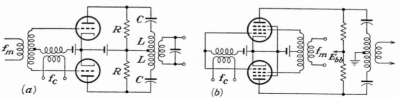

Fig. 12-9. Balanced modulators for producing suppressed-carrier modulation.

When this is done, the output contains frequencies $\omega_c + \omega_m$ and $\omega_c - \omega_m$, with the carrier term ω_c missing. Such modulated waves with carrier missing can be transmitted, as discussed in Chap. 1. The demodulation problem is more complicated than when the ω_c term is present. This will be discussed in Chap. 13. Two circuits of balanced modulators which suppress the carrier are illustrated in Fig. 12-9. In these circuits, the LC circuit is approximately in resonance for all frequencies in the neighborhood of the carrier frequency ω_c.

12-6. Single-sideband Suppressed-carrier Modulation. Suppose that the suppressed-carrier output from a balanced modulator were passed through a suitable filter network so that one of the sidebands was eliminated. The resulting wave would be a single-sideband suppressed-carrier signal. The demodulation of such a wave is feasible, but, because of fundamental limitations, such modulated waves are limited in their application to commercial telephony. The system is used extensively in point-to-point commercial communications.

In the case of signals for which the modulating signal frequency f_m is small, the construction of narrow band-pass filters with sharp cutoff is difficult. A method for producing the desired results by phase shifting rather than by means of filters has been developed[4] by the Bell Telephone Laboratories. The essentials of this method are indicated schematically in Fig. 12-10.

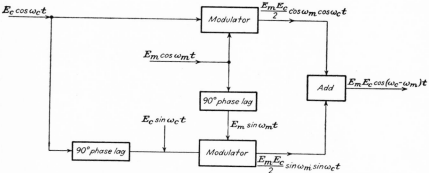

Fig. 12-10. A modulator for single-sideband suppressed-carrier signals.

12-7. Shunt Modulator. The Heising, or shunt, modulator was also one of the early devices for producing amplitude modulation. The circuit of this modulator is illustrated in Fig. 12-11. Observe that the circuit associated with $T2$ is just a simple tuned amplifier which is biased to operate under class C conditions. The carrier signal is applied to the grid of this amplifier. The circuit associated with $T1$ is a simple untuned power amplifier with a load consisting of the a-f choke and $T2$ in parallel, the bias E_{cc1} being so adjusted that this circuit operates under class A conditions at the modulating frequencies f_m. The effect of the amplifier $T1$ is to produce a varying plate potential to tube circuit $T2$. Hence in so far as $T2$ is concerned, the carrier signal e_c is impressed in the grid circuit, and the modulating signal e_m appears in the plate circuit. In essence, therefore, $T2$ is operating as a plate-modulated class C amplifier.

A detailed analysis of this circuit is not warranted, owing to its limited practical importance. Such an analysis is relatively straightforward if it is noted that the effect of $T1$ is to cause the plate potential of $T2$ to be of the form $e_b = E_{bb} + E_b \cos \omega_m t$. In so far as $T1$ is concerned, this tube functions as a class A amplifier which operates into an almost pure resistance load, which consists of the high reactance of the a-f choke shunted by the effective low resistance of the r-f stage.

Such a modulating system as this can produce a 100 per cent modulated carrier. Since the audio amplifier $T1$ serves principally to alter the effective plate potential to the r-f amplifier, and since a substantial portion of the power from the plate supply is absorbed by the $T1$ circuit, the system is quite inefficient. For this reason, it is suitable only for relatively low-level modulation.

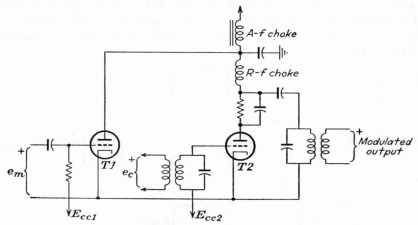

Fig. 12-11. The Heising, or shunt, modulator.

12-8. Linear Modulation.

The general principle of modulation discussed in the foregoing section is very important, particularly if the carrier and modulating potentials are large, or if the operation occurs near cutoff. Such a situation exists when a class C amplifier is series-modulated, whether this modulation is applied in the plate circuit, the grid circuit, the cathode circuit, or the suppressor circuit, if a tetrode or pentode is used. If a carrier potential were introduced into the grid of a class C amplifier, and if the modulating potential were introduced into the plate circuit, then because $\omega_c \gg \omega_m$, the variation in potential in the plate circuit caused by the signal could be considered to be the equivalent of a relatively slow change in plate supply potential. If the relationship between the output tank current is a linear function of the plate potential, for constant grid excitation, the output potential (which is a linear function of the tank current) would have the desired modulated characteristics.

With the proper design and adjustment, the modulation characteristic of a class C amplifier is such that 100 per cent modulation with distortion as low as 2 per cent in a plate-modulated amplifier and as low as 5 per cent in a linear grid amplifier may be attained. The distortion can be reduced below these values by the use of inverse feedback in the circuit.

12-9. Plate-modulated Class C Amplifier.   The basic circuit of a plate-modulated class C amplifier is given in Fig. 12-12.   It will be observed that it is essentially the circuit of the class C amplifier except for the introduction of the source of modulating potential in the plate circuit. The modulation characteristic of such a plate-modulated amplifier is the plot of the tank current as a function of the plate supply potential.   The

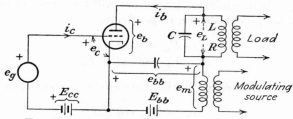

FIG. 12-12. A plate-modulated class C amplifier.

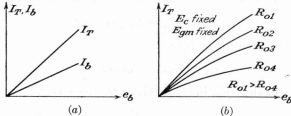

(a)   (b)

FIG. 12-13. (a) The ideal plate-modulation characteristic.   (b) The modulation characteristics, showing the effects of load impedance.

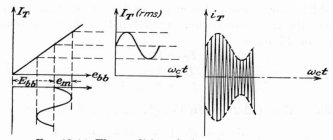

FIG. 12-14. The conditions during plate modulation.

ideal plate-modulation characteristic is illustrated in Fig. 12-13a.   Generally the situation is more nearly like that illustrated in Fig. 12-13b, which shows the effect of tank impedance.   The more nearly straight the lines, the less the modulation distortion.   A high value of tank impedance yields the smaller distortion, but the power output is also smaller.

If the frequency of the modulating signal is low compared with the carrier frequency, the impedance of the tank circuit at the modulating frequency will be negligible.   Consequently the properties of the circuit are not appreciably affected by the modulating frequency, and the plate and tank currents will follow the characteristics shown even when e_{bb} varies at the modulation frequency.

Suppose therefore that the carrier potential of angular frequency ω_c is modulated by a modulating potential of frequency ω_m. The behavior of the circuit is that illustrated in Fig. 12-14.

To analyze the modulation process, it will be supposed that $\omega_c \gg \omega_m$. The grid-circuit potentials are, respectively,

$$e_g = E_{gm} \cos \omega_c t$$

and
$$e_c = E_{gm} \cos \omega_c t + E_{cc}$$

(12-19)

If the modulating potential in the plate circuit is written in the form

$$e_m = E_{mm} \cos \omega_m t \qquad (12\text{-}20)$$

the resulting relatively slowly varying plate potential has the form

$$e_{bb} = E_{bb} + E_{mm} \cos \omega_m t \qquad (12\text{-}21)$$

This may be written in the form

$$e_{bb} = E_{bb}(1 + m \cos \omega_m t) \qquad (12\text{-}22)$$

where m, the modulation index, is given by the ratio

$$m = \frac{E_{mm}}{E_{bb}} \qquad (12\text{-}23)$$

It should be noted from the curves of Fig. 12-13 that the rms tank current and the d-c plate current are related to the plate potential by expressions of the form

$$I_T = k_T e_{bb}$$
$$I_b = k_b e_{bb} \qquad (12\text{-}24)$$
$$I_{bb} = k_b E_{bb}$$

By combining Eqs. (12-24) with Eq. (12-22), it follows that

$$I_T = k_T E_{bb}(1 + m \cos \omega_m t)$$
$$I_b = k_b E_{bb}(1 + m \cos \omega_m t) \qquad (12\text{-}25)$$
$$I_b = I_{bb}(1 + m \cos \omega_m t)$$

Also, corresponding to the rms tank current, the instantaneous tank current i_T will be chosen of the form

$$i_T = \sqrt{2}\, I_T \sin \omega_c t \qquad (12\text{-}26)$$

This may be expressed in the form

$$i_T = \sqrt{2}\, k_T E_{bb}(1 + m \cos \omega_m t) \sin \omega_c t \qquad (12\text{-}27)$$

But the output potential e_L that appears across the tank circuit is given with good approximation by

$$\mathbf{E}_L = jX_L I_T = X_L I_T \underline{/90°} \tag{12-28}$$

Therefore

$$e_L = \sqrt{2}\, X_L I_T \sin(\omega_c t + 90)$$
$$= \sqrt{2}\, X_L k_T E_{bb}(1 + m \cos \omega_m t) \cos \omega_c t \tag{12-29}$$

The corresponding plate-cathode potential of the tube is

$$e_b = e_{bb} - e_L$$

which is

$$e_b = E_{bb}(1 + m \cos \omega_m t)(1 - \sqrt{2}\, X_L k_T \cos \omega_c t) \tag{12-30}$$

Also, from the discussion in Secs. 10-2 and 10-3, the plate current is given by

$$\mathbf{I}_{p1} = \frac{\mathbf{E}_L}{R_0} \doteq j\frac{X_L I_T}{R_0} = j\frac{I_T}{Q} = \frac{I_T}{Q} \underline{/90°}$$

the instantaneous plate current has the form

$$i_{p1} = \frac{\sqrt{2}}{Q} k_T E_{bb}(1 + m \cos \omega_m t) \cos \omega_c t \tag{12-31}$$

Likewise, it follows from the curve of Fig. 12-13 and Eq. (12-25)

$$I_b = I_{bb}(1 + m \cos \omega_m t) \tag{12-32}$$

The above information may be used to analyze the performance of the modulated amplifier.

The average power supplied by the d-c plate power source is

$$P_{bb} = \frac{1}{T_m} \int_0^{T_m} E_{bb} I_b \, dt \tag{12-33}$$

where T_m is the period of the modulating cycle. This expression may be written as

$$P_{bb} = \frac{1}{T_m} \int_0^{T_m} E_{bb} I_{bb}(1 + m \cos \omega_m t) \, dt$$

This integrates to

$$P_{bb} = E_{bb} I_{bb} = k_b E_{bb}^2 \tag{12-34}$$

The power input by the modulating source is

$$P_m = \frac{1}{T_m} \int_0^{T_m} e_m I_b \, dt$$

This becomes

$$P_m = \frac{1}{T_m} \int_0^{T_m} E_{mm} \cos \omega_m t \, I_{bb}(1 + m \cos \omega_m t) \, dt$$

which integrates to the form

$$P_m = E_{mm}I_{bb}\frac{m}{2} = P_{bb}\frac{m^2}{2} \tag{12-35}$$

Clearly, for 100 per cent sinusoidal modulation, the modulating source must deliver one-half as much power as the d-c plate power supply. This requires, of course, that the modulating source must be an amplifier of large power capacity for a large power output.

The a-c power output at the tank circuit is given by the expression

$$P_L = \frac{1}{T_m}\int_0^{T_m} e_L i_{p1}\,dt = \frac{1}{T_m}\int_0^{T_m} R_0 i_{p1}^2\,dt \tag{12-36}$$

This becomes

$$P_L = \frac{1}{T_m}\int_0^{T_m} 2R_0\left(\frac{k_T E_{bb}}{Q}\right)^2 (1 + m\cos\omega_m t)^2 \cos^2\omega_c t\,dt$$

Consideration must be given to the fact that averaging over the audio cycle is being carried out, during which time the term of carrier frequency is varying rapidly, since $\omega_c \gg \omega_m$. It is implicitly assumed, therefore, that the net contribution to the average (the area under the appropriate curve) by the $\cos^2\omega_c t = (1 + \cos 2\omega_c t)/2$ term is the factor $\frac{1}{2}$, the trigonometric term at carrier frequency undergoing many cycles during the slow audio-cycle period, yielding a negligible contribution.

By performing the indicated integrations,

$$P_L = R_0\left(\frac{k_T E_{bb}}{Q}\right)^2 \left(1 + \frac{m^2}{2}\right)$$

This may be reduced to the form

$$P_L = \frac{R_0 k_T^2}{Q^2 k_b} P_{bb}\left(1 + \frac{m^2}{2}\right) \tag{12-37}$$

It may be concluded from this that the d-c plate power supply furnishes the power to produce the carrier wave and the modulating amplifier furnishes the power to produce the sidebands in the output.

The plate-circuit efficiency of the modulated amplifier is given by the expression

$$\eta = \frac{P_L}{P_{bb} + P_m} \tag{12-38}$$

which becomes

$$\eta = \frac{R_0 k_T^2}{Q^2 k_b}\frac{P_{bb}(1 + m^2/2)}{P_{bb}(1 + m^2/2)}$$

or

$$\eta = \frac{R_0 k_T^2}{Q^2 k_b} \tag{12-39}$$

This result shows that the plate-circuit efficiency is independent of the degree of modulation. Therefore one may calculate the efficiency from considerations of the unmodulated amplifier as a simple class C device. To find an expression for the power dissipated in the plate of the tube, it is evident that

$$P_p = P_{bb} + P_m - P_L$$

which may be written in the form

$$P_p = P_{bb}(1 - \eta)\left(1 + \frac{m^2}{2}\right) \qquad (12\text{-}40)$$

Consider the results when the modulation index m is zero. The foregoing become, in this case,

$$\begin{aligned}
P_{bb} &= k_b E_{bb}^2 \\
P_m &= 0 \\
P_L &= \eta P_{bb} \\
P_p &= (1 - \eta)P_{bb} \\
\eta &= \frac{R_0 k_T^2}{Q^2 k_b}
\end{aligned} \qquad (12\text{-}41)$$

By comparing these expressions with the corresponding expressions when m is not zero, it is observed that the addition of modulation increases the plate dissipation. This requires that a given tube when operated under modulated conditions must be operated with a reduced plate potential and current, if a specified maximum allowable plate dissipation is not to be exceeded. That is, since the input power to the plate circuit is $P_{bb} + P_m$, then, for a given plate-circuit efficiency η_p, the losses are increased. For a specified maximum allowable plate dissipation P_p, it is then necessary to reduce $P_{bb} + P_m$.

In order to design the modulating amplifier, a knowledge of the effective impedance across the secondary terminals of the output transformer of this amplifier is needed. This will permit a specification of the turns ratio of the modulating transformer in order to reflect the optimum value of impedance into the plate circuit of the modulating tubes. This impedance is readily obtained by observing that the plate impedance is substantially resistive and must be given by

$$R_m = \frac{E_m^2}{P_m} = \frac{E_{mm}^2/2}{E_{mm}I_b(m/2)} = \frac{E_{bb}}{I_b} = \frac{1}{k_b} = R_b \qquad (12\text{-}42)$$

This shows that the effective impedance is independent of the modulation.

The plate-modulated amplifier is used extensively in radio transmitters. It has the advantage that modulation without excessive distortion is possible in practice by reasonably simple methods. Also, it operates at high efficiency and is relatively easy of adjustment. It has the disadvantage that a comparatively large amount of power at the modulating frequency is required. The resulting cost of the heavy and bulky modulating equipment is sometimes greater than that of other methods. It might be of interest to know that the two modulating transformers at

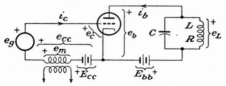

the 500-kw radio station WLW weigh approximately 19 tons each and that an audio choke weighs 12 tons.[5]

FIG. 12-15. A grid-bias modulated class C amplifier.

12-10. Grid-bias Modulation.

Amplitude modulation may be accomplished by connecting the modulating source in the grid instead of the plate circuit. The basic circuit of such a grid-bias modulated amplifier is illustrated in Fig. 12-15. Typical linearity curves of such an amplifier for several different conditions are illustrated in the curves of Fig. 12-16. The general character of the operation is illustrated graphically in Fig. 12-17.

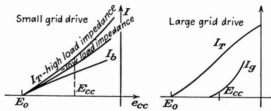

FIG. 12-16. Typical linearity curves of a grid-bias modulated class C amplifier under different conditions of load.

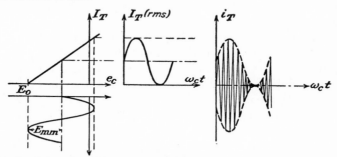

FIG. 12-17. Conditions for 100 per cent modulation in a grid-bias modulated class C amplifier.

To analyze the operation, the procedure is essentially parallel to that of Sec. 12-9 for the plate-modulated amplifier. It is assumed that the modulation characteristic is linear and that $\omega_c \gg \omega_m$. The carrier signal is chosen of the form

$$e_g = E_{gm} \cos \omega_c t \tag{12-43}$$

and the modulating potential is of the form

$$e_m = E_{mm} \cos \omega_m t \qquad (12\text{-}44)$$

The total grid-cathode potential has the form

$$e_c = E_{gm} \cos \omega_c t + E_{mm} \cos \omega_m t + E_{cc} \qquad (12\text{-}45)$$

the slowly varying grid component being specified as

$$e_{cc} = E_{mm} \cos \omega_m t + E_{cc} \qquad (12\text{-}46)$$

Over the linear range of operation, the analytic form for the rms tank current is

$$I_T = k_T(e_{cc} + E_0) \qquad (12\text{-}47)$$

Also, if the instantaneous value of the tank current is chosen as

$$i_T = \sqrt{2}\, I_T \sin \omega_c t$$

this may be written as

$$i_T = \sqrt{2}\, k_T(e_{cc} - E_0) \sin \omega_c t$$

or

$$i_T = \sqrt{2}\, k_T(E_{mm} \cos \omega_m t + E_{cc} - E_0) \sin \omega_c t \qquad (12\text{-}48)$$

But when the modulation is zero, the tank current has the form

$$i_T = \sqrt{2}\, k_T(E_{cc} - E_0) \sin \omega_c t$$

which may be written as

$$i_T = I_{Tm} \sin \omega_c t$$

where

$$I_{Tm} = \sqrt{2}\, k_T(E_{cc} - E_0) \qquad (12\text{-}49)$$

Note that, when the modulation exists, the value of the tank current at the peak of the modulating cycle is

$$I'_{Tm} = \sqrt{2}\, k_T(E_{mm} + E_{cc} - E_0) \qquad (12\text{-}50)$$

The conditions are best examined graphically as in Fig. 12-18. Clearly, the degree of modulation is seen to be

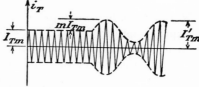

Fig. 12-18. The tank current during grid-bias modulation.

$$m = \frac{I'_{Tm} - I_{Tm}}{I_{Tm}} \qquad (12\text{-}51)$$

which may be written as

$$m = \frac{\sqrt{2}\, k_T(E_{mm} + E_{cc} - E_0) - \sqrt{2}\, k_T(E_{cc} - E_0)}{\sqrt{2}\, k_T(E_{cc} - E_0)}$$

which reduces to

$$m = \frac{E_{mm}}{E_{cc} - E_0} \tag{12-52}$$

By combining Eq. (12-52) with Eq. (12-48), the instantaneous tank current assumes the form

$$i_T = \sqrt{2}\, k_T[(E_{cc} - E_0)m \cos \omega_m t + (E_{cc} - E_0)] \sin \omega_c t$$

which is

$$i_T = \sqrt{2}\, k_T(E_{cc} - E_0)(1 + m \cos \omega_m t) \sin \omega_c t \tag{12-53}$$

In an entirely parallel way, it is possible to derive for the plate circuit the expressions

$$\begin{aligned} I_b &= k_b(e_{cc} - E_0) \\ I_{bb} &= k_b(E_{cc} - E_0) \end{aligned} \tag{12-54}$$

which may be written as

$$\begin{aligned} I_b &= k_b(E_{cc} - E_0)(1 + m \cos \omega_m t) \\ &= I_{bb}(1 + m \cos \omega_m t) \end{aligned} \tag{12-55}$$

The potential across the tank circuit is

$$\mathbf{E}_L = jX_L I_T$$

which is

$$\mathbf{E}_L = jX_L k_T(E_{cc} - E_0)(1 + m \cos \omega_m t) \tag{12-56}$$

Therefore the instantaneous potential across the tank circuit is given by

$$e_L = \sqrt{2}\, X_L k_T(E_{cc} - E_0)(1 + m \cos \omega_m t) \sin (\omega_c t + 90)$$

or

$$e_L = \sqrt{2}\, X_L k_T(E_{cc} - E_0)(1 + m \cos \omega_m t) \cos \omega_c t \tag{12-57}$$

It is now possible to complete the analysis of the circuit.

Expressions for the various important values of power in the circuit are readily obtained. The average power input to the plate circuit by the d-c plate supply, over the modulating cycle, is

$$P_{bb} = \frac{1}{T_m} \int_0^{T_m} E_{bb} I_b \, dt$$

This becomes, by Eq. (12-55),

$$P_{bb} = \frac{1}{T_m} \int_0^{T_m} E_{bb} I_{bb}(1 + m \cos \omega_m t) \, dt$$

which integrates to

$$P_{bb} = E_{bb} I_{bb} \tag{12-58}$$

Since this result shows no dependence on the modulation index m, it follows that the plate supply power is independent of the degree of modulation.

The average output at the tank circuit is given by

$$P_L = \frac{1}{T_m} \int_0^{T_m} e_L i_{p1}\, dt = \frac{1}{T_m} \int_0^{T_m} R_0 i_{p1}^2\, dt$$

which becomes, by Eq. (12-53),

$$P_L = \frac{1}{T_m} \int_0^{T_m} \frac{2R_0 k_T^2}{Q^2} (E_{cc} - E_0)^2 (1 + m \cos \omega_m t)^2 \sin^2 \omega_c t\, dt$$

The problem that exists here in examining the effect of the term of carrier frequency when integrating over the modulating cycle is the same as that discussed in connection with the comparable integration of Eq. (12-36). Similar reasoning allows the present integral to be evaluated. The integral yields

$$P_L = \frac{R_0 k_T^2}{Q^2} (E_{cc} - E_0)^2 \left(1 + \frac{m^2}{2}\right) = I_T^2 R \left(1 + \frac{m^2}{2}\right) \qquad (12\text{-}59)$$

This shows that the r-f power increases with percentage modulation.

The plate-circuit efficiency of the modulated amplifier is given by

$$\eta = \frac{P_L}{P_{bb}} = \frac{(R_0 k_T^2/Q^2)(E_{cc} - E_0)^2(1 + m^2/2)}{E_{bb} k_b (E_{cc} - e_0)}$$

which becomes

$$\eta = \frac{R k_T^2}{k_b E_{bb}} (E_{cc} - E_0) \left(1 + \frac{m^2}{2}\right) \qquad (12\text{-}60)$$

This expression shows that the plate efficiency increases as the modulation index increases. To realize the highest efficiency for a given modulation index ($= 1$) it is necessary that the quantity $E_{cc} - E_0$ be made as large as possible. This requires that the load impedance of the modulated amplifier be so adjusted that the peak amplitude of the output wave is only slightly less than the d-c plate supply.

The plate dissipation of the tube is given by the expression

$$P_p = P_{bb} - P_L$$

which is

$$P_p = k_b E_{bb} (E_{cc} - E_0) - R k_T^2 (E_{cc} - E_0)^2 \left(1 + \frac{m^2}{2}\right) \qquad (12\text{-}61)$$

This may be written in the form

$$P_p = E_{bb} I_b - I_T^2 R \left(1 + \frac{m^2}{2}\right) \qquad (12\text{-}62)$$

It should be noted that the plate dissipation decreases as the percentage modulation increases. Clearly, therefore, the plate dissipation is a maximum when the amplifier is unmodulated.

Grid-bias modulation has the advantage that only a small amount of modulating power is required. However, the carrier power that is obtainable from the amplifier is approximately one-quarter of that from the same tube when operating as a simple class C amplifier. This is so because the peak power of the modulated amplifier corresponds to class C operation, and with a completely modulated wave the peak current is twice the unmodulated current and the corresponding peak power is four times the unmodulated, or carrier, power. Also, the plate efficiency during the unmodulated intervals is approximately one-half the efficiency obtained with simple class C operation. This results from the fact that, if the amplifier is so adjusted that the plate potential is small at the crest of the modulation cycle, then, when there is no modulation, the potential across the load is halved. This results in a high potential across the tube, with a corresponding large plate loss. As a result, the plate-circuit efficiency in the absence of modulation is of the order of 34 per cent. During 100 per cent modulation by a sinusoidal signal, the r-f power output increases by a factor of $\frac{1}{2}$, and the plate-circuit efficiency increases to approximately 51 per cent.

It is interesting to compare the operating features of a plate and a grid-bias modulated amplifier. These are

Grid-bias modulated amplifier:
    Relatively low plate efficiency.
    Low power output in proportion to the capabilities of the modulated tube.
    Low grid-modulating power.
Plate-modulated amplifier:
    Large power output in proportion to the power capabilities of the modulated tube.
    Large modulator power.

In consequence, the over-all efficiency, considering both the modulating and the modulated tube capabilities, is roughly the same. The choice between the two methods of modulation is largely one of convenience, since both methods of modulation will give sensibly 100 per cent modulated waves with low distortion, although it is more difficult to achieve a linear modulating characteristic with control-grid modulation than with other modulation methods. The circuit adjustments are more difficult with grid-bias modulation, as they are sensitive to variations in the carrier exciting potential, the plate supply potential, and the magnitude of the tuned load impedance. Despite these difficulties, control-grid modulation is used in high-power television transmission, since a plate modulator would be very complicated, in view of the width of the frequency band required for this TV service.   Control-grid modulation is generally used in the last r-f stage.

12-11. Cathode Modulation.   A modulated output wave is produced if the modulating potential is introduced into the cathode of the amplifier. The basic circuit for cathode modulation is given in Fig. 12-19.   It should be observed that in such a circuit the modulating potential appears in both the plate and the grid circuits.   Consequently, it is to be anticipated that the characteristics are a combination of those of the plate-modulated and the grid-bias modulated amplifiers, with a plate efficiency and modulating power requirements intermediate between the corresponding requirements for the plate-modulated and the grid-bias modulated amplifiers.

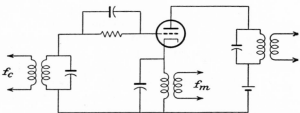

FIG. 12-19. The basic circuit for cathode modulation.

The proportion of plate relative to grid-bias modulation can be increased by increasing the modulating potential E_{mm} and making the grid bias large (by increasing R_g).   By reducing the grid-bias potential, a smaller modulating potential will have a greater influence in the grid circuit, and the system becomes more nearly of the grid-bias modulated type.

The plate-circuit efficiency of such a cathode-modulated amplifier should lie between the roughly 40 per cent of the grid-bias modulated amplifier and the roughly 70 per cent of the plate-modulated amplifier. Also, the power requirements of the modulator will lie between the roughly 5 per cent of the output power for the grid-bias modulated amplifier to the 50 per cent of the output power for the plate-modulated amplifier.   The conditions which prevail will depend on the relative potentials at various points in the amplifier, the percentage modulation, and the degree of linearity of operation.

An interesting point to be noted is that the carrier excitation potential E_{gm} is approximately half that required to operate the circuit as a simple class C amplifier to full output, and the grid bias is usually much greater than the normal class C bias.   This means, of course, that the amplifier is being only lightly driven.

12-12. Other Methods of Modulating a Class C Amplifier.   If a pentode is employed, the modulation potential may be applied in the suppressor-grid circuit.   The general characteristics of such a suppressor-grid modulated class C amplifier are similar to those for control-grid modulation. However, adjustment of the amplifier is simpler. Fairly linear modulation up to 100 per cent may be obtained.

Suppressor-grid modulation possesses the unusual feature that the modulation characteristic lies wholly within the region of negative suppressor potential. The suppressor-grid current is substantially zero; hence the modulation power is zero.

Modulation may be accomplished by injecting the modulation in the screen circuit of a tetrode or pentode. Some power is required from the modulating source, and 100 per cent modulation usually cannot be achieved without some distortion.

12-13. Cross-modulation Distortion. One of the most undesirable forms of distortion which may occur in r-f amplifiers is known as "cross modulation." This effect may occur if a powerful transmitter is in the vicinity of a receiver and arises if the signal due to the transmitter at the grid of the first tube is sufficient to modulate other signals over a substantial tuning range of the receiver. It also occurs over a limited range when an unwanted modulated signal is applied to the grid of the first tube along with the desired signal. If the curvature of the dynamic characteristic contains a third-order term in its series representation, the undesired modulation is transferred to the desired carrier.

Suppose that the dynamic characteristic of the tube may be written in the form

$$i_p = a_1 e_g + a_2 e_g^2 + a_3 e_g^3 + a_4 e_g^4 + \cdots \tag{12-63}$$

and suppose that the signal applied to the grid circuit has the form

$$e_g = E_{c1} \cos \omega_{c1} t + E_{c2}(1 + m \cos \omega_m t) \cos \omega_{c2} t \tag{12-64}$$

To avoid unnecessary complication, the desired carrier E_{c1} is written without modulation, although in general this carrier will be modulated. No loss of generality results by doing this. Consider the third-order term in the series. This is

$$a_3 e_g^3 = a_3 [E_{c1} \cos \omega_{c1} t + E_{c2}(1 + m \cos \omega_m t) \cos \omega_{c2} t]^3$$

which contains the following term, upon expanding the expression:

$$3a_3 E_{c1} \cos \omega_{c1} t [E_{c2}(1 + m \cos \omega_m t) \cos \omega_{c2} t]^2$$

This may be written as

$$3a_3 E_{c1} \cos \omega_{c1} t \left[E_{c2}^2 \frac{1 + \cos 2\omega_{c2} t}{2} (1 + m \cos \omega_m t)^2 \right]$$

and this contains a component

$$\frac{3a_3}{2} E_{c1} E_{c2}^2 \cos \omega_{c1} t \left(1 + \frac{m^2}{2} + 2m \cos \omega_m t + \frac{m^2}{2} \cos 2\omega_m t \right)$$

Observe that the desired carrier is now modulated by the undesired modulation and its second harmonic.

To reduce such cross modulation requires that the selectivity of the total input circuit to the first r-f stage must be high. Of course, by reducing the higher factors a_3, a_4, etc., in the power-series expansion of the tube characteristic will also result in a decreased cross-modulation effect.

REFERENCES

1. Standards on Transmitters and Antennas, Institute of Radio Engineers, 1933.
2. Carson, J. R., *Proc. IRE*, **9**, 243 (1921).
3. Peterson, E., and C. R. Keith, *Bell System Tech. J.*, **7**, 131 (1928).
4. Black, H. S., "Modulation Theory," D. Van Nostrand Company, Inc., New York, 1953.
5. Chambers, J. A., L. F. Jones, G. W. Fyler, R. H. Williamson, E. A. Leach, and J. A. Hutcheson, *Proc. IRE*, **22**, 1151 (1934).
6. As general references, see:
   Massachusetts Institute of Technology Staff, "Applied Electronics," 1st ed., secs. 12-4 to 12-6, John Wiley & Sons, Inc., New York, 1943.
   Cruft Laboratory, War Training Staff, "Electronic Circuits and Tubes," chap. XV, secs. 15-18, 15-19, McGraw-Hill Book Company, Inc. New York, 1947.

PROBLEMS

12-1. The equation of a modulated wave is

$$e = (15 + 10 \sin 3{,}000t - 8 \cos 10{,}000t) \cos 2\pi \times 10^6 t$$

a. What frequencies are contained in the modulated wave?
b. What is the amplitude of each?

12-2. Carry out the analysis to show that amplitude modulation results in a square-law circuit when the carrier potential is applied in the grid circuit and the modulating potential is applied in the plate circuit.

12-3. A shunt modulator using a bridge connection which requires no transformer is illustrated.*

a. Derive an expression for the signal to the load R_l.
b. If $\omega_c = \omega_m$, what is the output?

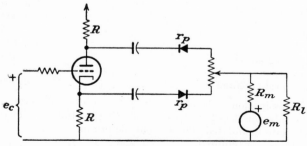

* D. G. Tucker, *Electronic Eng.*, **22**, 139 (1950).

12-4. Prove that the carrier term is missing in the balanced modulator of Fig. 12-9.

12-5. The balanced modulator of Fig. 12-9a is used for carrier suppression. In this circuit, the potentials applied are the following:

$$e_c = E_c \cos \omega_c t$$
$$e_m = E_m \cos \omega_m t$$

with $\omega_c \gg \omega_m$ and with $E_m = 0.5E_c$. Assume that the transconductance g_m varies linearly with grid potential.

  a. Obtain an expression for the output potential from the modulator.
  b. Plot the envelope of this potential.

12-6. Suppose that a band-pass filter is connected in the output of Prob. 12-5 of such characteristics that the lower sidebands are eliminated.

  a. What is the expression for the resulting output?
  b. Plot the envelope of this wave.

12-7. An ideal diode for which $r_p = 1,000$ ohms in the forward direction and $r_p = \infty$ in the inverse direction is used as a modulator. There are applied to this circuit the two potentials

$$e = E_c \cos \omega_c t + E_m \cos \omega_m t$$

with $\omega_c \gg \omega_m$ and with $E_m = 0.5E_c$.

  a. Determine the amplitude of the component of current of angular frequency $\omega_c = \omega_m$.
  b. Repeat for the component of frequency $\omega_c + \omega_m$.

12-8. Repeat Prob. 12-7 for the case where the single diode is replaced by four diodes connected in a bridge circuit.

12-9. A type 851 power triode operates with a bias of -300 volts and with a peak r-f signal of 525 volts. The load impedance $R_0 = 1,500$ ohms. Determine and plot the a-c plate potential across the tank as a function of the d-c plate supply potential, for the following values of plate potential: $E_{bb} = 500, 1,500, 2,500, 3,500$ volts.

12-10. Repeat Prob. 12-9 for $R_0 = 1,000$ ohms.

12-11. An 851 triode is used in a plate-modulated class C amplifier. It operates with a bias of -300 volts, a peak r-f signal of 525 volts, and a plate supply $E_{bb} = 2,000$ volts. When $e_{bb} = E_{bb}$, the peak plate swing is 1,750 volts. Determine the plate-current waveforms at the values of $e_{bb} = 1,000, 2,000, 3,000$ volts.

12-12. A type 891 r-f power triode has the following ratings as a class C oscillator for telegraphy:

D-c plate potential................................	10,000 volts
D-c grid potential.................................	$-2,000$ volts
D-c plate current..................................	1.45 amp
D-c grid current...................................	0.105 amp
Grid driving power................................	310 watts
Power output......................................	10 kw
Peak r-f grid potential............................	2,900 volts

If the plate dissipation is the only limiting factor, determine the corresponding ratings of the tube for class C telephony, allowing for 100 per cent plate modulation. When plate-modulated 100 per cent, determine:

  a. The audio power required.
  b. The impedance offered to the audio source.

c. Power output.

d. Plate-circuit efficiency.

12-13. An 852 transmitting triode has the following ratings as a plate-modulated r-f amplifier under carrier conditions that allow for 100 per cent modulation:

D-c plate potential	2,000 volts
D-c grid potential	−500 volts
D-c plate current	67 ma
D-c grid current	30 ma
Peak r-f grid potential	750 volts
Grid driving power	23 watts
Power output	75 watts

The amplifier is sinusoidally plate-modulated 75 per cent.   Determine:

a. Audio power required.

b. Impedance offered to the audio source.

c. Plate efficiency.

d. Average plate dissipation.

e. Grid dissipation at the tube terminal.

If the amplifier were unmodulated, what would be the maximum allowable r-f power output, assuming that the plate dissipation is the limiting factor, and that the plate-circuit efficiency remains constant?

12-14. The results on a plate-modulated class C amplifier are given in the figure.   Suppose that this modulated amplifier is operated at 1,600 volts d-c,

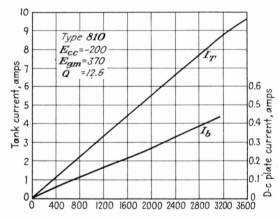

with 75 per cent modulation.   Assume a constant plate efficiency of 60 per cent. Calculate the following:

a. The power supplied by the d-c plate source.

b. The power supplied by the audio source.

c. The r-f carrier power.

d. The r-f sideband power

e. The resistance of the class C amplifier to the modulating source.

f. The maximum and minimum instantaneous voltage between plate and cathode when the carrier is unmodulated.

g. Repeat (*f*) for $m = 0.75$.

12-15. The essential elements of a plate-modulated class C amplifier are illustrated in the diagram. The tubes are operated under the following conditions:

843 tube:

$f_c = 1.2$ Mc

$E_{bb} = 350$ volts d-c

$I_b = 30$ ma d-c

6N7 tube:

$E_{bb} = 300$ volts d-c

Effective plate-plate resistance 8,000 ohms

Impedance of 843 tank circuit at 1.2 Mc is 10,000 ohms.

Effective Q of 843 tank is 15.

The carrier output is to be 5 watts 100 per cent modulated.

Calculate the following:

a. The plate-circuit efficiency of the 843.

b. The power required from the 6N7.

c. The load impedance presented by the 843 to the secondary of the modulating transformer.

d. The transformer ratio that should be used.

e. If the output is to be down 1 db 5,000 cycles off resonance, what must the effective Q of the 843 tank circuit be?

f. The value of C.

g. The approximate value of the r-f choke *RFC*.

h. With a loaded Q of 15, calculate the value of L and C of the 843 tank circuit.

i. If the actual resistance in the 843 tank is 5 ohms, how much resistance is coupled into this tank from its load?

j. What is the efficiency of power transfer from the tank to the load?

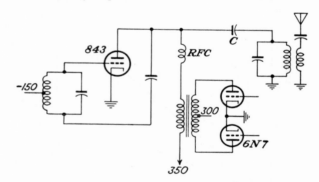

12-16. An 806 tube is to be used as the plate-modulated class C power amplifier of a transmitter. It operates from a 2,500-volt power supply. Carry out the design of this and the associated transformer-coupled class B modulator. The design must fulfill the following specifications:

a. The plate dissipation is not to exceed 150 watts.

b. The transmitter is to be plate-modulated 70 per cent.

c. The distortion in the modulating envelope is not to exceed 10 per cent.

d. The transmitter frequency is 2 Mc.

e. The grid bias may be obtained with grid leak, fixed bias, or a combination of both.

f. Specify the plate supply potential, grid bias, and excitation potential.

g. The output is to feed a 76-ohm antenna.

h. Specify the primary inductance, secondary inductance, tuning capacitance, and mutual inductance. Assume that the unloaded Q of the coils is 300 and that the loaded Q is 12.

i. Give the modulation-transformer requirements.

Be sure that any assumptions that are made are clearly stated.

12-17. The characteristics of an 802 tube when used as a grid-bias modulated class C amplifier are given in the sketch. Calculate for $m = 1.0$ the following:

a. The power supplied by the d-c source.

b. The r-f carrier power.

c. The sideband power.

d. The plate efficiency.

e. The plate dissipation.

f. The maximum and minimum instantaneous potential between cathode and plate when the carrier is unmodulated.

g. Repeat (*f*) for $m = 0.75$.

h. What is the amplitude of the a-f signal to achieve the desired degree of modulation?

i. What is the a-f driving power?

j. What is the grid-cathode power loss?

Choose $R_L = 12.6$ ohms; $Q = 26.5$.

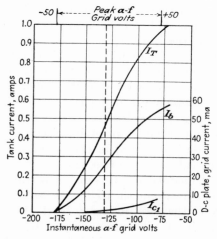

12-18. Consider a class C amplifier that is modulated 100 per cent. Assume the output power to be 1,000 watts. Assume reasonable values of plate-circuit efficiency for each of the tubes involved, and calculate (1) the total power required by the modulated tube, (2) the total power required by the modulator tubes, and (3) the over-all plate-circuit efficiency when the amplifier is:

a. Plate-modulated, using a class A modulator.

b. Plate-modulated, using a class B modulator.

c. Grid-bias modulated.

Repeat the calculations for zero per cent modulation.

CHAPTER 13

DEMODULATION

13-1. Introduction. When a radiated modulated carrier signal reaches the receiving point, the signal, or intelligence, must be extracted therefrom. The process by which the signal is recovered from the modulated wave is broadly known as demodulation or detection.

Before considering methods of detection, it is desirable that the processes of modulation and demodulation be reviewed. As already discussed in Chap. 12, the process of modulation may be considered to be one in which the signal frequencies ω_m, which are specified relative to the zero-frequency reference level, are shifted upward on the frequency scale and the sidebands are symmetrically disposed about the carrier frequency ω_c. This frequency shifting is accomplished by mixing the signal-frequency group, centered about the zero frequency, with the carrier frequency in appropriate multiplying circuits. The existence of a nonlinear characteristic is essential in the modulator in order to effect the mixing or multiplication of the two waves.

In the process of demodulation the signal spectrum, which is centered about ω_c, is shifted downward on the frequency scale so that it is centered, once again, relative to the zero-frequency level, thus returning it to its original frequency position. This frequency shifting is accomplished by mixing the signal-frequency group which is centered about the carrier frequency ω_c with the carrier frequency ω_c in appropriate multiplying circuits. The existence of a nonlinear characteristic in the demodulator is essential in order to effect the mixing or multiplication of the two waves.

Observe, therefore, that both the modulating and the demodulating processes involve frequency shifting; both frequency shifts are by an amount ω_c; and both processes are accomplished in circuits which possess nonlinear characteristics, in order to effect multiplication of the waves. In fact, similar circuits are used in certain cases for both processes, although certain essential differences exist. In the modulating process the carrier signal is generated in one channel, and this is combined in the modulator with the audio signal, which has been generated in a second

348

channel.   In the demodulating process, the required carrier wave is ordinarily contained in the incoming modulated carrier, and no separate carrier-generating circuit is necessary.   Of course, if the carrier is missing from the incoming wave, as is true in suppressed-carrier transmission, it is necessary that a separate locally generated carrier be made available if the original signal frequencies are to be extracted.   This matter will be discussed later.

It is customary to consider frequency changing, which is the process of eliminating the original carrier from the modulated signal and substituting for it a new carrier, as demodulation.   In essence, therefore, frequency shifting in which the signal frequency does not play a direct part is also classified as demodulation.

13-2. Plate Detection.   Detection is possible when a modulated potential is applied to the grid of a tube which is biased to the nonlinear portion of its transfer characteristic.   The general features of such plate detection are made evident by an examination of Fig. 13-1.   The output curve

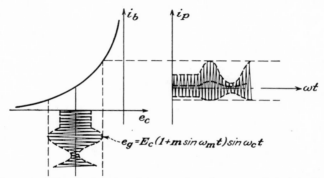

Fig. 13-1. Sketch showing the operation of a square-law detector.

clearly shows the presence in the output of a component that varies at the modulating frequency rate.   Of course the h-f carrier component must be eliminated, but this is readily accomplished by using an appropriately placed low-pass filter in the circuit.

To examine the operation of the circuit analytically, it will be supposed that the transfer curve with respect to the operating point is a simple square-law characteristic of the form

$$i_p = ae_g^2 \qquad (13\text{-}1)$$

Suppose that the signal is an a-m wave of the form

$$e_g = E_c(1 + m \cos \omega_m t) \cos \omega_c t \qquad (13\text{-}2)$$

Then the output current will contain the terms

$$
\begin{aligned}
i_p &= aE_c^2(1 + m \cos \omega_m t)^2 \cos^2 \omega_c t \\
&= \frac{aE_c^2}{2}(1 + m \cos \omega_m t)^2(1 + \cos 2\omega_c t) \\
&= aE_c^2 \left[\frac{1}{2} + m \cos \omega_m t + \frac{m^2}{4} + \frac{m^2}{4} \cos 2\omega_m t \right. \\
&\qquad + \frac{1}{2} \cos 2\omega_c t + \frac{m}{2} \cos (2\omega_c + \omega_m)t + \frac{m}{2} \cos (2\omega_c - \omega_m)t \\
&\qquad + \frac{m^2}{2} \cos 2\omega_c t + \frac{m^2}{8} \cos (2\omega_c + 2\omega_m)t \\
&\qquad \left. + \frac{m^2}{8} \cos (2\omega_c - 2\omega_m)t \right]
\end{aligned}
\tag{13-3}
$$

Clearly, there will be included in the output a number of steady components, a term of modulating frequency, a number of components of frequencies equal to the sums and differences of the carrier and side frequencies, and a number of components of twice the carrier and side frequencies.

Suppose that a selective network is used which attenuates all components except those in the neighborhood of the modulating frequency ω_m. The terms that appear in the output will then be

$$
i_1 \doteq amE_c^2 \left(\cos \omega_m t + \frac{m}{4} \cos 2\omega_m t \right)
\tag{13-4}
$$

which consists of the desired term plus one of second harmonic of this frequency. If the second-harmonic amplitude is to be kept smaller than, say, 10 per cent of the fundamental, it is necessary that the modulation index be less than 0.4 for sinusoidal modulation. Despite this limitation, such detectors have been used extensively with generally satisfactory results, probably because the average modulation of the ordinary radio program is of the order of 40 per cent.

It is of interest and significance in subsequent work to examine those terms in the neighborhood of the second harmonic of the carrier $2\omega_c$, although these results are not of importance at this particular point. The terms are

$$
\begin{aligned}
i_2 &= \frac{aE_c^2}{2} \left[(1 + m^2) \cos 2\omega_c t + m \cos (2\omega_c + \omega_m)t + m \cos (2\omega_c - \omega_m)t \right. \\
&\qquad \left. + \frac{m^2}{4} \cos (2\omega_c + 2\omega_m)t + \frac{m^2}{4} \cos (2\omega_c - 2\omega_m)t \right]
\tag{13-5}
\end{aligned}
$$

If m is small, this equation can be written as

$$i_2 \doteq \frac{aE_c^2}{2} \left[\cos 2\omega_c t + m \cos (2\omega_c + \omega_m)t + m \cos (2\omega_c - \omega_m)t \right]$$

which is

$$i_2 = \frac{aE_c^2}{2} (1 + 2m \cos \omega_m t) \cos 2\omega_c t \qquad (13\text{-}6)$$

Therefore, if one were to use a tuned circuit at the output of a square-law circuit which is tuned to $2\omega_c$, the output would be of second harmonic of the carrier but the modulation frequency would be unchanged. Frequency doublers of this type find extensive use in h-f operations.

13-3. Diode Detection. Diode detectors have almost completely supplanted other types of detectors in home radio-receiver use. They operate very satisfactorily, although the modulated input to the detector

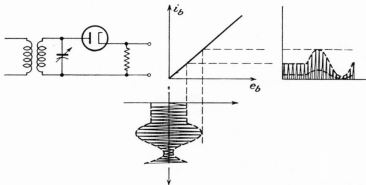

Fig. 13-2. The circuit and the operational characteristics of an average diode detector.

must be large—in excess of 1 or 2 volts. Otherwise excessive distortion may result because of the nonlinear dynamic curve of the diode circuit. Since the diode detector possesses characteristics in common with ordinary rectification, it is possible to present a qualitative discussion of its operation on this basis.

There are two important types of operation of a diode detector. One is known as *average detection,* and the other is *envelope detection.* The circuit for average detection is illustrated in Fig. 13-2. Also illustrated in this figure is the character of input and output waves. It will be observed that this is just a simple diode rectifier without a filter in the output. The application of a modulated wave to the circuit yields an output the average value of which contains the modulating frequency. It follows from simple rectifier theory (refer to Chap. 3) that the output potential is of the form

$$E_m = \frac{R}{\pi(R + r_p)} E_c(1 + m \cos \omega_m t) \qquad (13\text{-}7)$$

The use of appropriate circuits permits the modulating-frequency component to be extracted from the output.

The circuit for envelope detection is illustrated as Fig. 13-3. It will be observed that such circuits are essentially those of a simple diode rectifier with a capacitor filter. The operation of this circuit is substantially the same as that for the simple rectifier, with the additional fact that the a-c input potential varies in amplitude. With the proper choice of the filter capacitor, the waveforms of the input potential, the output potential, and the tube current are roughly those shown in Fig. 13-4. Since the carrier frequency is much greater than the modulating frequency, the jagged appearance of the curves is considerably worse than is actually the case. In effect, therefore, the output potential of the detector follows the envelope of the modulated input wave and has the waveform of the modulating potential.

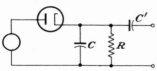

Fig. 13-3. A circuit for envelope detection.

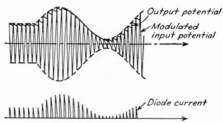

Fig. 13-4. Waveforms of the input potential, output potential, and plate current in a diode-detector circuit.

13-4. Analysis of Diode Detection.[1] An analytic expression that gives certain of the properties of the diode detector is possible if several reasonable assumptions are made. In particular, it will be assumed that the d-c potential across the diode load, which arises from the tube current during the portion of the cycle when the input potential exceeds the potential across the output capacitor, will remain constant over the carrier-frequency cycle. It will also be assumed that the static characteristic of the diode is linear. The conditions that apply during one cycle of the impressed modulated r-f signal wave are as illustrated in Fig. 13-5.

The equation of the assumed characteristic is

$$i_b = \frac{e_b}{r_p} = g_p e_b \qquad e_b > 0$$
$$i_b = 0 \qquad e_b < 0$$

(13-8)

But the instantaneous potential applied to the diode is given by the equation

$$e_b = E_c(1 + m \cos \omega_m t) \cos \omega_c t - E_a$$

which is written for convenience as

$$e_b = E' \cos \omega_c t - E_a \qquad (13\text{-}9)$$

where E' is the instantaneous amplitude of the modulated carrier and E_a is the average value of the rectifier carrier signal and appears across

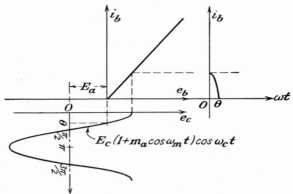

Fig. 13-5. The approximate action of a diode detector.

the capacitor.   The plate current will be of the form

$$\begin{aligned} i_b &= g_p(E' \cos \omega_c t - E_a) & e_b &> 0 \\ i_b &= 0 & e_b &< 0 \end{aligned} \qquad (13\text{-}10)$$

The shift from one equation to the other occurs at the angle θ, which is that angle defined by

$$E' \cos \omega_c t_0 = E' \cos \theta = E_a \qquad (13\text{-}11)$$

The instantaneous current i_b will contain a number of harmonic components, but those of interest are the d-c or average component and the a-c term at the driving frequency.   The d-c component of i_b is given by

$$I_b = \frac{1}{2\pi} \int_0^{2\pi} i_b \, d\theta$$

which is, because of the symmetry that exists,

$$I_b = \frac{1}{\pi} \int_0^{\theta} i_b \, d\theta$$

This may be written as

$$I_b = \frac{1}{\pi} \int_0^{\theta} g_p(E' \cos \theta - E_a) \, d\theta \qquad (13\text{-}12)$$

which becomes

$$I_b = \frac{g_p}{\pi} (E' \sin \theta - E_a \theta) \tag{13-13}$$

This becomes, by Eq. (13-11),

$$I_b = \frac{g_p}{\pi} E'(\sin \theta - \theta \cos \theta) \tag{13-14}$$

Also, it is initially assumed that

$$E_a = I_b R$$

By combining Eqs. (13-14) and (13-15), there results

$$I_b = \frac{E_a}{R} = \frac{E' \cos \theta}{R} = \frac{g_p E'}{\pi} (\sin \theta - \theta \cos \theta) \tag{13-15}$$

from which

$$\frac{r_p}{R} = \frac{1}{\pi} (\tan \theta - \theta) \tag{13-16}$$

This expression shows that there is a direct functional relationship between the operating angle θ and the ratio of the plate resistance of the diode to the external resistance. An explicit expression for θ as a function of r_p/R is very difficult, but the information may be given graphically.

The detection efficiency of the diode detector is defined as the ratio of the average value of the load potential E_a to the peak a-c input E'. That is,

$$\eta = \frac{E_a}{E'} = \cos \theta \tag{13-17}$$

This may be written, by Eq. (13-15), as

$$\eta = \frac{R}{\pi r_p} (\sin \theta - \theta \cos \theta) \tag{13-18}$$

so that η appears as a function of the ratio R/r_p. Clearly, therefore, the detection efficiency for a specified choice of diode and load, i.e., for a specified ratio r_p/R, is obtained from a plot of Eq. (13-18), which is contained in Fig. 13-6. Observe that since r_p/R is a constant of the circuit, the conduction angle θ is likewise a constant for the circuit. This means, of course, that θ is independent of the degree of modulation or the amplitude E_c.

The detection efficiency is readily computed for the case when the by-pass or output capacitor is not used, i.e., for the average detector. In this case, the output potential is given by Eq. (13-7) and is

$$E_a = \frac{R}{\pi(R + r_p)} E_c(1 + m \cos \omega_m t) \tag{13-19}$$

when the peak value is

$$E' = E_c(1 + m \cos \omega_m t) \tag{13-20}$$

The detection efficiency is the ratio of Eq. (13-19) to (13-20) and is

$$\eta = \frac{R/r_p}{\pi(1 + R/r_p)} \tag{13-21}$$

The detection efficiency for this case is seen to approach $1/\pi$ as a maximum value.

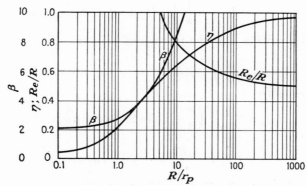

Fig. 13-6. Various important terms in the analysis of diode detectors.

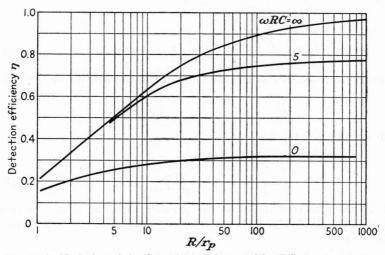

Fig. 13-7. Variation of the detection efficiency with ωRC as a parameter.

It is possible to compute[2] the values of detection efficiency for values of C between the value specified as $\omega RC = \infty$ in Fig. 13-7, as specified in Eq. (13-18), and the value $\omega RC = 0$, the value specified in Eq. (13-21). The curve for $\omega RC = 5$ is also shown in Fig. 13-7. The designer's problem is to choose as large a value of C as possible, consistent with no diagonal clipping (see Sec. 13-5). The other curves of Fig. 13-7 will be discussed later.

Another quantity of importance in detector operation is the power absorbed by the detector, or the power loss in the diode circuit. To evaluate this requires a knowledge of the fundamental-frequency component of the current. The maximum value of the current is given by the Fourier coefficient

$$I_{p1m} = \frac{1}{\pi} \int_0^{2\pi} i_b \cos \omega t \, d(\omega t)$$

This becomes, writing α as the parameter of integration,

$$I_{p1m} = \frac{2}{\pi} \int_0^\theta g_p(E' \cos \alpha - E_a) \cos \alpha \, d\alpha \qquad (13\text{-}22)$$

which integrates to

$$I_{p1m} = \frac{2g_p E'}{\pi} \left(\frac{\theta}{2} + \frac{1}{4} \sin 2\theta - \sin \theta \cos \theta \right)$$

or

$$I_{p1m} = \frac{g_p E'}{\pi} (\theta - \sin \theta \cos \theta) \qquad (13\text{-}23)$$

The power input to the diode and its load is

$$P = \frac{1}{T} \int_0^T e i_b \, dt$$

$$P = \frac{E' I_{p1m}}{2} = \frac{g_p E'^2}{2} (\theta - \sin \theta \cos \theta) \qquad (13\text{-}24)$$

The effective resistance of the diode circuit is defined by the relation

$$R_e \equiv \frac{E'^2}{2P} = \frac{\pi}{g_p(\theta - \sin \theta \cos \theta)} \qquad (13\text{-}25)$$

which may be written as

$$R_e = r_p \beta$$

$$\beta \equiv \frac{\pi}{\theta - \sin \theta \cos \theta} \qquad (13\text{-}26)$$

That is, the effective resistance in parallel with the capacitor due to the loss in the diode circuit is equal to βr_p. A plot of β is also contained in Fig. 13-6.

By combining Eqs. (13-26) with (13-16), an expression for the equivalent resistance that shunts the diode input circuit is possible. This is

$$\frac{R_e}{R} = \frac{R_e}{r_p} \frac{r_p}{R} = \frac{\tan \theta - \theta}{\theta - \sin \theta \cos \theta}$$

This expression is plotted as a function of R/r_p in Fig. 13-6.

For the case when η is high, the equivalent input resistance reduces to a simple form.   Noting that for η high θ is small,

$$\sin \theta \doteq \theta - \frac{\theta^3}{6} \qquad \cos \theta \doteq 1 - \frac{\theta^2}{2}$$

and

$$\frac{R_e}{R} = \frac{1}{\cos \theta} \frac{\sin \theta - \theta \cos \theta}{\theta - \sin \theta \cos \theta} \doteq \frac{1}{2\eta} \tag{13-27}$$

Hence the effective input resistance becomes $R/2\eta$ for large η.   Since $\eta \doteq 1$, then R_e is slightly greater than one-half the load resistance.

13-5. Distortion in Diode Detectors.   There are two sources of distortion in a simple diode detector.   One results from the curvature in the tube characteristic, making the efficiency of rectification vary according to the amplitude of the envelope.   This source of distortion may be minimized by making the load resistance large compared with the diode plate resistance and by making the amplitude of the carrier envelope applied to the diode reasonably large.   Under practical conditions, when the detection efficiency exceeds 80 per cent, the distortion from this source is of the order of 2 per cent for a completely modulated wave.   With small signals the distortion may reach as high as 25 per cent for a completely modulated wave when the signal potential is a fraction of a volt.

The second source of distortion arises from the fact that the potential across the capacitor in the output can die away only as fast as the charge can leak off through the load resistor.   Hence, unless the time constant of this circuit is properly chosen, clipping may result during the troughs of the modulated signal.

If the h-f variations of the output potential are to be small, the time constant of the load circuit RC must be large compared with the period of the carrier-frequency cycle. However, if this value is made too large, the output potential cannot decay as rapidly as the envelope decreases, and clipping occurs.   The conditions discussed are illustrated in Fig. 13-8.

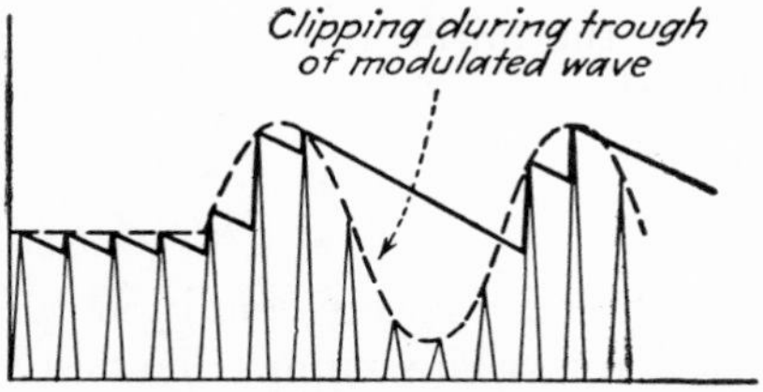

Fig. 13-8. Diagonal clipping in a diode detector when the load-circuit time constant is too large.

To ascertain the maximum allowable value of the time constant, it should be noted that this value must be such as to permit the capacitor to discharge at the same rate as the decrease of the modulation envelope. This may be estimated in the following manner.[3]   The most unfavorable condition occurs at the highest modulation frequency ω_m that the detector is designed to handle and is that for which the equation of the envelope is

$$e = E_c(1 + m \cos \omega_m t) \tag{13-28}$$

At any particular time $t = t_0$, the value and the slope of the modulation envelope are

$$e = E_c(1 + m \cos \omega_m t_0)$$
$$\left(\frac{de}{dt}\right)_{t_0} = -\omega_m m E_c \sin \omega_m t_0 \qquad (13\text{-}29)$$

If the potential across the capacitor equals the modulation potential at the time $t = t_0$,

$$e_a = E_c(1 + m \cos \omega t_0) \qquad (13\text{-}30)$$

and it decays thereafter according to the exponential expression

$$e_a = e_{a0} e^{-(t-t_0)/RC} \qquad (13\text{-}31)$$

The initial rate of change is

$$\left(\frac{de_a}{dt}\right)_{t_0} = -\frac{1}{RC} e_a = -\frac{E_c}{RC}(1 + m \cos \omega_m t_0) \qquad (13\text{-}32)$$

To avoid the diagonal clipping illustrated in Fig. 13-8, the capacitor potential must be less than the value of the envelope for time $t > t_0$, and the slope of e_a must be less than that of the envelope at $t = t_0$. This requires that

$$-\frac{E_c}{RC}(1 + m \cos \omega_m t_0) \leqq -\omega_m m E_c \sin \omega_m t_0$$

or

$$\frac{1}{RC} \geqq \omega_m \frac{m \sin \omega_m t_0}{1 + m \cos \omega_m t_0} \qquad (13\text{-}33)$$

For the initial rate of decay of the capacitor potential to be greater than the rate of decay of the envelope potential, it is necessary that

$$\frac{1}{RC} > \omega_m \frac{m \sin \omega_m t_0}{1 + m \cos \omega_m t_0}$$

But the most severe condition on the RC constant is that for which the fraction is a maximum. To find this, consider the expression

$$\frac{d}{dt} \frac{m \sin \omega_m t_0}{1 + m \cos \omega_m t_0} = 0$$

This yields

$$\cos \omega_m t_0 = -m$$
$$\sin \omega_m t_0 = \sqrt{1 - m^2}$$

from which

$$\frac{1}{RC} > \omega_m \frac{m}{\sqrt{1 - m^2}} \qquad (13\text{-}34)$$

If this equation is satisfied, the output potential follows the waveform of the envelope. According to this equation, as the modulation approaches

100 per cent, the required time constant approaches zero.   Consequently, at 100 per cent modulation, the output potential contains the carrier as well as the modulating frequency.

By taking into account a number of factors that were neglected in the above analysis, such as the impedance of the source supplying the modulated potential, the results must be modified somewhat.   Experimentally it has been found that the amount of harmonic generation is not excessive for sound reproduction if

$$\frac{1}{RC} \geqq \omega_m m \tag{13-35}$$

This equation expresses the relation among the circuit parameters which permits the detector to follow the modulation envelope.

13-6. Diodes with Complex Load Impedance. A detector stage is normally provided with a filter in the output in order to prevent any r-f

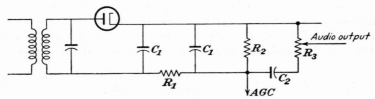

Fig. 13-9. Diode-detector circuit.

potential from reaching the subsequent stages, since only the d-c and modulation-frequency terms are desired.   The d-c component that is developed across the diode is ordinarily used for the purpose of automatic gain control (see Sec. 13-8); the a-c component is fed to the audio amplifiers to provide the a-c signals at a potential and power level dictated by the output device.

To achieve the requisite filtering necessitates the addition of circuit elements, with the result that the impedance that the complex load offers to the diode at the modulation frequency is quite different from that offered to the d-c component.   A typical circuit, which includes the r-f filter, which is usually a simple Π-type resistance-capacitance filter, and the coupling network to the first audio stage, is illustrated in Fig. 13-9. Observe from this circuit that the a-c impedance at the modulating frequency is smaller than the d-c resistance, owing to the shunting effect of the filter capacitors and also because of the fact that the grid resistor of the next stage parallels the load resistor.   Because of this, the properties of the diode rectifier are not precisely those discussed in Sec. 13-5.

Consider the situation for a sinusoidal modulation envelope to the input of the diode circuit.   A sinusoidal component of current at the modulation frequency and a d-c component of current due to the carrier level will exist in the diode circuit. It is necessary that the negative peak of the a-c component of current should never exceed the d-c component; otherwise the diode will cut off, with an a-c waveform distortion. The a-c waveform will have the negative peaks clipped if this happens.

Equation (13-15) may be used as a starting point for obtaining significant results in the present connection. It follows from Eq. (13-15) that the ratio

$$\frac{\text{Peak } E_{ac}}{E_{dc}} = m \tag{13-36}$$

which may be written as

$$\frac{\text{Peak } I_{ac}|Z_m|}{I_{dc}R} = m \tag{13-37}$$

In this expression Z_m is impedance of the total diode output circuit at the modulating frequency and R is the total diode output-circuit resistance at the d-c or zero-frequency level. Now from the discussion given above, the maximum value that m may have and still avoid negative clipping is that for which the peak I_{ac} current is just equal to the d-c component I_{dc}. Clearly, the maximum value of m without negative clipping is then

$$m_{\text{max}} = \frac{|Z_m|}{R} = \frac{\text{impedance of load to } \omega_m}{\text{resistance of load to d-c}} \tag{13-38}$$

Figure 13-9 is examined in the light of Eq. (13-36). For the usual choice of circuit parameters (see Fig. 13-13 for a detailed circuit) the reactance of C_1 is high at the modulating frequencies, and the reactance of C_2 is very low. Approximately, therefore, for this circuit

$$m_{\text{max}} \doteq \frac{R_1 + \dfrac{R_2 R_3}{R_2 + R_3}}{R_1 + R_2}$$

The actual choice of the parameters R_1, R_2, and R_3 is a compromise between detection efficiency and the effect of possible nonlinearity of the diode.

13-7. Rectification Characteristics. It is clear from the discussion in Sec. 13-5 and also from the discussion leading to Eq. (13-38) that the signal output from the diode detector consists of a d-c potential E_a, which is the average value of the rectified carrier signal, and this appears across the capacitor C, and an a-c term of modulating frequency, this being a measure of the amplitude of the envelope of the incoming modulated carrier. Thus one might consider C as an effective by-pass for carrier-frequency currents, with two potential components across the output, the d-c and the a-c terms. The quantitative relationships among the amplitude of the r-f potential, the average rectified current, and the average plate potential E_a are contained in the rectification characteristic of the diode. A circuit for obtaining these curves and the results on a 6H6 are illustrated in Fig. 13-10. In the circuit shown, the a-c potential E is maintained constant, while the bias potential E_a, which simulates the drop across the load resistor, is varied, and the rectified current is read on the microammeter.

Indicated on this characteristic are a series of load lines, which correspond to different static load resistances R. These are drawn on the curves in the customary way. Their use permits one to obtain the output potential as the carrier potential varies. Thus, by plotting the current as a function of time as the carrier amplitude varies because of

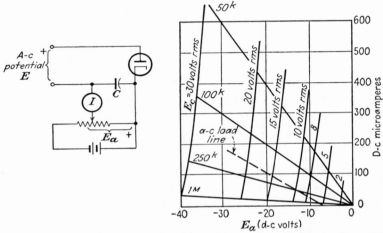

Fig. 13-10. The rectification characteristic of a 6H6 diode, and the circuit used for its determination.

the modulation, it is possible to determine both the output and the distortion. For example, if the unmodulated carrier amplitude is 10 volts rms, with the modulation causing the amplitude to vary between 5 and 15 volts rms, with, say, $R = 100$ kilohms, the load current will vary between approximately 60 and 180 μa, with the output potential varying between 6 and 18 volts. The detection efficiency in this case is

$$\frac{12 - 6}{10} = 0.6$$

Attention is called to the fact that, in addition to the several static load lines which are drawn on the curves of Fig. 13-10, there is also shown an "a-c load line." The line shown represents a 0.25-megohm static load that is shunted through a coupling capacitor by a second 0.25-megohm load, which might be the grid resistor of the first audio amplifier. At the audio frequencies, the actual load is the parallel combination of these two resistors. The circuit of Fig. 13-13 indicates a static load of 250 kilohms with a dynamic load consisting of the series combination of a 50-kilohm resistance and a 250-kilohm resistor paralleled by two 500-kilohm resistors. The a-c load line illustrated has been drawn for an effective value of the unmodulated signal of 10 volts. Observe that the load line does not pass through the point (0,0). Consequently, if the operation is carried to the region of no current, severe distortion may result. The curves of Fig. 13-11 show the character of the variation of the distortion with per cent modulation.

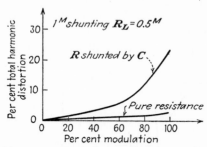

Fig. 13-11. Variation of distortion with per cent modulation. (*From F. Langford-Smith, "Radiotron Designer's Handbook," 1st ed., chap. 18, Amalgamated Wireless Valve Company Pty. Ltd., Sydney, Australia, 1941.*)

13-8. Automatic Gain Control. The average amplitude of the modulated carrier wave that reaches the detector stage will depend upon a number of factors, including the field strength at the receiver of the station to which the receiver is tuned, and the propagation conditions between the transmitter and receiver. It is desirable, therefore, to incorporate some means within the receiver for maintaining the average modulated carrier amplitude at the detector at a constant level so as to avoid the effects of fading. Such an automatic gain control (agc) (often called automatic volume control, avc) will automatically vary the gain of the r-f or i-f stages to yield a substantially constant level at the detector. Figure 13-12 shows a block diagram of a receiver incorporating automatic gain control.

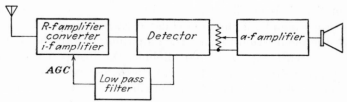

Fig. 13-12. Block diagram of a receiver incorporating automatic gain control.

The details of a circuit in which a diode is used both as a linear detector and to supply a d-c potential for automatic-gain-control purposes are illustrated in Fig. 13-13. In this circuit the use of a separate isolating resistor and capacitor filter (R_1, C_1) permits the extraction of a d-c potential that is proportional to the average modulated carrier level. Also, the d-c potential across the diode load resistance is blocked by the use of a capacitor-and-resistor combination (R_2, C_2), the a-f component being made available for the following a-f amplification stages.

The time constant of the automatic-gain-control network RC_1 is made long enough to average out the variations in carrier amplitude corresponding to the modulation, but short enough so that the automatic-gain-control potential varies with the average amplitude of the carrier, dropping off as the carrier fades and increasing as the carrier becomes stronger.

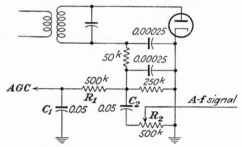

Fig. 13-13. A diode detector and automatic-gain-control circuit.

This potential is used to vary the bias, and hence the transconductance, of the r-f and i-f amplifier tubes, to maintain a substantially constant level. In this way, fluctuations in the average amplitude of the modulated carrier delivered to the diode are greatly reduced. The r-f and i-f amplifier tubes that have automatic gain control applied to them should be of the remote-cutoff or variable-mu type; otherwise the system may be very critical of adjustment, owing to the extremely marked sensitivity of transconductance with bias of the sharp-cutoff type of tubes.

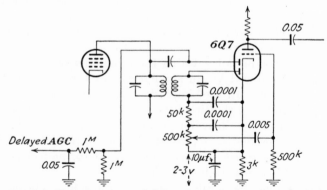

Fig. 13-14. A diode detector and delayed automatic-gain-control circuit.

If it is desired to have the automatic gain control operate only after the carrier strength reaches a specified minimum, so that the reception of weak signals will not be affected by the automatic-gain-control system, a *biased* or *delayed* automatic-gain-control circuit may be used. A circuit with delayed automatic-gain-control potential is shown in Fig. 13-14. In this circuit the automatic-gain-control potential is obtained from a separate diode. Also, the automatic-gain-control potential is obtained from the output of the previous stage in order that a potential—that across the cathode resistor of the triode element of the duodiode triode—may be used as the reference level, below which no automatic gain control is applied.

13-9. Superregenerative Detector. If the quality of reproduction of a receiver is not critical, and high sensitivity is required from relatively simple apparatus, the superregenerative receiver possesses considerable merit. In such a receiver, regenerative feedback is incorporated in the detector circuit. The amount of regeneration that is provided sets the detector at the point of oscillation, and the smallest signal is capable of initiating the oscillations. Once the oscillations have been initiated, they will increase in amplitude until the nonlinear characteristic of the tube sets the amplitude level, exactly as for the simple oscillator. Moreover, the oscillations will continue to exist, unless a means is provided for controlling them. The effect of the feedback is to produce a negative input conductance, precisely in the manner of the discussion of Sec. 11-14. With sufficient negative conductance, oscillations of the type discussed in Sec. 11-14 will occur, whence the rate of rise of the oscillation amplitude, which is exponential, is inversely proportional to the inductance of the tuning circuit. Also, the rate of rise is found to be proportional to the amplitude of the initiating signal.

To make such a regenerative detector useful, it is necessary to interrupt the oscillations periodically and reset the detector to its sensitive position. The usual method of obtaining the desired control is to add an a-c potential to the plate supply of the detector. In this way the circuit can be made to yield negative conductance for at least a part of the half cycle during which the a-c potential adds to the plate potential, though it has a positive conductance during the remainder of the period. The a-c potential is produced by an auxiliary oscillator, which is known as the *quench* oscillator. In the simplest case, the detector may be made self-setting by adjusting the circuit to be of the self-blocking type. The general character of the operation is illustrated in Fig. 13-15. Observe that the pulses of oscillation repeat at the quench frequency. A typical superregenerative detector is shown in Fig. 13-16, in which $T1$ is the detector and $T2$ is the quench oscillator.

When the circuit is so adjusted that the quench oscillator stops the growth of oscillations before they reach the optimum value determined by the tube characteristics, it is said to be operating in the linear mode. This is the operation that is illustrated in Fig. 13-15. If the growth of oscillations continues until they are limited by the tube curvature before the quench oscillator causes them to decay, the system is said to be operating in the logarithmic mode. The basis for this name is found in the fact that all signals above a certain minimum value will produce the same pulse amplitude, but the area under the pulse envelope is proportional to the logarithm of the signal amplitude.

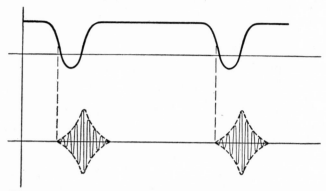

FIG. 13-15. The general character of the action of the superregenerative detector.

Suppose that the incoming signal is modulated. The rate of rise of oscillations is proportional to the amplitude of the initiating signal, and if the quench frequency is considerably higher than the modulation frequency, the amplitude of the pulses will follow the modulation envelope

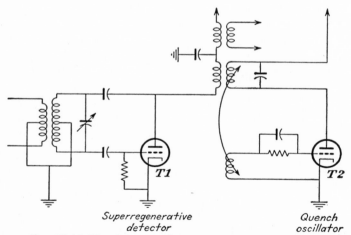

Superregenerative
detector

Quench
oscillator

FIG. 13-16. The elements of a superregenerative receiver.

of the signal. The need for the high quench frequency arises from the fact that the quenched pulses are of varying amplitude and so introduce additional sidebands. It is necessary to choose the quench frequency to be several times greater than the modulating frequency if the added sidebands are not to interfere with the original sidebands and thereby produce distortion in the rectified output. The quench frequency is ordinarily chosen to be five to fifty times the modulation frequency.

Owing to the sensitive state of the detector, noise potentials due to thermal agitation and shot effect will also initiate the oscillations and produce pulses at the quench frequency. Since the initiating noise signals fluctuate, there will be a noise signal in the output. As a result, the noise level of the receiver is high. In addition, external noise which is received with the signal will alter the value of the total signal at the instant when the oscillations begin to build up. The amplitudes of the pulses are thereby affected, with a consequent noise in the output.

The selectivity of the superregenerative receiver is low, owing to the loading of the input tuned circuit of the detector by the low conductance. Moreover, the selectivity cannot be increased by the addition of r-f amplification because the regenerative feedback from the detector will cause shock excitation of the added tuned circuits. For short-wave applications this lack of selectivity is actually desirable, both because the available frequency band is great and tuning is necessary over a very wide band, and because many transmitters might not be very stable.

13-10. Suppressed-carrier Demodulation. Some general comments concerning suppressed-carrier transmission were given in Sec. 1-5. Also, it was shown in Sec. 12-3 that the output from a balanced modulator which was arranged to suppress the carrier contained the sidebands of an a-m carrier. Clearly, the transmission of suppressed-carrier signals is accomplished at high efficiency since the greater part of the power of an a-m wave is in its carrier, and with its suppression a saving in power is effected.

The process of demodulation for suppressed-carrier transmission proves to be rather difficult. The production of a carrier at low power in the receiver which will maintain the proper phase relation between it and the sidebands over a period of time is extremely difficult. It is important to examine the effects of phase shifts between the carrier and the sidebands in order to evaluate the suppressed-carrier system of transmission. The situation may best be examined by reference to the sinor representation of the process.

Consider the particular case when the reintroduced carrier is 90 deg away from its required phase position for the exact reproduction of the modulated carrier. Also, it is supposed that the carrier amplitude is large compared with the sideband amplitudes, as it would be if the modulation index were small. The situation is illustrated graphically in Fig. 13-17 for several positions during the modulating cycle. An examination of these figures shows that the resultant potential E_R does not vary appreciably from the reintroduced carrier. However, E_R does undergo periodic phase variations with respect to E_c, since, during one half cycle

E_R leads E_c, and during the other half cycle E_R lags E_c. Under these conditions the resulting wave is no longer constant in frequency but varies at the modulation-frequency rate, and the frequency variation is accompanied by a cyclic change in amplitude.

The effect of phase shifting of the carrier of an a-m wave is the reduction of the modulation index and the introduction of a phase or frequency modulation. When the carrier phase shift is 90 deg, the amplitude modulation may almost disappear and the phase modulation that results may be considerable. In fact, this latter case is the method for producing a p-m wave as one step in the production of a f-m output in the Armstrong system of frequency modulation, which will be discussed in Chap. 14.

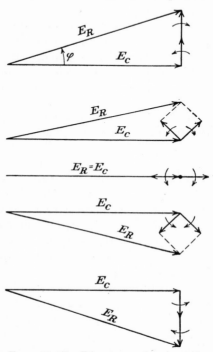

If the reintroduced carrier is of a different frequency from the original carrier, there will be a beating with the sidebands and only a transient condition will prevail.

For the proper reproduction of the original signal, the carrier phase must be maintained, relative to those of the sidebands, to within a fraction of a cycle. If a pilot carrier is transmitted, control circuits might be possible to achieve the required frequency and phase stability between the pilot and the locally generated carrier. If no pilot carrier is available, then the frequency stability of both the transmitting and receiving

Fig. 13-17. Diagrams showing the instantaneous amplitude of a reintroduced carrier which is 90 deg out of phase with the sidebands.

oscillators must be controllable with a very high degree of precision. This latter condition cannot be achieved even with present-day techniques. Consequently, completely suppressed carrier transmission is not practical.

13-11. Single-sideband Suppressed-carrier Demodulation. If a suppressed-carrier signal were passed through a suitable filter network or through appropriate circuits so that one of the sidebands was eliminated, the resulting wave would be a single-sideband signal. The demodulation of such single-sideband signals proves to be feasible, and such a communication system is used commercially. Actually, of course, the suppression of the sideband is accomplished at the transmitter, so that only a single-sideband suppressed-carrier signal is radiated. For a given signal strength at the receiver, this system has the same power economy as the suppressed-carrier system. In addition, it effects a saving in the bandwidth required in the r-f spectrum.

In the case of a pure tone, the reintroduction of a carrier ω_c to the signal of frequency $\omega_c + \omega_m$ (assuming that the upper sideband $\omega_c + \omega_m$ is transmitted) will return the frequency ω_m in the output. However, it is necessary that the amplitude of the reintroduced carrier must be properly chosen if the envelope of the reconstructed signal is to be a replica of the original signal. Moreover, the phase of the reintroduced carrier and that of the sideband are important, since the resultant amplitude will depend on the relative phases of these component waves which are to be combined.

If the signal is a complex wave, as is usually the case, the effects of the frequency and the phase of the reintroduced carrier become more difficult to discuss qualitatively. The general effects of an inadequate carrier amplitude and incorrect carrier phase are a distortion of the resulting amplitude, owing to the different components contained in the signal being affected by differing amounts. In general, the phase of the different frequencies will be shifted by different amounts. Also, the amplitudes may be differently affected.

The shape of the resulting envelope depends on the relative phases of the different components of the signal; hence the resulting waveshape will vary with the phase of the reintroduced carrier. However, since the human ear recognizes only amplitude and frequency, distortion due to phase will not be recognized. Consequently such single-sideband suppressed-carrier operation is generally satisfactory for speech transmission. In fact, if the reintroduced carrier is altered in frequency, the pitch of the signal will change, because the signal frequency will not be translated to the proper zero position. A translation of several cycles from the zero is not particularly objectionable.

While a translation of several cycles might not influence too seriously a speech signal, it will seriously affect the transmission of music. This follows from the fact that, for music, the fundamental and its harmonics are important in presenting the tonal qualities of each instrument. If the frequency and amplitude of the reproduced harmonic components are altered, the character of each instrument will be lost.

Because of its limitations, single-sideband suppressed-carrier transmission is limited in its application to commercial telephony. It is used extensively in point-to-point commercial communication.[4]

13-12. Mixers and Converters. A superheterodyne receiver (see Sec. 1-8 and also Prob. 13-8) incorporates a mixing element, a device in which the incoming modulated signal is combined with the signal from a local oscillator in order to shift the carrier level from one frequency to another. The use of such a device permits the carrier level of any signal to be shifted to a preset i-f value and then to provide i-f amplification to bring the potential level to the 10 volts or so desired at the input of the diode detector.   The use of the superheterodyne is widespread because it provides a higher selectivity than a tuned r-f circuit, primarily because of the use of double-tuned amplifiers.

As was noted in Sec. 7-2, the equivalent noise resistance of a mixer or converter is relatively high.   Owing to this, a noise potential of 1 μv or more may exist on the grid.   Moreover, since the second detector potential level is perhaps 10 volts, the maximum gain that can be used between the mixer grid and i-f amplifier output is then determined by the allowable signal/noise potential ratio.   For example, if a signal/noise ratio of 100 is required, the largest useful mixer-amplifier gain is about 10^5.   Since some gain occurs in the mixer and is roughly 25 per cent of that of the i-f amplifier stage, two i-f amplifier stages will provide all the requisite gain.

If a separate local or beating oscillator tube is used, the tube in which the combining is accomplished is called a *mixer*.   If a multigrid tube is used to serve as both the local oscillator and the mixing element simultaneously, it is referred to as a *converter*.   In both cases the effectiveness with which mixing is accomplished, i.e., the ratio of the i-f current in the output to the signal potential input to the circuit, is an important quantity.   This quantity is called the *conversion transconductance* and is, by definition,

$$g_c \equiv \frac{i_{i\text{-}f}}{E'} = \frac{\partial i_{b,\,i\text{-}f}}{\partial e_{c,\,r\text{-}f}} \tag{13-39}$$

It should be noted that this quantity is quite different from the mutual conductance of the tube.

13-13. Square-law Conversion.   To examine certain of the aspects of the conversion process, it will be supposed that the output from the local oscillator is combined with the modulated carrier potential, and this combined potential is supposed impressed directly on the grid of a square-law tube.   If the tube characteristic is represented by an expression of the form

$$i_p = ae_g^2 \tag{13-40}$$

then with the application of the potential

$$e_g = E_c(1 + m \cos \omega_m t) \sin \omega_c t + E_0 \sin \omega_0 t \tag{13-41}$$

the following terms will appear in the output:

$$i = a\left[E_c^2 \sin^2 \omega_c t + E_0^2 \sin^2 \omega_0 t + \frac{m^2 E_c^2}{4} \sin^2 (\omega_c + \omega_m)t \right.$$

$$+ \frac{m^2 E_c^2}{4} \sin^2 (\omega_c - \omega_m)t + 2E_c E_0 \sin \omega_c t \sin \omega_0 t$$

$$+ mE_c^2 \sin \omega_c t \sin (\omega_c + \omega_m)t + mE_c^2 \sin \omega_c t \sin (\omega_c - \omega_m)t$$

$$+ mE_c E_0 \sin \omega_0 t \sin (\omega_c + \omega_m)t + mE_c E_0 \sin \omega_0 t \sin (\omega_c - \omega_m)t$$

$$\left. + \frac{m^2 E_c^2}{2} \sin (\omega_c + \omega_m)t \sin (\omega_c - \omega_m)t \right] \tag{13-42}$$

By the use of frequency-selective circuits, all terms will be eliminated except those having frequencies in the neighborhood of $\omega_0 - \omega_c = \omega_i$. Thus there will remain in the output the following:

$$i = a[E_c E_0 \cos \omega_i t + \tfrac{1}{2}mE_c E_0 \cos (\omega_i - \omega_m)t$$
$$+ \tfrac{1}{2}mE_c E_0 \cos (\omega_i + \omega_m)t] \tag{13-43}$$

which may be written as

$$i = aE_c E_0(1 + m \cos \omega_m t) \cos \omega_i t \tag{13-44}$$

That is, the only signal that can get through the tuning circuits which have been tuned to the i-f frequency and which have a bandwidth sufficiently wide to accommodate the a-f spread is essentially the modulation amplitude at the i-f frequency.

As noted in Sec. 13-1, frequency changing is classed as detection, whence the converter is frequently called the "first detector." Actually it is a detector only in the sense that it permits obtaining output frequencies that are different from the input frequencies or, rather, that it shifts the frequency from the r-f level to the i-f level.

The problem of keeping the difference between the local oscillator and the input r-f frequencies constant as one varies the antenna tuning from a position corresponding to one end of the band (say 550 kc) to one corresponding to the other end of the band (say 1,600 kc) is not a simple matter if one wishes to adjust a single control. It requires careful construction of the variable capacitors and the choice of constants so that they "track" together. In general, perfect tracking is not possible over the entire band. Ordinarily provision is possible for ensuring perfect tracking at only three specific points. The errors over the intervening ranges are not great enough to throw the beat frequency out of the i-f pass band.

13-14. Generalized Conversion Theory.[5] In the foregoing discussion it was assumed that both the broadcast signal and the local oscillator signal were impressed on the grid of a square-law amplifier. Under these circumstances the conversion is distortionless. To reduce the interaction between the two circuits, electron coupling is ordinarily employed in modern practice.   Consequently the only coupling is that through the electron stream.

Under the assumption that the signal potential is small and that the local oscillator potential is large, the signal-electrode transconductance may be considered as a function of the oscillator potential only.   Then the signal-electrode plate transconductance g_m may be considered as varying periodically at the oscillator frequency.   The situation is then

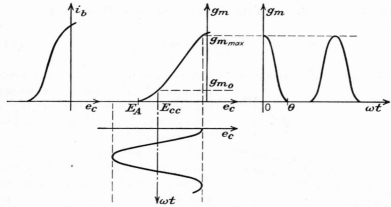

FIG. 13-18. Illustrating the variation of plate-grid transconductance of a converter tube with a large oscillator potential on the grid.

somewhat as illustrated in Fig. 13-18.   Because of the periodic variation that occurs in g_m, this may be represented by a Fourier series of the form

$$g_m = \frac{b_0}{2} + b_1 \cos \omega_0 t + b_2 \cos 2 \omega_0 t + \cdots \qquad (13\text{-}45)$$

When a small signal is applied to the tube, the resulting a-c plate current has the form

$$i_p = g_m E' \cos \omega_c t \qquad (13\text{-}46)$$

This may be written in the form

$$i_p = E' \cos \omega_c t \left(\frac{b_0}{2} + \sum_n b_n \cos n\omega_0 t \right)$$

or

$$i_p = \frac{b_0}{2} E' \cos \omega_c t$$
$$+ E' \left(b_1 \cos \omega_c t \cos \omega_0 t + \sum_{\substack{n \\ n \neq 1}} b_n \cos n\omega_0 t \cos \omega_c t \right) \qquad (13\text{-}47)$$

For a circuit tuned to the frequency $\omega_0 - \omega_c$, the i-f frequency, the output is

$$i_{p,i\text{-}f} = \frac{b_1}{2} E' \cos (\omega_0 - \omega_c)t = \frac{b_1}{2} E' \cos \omega_i t \qquad (13\text{-}48)$$

whence the conversion transconductance is

$$g_c \equiv \frac{i_{p,i\text{-}f}}{E'} = \frac{b_1}{2} \qquad (13\text{-}49)$$

Upon combining this with the known form for b_1, there results

$$g_c = \frac{1}{2\pi} \int_0^{2\pi} g_m \cos \omega_0 t \, d(\omega_0 t) \qquad (13\text{-}50)$$

This expression indicates that the value of g_c depends on the magnitude of the mutual conductance at the operating point and also on the way that this conductance is varied by the local oscillator potential.

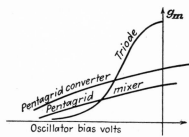

FIG. 13-19. Typical transconductance curves for different types of tubes.

The continued development of Eq. (13-50) is possible by examining curves showing typical variations of the plate-grid transconductance with the oscillator bias potential. These are given in Fig. 13-19. It is found that in most practical cases, the (g_m, e_c) curves can be represented with reasonable approximation over the operating range by an expression of the form

$$g_m = g_{m0} \left(1 + \frac{e_c}{E_A} \right)^\alpha \qquad \text{with } 0.5 < \alpha < 1.5 \qquad (13\text{-}51)$$

(see Fig. 13-18 for notation). Suppose that the oscillator potential is of the form

$$e_c = E_{0m} \cos \omega_0 t \qquad (13\text{-}52)$$

Equation (13-50) then becomes

$$g_c = \frac{2g_{m0}}{2\pi} \int_0^\theta \left(\frac{1 + E_{0m} \cos \omega_0 t}{E_A} \right)^\alpha \cos \omega_0 t \, d(\omega_0 t) \qquad (13\text{-}53)$$

For convenience, this expression is written in the form

$$g_c = \tfrac{1}{2} g_{m,\max} f(\theta)$$

where

$$f(\theta) = \frac{2g_{m0}}{\pi g_{m,\max}} \int_0^\theta \left(\frac{1 + E_{0m} \cos \omega_0 t}{E_A} \right)^\alpha \cos \omega_0 t \, d(\omega_0 t) \qquad (13\text{-}54)$$

But since

$$g_{m,\text{max}} = g_{m0}\left(1 + \frac{E_{0m}}{E_A}\right)^{\alpha} \tag{13-55}$$

then

$$f(\theta) = \frac{2}{\pi}\int_0^{\theta}\left[\frac{1 + (E_{0m}\cos\omega_0 t/E_A)}{1 + E_{0m}/E_A}\right]^{\alpha}\cos\omega_0 t\,d(\omega_0 t) \tag{13-56}$$

The function $f(\theta)$ can be evaluated for different values of α. Plots of such results[6] are given in Fig. 13-20.

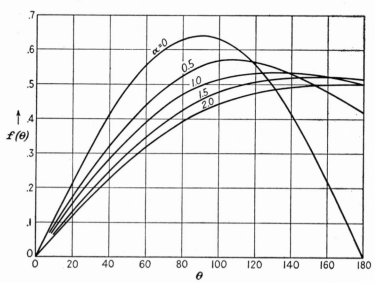

Fig. 13-20. Plot of the function $f(\theta)$ for various values of α.

Observe from these curves that the values of $f(\theta)$ for a given value of θ do not vary markedly from each other for different values of α. The maximum value of conversion transconductance occurs in the neighborhood of 90 deg. Specifically, for $\alpha = 0$, which occurs for constant $g_m = g_{m,\text{max}}$ over the full operating range, $f(\theta) = 2/\pi$, and so

$$g_c = \frac{1}{2}\,g_{m,\text{max}}\,\frac{2}{\pi} = 0.32 g_{m,\text{max}} \tag{13-57}$$

For a linear transconductance variation ($\alpha = 1$), which corresponds to a quadratic transfer characteristic, the optimum θ is approximately 120 deg, in which case

$$g_c = \tfrac{1}{2}g_{m,\text{max}} \times 0.53 = 0.27 g_{m,\text{max}} \tag{13-58}$$

Finally, for the transconductance variation specified by $\alpha = 0.5$, which corresponds to a space-charge (three-halves power) variation, the optimum

θ is approximately 105 deg, in which case

$$g_c = \frac{1}{2}g_{m,\text{max}} \times 0.57 = 0.29g_{m,\text{max}} \qquad (13\text{-}59)$$

Note that all values of $g_c/g_{m,\text{max}}$ are roughly the same, so that, for conduction angles $90 < \theta < 180$ deg, the conversion-transconductance ratio varies over the range from 0.25 to 0.30.

If an exact determination of g_c for a specific tube is required, this can be accomplished by a numerical evaluation of the Fourier coefficient given by Eq. (13-50).

REFERENCES

1. Everitt, W. L., "Communication Engineering," 2d ed., pp. 427-433, McGraw-Hill Book Company, Inc., New York, 1937.
2. Marique, J., *Wireless Eng.*, **12**, 17 (1935).
3. Terman, F. E., and N. R. Morgan, *Proc. IRE*, **18**, 2160 (1930).
4. Nichols, H. W., *Elec. Commun.*, **2**, 11 (1923).
5. Peterson, E., and F. B. Llewellyn, *Proc. IRE*, **18**, 38 (1930).
   Herold, E. W., *Proc. IRE*, **30**, 84 (1942).
   Peterson, L. C., and F. B. Llewellyn, *Proc. IRE*, **33**, 458 (1945).
6. Rothe, H., and W. Kleen, "Elektronenrohren als Anfangsstufen Verstarker," Akademische Verlagsgesellschaft, m.b.H., Leipzig, 1948.

PROBLEMS

13-1. A sinusoidal potential is applied to the average detector of Fig. 13-2, with $R_l = 100$ kilohms. Determine the variation of the rectified output potential with applied signal.

13-2. The envelope detector of Fig. 13-3 has

$$R_l = 100 \text{ kilohms} \qquad \text{and} \qquad C = 200 \ \mu\mu\text{f}$$

The impressed potential is

$$e = 12 \cos 2\pi \times 1.5 \times 10^6 t + 1 \cos 2\pi \times 1.51 \times 10^6 t$$

Write an expression for the instantaneous potential across C. Neglect tube drop in the diode.

13-3. A carrier is sinusoidally modulated 80 per cent by a 7.5-kc signal. The signal input to the envelope detector of Fig. 13-3 with $R_l = 100$ kilohms has a carrier component of 12 volts peak. What should be the maximum value of C for no distortion? Neglect the tube resistance.

13-4. The input to the detector of Prob. 13-3, with

$$C = 100 \ \mu\mu\text{f} \qquad R_l = 100 \text{ kilohms} \qquad R_g = 1 \text{ megohm} \qquad C' = \infty$$

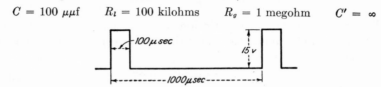

is a pulsed r-f signal, the carrier frequency being 5 Mc. Sketch the waveform of the potential across R_g.

13-5. In the circuit of Fig. 13-3, the diode efficiency is 0.90. Calculate and plot as a function of the modulating frequency ω_m the maximum degree of modulation of the input signal e for distortionless rectification.

13-6. Suppose that the d-c load resistance of a peak diode detector is 250 kilohms and $\eta = 0.90$.

a. Calculate and plot the maximum degree of modulation of a signal without negative peak clipping as a function of the ratio of a-c to d-c load impedances for ratios between 1 and 0.5.

d. If the signal is 100 per cent modulated, plot the approximate distortion under these conditions.

13-7. Determine from the rectification characteristics of a 6H6 diode the largest permissible modulation without clipping if the d-c impedance of the load is 100 kilohms and the modulation frequency impedance is 50 kilohms. If the effective modulation is 70 per cent with a carrier of 10 volts rms, determine the approximate percentage distortion.

13-8. A superheterodyne as indicated in the diagram in block form gives for an unmodulated carrier-frequency signal of $5\mu v$ input to the r-f amplifier a detector

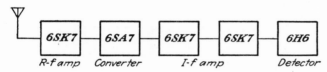

output of 5 volts. If automatic gain control is used on all tubes, what must the carrier level be to give a 5-volt output; a 10-volt output? Assume that the full d-c output potential is used for automatic gain control.

13-9. A receiver is provided with a square-law detector, which is represented by the expression

$$i = ke^2$$

Calculate the form of the output, and specify whether or not an intelligible a-f signal results when the following are applied to the input:

a. One sideband is eliminated from the transmitted wave.
b. The carrier is eliminated from the transmitted wave.
c. One sideband and the carrier are eliminated from the transmitted wave.

13-10. A single-sideband transmitted wave is applied to a square-law detector for which

$$i_p = 0.5(6 + e_g)^2 \quad ma$$

If the input consists of a supplied carrier of 2.5 volts peak and the sideband amplitude is 1 volt peak, calculate the signal current in the output.

13-11. A 6L7 pentagrid tube is used as a converter. A plot of the curve of

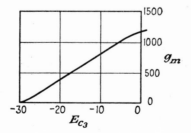

plate–grid 1 transconductance as a function of grid 3 bias is sketched in the diagram for this problem.   A beating oscillator signal of 24 volts peak, which causes a bias of −20 volts to be developed, is applied to grid 3.   The incoming signal of 100 μv is applied to grid 1, which is maintained at a bias of −6 volts.

   a. Evaluate the conversion transconductance under these conditions by a graphical solution.

   b. Compare with the results obtained by applying the appropriate results of Sec. 13-15.

CHAPTER 14

FREQUENCY MODULATION AND DETECTION

14-1. Introduction. Chapter 12 was confined to a discussion of amplitude modulation, in which the amplitude of the transmitted wave is altered in a manner dictated by the amplitude and frequency characteristics of the signal. It was there pointed out that in addition to such amplitude variations it is possible to effect changes in the frequency or in the phase of the transmitted signal. In particular, however, if intelligence is to be transmitted, it is essential that the two features that characterize intelligence, viz., amplitude, or loudness, and frequency, must be available.

In frequency modulation the transmitting frequency is varied by an amount depending on the signal amplitude, and the signal frequency determines the rate at which the variation takes place. In phase modulation the phase of the transmitted wave is shifted by an amount that depends on the signal amplitude, and the rate at which this shift occurs is made proportional to the signal frequency. In general, any system that can transmit the two aspects of information required for the intelligence could serve as an acceptable system of communication. A variety of pulse systems have been devised which are satisfactory and which possess certain advantages over the a-m, f-m, and p-m systems. Certain aspects of these systems have been discussed in Chap. 1.

It should be particularly noted that the amplitude of the oscillations in the f-m system is not involved in the actual process of transmitting intelligence. Consequently, it is possible to make the system insensitive to any a-m disturbances. This is a particularly desirable feature since atmospheric and man-made disturbances are largely amplitude-modulated. Owing to the difference in character between a-m and f-m signals, it is possible to separate and extract the signal from the interference.

14-2. Basic Characteristics of Frequency Modulation. To examine graphically the fundamental principles of frequency modulation, suppose that a telegraph dot and dash are applied to an a-m and to an f-m system. The results have the forms illustrated in Fig. 14-1. For the a-m system, the frequency of oscillation remains constant, but the amplitude is zero or a constant, depending upon the time in the cycle. In the f-m system, the amplitude remains constant, but the frequency changes from a value f_2 to a value f_1 or f_3 when the signal is applied.

If the applied signal is sinusoidal and of frequency f_m, the effect produced in an a-m system has the form illustrated in Fig. 14-2b and the

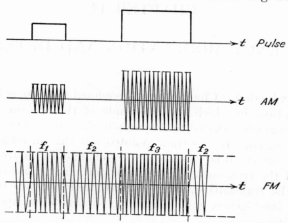

Fig. 14-1. The primary features of a-m and f-m waves.

effect produced in an f-m system has the form illustrated in Fig. 14-2c.

14-3. Instantaneous Phase and Frequency. The general expression for an unmodulated carrier wave is given by

$$e_c = E_c \sin (\omega_c t + \theta) \tag{14-1}$$

In this expression the period of the wave is given by

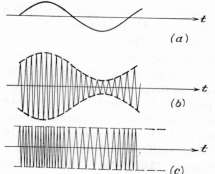

Fig. 14-2. The output of a sinusoidally modulated a-m and f-m transmitter.

$$T = \frac{1}{f} = \frac{2\pi}{\omega_c}$$

The quantity

$$\omega_c t + \theta = \varphi \tag{14-2}$$

is the total instantaneous "phase" of the function. If the phase is written as $\varphi(t)$, the value of the potential at any instant is represented by the expression

$$e_c = E_c \sin \varphi(t) \tag{14-3}$$

But, clearly, the angular frequency is related to the phase by the expression

$$\omega = \frac{d\varphi}{dt} \tag{14-4}$$

This expression agrees with the usual definitions of frequency, and in the unmodulated case

$$\omega = \frac{d}{dt}(\omega_c t + \theta) = \omega_c$$

14-4. Frequency Modulation. Frequency modulation is produced by varying the instantaneous frequency of a carrier by an amount that is proportional to the amplitude of the modulating signal and at a rate given by the frequency of the modulating source. The amplitude of the carrier is assumed to remain constant in the process. That is, if the modulating signal has the form

$$e_m = E_m \cos \omega_m t \tag{14-5}$$

the f-m wave has an instantaneous frequency given by the expression

$$\omega(t) = \omega_c + k_f E_m \cos \omega_m t \tag{14-6}$$

The proportionality factor k_f determines the maximum variation in frequency for a given signal strength E_m.

To determine the expression for the f-m wave, use is made of Eq. (14-4). This requires that

$$\omega = \frac{d\varphi}{dt} = \omega_c + k_f E_m \cos \omega_m t$$

from which it follows that

$$\varphi(t) = \int_0^t \omega \, dt$$

which yields the expression

$$\varphi(t) = \omega_c t + k_f \frac{E_m}{\omega_m} \sin \omega_m t + \theta_0 \tag{14-7}$$

The initial phase θ_0 is neglected in what follows, for it plays no part in the modulating process. Thus, for the f-m wave,

$$e = E_c \sin\left(\omega_c t + k_f \frac{E_m}{\omega_m} \sin \omega_m t\right) \tag{14-8}$$

The instantaneous frequency of the f-m wave is

$$f = \frac{\omega}{2\pi} = f_c + k_f \frac{E_m}{2\pi} \cos \omega_m t \tag{14-9}$$

which has a maximum value of

$$f_{\max} = f_c + k_f \frac{E_m}{2\pi} \tag{14-10}$$

and a minimum value of

$$f_{\min} = f_c - k_f \frac{E_m}{2\pi} \tag{14-11}$$

The maximum swing of the frequency from its mean value is called the *frequency deviation* and is denoted by f_d.   It is

$$f_d \equiv f_{\max} - f_c = f_c - f_{\min} = k_f \frac{E_m}{2\pi} \qquad (14\text{-}12)$$

By analogy with amplitude modulation, the *modulation index* is defined as

$$m_f \equiv \frac{f_d}{f_c} = \frac{\omega_d}{\omega_c} = k_f \frac{E_m}{\omega_c} \qquad (14\text{-}13)$$

Also, the ratio of f_d to the modulating frequency f_m is called the *deviation ratio* and has the value

$$\delta \equiv \frac{f_d}{f_m} = \frac{\omega_d}{\omega_m} = m_f \frac{\omega_c}{\omega_m} = k_f \frac{E_m}{\omega_m} \qquad (14\text{-}14)$$

In terms of these factors, the expression for the f-m wave assumes the form

$$e = E_c \sin (\omega_c t + \delta \sin \omega_m t) \qquad (14\text{-}15)$$

14-5. Frequency Spectrum of F-M Wave.   To examine the spectrum of the f-m wave, it is necessary to expand the expression [Eq. (14-15)] that represents the f-m wave.   This is done as follows:

$$e = E_c[\sin \omega_c t \cos (\delta \sin \omega_m t) + \cos \omega_c t \sin (\delta \sin \omega_m t)] \qquad (14\text{-}16)$$

Use is now made of the following expansions,

$$\cos (\delta \sin \omega_m t) = J_0(\delta) + 2 \sum_{n=1}^{\infty} J_{2n}(\delta) \cos 2n\omega_m t$$

$$\sin (\delta \sin \omega_m t) = 2 \sum_{n=0}^{\infty} J_{2n+1}(\delta) \sin (2n + 1)\omega_m t \qquad (14\text{-}17)$$

where the function $J_n(\delta)$ is the Bessel function of the first kind and of order n.   The f-m waveform then becomes

$$\begin{aligned} e = {}&E_c \sin \omega_c t[J_0(\delta) + 2J_2(\delta) \cos 2\omega_m t + 2J_4(\delta) \cos 4\omega_m t + \cdots] \\ &+ E_c \cos \omega_c t[2J_1(\delta) \sin \omega_m t + 2J_3(\delta) \sin 3\omega_m t + \cdots] \end{aligned} \qquad (14\text{-}18)$$

which may be written in the form

$$\begin{aligned} e = {}&J_0(\delta)E_c \sin \omega_c t \\ &+ J_1(\delta)E_c[\sin (\omega_c + \omega_m)t - \sin (\omega_c - \omega_m)t] \\ &+ J_2(\delta)E_c[\sin (\omega_c + 2\omega_m)t + \sin (\omega_c - 2\omega_m)t] \\ &+ J_3(\delta)E_c[\sin (\omega_c + 3\omega_m)t - \sin (\omega_c - 3\omega_m)t] \\ &+ \cdots \end{aligned} \qquad (14\text{-}19)$$

where use has been made of the trigonometric expansions

$$\begin{aligned} \sin x \cos y &= \tfrac{1}{2}[\sin (x + y) + \sin (x - y)] \\ \cos x \sin y &= \tfrac{1}{2}[\sin (x + y) - \sin (x - y)] \end{aligned} \qquad (14\text{-}20)$$

The Bessel function $J_n(\delta)$ is defined by the series

$$J_n(\delta) = \frac{\delta^n}{2^n n!} \left[1 - \frac{\delta^2}{2(2n+2)} + \frac{\delta^4}{2(4)(2n+2)(2n+4)} \right.$$
$$\left. - \frac{\delta^6}{2(4)(6)(2n+2)(2n+4)(2n+6)} + \cdots \right] \quad (14\text{-}21)$$

It follows from Eq. (14-19) that the spectrum of the f-m wave consists of a carrier and an infinite number of sidebands all of whose amplitudes are various-order Bessel functions. Graphs of several of these functions are contained in Fig. 14-3. It will be noticed that $J_0(\delta)$ has a root at

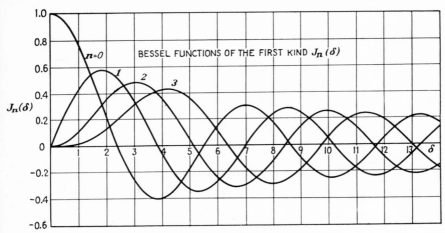

FIG. 14-3. Bessel functions of the first kind.

about 2.40. This means that the carrier will vanish when the frequency deviation is equal to 2.4 times the audio frequency. This fact provides a method for measuring the frequency deviation since the zero point of the carrier can be observed by a selective radio receiver.

A list of the roots of various Bessel functions is given in Table 14-1.

TABLE 14-1

ROOTS OF $J_n(\delta)$

$n = 0$	1	2	3	4	5
2.4048	3.882	5.135	6.379	7.586	8.780
5.520	7.016	8.417	9.760	11.064	12.339
8.654	10.173	11.620	13.017	14.373	15.700
11.792	13.323	14.796	16.224	17.616	18.982
14.931	16.470	17.960	19.410	20.827	22.220
18.071	19.616	21.117	22.583	24.018	25.431
21.212	22.760	24.270	25.749	27.200	28.628

It is instructive to examine a particular situation in some detail. Consider an r-f signal that is modulated ± 75 kc by an a-f signal of 7.5 kc. The corresponding deviation ratio is 10.0. The important Bessel function that occurs in the expression for such an f-m wave is $J_n(10.0)$. A plot of $J_n(10.0)$ as a function of n is given in Fig. 14-4. Notice that

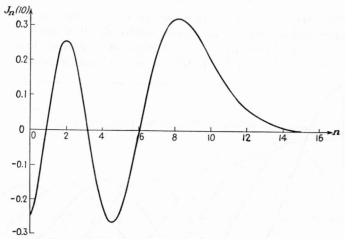

Fig. 14-4. A plot of $J_n(10.0)$ as a function of n.

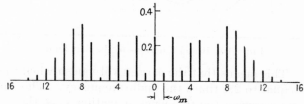

Fig. 14-5. The spectral distribution in an f-m wave with $\delta = 10$.

$J_n(10.0)$ falls off toward zero rapidly for n greater than 10, but that the amplitudes are significant out to about 14, which corresponds to

$$14 \times 7.5 = 105 \text{ kc}$$

A plot of the spectrum corresponding to Eq. (14-19) is given in Fig. 14-5. Notice that this is just a plot of the spectral lines, without regard for sign, as dictated by the Bessel-function plot of Fig. 14-4. The separation between individual sidebands is 7.5 kc, the modulating frequency. It is evident from this plot that the total bandwidth necessary to include all significant sidebands is 210 kc.

Two similar plots are also included. In Fig. 14-6 is illustrated a series of plots for constant modulating frequency f_m but for various values of frequency-deviation ratio δ. The increasing number of sidebands with

δ is clearly seen. Likewise, the disappearance of the carrier is plainly seen.

The plots of Fig. 14-7 show the spectra for a constant frequency deviation but for various modulation frequencies. It should be observed that the total bandwidth required to include all significant sidebands decreases somewhat with increasing deviation ratio. For a given frequency deviation f_d, except for the very small value of δ, almost all significant sidebands are contained within the range f_d. The curve of Fig. 14-8 indicates the number of significant sidebands (those with amplitudes exceeding 1

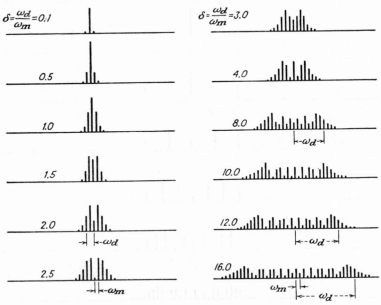

FIG. 14-6. The spectral distribution in an f-m wave for different values of δ, different ω_d, and fixed ω_m.

per cent of the largest sideband component) in an f-m spectrum for different values of n and δ. In particular, if $\delta = 5$, then n must be about 8 for $J_n(\delta)$ to be negligible compared with unity.

Some very important information is contained in Fig. 14-8. To appreciate this, consider the present Federal Communications Commission (FCC) regulations on frequency modulation. These regulations specify:

1. Maximum frequency deviation, $f_d = \pm 75$ kc.
2. Allowable bandwidth, $B = 200$ kc (including a 25-kc band at each end).
3. Frequency stability of carrier, ± 2 kc.

Remembering that the frequency deviation is related to the amplitude and frequency of the modulating potential according to the relation

$$\omega_d = k_f E_m$$

then for that amplitude which provides a frequency deviation of 75 kc the bandwidth requirements increase with decreasing f_m. But from Fig.

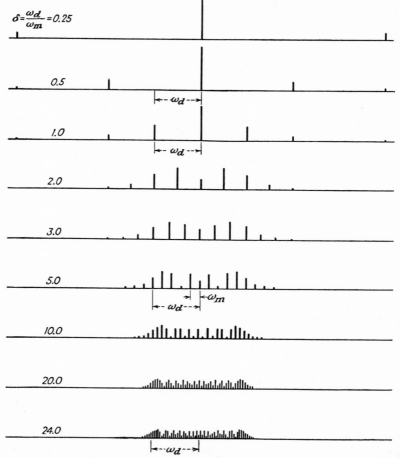

Fig. 14-7. The spectral distribution in an f-m wave for different values of fixed ω_d and different ω_m.

14-8 it is clear that all of the significant sidebands or energy is contained within f_d for values of $\delta = 10$ or higher. For δ lower than 10, the number of sidebands outside of f_d begins to increase rather seriously. This occurs for frequencies of 7.5 or higher. Note, however, that with ordinary broadcasts the amplitude of the frequencies in the range of 7.5 kc and higher is considerably smaller than with the frequencies in the middle or lower registers. Clearly, therefore, E_m for these higher frequencies is smaller than for the mid-frequency band, and hence the total active f_d is materially less than the allowable 75 kc and the system is operating within a narrower bandwidth than might otherwise be required. In fact, the bandwidth is so much less than that allowed that it is found convenient to include weighting or preemphasis networks in the transmitter. These have such properties that they tend to accentuate the higher frequencies.

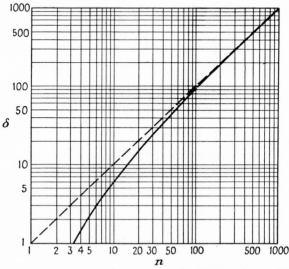

Fig. 14-8. Values of n for a given value of δ to make $J_n(\delta) < 0.01$. Note that n may assume only integral values. (*From L. Mautner, "Mathematics for Radio Engineers," Pitman Publishing Corporation, New York, 1947.*)

In this way, the higher-frequency components, which ordinarily do not contain much energy, are expanded beyond their natural level. This proves to be a desirable practice in that it tends to give an improved signal/noise ratio, for the noise generated within the tube circuits is uniformly distributed over the frequency band. Of course, for fidelity in reproduction, the receiver must have networks which deemphasize the incoming signal to yield the proper energy distribution. More will be said about this when the circuits for effecting preemphasis and deemphasis are discussed.

14-6. Phase Modulation. Phase modulation is produced by varying the instantaneous phase of the carrier at a rate that is proportional to the modulating frequency and by an amount that is proportional to the strength of this modulating signal. The amplitude of the carrier remains unaltered in this process. If the modulating signal has the form

$$e_m = E_m \sin \omega_m t$$

the instantaneous phase of the wave is given by the expression

$$\theta = \theta_0 + k_p E_m \sin \omega_m t \qquad (14\text{-}22)$$

where k_p is a proportionality factor that determines the maximum variation in phase for a given signal strength.

To find the analytic expression for the p-m wave, use is made of the fact that the instantaneous phase is given by

$$\varphi(t) = \omega_c t + \theta_0 + k_p E_m \sin \omega_m t \qquad (14\text{-}23)$$

Equation (14-3) for the present case, when written in full, becomes

$$e = E_c \sin (\omega_c t + k_p E_m \sin \omega_m t) \qquad (14\text{-}24)$$

The constant phase θ_0 is taken as zero, as it plays no part in the modulating process. This expression is written in the form

$$e = E_c \sin (\omega_c t + \theta_d \sin \omega_m t) \qquad (14\text{-}25)$$

where the maximum deviation in phase is

$$\theta_d \equiv k_p E_m \qquad (14\text{-}26)$$

A comparison of Eq. (14-25) with Eq. (14-15) for the f-m wave indicates that the two forms are identical. Consequently the entire discussion of the spectral distribution of the energy contained in an f-m wave can be extended to p-m waves. Therefore the frequency spectrum of a p-m wave having a maximum phase deviation of, say, 10 rad will be identical in form with the frequency spectrum of an f-m wave having a deviation ratio of 10.

There is one very significant difference between the f-m and the p-m waves, however. This difference is contained in the form of the phase deviation θ_d and the deviation ratio δ that appears in Eqs. (14-25) and (14-15), respectively. The differences lie in the definitions of θ_d and δ, namely,

$$\theta_d = k_p E_m \qquad \text{for p-m waves}$$
$$\delta = \frac{k_f E_m}{\omega_m} \qquad \text{for f-m waves}$$

Clearly, for p-m waves the phase deviation depends only on the amplitude of the modulating signal, and all modulating frequencies of equal E_m will possess equal values of θ_d, independently of the frequency ω_m. As a result, the spectral distribution will be the same in each case, although the separation of the spectral lines will depend on the modulating frequency. In particular, if it is supposed that the maximum phase deviation of a particular wave is 5 rad, there will then be approximately 8 significant sideband components present. If the modulating frequency is 5 kc, then the bandwidth is $2 \times 8 \times 5,000 = 80,000$ cps. If the modulating frequency for the 5-rad maximum deviation is 50 cps, then the bandwidth is $2 \times 8 \times 50 = 800$ cps.

In the case of frequency modulation, if the value of E_m is such that the deviation ratio is $\delta = 5$ for a modulating frequency of 5 kc, then for an equal E_m at 50 cps the corresponding deviation ratio is 500. The resulting spectral distribution in these two cases will be altogether different, there being 8 significant sidebands for $\delta = 5$, and there being in excess of 500 significant sidebands for $\delta = 500$. The bandwidth is $2 \times 8 \times 5,000 = 80$ kc under the first conditions and is approximately $2 \times 500 \times 50 = 50$ kc in the second case.

Owing to the simple difference in form between θ_d and δ, it might appear that it should be possible to use p-m waves to produce f-m waves. This would be possible if one could arrange, by means of appropriate circuits, to cause the apparent phase deviation to vary inversely as the modulating frequency. Such circuits are possible, and the Armstrong method of producing frequency modulation operates on this principle. The details of this method will be discussed below.

14-7. F-M Transmitters—Reactance-tube Types. A variety of methods for the production of frequency modulation exist, although they do not all enjoy very great flexibility. In principle at least, the most direct way of producing an f-m wave is to alter the capacitance in the tank circuit of an oscillator. This might conceivably be done by incorporating a capacitor microphone as part of the tank capacitor in an oscillator circuit. A considerably more satisfactory method, and one which accomplishes the same result in substantially the same way, is to incorporate a *reactance tube* in the tank circuit.

A reactance-tube circuit is an electron-tube circuit which is so designed that the effective output-terminal impedance is largely reactive, either inductive or capacitive depending upon its manner of connection, the magnitude of the reactance being varied by varying the potential on one grid of the tube. By incorporating such a circuit as part of the tank circuit of an oscillator, the effective tank-circuit inductance or capacitance, and so the resonant frequency of the oscillator, may be varied by electrical means. Moreover, it will be shown below that the instantaneous carrier frequency of such a reactance-tube transmitter is directly proportional to the instantaneous potential on the control electrode of the reactance tube. As a result, therefore, the instantaneous frequency of the transmitter is directly proportional to the amplitude of the control signal, which is proportional to the modulating-signal amplitude.

A block diagram of a simple reactance-tube f-m transmitter is shown in Fig. 14-9. The essential features of certain of the elements of the circuit are examined below in some detail. In particular, the operation of the reactance-tube circuit, and the operation of the preemphasis circuit, will be examined analytically.

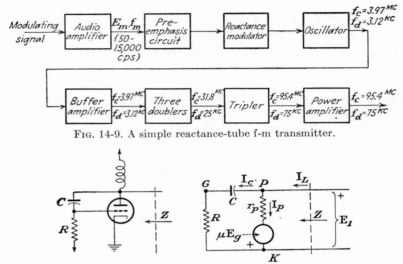

FIG. 14-9. A simple reactance-tube f-m transmitter.

FIG. 14-10. The reactance tube and its equivalent circuit.

14-8. The Reactance Tube. A schematic diagram of a simple react-ance-tube circuit and its equivalent circuit is given in Fig. 14-10. It is desired to determine the effective output-terminal impedance of this circuit. This is readily accomplished. Note from the equivalent circuit the following relations:

$$\mathbf{I}_c = \frac{\mathbf{E}_1}{R - jX_c} \tag{14-27}$$

with

$$X_c = \frac{1}{\omega C}$$

Also, the grid potential is

$$\mathbf{E}_g = R\mathbf{I}_c = \frac{R\mathbf{E}_1}{R - jX_C} \tag{14-28}$$

The plate current is

$$\mathbf{I}_p = \frac{\mathbf{E}_1 + \mu\mathbf{E}_g}{r_p}$$

which may be expressed as

$$\mathbf{I}_p = \frac{\mathbf{E}_1}{r_p} + \frac{\mu}{r_p}\frac{R\mathbf{E}_1}{R - jX_C} \tag{14-29}$$

The total current is then

$$\mathbf{I}_L = \mathbf{I}_p + \mathbf{I}_c = \frac{\mathbf{E}_1}{R - jX_C} + \frac{\mathbf{E}_1}{r_p} + g_m\frac{R\mathbf{E}_1}{R - jX_C} \tag{14-30}$$

The output-terminal admittance of the circuit is given by the relation

$$\mathbf{Y} = \frac{1}{\mathbf{Z}} = \frac{\mathbf{I}}{\mathbf{E}_1} = \frac{1}{R - jX_C} + \frac{1}{r_p} + g_m \frac{R}{R - jX_C} \qquad (14\text{-}31)$$

which may be expressed in the form

$$\mathbf{Y} = \frac{1}{R - j(1/\omega C)} - \frac{1}{r_p} + \frac{1}{(1/g_m) - j(1/g_m RC\omega)} \qquad (14\text{-}32)$$

This expression indicates that, in so far as the output circuit of the reactance tube is concerned, it may be represented by the circuit of Fig. 14-11. Clearly, if the impedances r_p and $R - jX_C$ are large compared with

$$\frac{1}{g_m} - j\,\frac{1}{g_m RC\omega}$$

and if $1/\omega CR$ is large compared with unity, the output-terminal

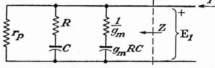

Fig. 14-11. The equivalent output circuit of a capacitive reactance tube.

admittance becomes purely capacitive and arises from an equivalent capacitor having a capacitance $g_m RC$.

Since the output impedance of the reactance-tube circuit above may be made to appear as a pure capacitance $g_m RC$, then if the modulating signal is made to vary the g_m of the tube, and this is readily accomplished by applying the modulating signal to the grid of the tube, the effective capacitance will then change with changes in grid potential. The circuit of such a reactance-tube f-m oscillator is given in Fig. 14-12. Also

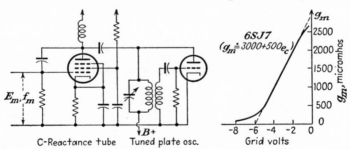

Fig. 14-12. A reactance-tube f-m oscillator, and the curve showing the variation of g_m with grid potential.

included is a curve showing the variation of g_m of the tube with changes in grid potential.

A reactance tube may be connected to yield an effective inductance, rather than an effective capacitance, across the output terminals. Such a circuit, with its electrical equivalent, is given in Fig. 14-13. By proceeding in the same general manner as for the capacitive reactance-tube

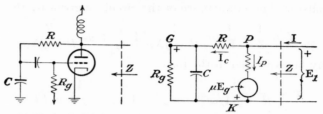

Fig. 14-13. An inductive reactance tube and its equivalent circuit.

circuit, it can be shown that the equivalent output admittance has the form

$$Y = \frac{1}{R + \dfrac{R_g/j\omega C}{R_g + 1/j\omega C}} + \frac{1}{r_p} + \frac{1}{\dfrac{1}{g_m} + \dfrac{R}{g_m R_g} + j\dfrac{\omega CR}{g_m}} \qquad (14\text{-}33)$$

for which an equivalent circuit exists. This equivalent circuit has the form illustrated in Fig. 14-14. By the proper choice of the various

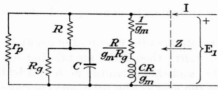

Fig. 14-14. The equivalent output circuit of an inductive reactance tube.

elements in the circuit, the circuit reduces to the simple form, comprising only an equivalent inductance CR/g_m.

A reactance-tube oscillator that incorporates an inductive reactance-tube circuit as part of a Hartley oscillator is illustrated in Fig. 14-15. Also included is a graph showing the variation of g_m with changes in grid 3 potential.

An approximate expression for the variation of the frequency of a reactance-tube oscillator as the potential on the control electrode is varied is readily possible. The transconductance may be expressed analytically as a function of the potential of the control electrode. Note from the

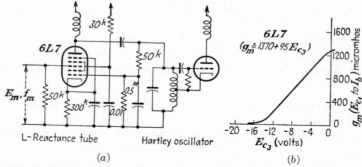

Fig. 14-15. An inductive-reactance-tube f-m oscillator, and the curve showing the variation of g_m with grid 3 potential of the 6L7 heptode.

curve that

$$g_m = \frac{G_0}{E_0} e_c + G_0 \qquad (14\text{-}34)$$

But since

$$e_c = E_{cc} + e_m$$
$$= E_{cc} + E_m \cos \omega_m t \qquad (14\text{-}35)$$

then

$$g_m = G_0 \frac{E_{cc}}{E_0} + G_0 + \frac{G_0}{E_0} E_m \cos \omega_m t \qquad (14\text{-}36)$$

For the capacitive reactance-tube circuit, the effective output capacitance is

$$C_e \doteq g_m C R = G_0 C R \left(1 + \frac{E_{cc}}{E_0} + \frac{E_m}{E_0} \cos \omega_m t \right) \qquad (14\text{-}37)$$

If it is assumed that the frequency of oscillation of the oscillator is that of the tank circuit alone, then

$$f = \frac{1}{2\pi \sqrt{L_0(C_0 + C_e)}}$$

$$f = \frac{1}{2\pi \sqrt{L_0 C_0 + L_0 G_0 C R \left(1 + \dfrac{E_{cc}}{E_0} + \dfrac{E_m}{E_0} \cos \omega_m t \right)}} \qquad (14\text{-}38)$$

The carrier frequency is evidently the value of the frequency of the oscillator when the modulating-signal potential is zero.   This is

$$f_c = \frac{1}{2 \sqrt{L_0 \left[C_0 E_0 + G_0 C R \left(1 + \dfrac{E_{cc}}{E_0} \right) \right]}} \qquad (14\text{-}39)$$

The frequency ratio f/f_c is given by

$$\frac{f}{f_c} = \frac{1}{\sqrt{1 + \dfrac{L_0 G_0 C R E_m \cos \omega_m t}{L_0 [C_0 E_0 + G_0 C R (E_0 + E_{cc})]}}} \qquad (14\text{-}40)$$

By expanding this expression by the binomial theorem and retaining only the first term in the expansion, since the total frequency shift is small, then

$$\frac{f}{f_c} \doteq 1 - \frac{1}{2} \frac{E_m \cos \omega_m t}{C_0 E_0 / G_0 C R + E_{cc} + E_0} \qquad (14\text{-}41)$$

This expression may be written in the form

$$f = f_c(1 + m_f \cos \omega_m t)$$

where the modulation index is

$$m_f = -\frac{1}{2}\frac{E_m}{C_0E_0/G_0CR + E_{cc} + E_0} \qquad (14\text{-}42)$$

14-9. Preemphasis Circuits. As discussed in Sec. 14-4, there is a relatively small amount of energy contained in the h-f portion of the audio spectrum. As a result, the deviation at these high frequencies is far less than the maximum allowable value of 75 kc. The corresponding bandwidth requirement is correspondingly less than the allowable 150-kc total. In fact, the relative h-f amplitudes are so low that it is customary to include preemphasis networks in the circuit to accentuate the h-f terms. In this way the relative signal strength at these higher frequencies is improved relative to tube and circuit noise, which has a uniform distribution over the entire audio spectrum. Of course, corresponding deemphasis must be incorporated in the receiver in order to bring the relative amplitudes of all frequencies to their proper levels.

Preemphasis circuits are chosen to satisfy the equation

$$\frac{E_2}{E_1} = \frac{1}{\sqrt{1 + (\omega_1/\omega)^2}} \qquad (14\text{-}43)$$

The value of ω_1 was originally chosen to be $1/\omega_1 = 100$ μsec, but it is now taken as 75 μsec. With such a preemphasis circuit the amplitude of a 2,100-cps signal is increased in the ratio $\sqrt{2}/1$ over the normal level, and the relative amplitude of a 21-kc signal is increased in the ratio 10/1.

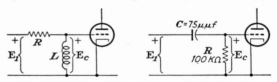

Fig. 14-16. Two different preemphasis circuits.

Either an RL or a CR circuit may be used to accomplish preemphasis. Two different circuits are illustrated in Fig. 14-16. In the RL circuit, the potential ratio E_c/E_1 is readily found to be

$$\frac{E_c}{E_1} = \frac{j\omega L}{R + j\omega L} = \frac{1}{\sqrt{1 + (R/\omega L)^2}}\;\underline{/\tan^{-1}(-R/\omega L)} \qquad (14\text{-}44)$$

By writing $\omega_1 = R/L$, this becomes

$$\frac{E_c}{E_1} = \frac{1}{\sqrt{1 + (\omega_1/\omega)^2}} \qquad (14\text{-}45)$$

Similarly, for the CR circuit, the mathematical development becomes

$$\frac{E_c}{E_1} = \frac{R}{R + 1/j\omega C} \qquad (14\text{-}46)$$

which is

$$\frac{E_c}{E_1} = \frac{1}{1 + 1/j\omega CR} \tag{14-47}$$

By writing $\omega_1 = 1/CR_1$

$$\frac{E_c}{E_1} = \frac{1}{1 - j\omega_1/\omega} \tag{14-48}$$

or

$$\frac{E_c}{E_1} = \frac{1}{\sqrt{1 + (\omega_1/\omega)^2}} \tag{14-49}$$

14-10. Frequency Stabilization of F-M Transmitters. Just as in the case of the a-m transmitter, it is necessary that the average or carrier frequency of an f-m transmitter be maintained very nearly constant, even though the instantaneous frequency of the f-m transmitter varies with the modulating signal. When a reactance-tube modulator is used to modulate the carrier, the carrier cannot be crystal-controlled and the average frequency will depend to some extent on the temperature, the tube characteristics, and the various potentials. Slight drifts in the operating characteristics of the reactance tube or slight changes in any of the circuit elements will be accompanied by an appreciable change in the average frequency. It is possible to minimize the effects of the drift in the reactance-tube characteristics by employing two such tubes in a balanced connection. Nevertheless the stability is not sufficient without employing some type of stabilization to maintain the carrier frequency within the 2-kc deviation specified by the FCC regulations.

Two basically different methods of stabilizing a reactance-tube modulator are in present-day use. In both cases a standard reference frequency is provided by a crystal-controlled oscillator, and the fundamental or some subharmonic of the transmitter frequency is compared with this reference frequency. Deviations between the two serve to actuate control circuits which operate in such a manner as to reduce these deviations. The RCA and Federal Telecommunications Laboratory schemes employ somewhat similar all-electronic methods to effect the frequency stabilization, and the Bell Telephone Laboratories method employs a frequency-sensitive servomechanism which drives a small motor to which is geared the tuning capacitor, the direction of rotation of the motor being determined by the relative frequency of the transmitter and the reference standard.

The RCA method of stabilizing a reactance-tube f-m modulator[1] is shown schematically in Fig. 14-17. In this circuit the frequency of the reference crystal differs from the center frequency of the f-m transmitter by some definite amount, say 1 Mc. The two frequencies are mixed, and the difference frequency is applied to a discriminator (the operation of the discriminator will be discussed in Sec. 14-16). The d-c output from the discriminator, which is a direct measure of the difference frequency, is then applied to the grid of the reactance-tube modulator in such a manner as to make the net control potential equal to zero when the difference frequency is exactly 1 Mc. Any frequency drifts can then be appreciably reduced. Clearly, the method cannot yield perfect stability, for unless there is a slight frequency difference, no control potential is applied to the modulator. However, the improvement that results is sufficient to maintain the frequency stability within the FCC regulations.

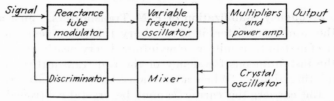

Fig. 14-17. RCA method of stabilizing a reactance-tube frequency modulator.

The Federal center-frequency-stabilization system is shown schematically in Fig. 14-18. In this system the frequencies of the crystal oscillator and the master oscillator are each divided to a common frequency and are then combined in a balanced phase detector. The d-c output potential, which is a measure of the phase difference between the two oscillators, is used to actuate the reactance-tube modulator in a manner to lock the oscillator mean frequency to that of the crystal reference frequency. This system maintains the center frequency constant within about 1 kc.

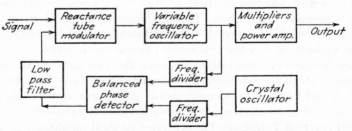

Fig. 14-18. The Federal center-frequency stabilization system.

The schematic diagram of the Bell Laboratories method of stabilizing the frequency of an f-m transmitter[2] is illustrated in Fig. 14-19. Here the output is frequency-divided, and the resulting subharmonic is then modulated by the output of the crystal-controlled oscillator in such a manner as to produce two-phase beat currents. These currents are used to operate a small synchronous motor to which is geared a tuning capacitor, which is part of the f-m oscillator circuit. If the subharmonic remains in synchronism with the crystal reference, the motor does not move.   If the carrier frequency drifts, the armature rotates, the direction of rotation being set so as to readjust the carrier to the correct frequency. This method of stabilization proves to be very satisfactory and operates over a very wide range of drifts to yield satisfactory results.

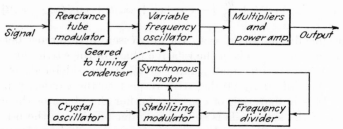

Fig. 14-19. The Bell Laboratories method of stabilizing a reactance-tube frequency modulator.

14-11. F-M Transmitters—Armstrong System.   The Armstrong phase-shift method of obtaining frequency modulation incorporates a crystal-controlled oscillator as a basic element of the system.   Consequently this system has an intrinsic stability as good as that of its crystal, and no additional frequency stabilization is required.

Before the specific features of this method of producing frequency modulation are examined, it is pertinent to examine the spectrum of p-m waves with small value of maximum phase deviation.   For the particular case where $\theta_d = 0.5$, which is illustrated in Fig. 14-6, the significant terms depend on the following values of Bessel functions,

$$J_0(0.5) = 0.9385$$
$$J_1(0.5) = 0.2423$$
$$J_2(0.5) = 0.0306$$
$$J_n(0.5) \doteq 0 \quad \text{for } n > 2$$

and the modulated wave has the explicit form

$$e = E_c \sin (\omega_c t + 0.5 \sin \omega_m t) \tag{14-50}$$

which is

$$e = 0.9385 E_c \sin \omega_c t + 0.2423 E_c [\sin (\omega_c + \omega_m)t - \sin (\omega_c - \omega_m)t]$$
$$+ 0.0306 E_c [\sin (\omega_c + 2\omega_m)t + \sin (\omega_c - 2\omega_m)t] \tag{14-51}$$

Note, however, that the second sideband components are quite small and that the expression may be written approximately as

$$e \doteq 0.9385 \left\{ E_c \sin \omega_c t + \frac{\theta_d}{2} [\sin (\omega_c + \omega_m)t - \sin (\omega_c - \omega_m)t] \right\} \tag{14-52}$$

Clearly, this expression will be more accurate for values of θ_d less than 0.5.

Now consider the corresponding a-m wave, having the form

$$e = E_c(1 + m_a \sin \omega_m t) \sin \omega_c t \qquad (14\text{-}53)$$

which may be written as

$$e = E_c \sin \omega_c t + \frac{m_a}{2} [- \cos (\omega_c + \omega_m)t + \cos (\omega_c - \omega_m)t] \quad (14\text{-}54)$$

Note specifically that, if $m_a = \theta_d$, the only essential difference between the a-m and the p-m waves is in the relative phase of the carrier and the sidebands. Evidently for small values of θ_d, if the sidebands of the a-m wave can be shifted by 90 deg with respect to the carrier, a p-m wave results. It is immaterial, of course, whether the phase of the carrier or the phase of the sidebands is shifted in order to achieve the p-m waves.

The process here discussed can be given graphically in a manner that is quite illuminating. It was shown in Sec. 12-2 that amplitude modulation

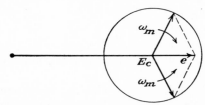

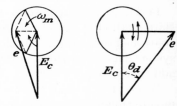

FIG. 14-20. The sinor representation of an a-m wave.

FIG. 14-21. The sinor representation of a p-m wave.

could be represented by means of a sinor diagram. In this diagram, the carrier potential is represented by a fixed sinor, and the sideband components are represented by two sinors which rotate in opposite directions. This sinor representation is redrawn for convenience in Fig. 14-20. The resultant sinor e represents the a-m wave at any instant.

A corresponding sinor representation of the process of p-m production is possible. Here, as shown in Eq. (14-52), the carrier must be shifted in phase by 90 deg relative to the sidebands. The resultant sinor diagram then has the form shown in Fig. 14-21. It is evident from this diagram that a p-m wave does result. Moreover, since θ_d is chosen to be small, the amplitude variations that result in this process are very small. For large deviations θ_d, distortion is introduced. Figure 14-22 shows the percentage distortion vs. maximum phase deviation which results.

A block diagram of an Armstrong type f-m transmitter is given in Fig. 14-23. The essential features of the system are the following: A stabilized 200-kc primary frequency oscillator is used to control the mean or carrier frequency of the radiated wave. Part of this 200-kc signal is mixed in a balanced modulator with a signal representing a frequency-distorted version of the audio signal, the predistorted signal being such that the ampli-

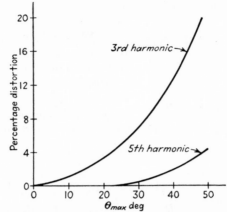

FIG. 14-22. Per cent distortion vs. maximum phase deviation in degrees, which results in the Armstrong modulator.

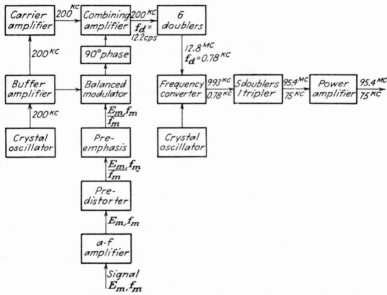

FIG. 14-23. Block diagram of an Armstrong f-m transmitter.

tude is made to vary inversely with its frequency. The output from the balanced modulator is the a-m sidebands with the carrier-frequency component missing. The modulation products are shifted through 90 deg in phase and are then combined with the carrier in the combining buffer amplifier. The result is an f-m wave, which has been achieved from the p-m wave, the phase deviation of which has been made to vary inversely with the modulating frequency. The resulting frequency modulation is multiplied in frequency until it is brought to the desired frequency level for final amplification and transmission.

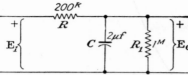

Fig. 14-24. A predistorter circuit.

14-12. Predistorter Circuit. The function of the predistorter circuit is to provide an output potential the amplitude of which varies inversely with the frequency of the input potential. A circuit which achieves the desired results is given in Fig. 14-24. The ratio of the output to the input potential is given by

$$\frac{E_c}{E_1} = \frac{\dfrac{R_1/j\omega C}{R_1 + 1/j\omega C}}{R + \dfrac{R_1/j\omega C}{R_1 + 1/j\omega C}} = \frac{\dfrac{R_1}{1 + j\omega C R_1}}{R + \dfrac{R_1}{1 + j\omega C R_1}} = \frac{1}{1 + R\dfrac{1 + j\omega C R}{R_1}} \quad (14\text{-}55)$$

or

$$\frac{E_c}{E_1} = \frac{1}{1 + R/R_1 + j\omega C R} \quad (14\text{-}56)$$

This becomes, for the specific circuit constants indicated on the diagram,

$$\frac{E_c}{E_1} = \frac{1}{1.02 + j2.51f} \quad (14\text{-}57)$$

Note particularly that for all frequencies in excess of 50 cps the results are given within 1 per cent by the expression

$$\frac{E_c}{E_1} \doteq \frac{1}{j2.51f} \quad (14\text{-}58)$$

14-13. F-M Transmitters—The Phasitron. A cutaway sketch of the General Electric GL-2H21 phasitron is shown in Fig. 14-25. It consists of a cathode, an electrostatic focus and deflection system, and an anode structure. The electrons that are drawn from the cathode surface to the anode assembly are acted on by the focus elements to form a tapered, thin-edged disk, whose axis is the cathode and whose focus is at anode 1 of the anode assembly. The deflection system consists of 36 rigidly mounted elements whose active portions lie in a radial plane below the electron disk and a solid neutral plane located above the disk. Every third deflector is connected together and to one phase of a three-phase excitation source. The three-phase potential source comprises a crystal oscillator and phase-splitting network.

The action of the deflection system is such that portions of the electron disk are deflected above or below the normal plane by the magnetic field of the three-phase system to form a sinusoidal edge. The appearance of the disk is clearly illustrated in Fig. 14-25. The disk may be considered as rotating at a rate determined by the crystal oscillator.

Anode 1 is a cylinder with 24 holes punched alternately above and below the normal plane of the disk. Electrons striking the surface of the cylinder are collected by it, while those which pass through the holes are collected by the solid anode 2. Figure 14-26 shows a developed portion of anode 1. The solid sine curve represents the edge of the electron disk at the time the maximum number of electrons passes through the openings to anode 2. The dotted curve shows the situation one-half cycle later, and almost no electrons pass through the openings to anode 2. If, therefore, the two anodes are connected to opposite ends of a resonant circuit, the circuit will be excited at the crystal driving frequency and in a time-phase sense that is determined by the phase of the anode-current pulses.

Frequency modulation of the resonant anode circuit is produced by phase modulation of the electron disk. This is accomplished by applying the audio signal to a solenoid which surrounds the phasitron. The axial magnetic field that is so produced causes the electron disk to be advanced or retarded about its axis relative to its zero-signal position. Consequently the phase of the oscillator is shifted, with a resultant production of p-m waves. Moreover, since the magnetic field is produced by a solenoid which is essentially a pure reactance at audio frequencies, then, for a constant potential input, the current, and hence the magnetic field that is produced, will vary inversely with the frequency of the impressed potential. Clearly, therefore, the output from the oscillator is an f-m wave.

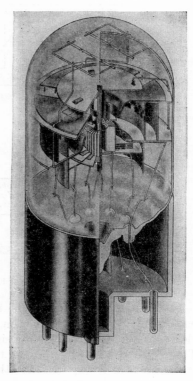

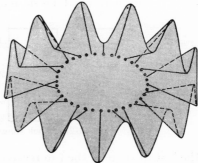

Fig. 14-25. The General Electric GL-2H21 phasitron.

A schematic diagram of the phasitron f-m transmitter is given in Fig. 14-27.

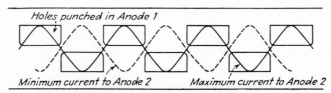

Fig. 14-26. A developed portion of anode 1.

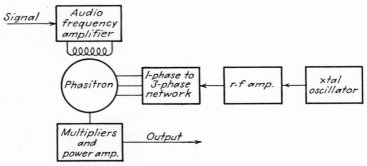

Fig. 14-27. The General Electric phasitron f-m transmitter.

14-14. F-M Receivers. The basic circuit of an f-m receiver is somewhat similar to that of an a-m receiver of the superheterodyne type. However, there are a number of significant differences in the two receivers. The required bandwidth in the f-m receiver is larger than that for a-m reception, which requires that the frequency converter and the r-f and the i-f amplifiers must be designed for this broader bandwidth. Also,

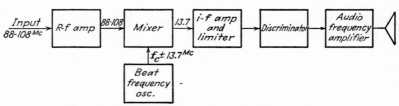

Fig. 14-28. Block diagram of a typical f-m receiver.

the last i-f stage of the f-m receiver is operated as a limiter, thus eliminating any fluctuations in the amplitude of the i-f carrier, however produced. The other outstanding difference is in the circuit used to demodulate the f-m carrier. The f-m discriminator that is used to convert from frequency modulation to amplitude modulation does not appear in an a-m receiver, and also the detector, while it uses conventional diode circuits, operates somewhat differently in the f-m circuit. The operation of this will be examined below.

A block diagram of a typical f-m receiver is shown in Fig. 14-28. Such a receiver must provide a high r-f gain in order to permit high sensitivity with amplitude limitation. Also, it is necessary to use a relatively high i-f frequency in order to permit the necessary 225-kc bandwidth. In addition, the high intermediate frequency has the feature that the image signals fall outside of the tuning range. In particular, in the block diagram shown for use in the range from 88 to 108 Mc, the image frequencies lie in the band 115.4 to 135.4 Mc.

14-15. The Limiter. It is the function of the limiter to remove any amplitude modulation that might exist in the signal. These fluctuations in the amplitude of the i-f carrier might have been produced either by

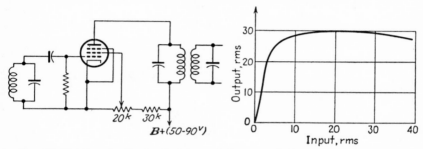

Fig. 14-29. The circuit of a limiter, and the general character of the results.

variations in the transmitting conditions or by man-made or natural static. Such a circuit, which usually operates on the nonlinear portion of its characteristic, provides an output potential that is sensibly independent of the amplitude of the input potential. Such limiter action is easily secured by operating the plate of a tube at a very low plate potential, by using a high series grid resistor, by using a low screen potential, or by a combination of these three.

As ordinarily used, the last i-f stage of the f-m receiver is usually operated at low screen and low plate potential, in a circuit of the type illustrated, to serve as the limiter. The operation of the circuit depends on the characteristic of pentodes with low applied potentials. With such low potentials the operation falls below the knee of the plate characteristic. The plate current becomes independent of the amplitude of the grid potential over wide ranges. The general character of the gain curve is also included in Fig. 14-29. Such a circuit as that illustrated will saturate at about 10 volts input to the grid, and at this point the stage has a gain of approximately 3.

14-16. The Discriminator. In demodulating an f-m wave, the method generally used is first to convert from frequency modulation to amplitude modulation and then to demodulate the amplitude modulation by conventional methods. The circuit that is used to effect this conversion is known as a *discriminator*. A variety of such circuits is possible, and several will be considered in some detail.

The simplest form of discriminator comprises an ordinary resonant circuit that is tuned to a frequency that differs somewhat from the average or carrier frequency of the f-m signal. An exact analysis of such a network is actually quite complicated owing to the fact that the frequency of the applied signal is a changing one, and the problem is therefore not a simple steady-state-frequency one but really requires a transient analysis. An analysis of the problem shows that if the bandwidth of the tank circuit is large compared with the audio rate at which the frequency of the applied potential is varied, the normal steady-state

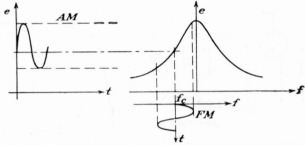

Fig. 14-30. A simple antiresonant circuit operating as a discriminator.

methods of analysis may be applied without serious error. If this quasi-steady-state method of analysis may not be used, the problem becomes exceedingly complicated.

The approximate action of such a *slope* detector is illustrated graphically in Fig. 14-30. Clearly, as the carrier frequency fluctuates, the current in the detuned circuit varies, increasing as the impressed frequency approaches the resonant frequency of the circuit, and decreasing as the impressed frequency departs from the resonant frequency. The output from such a circuit is an a-m wave. However, since the side of the simple resonance curve is not linear, the a-m output is distorted.

A second feature of such a simple circuit as an f-m detector is that it provides no a-m rejection. That is, if the applied potential is doubled, the current is also doubled. This means, therefore, that any amplitude modulation that exists in the applied signal will also produce an effect in the output. As will be seen later in Sec. 14-20, noise produces such an a-m effect, and in order to ensure noise-free performance a very good limiter is required ahead of this discriminator circuit. Because of its several shortcomings, such a simple discriminator is not used.

The linearity can be greatly improved by using two "off-tuned" or "stagger-tuned" circuits instead of one and then choosing the difference between the two outputs. Such a stagger-tuned discriminator circuit[3] is illustrated in Fig. 14-31. In this discriminator, the input A is tuned to

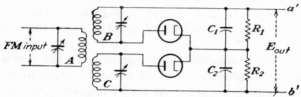

FIG. 14-31. A discriminator employing two stagger-tuned circuits.

the carrier frequency f_c, circuit B is tuned to a frequency that is somewhat higher than f_c, and circuit C is tuned to a frequency that is somewhat lower than f_c. The a-m output from such a circuit is without appreciable distortion, owing to the linear resulting characteristic around the point f_c. Such circuits suffer from the fact that reception is possible at three points, corresponding to each outer portion of the resonant curves and also to the center or desired linear operating region. The response from such a circuit is illustrated in Fig. 14-32.

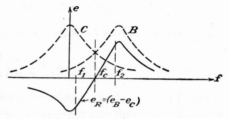

FIG. 14-32. The a-m output from the discriminator of Fig. 14-31.

As seen in the diagram, the output from each circuit is passed through a diode detector of the envelope or peak detection type. The capacitors C_1 and C_2 are equal and have negligible reactance at the carrier frequency. The resistances R_1 and R_2 are equal and are quite large. The

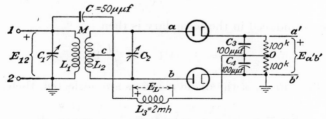

FIG. 14-33. A center-tuned discriminator circuit.

d-c potential across C_1R_1 is a measure of the amplitude of the output from circuit B, and the d-c potential across C_2R_2 is a measure of the amplitude of the output from circuit C. Also, the total output across $a'b'$ is then a measure of the difference between the outputs from circuits

B and C and has a form like the resultant curve e_R of Fig. 14-32. By careful adjustment of the circuit constants, and if the frequency deviation is limited to the range between f_2 and f_1, the rectified potential is an approximately linear function of the impressed frequency.

Another commonly used type of discriminator circuit[4] is shown in Fig. 14-33. It is possible to show that this circuit is substantially a staggertuned pair[5] and that the results illustrated in Fig. 14-32 also apply for this case.

A limited analytic solution of the operation of the center-tuned discriminator circuit is possible. Consider first the series circuit comprising CL_3C_4 across terminals 1 and 2. At the i-f frequency, assumed to be 4.3 Mc in this circuit,

$$X_C = \frac{10^{12}}{2\pi \times 4.3 \times 10^6 \times 50} = 800 \text{ ohms}$$
$$X_{C4} = 400 \text{ ohms}$$
$$X_{L3} = 2\pi \times 4.3 \times 10^6 \times 2 \times 10^{-3} = 50 \text{ kilohms}$$

The potential across L_3 is then seen to be

$$\mathbf{E}_L = \frac{jX_{L3}\mathbf{E}_{12}}{jX_{L3} - j(X_{C1} + X_{C4})} \doteq \mathbf{E}_{12} \tag{14-59}$$

Consider now the mutually coupled circuit. If the mutual inductance is small, the impedance coupled into the primary circuit is small and approximately, therefore,

$$\mathbf{I} \doteq \frac{\mathbf{E}_{12}}{R_1 + jX_{L1}}$$

which becomes, for high-Q coils,

$$\mathbf{I} \doteq \frac{\mathbf{E}_{12}}{jX_{L1}} \tag{14-60}$$

The potential induced in the secondary is then

$$\mathbf{E}_{sec} = \pm j\omega M\mathbf{I} = \pm \frac{M}{L_1}\mathbf{E}_{12} \tag{14-61}$$

If the loading effects of the diode rectifiers are neglected, then

$$\mathbf{E}_{ab} = \frac{-jX_{C2}\mathbf{E}_{sec}}{R_2 + jX_{L2} - jX_{C2}} = \pm \frac{jX_{C2}M/L_1}{R_2 + jX_2}\mathbf{E}_{12} \tag{14-62}$$

where $\qquad X_2 = \omega L_2 - \dfrac{1}{\omega C_2}$

Note now that the output d-c potential $E_{a'o}$ is proportional to the peak of the envelope of E_{ao}, and correspondingly the output potential $E_{b'o}$ is proportional to the peak of the envelope of E_{bo}. The total output d-c potential is

$$E_{a'b'} = E_{a'o} + E_{ob'} = E_{a'o} - E_{b'o} \qquad (14\text{-}63)$$

However, the a-c envelopes can be represented in terms of the potentials E_{ab} and E_{12}, namely,

$$\mathbf{E}_{ao} = \mathbf{E}_{ac} + \mathbf{E}_L = \mathbf{E}_{ac} + \mathbf{E}_{12} = \frac{\mathbf{E}_{ab}}{2} + \mathbf{E}_{12}$$

$$\mathbf{E}_{bo} = \mathbf{E}_{bc} + \mathbf{E}_L = -\mathbf{E}_{cb} + \mathbf{E}_{12} = \frac{-\mathbf{E}_{ab}}{2} + \mathbf{E}_{12} \qquad (14\text{-}64)$$

Consider the situation when the instantaneous frequency equals the carrier frequency. At this frequency, the secondary circuit is resonant, and the quantity X_2 is zero. The potential $\mathbf{E}_{ab}$ is then given by the following expression, obtained from Eqs. (14-62). The positive sign is chosen arbitrarily.

$$\mathbf{E}_{ab} = j\,\frac{X_{C2}}{R_2}\frac{M}{L_1}\,\mathbf{E}_{12} = j\,\frac{M}{\omega C_2 L_1}\,\mathbf{E}_{12}\,Y\underline{/0} \qquad (14\text{-}65)$$

The potentials $\mathbf{E}_{ao}$ and $\mathbf{E}_{bo}$ then have the amplitudes and phase somewhat as illustrated in the accompanying sinor diagram. Note that since

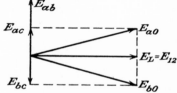

$$E_{ao} = E_{bo}$$

and

$$E_{a'o} = E_{b'o}$$

then

$$E_{a'b'} = 0$$

When the instantaneous frequency is greater than the carrier frequency, the secondary reactance X_2 is positive and Eqs. (14-62) may be written in the form

$$\mathbf{E}_{ab} = j\,\frac{M}{\omega C_2 L_1}\,\mathbf{E}_{12}\,\frac{1}{R_2 + jX_2} = j\,\frac{M}{\omega C_2 L_1}\,\mathbf{E}_{12}Y\underline{/-\theta} \qquad (14\text{-}66)$$

The corresponding sinor diagram has the form shown.

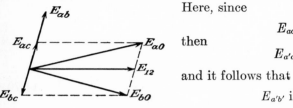

Here, since

$$E_{ao} > E_{bo}$$

then

$$E_{a'o} > E_{b'o}$$

and it follows that

$$E_{a'b'} \text{ is positive}$$

When the instantaneous frequency is less than the carrier frequency, X_2 is negative and Eqs. (14-62) become

$$\mathbf{E}_{ab} = j\,\frac{M}{\omega C_2 L_1}\,\mathbf{E}_{12}\,\frac{1}{R_2 - jX_2} = j\,\frac{M}{\omega C_2 L_1}\,\mathbf{E}_{12}Y\underline{/\theta} \qquad (14\text{-}67)$$

The corresponding sinor diagram in this case is as shown. In this case

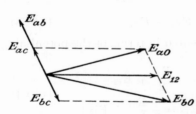

$$E_{ao} < E_{bo}$$

and

$$E_{a'o} < E_{b'o}$$

so that

$$E_{a'b'} \text{ is negative}$$

An analytical solution is also possible, the details of which more or less duplicate the foregoing semiquantitative graphical solution. This development proceeds from Eq. (14-62), which is written in the form

$$\frac{\mathbf{E}_{ab}}{\mathbf{E}_{12}} = \mp j \frac{X_{C2}k \sqrt{L_2/L_1}}{R_2 + jX_2}$$

Also, noting that

$$R_2 + jX_2 \doteq R_2(1 + j2\delta Q_2)$$

and

$$\frac{X_{C2}}{R_2} = \frac{1}{\omega C_2 R_2} \doteq Q_2$$

and choosing the positive sign, then

$$\frac{\mathbf{E}_{ab}}{\mathbf{E}_{12}} = j \sqrt{\frac{L_2}{L_1}} \frac{kQ_2}{1 + j2\delta Q_2} \tag{14-68}$$

Combine the foregoing with Eqs. (14-64), and recalling that the audio output from a peak diode detector is related to the impressed modulated signal through the detector efficiency (see Sec. 13-4), then directly

$$E_{a'o} = \eta \left| 1 + j \frac{1}{2} \sqrt{\frac{L_2}{L_1}} \frac{kQ_2}{1 + j2\delta Q_2} \right| E_{12}$$

and

$$E_{b'o} = \eta \left| 1 - j \frac{1}{2} \sqrt{\frac{L_2}{L_1}} \frac{kQ_2}{1 + j2\delta Q_2} \right| E_{12} \tag{14-69}$$

Therefore, since

$$E_{a'b'} = E_{a'o} - E_{b'o}$$

then

$$E_{a'b'} = \eta E_{12} \left(\left| 1 + j \frac{1}{2} \sqrt{\frac{L_2}{L_1}} \frac{kQ_2}{1 + j2\delta Q_2} \right| \right.$$
$$\left. - \left| 1 - j \frac{1}{2} \sqrt{\frac{L_2}{L_1}} \frac{kQ_2}{1 + j2\delta Q_2} \right| \right) \tag{14-70}$$

A plot of this expression has the general form illustrated in Fig. 14-32.

The foregoing analysis is subject to the very serious limitation that the potential $\mathbf{E}_{12}$ does not remain constant with frequency. As a result, Eq. (14-70) does not represent too well the action over the entire range.

As a matter of fact, by careful design the effect of a varying E_{12} may serve to improve the performance of the discriminator, by extending the linear range considerably beyond that given by this expression.

The complete expression for the discriminator may be obtained in the following way: Refer to Fig. 14-34, which isolates the inductively

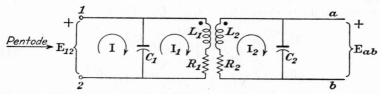

FIG. 14-34. The inductively coupled portion of the center-tuned discriminator.

coupled portion of the network. The controlling equations of this network are the following

$$+j\frac{1}{\omega C_1}\mathbf{I} + \left[R_1 + j\left(\omega L_1 - \frac{1}{\omega C_1}\right)\right]\mathbf{I}_1 - j\omega M\mathbf{I}_2 = 0$$
$$-j\omega M\mathbf{I}_1 + \left[R_2 + j\left(\omega L_2 - \frac{1}{\omega C_2}\right)\right]\mathbf{I}_2 = 0 \qquad (14\text{-}71)$$

In the neighborhood of the resonant frequency ω_0, these may be written as

$$R_1(1 + j2\delta Q_1)\mathbf{I}_1 - j\omega_0 M\mathbf{I}_2 = -j\frac{1}{\omega_0 C_1}\mathbf{I}$$
$$-j\omega_0 M\mathbf{I}_1 + R_2(1 + j2\delta Q_2)\mathbf{I}_2 = 0 \qquad (14\text{-}72)$$

Now solve for $\mathbf{I}_1$ in terms of $\mathbf{I}$. The result is

$$\frac{R_1 R_2(1 + j2\delta Q_1)(1 + j2\delta Q_2) + (\omega_0 M)^2}{R_2(1 + j2\delta Q_2)}\mathbf{I}_1 = -j\frac{1}{\omega_0 C_1}\mathbf{I}$$

Dividing both sides by $R_1 R_2$, the resulting expression may be written as

$$\frac{(1 + j2\delta Q_1)(1 + j2\delta Q_2) + k^2 Q_1 Q_2}{R_2(1 + j2\delta Q_2)}\mathbf{I}_1 = -j\frac{Q_1}{R_2}\mathbf{I} \qquad (14\text{-}73)$$

Hence

$$\mathbf{I}_1 = -jQ_1\frac{1 + j2\delta Q_2}{(1 + j2\delta Q_1)(1 + j2\delta Q_2) + k^2 Q_1 Q_2}\mathbf{I} \qquad (14\text{-}74)$$

from which it follows that $\mathbf{I}_1 \gg \mathbf{I}$. Therefore

$$E_{12} \doteq j\frac{1}{\omega_0 C_1}\mathbf{I}_1 \qquad (14\text{-}75)$$

so that

$$E_{12} \doteq \frac{1 + j2\delta Q_2}{(1 + j2\delta Q_1)(1 + j2\delta Q_2) + k^2 Q_1 Q_2}R_1\mathbf{I} \qquad (14\text{-}76)$$

Combine this expression with (14-68) to obtain $\mathbf{E}_{ab}$, namely,

$$\mathbf{E}_{ab} = j \sqrt{\frac{L_2}{L_1}} \frac{kQ_2}{(1 + j2\delta Q_1)(1 + j2\delta Q_2) + k^2 Q_1 Q_2} R_1 \mathbf{I} \qquad (14\text{-}77)$$

Equations (14-76) and (14-77) determine $\mathbf{E}_{12}$ and $\mathbf{E}_{ab}$ quite accurately for ordinary primary and secondary values of Q.

It is customary to choose $Q_1 = Q_2 = Q$. Then

$$\mathbf{E}_{12} = \frac{1 + j2\delta Q}{(1 + j2\delta Q)^2 + kQ^2} R_1 \mathbf{I}$$
$$\mathbf{E}_{ab} = j \sqrt{\frac{L_2}{L_1}} \frac{kQ}{(1 + j2\delta Q)^2 + kQ^2} R_1 \mathbf{I} \qquad (14\text{-}78)$$

For completeness, the ratio $\mathbf{E}_{ab}/\mathbf{E}_{12}$ is noted,

$$\frac{\mathbf{E}_{ab}}{\mathbf{E}_{12}} = j \sqrt{\frac{L_2}{L_1}} \frac{kQ}{1 + j2\delta Q} \qquad (14\text{-}79)$$

This latter expressions shows that the form given in Eq. (14-68) is not altered by the more complete analysis. However, the first of Eqs. (14-78)

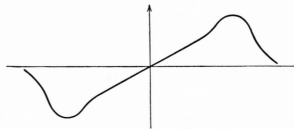

FIG. 14-35. Response obtained from an overcoupled discriminator.

shows that $\mathbf{E}_{12}$ is not a constant but varies with frequency, under the assumption of a constant pentode current $\mathbf{I}$. In place of Eqs. (14-69) there now follows

$$E_{a'o} = \eta \left| \frac{1 + j2\delta Q}{(1 + j2\delta Q)^2 + kQ^2} \left(1 + j\frac{1}{2} \sqrt{\frac{L_2}{L_1}} \frac{kQ}{1 + j2\delta Q} \right) \right| R_1 I$$
$$E_{b'o} = \eta \left| \frac{1 + j2\delta Q}{(1 + j2\delta Q)^2 + kQ^2} \left(1 - j\frac{1}{2} \sqrt{\frac{L_2}{L_1}} \frac{kQ}{1 + j2\delta Q} \right) \right| R_1 I \qquad (14\text{-}80)$$

whence finally

$$E_{a'b'} = \eta R_1 I \left| \frac{1 + j2\delta Q}{(1 + j2\delta Q)^2 + kQ^2} \right|$$
$$\left(\left| 1 + j\frac{1}{2} \sqrt{\frac{L_2}{L_1}} \frac{kQ}{1 + j2\delta Q} \right| - \left| 1 - j\frac{1}{2} \sqrt{\frac{L_2}{L_1}} \frac{kQ}{1 + j2\delta Q} \right| \right) \qquad (14\text{-}81)$$

This expression gives a good representation of the discriminator curve.

A complete discussion for the determination of the optimum values of kQ and $\sqrt{L_2/L_1}$ will not be undertaken. Such an analysis shows that $kQ = 1$ and $\sqrt{L_2/L_1} = 1$ are desirable values. If kQ is less than unity, which is the condition for loose coupling, the linear portion of the discriminator curve is relatively small. If kQ is greater than unity, which is the overcoupled condition, the results obtained have the form illustrated in Fig. 14-35.

14-17. The Ratio Detector.[6] The ratio detector has found extensive use in f-m receivers, since a very good noise-free performance is possible with relatively few components, and with no requirement for limiter circuits. To understand the basic operation of the ratio detector, refer to Fig. 14-36. This is not the complete circuit of the device, but it does

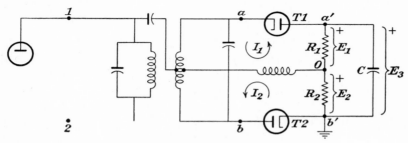

FIG. 14-36. The basic ratio-detector circuit.

permit a direct discussion of its operation. It should be noted that this circuit is quite similar to the Foster-Seeley circuit of Fig. 14-33, except that the diode $T1$ is reversed in polarity.

Suppose that the potential developed across R_1 is $E_1 = -E$ volts at the center frequency. The potential developed across R_2 is $E_2 = -E$ volts. The net potential E_3 is $-2E$, instead of zero, as in the Foster-Seeley circuit. If the input signal is detuned slightly, the potential across R_1 changes to, say, $-E + \Delta E$, while that across R_2 changes to $-E - \Delta E$. The net potential E_3 remains $-2E$. Now, however, the potential across R_2 has changed by an amount $-\Delta E$ and may be used as an audio output. Observe that since E_3 has not changed, the capacitor C may be made very large and is usually an electrolytic capacitor with a capacitance of 10 μf or more.

The foregoing paragraph shows that the output potential E_3 remains constant for changes in frequency. It is now of interest to examine the effect of a change of amplitude of the input signal which occurs at an audio rate. The presence of the large capacitor C prevents E_3 from varying over the audio cycle. Similarly, the potential E_2 cannot follow variations in amplitude of the input signal. Thus, since E_2 is independent of amplitude variations in the input, it is expected that changes in E_2

will be proportional only to the ratio of the magnitudes of the potentials applied to the two diodes, which in turn depend on the frequency.

To show these results analytically, it is convenient to use certain of the results of the analysis of Sec. 14-16. By comparing Figs. 14-36 and 14-33, the essential difference is seen to lie in the polarities of $E_{a'o}$ and $E_{b'o}$ of the two circuits. However, in both cases $\mathbf{E}_{12}$ and $\mathbf{E}_{ab}$ are the same as before, and Eqs. (14-78) apply here. For the ratio detector

$$E_{a'b'} = E_{a'o} + E_{ob'} = \eta(|E_{ao}| + |E_{bo}|)$$

and

$$E_{a'b'} = \eta R_1 I \left| \frac{1 + j2\delta Q}{(1 + j2\delta Q)^2 + kQ^2} \right| \left(\left| 1 + j\frac{1}{2}\sqrt{\frac{L_2}{L_1}}\frac{kQ}{1 + j2\delta Q} \right| + \left| 1 - j\frac{1}{2}\sqrt{\frac{L_2}{L_1}}\frac{kQ}{1 + j2\delta Q} \right| \right) \quad (14\text{-}82)$$

This expression shows that the total output differential potential is a function of the tube current I, and so of the input-signal amplitude. In so far as the variation with frequency is concerned, this expression varies very slowly, and over the range of operation it is substantially constant.

Now examine the ratio

$$\frac{E_{a'o}}{E_{ob'}} = \frac{\left| 1 + j\frac{1}{2}\frac{L_2}{L_1}\frac{kQ}{1 + j2\delta Q} \right|}{\left| 1 - j\frac{1}{2}\frac{L_2}{L_1}\frac{kQ}{1 + j2\delta Q} \right|} \quad (14\text{-}83)$$

This ratio is independent of I, and so of the input-signal amplitude. Also over the range of operation the expression on the right approximates to

$$\frac{E_{a'o}}{E_{ob'}} = \text{const} + A\delta \quad (14\text{-}84)$$

where A is a constant. This expression shows that the ratio depends directly on the frequency deviation from the center frequency.

The more complete form of the ratio detector is shown in Fig. 14-37. The changes that have been introduced in this circuit are designed to overcome the tendency of the diodes to cutoff. This is precisely the problem that exists for the simple peak diode detector, and as a result the load resistors must be made quite low, the ordinary values ranging from 2 to 10 kilohms. Actually a single load resistor R_3 is used, since the diodes are essentially in series.

It should be noticed also that, because of the low load resistance R_3 with its consequent heavy primary loading, it is expedient to tap down on the primary winding. While this produces a loss in secondary potential, the reduced loading more than overcomes this loss of potential. While the change discussed effects a substantial improvement, a sudden change in applied-signal amplitude will still result in diode cutoff.

The second change that is made is the addition of a second time constant, represented by R_1C_1 and R_2C_2. The resistances R_1 and R_2 are ordinarily much smaller than R_3, and C_1 and C_2 are essentially i-f by-pass capacitances. The d-c potential across C_3 may now discharge rapidly with a large reduction in input amplitude, and cutoff likelihood is substantially reduced. Because of this loading, the ability of the detector to reject a large increase in input amplitude is slightly impaired.

In addition to the elimination of the need for the limiter with the ratio detector, the small signal a-m rejection is so improved, owing to the fact that the limiter is eliminated, that the required input to the ratio

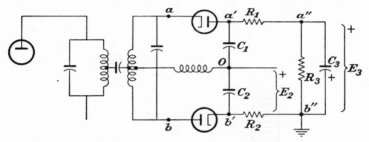

FIG. 14-37. The practical form of the ratio-detector circuit.

detector may be considerably smaller than with the discriminator for noise-free operation.

14-18. The Bradley Detector.[7] The Bradley detector is a single heptode which combines the function of limiter, discriminator, and amplifier. It operates essentially on the locked-oscillator principle, a local oscillator being forced to synchronize with the incoming f-m signal, the synchronization current being used as a measure of the frequency deviation of the oscillator from the mean or carrier level.

A typical Bradley detector circuit is illustrated in Fig. 14-38. The essential oscillator-circuit elements of this detector circuit are redrawn for detailed consideration in Fig. 14-39. This circuit shows a simple Colpitts oscillator circuit which is operating normally at the center i-f level. Coupled to the oscillator tank is a second tank circuit, the effect of which will be shown to couple an inductive reactance into the tank. The resulting frequency of the oscillator is determined by the two capacitors C_1 and C_1' in series and the effective inductance of the oscillator tank. It will be shown that an a-f component is contained in the plate current and moreover that its amplitude is controlled by the signal.

Owing to the amplitudes of the signals involved, the complete analysis would follow that employed in discussing the operation of an oscillator. Instead of a complete analysis, a simplified analysis is included here, although this is sufficient to indicate the general aspects of the circuit behavior. Consider Fig. 14-40, which shows a portion of the tank circuit

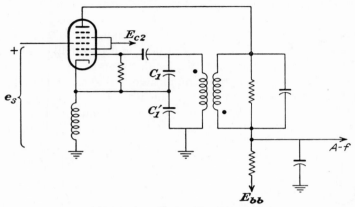

Fig. 14-38. The Bradley detector.

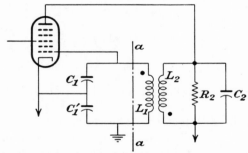

Fig. 14-39. The oscillator and reactance varying winding.

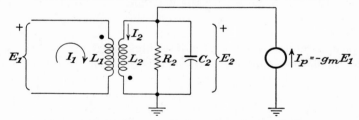

Fig. 14-40. Oscillator tank L_1 and reactance winding.

of the oscillator and coupled tank circuit. This is the portion of the circuit to the right of a-a. It is desired to evaluate the input impedance to this network.

If the secondary circuit were absent, then evidently

$$\mathbf{Z}_1 = j\omega L_1$$

To find the value of $\mathbf{Z}_1$ when the secondary circuit is coupled, use will be made of the fact that the fundamental component of $\mathbf{I}_p$ is in phase with the oscillator tank potential $\mathbf{E}_1$ but is controlled in amplitude by the signal. This fact will be justified later. Tentatively, therefore, $\mathbf{I}_p$ is written

$$\mathbf{I}_p = -g_m\mathbf{E}_1 \qquad (14\text{-}85)$$

Here, as for the oscillator, g_m is a variable factor, and its value is dependent on the signal conditions.

It is assumed that the secondary is very heavily loaded so that the secondary tank appears as a resistance R_2 over the range of operating frequencies. In practice R_2 is chosen small and provides a bandwidth approximately six times the operating range. It will also be assumed that the coupling M is small and that $\mathbf{I}_p$ is large, so that the current $\mathbf{I}_2$ is not affected by the current $\mathbf{I}_1$. This latter is actually a poor approximation, since the coupling is made fairly tight in order to provide good sensitivity. With these assumptions, then

$$\mathbf{E}_2 = R_2\mathbf{I}_p = -g_mR_2\mathbf{E}_1$$

Also

$$\mathbf{I}_2 = \frac{\mathbf{E}_2}{j\omega L_2} = -\frac{g_mR_2}{j\omega L_2}\mathbf{E}_1$$

From the diagram

$$j\omega L_1\mathbf{I}_1 - j\omega M\mathbf{I}_2 = \mathbf{E}_1$$

Combine equations to get

$$j\omega L_1\mathbf{I}_1 + \frac{j\omega M g_m R_2}{j\omega L_2}\mathbf{E}_1 = \mathbf{E}_1$$

from which

$$j\omega L_1\mathbf{I}_1 = \mathbf{E}_1\left(1 - \frac{g_m R_2 M}{L_2}\right)$$

or

$$j\omega L_1\mathbf{I}_1 = \mathbf{E}_1\left(1 - g_m R_2 k\sqrt{\frac{L_1}{L_2}}\right)$$

The input impedance is then given by

$$\mathbf{Z}_1 = j\omega L_1\frac{1}{1 - g_m R_2 k\sqrt{L_1/L_2}} \qquad (14\text{-}86)$$

which is written as

$$\mathbf{Z}_1 = j\omega L_1\frac{1}{1 - x}$$

$$\qquad (14\text{-}87)$$

where

$$x = g_m R_2 k\sqrt{\frac{L_1}{L_2}}$$

The total oscillator tank capacitance (C_1 and C_1' in series) is denoted C. The oscillator frequency is given approximately by

$$\omega_0 = \frac{1}{\sqrt{CL_1/(1-x)}} = \frac{1}{\sqrt{CL_1}}\sqrt{1-x}$$

Ordinarily x is small compared with unity, and, with good approximation,

$$\omega_0 \doteq \frac{1}{\sqrt{CL_1}}\left(1 - \frac{x}{2}\right) = \frac{1}{\sqrt{CL_1}}\left(1 - \frac{g_m R_2 k}{2}\sqrt{\frac{L_1}{L_2}}\right) \quad (14\text{-}88)$$

This expression shows that the oscillator frequency varies linearly with g_m, since g_m is the only variable term in the right-hand member.

According to Eqs. (14-87) only a reactance is reflected into the primary circuit. With conventional design, as is expected, a resistive term is also reflected into the primary. With the proper adjustment of the circuits, the resistive term may be made invariant with the value of g_m.

The effect of the signal potential e_s that is applied to grid 3 is to be examined. To do so, refer to Fig. 14-41, which shows a portion of the complete circuit. Recall that it is the function of grid 1 to control the cathode current. Also, grid 3 controls the portion of the cathode current which reaches the plate. That portion of the cathode current which does not reach the plate is collected by the screen. Recall also that, since grid 1 is part of the oscillator circuit, the cathode current will consist of current pulses of the usual class C variety. The waveshapes

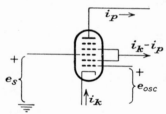

Fig. 14-41. The heptode in the Bradley detector.

at various points of the oscillator are precisely those which exist in the class C tuned amplifier and have the shapes illustrated in Fig. 10-8. The important waves for the fundamental-harmonic component of current and the grid driving potential are

$$i_k = I_{km}\cos\omega_0 t$$
$$e_g = E_{gm}\cos\omega_0 t \quad (14\text{-}89)$$

and

these two waves being in phase.

In so far as the current reaching the plate is concerned, this is affected by the potential of grid 3. From a curve such as Fig. 14-15b the instantaneous value of g_m, and so the effective $\overline{g_m}$ of Eq. (11-14) or $\overline{\overline{g_m}}$ of Eq. (11-21), and in consequence the current to the plate, will depend on the phase of the potential e_s and the potential e_g. If these potentials are in phase, the plate current is a maximum. As the relative phase varies, the plate current also varies and becomes a minimum when the two potentials are 180 deg out of phase.

Suppose now that the phase of e_s is such that the current is a maximum. The corresponding value of g_m is a maximum, and the oscillator frequency, from Eq. (14-88), is at some particular minimum value. Let the phase of e_s now vary, with a resulting decrease in the plate current i_p. The reduced value of g_m results in an increase in the oscillator frequency. With a properly designed system, the phase of the system will vary until the plate current, and so the value of g_m, will assume such a value that the oscillator will synchronize, or lock in, with the signal frequency. If the signal frequency changes to a value beyond which the system can follow, "breakout" will occur.

Suppose that the circuit is properly designed and adjusted so that lock-in does occur between the signal frequency and the oscillator. It still remains to show that the audio-modulating signal can be recovered. To do this, examine the Fourier expression for the amplitude of the fundamental component of plate current. This is given by the standard expression

$$I_{p1m} = \frac{2}{T} \int_0^T i_p \cos \omega_0 t \, dt \tag{14-90}$$

Now if the current pulse i_p is of sufficiently short duration, then the factor $\cos \omega_0 t$ will be approximately unity during the time when i_p has any important value. As a result, the integral is given, with good approximation, by the form

$$I_{p1m} = \frac{2}{T} \int_0^T i_p \, dt \tag{14-91}$$

But it is noted that this is just the form relating the d-c component of the plate-current pulse with the functional form, except for the factor 2. Therefore

$$I_{dc} = 0.5 I_{p1m} \tag{14-92}$$

It is now possible to argue a correlation between the signal frequency and the d-c plate current, as follows: (1) By Eq. (14-88) the oscillator frequency is linear with g_m. (2) If e_g remains fixed in peak value, which it does since e_1 does not vary, then g_m varies directly as i_p [see Eq. (14-85)]. (3) I_{dc} varies linearly with I_{p1m} [Eq. (14-92)]. Therefore

$$I_{dc} \text{ varies as the frequency of } e_s \tag{14-93}$$

To make practical use of this result, it is necessary only to include a resistor in the plate circuit of the heptode, across which will appear the audio signal.

The process of a-m rejection in the Bradley detector is readily understood. Suppose that the oscillator is locked in with the incoming signal, and suppose now that the amplitude of the input signal changes. The plate current i_p will change, since i_p depends on the amplitude of the signal e_s on grid 3. Such a change will momentarily change the oscillator frequency, and a new equilibrium phase condition between e_s and e_g will be reached. When the new equilibrium condition is reached, the oscillator frequency will still be that of the signal. That is, the amplitude variations are translated into phase variations of the oscillator, but not into frequency variations. Since the normal modulation produces many kilocycles per second of frequency change, the phase variations due to amplitude changes which occur at a relatively low frequency rate do not produce a significant audio output.

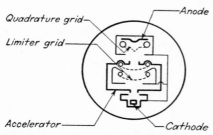

FIG. 14-42. Schematic of the gated-beam tube showing arrangement of the elements.

14-19. The Gated-beam Tube as a Limiter-Discriminator. The cross-section schematic of the gated-beam tube, showing the arrangement of elements, is given in Fig. 14-42. In normal operation, the plate and accelerator are operated at positive potentials, with the limiter grid and the quadrature grid serving to control the beam current.

In this tube electrons from the cathode are accelerated by the accelerator. The limiter grid exercises complete control of the electron beam and determines the extent of the electron drift out of the accelerator structure. The character of the control of the limiter grid is illustrated graphically in Fig. 14-43. Observe from this figure that when the limiter-grid potential is positive, the electron beam reaches the plate without difficulty. However, if the limiter grid is made more than a few volts negative, cutoff of the plate current occurs.

A feature of the design of the tube is that when the limiter grid is made negative, this tends to produce a space-charge cloud in the accelerator-limiter grid-shield region. This space-charge cloud causes a reflection of the cathode current, which diverges and is collected by the accelerator. That is, very few of the electrons are able to return to the cathode owing to the concentration of space charge and the divergence of the beam path.

As the electron beam emerges from the accelerator, it is converged by the electron-lens system, comprising the accelerator structure and the various grids, and is acted upon by the quadrature grid. The characteristics of the quadrature grid are somewhat like those of the limiter grid, as shown in Fig. 14-44. The design here too is such that, with the application of a negative potential to the quadrature grid, the electron beam is reflected away from the quadrature grid and returns to the outside surface of the accelerator structure.

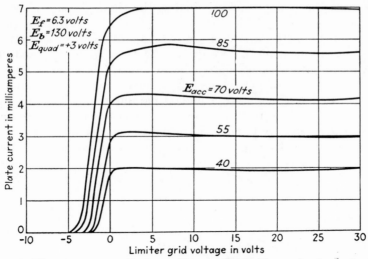

Fig. 14-43. Plate current vs. limiter grid potential, with accelerator potential as parameter.

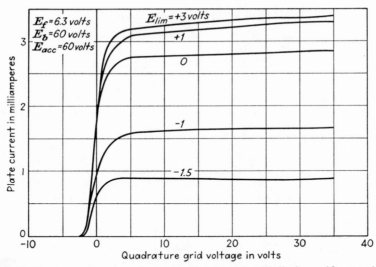

Fig. 14-44. Plate current vs. quadrature grid potential, with limiter grid potential as a parameter.

Owing to the control characteristics of the limiter and quadrature grids, it appears that both exert nearly step-function control over the plate current. In effect, therefore, each grid acts like a potential-controlled gate. If both gates are open, plate current exists. If either or both of the gates are closed, the flow of plate current is blocked.

When used as a limiter-discriminator, the circuit is substantially the following (Fig. 14-45). The cathode resistor R_k is so adjusted that the self-bias sets the plate current on the curved portion of the characteristic. The i-f signal then alternately drives the tube from the condition of plate-current cutoff to plate-current saturation. The result is essentially a square-wave variation of beam-current density beyond the limiter grid.

As indicated in Fig. 14-45, a high-Q parallel-resonant circuit is connected to the quadrature grid. The circuit is tuned to the center frequency of the f-m wave. The current pulses transfer some energy to the quadrature-grid tank circuit, which produces a quadrature-grid potential,

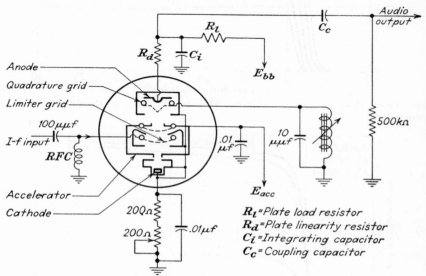

FIG. 14-45. Circuit of the gated-beam limiter-discriminator.

which also acts on the beam current. Because a phase difference exists between the limiter-grid potential and the quadrature-grid potential, only a fraction of each square-wave beam-current pulse reaches the plate.

When a center-frequency signal is applied to the limiter grid, the potential developed on the quadrature grid lags the input signal potential by approximately 90 deg. In this case, half of each square-wave current pulse reaches the plate. When the signal to the limiter grid is slightly above the center frequency, the potential on the quadrature grid lags the input signal by less than 90 deg. Now less than half the square-wave current pulse reaches the plate. Correspondingly, for a frequency less than the center frequency, the limiter grid–quadrature grid potentials are more than 90 deg apart, and more than half the square-wave current pulse reaches the plate. An essentially linear relationship exists between frequency deviation and average plate current, within the desired range of frequency deviation, as seen in Fig. 14-46. Therefore, the modulation content of an f-m signal is available as variations in the average plate current.

Limiting is accomplished because the beam current is limited in passing through the accelerator assembly. That is, if the minimum signal to be received appears on the limiting grid with sufficient amplitude to drive the tube from cutoff to saturation, the desired square-wave current pulses are produced. The only differences that might occur due to differences in amplitude of the input signal will be in the slopes of the pulse sides. Consequently, limiting and a-m rejection are realized.

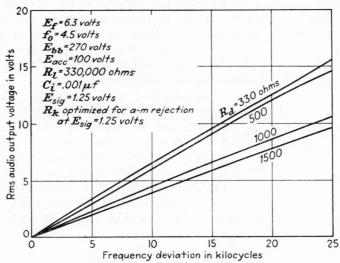

FIG. 14-46. Frequency deviation vs. audio output potential.

14-20. Comparison of Modulation Systems.

It is desired to examine certain significant factors of a-m and f-m systems, in order to compare the two systems of modulation.

Amplitude-modulated transmission is the oldest method of radio transmission and is still used very extensively. A considerable amount of f-m transmission exists, although it represents a relatively small part of the total transmission. Amplitude modulation is used over a very wide range of carrier frequencies, extending from the very low (say several hundred kilocycles) to the ultra-high-frequency bands in the hundreds of megacycles region. While a-m transmission is inferior to f-m transmission when considered from the point of view of receiver noise and certain transmitter considerations, it has not been displaced by f-m transmission owing to many factors, a number of which will be examined.

Consider first the transmitter output stages. The r-f amplitude of an f-m transmitter is a constant, independent of the modulation index, whereas the peak power will be four times the mean value in an a-m transmitter with modulation index $m = 1$. For a total fixed allowable plate dissipation and for fixed plate-circuit efficiency, the output power of the f-m transmitter with given output tubes will be twice that if a-m is employed.

The signal/noise ratio in the receiver is very important in the over-all comparison. It will be found that the f-m system possesses distinct advantages over the a-m system. Likewise, in the matter of interference by two transmissions on the same carrier frequency, the interference is far less with frequency modulation than with amplitude modulation.

To compare the relative effects of internal noise on f-m and a-m systems, the usual approach is the following: The effect of a single sinusoidal component of noise of arbitrary frequency is examined for each system. The results are then generalized to account for the complete band of frequencies contained in the noise spectrum.

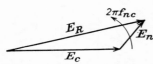

Fig. 14-47. The combination of signal and noise in an a-m system.

Consider first an a-m system. The input carrier signal is specified by the peak amplitude E_c and the angular frequency ω_c. Also, it will be supposed that there is a single frequency noise or interfering signal, specified by E_n and ω_n. It will be assumed that $E_c \gg E_n$. The resultant signal at the input of the receiver is the combination of the two, and they combine in the manner illustrated graphically in Fig. 14-47. Analytically the resultant signal is

$$e_R = E_n \cos \omega_n t + E_c \cos \omega_c t \qquad (14\text{-}94)$$

But since ω_n does not differ too markedly from ω_c, it is convenient to write

$$\omega_n = \omega_c + \omega_{nc} \qquad (14\text{-}95)$$

Also, for convenience, write

$$E_n = aE_c \qquad (14\text{-}96)$$

where, as specified above, $a \ll 1$. Equation (14-94) may then be written as

$$e_R = aE_c \cos (\omega_c + \omega_{nc})t + E_c \cos \omega_c t \qquad (14\text{-}97)$$

which may be recombined to the form

$$e_R = E_c(1 + a \cos \omega_{nc}t) \cos \omega_c t - aE_c \sin \omega_{nc}t \sin \omega_c t$$

This may be written as

$$e_R = E_c \sqrt{(1 + a \cos \omega_{nc}t)^2 + a^2 \sin \omega_{nc}t} \cos (\omega_c t + \varphi)$$

where
$$\varphi = - \tan^{-1} \frac{a \sin \omega_{nc}t}{1 + a \cos \omega_{nc}t} \tag{14-98}$$

For the specified condition that $a \ll 1$, these latter equations reduce to

$$e_R = E_c(1 + a \cos \omega_{nc}t) \cos (\omega_c t + \varphi)$$
$$\varphi = - \tan^{-1} (a \sin \omega_{nc}t) = -a \sin \omega_{nc}t \tag{14-99}$$

As illustrated in Fig. 14-47, the magnitude of the resultant signal E_R varies from $E_c + E_n$ through $E_c - E_n$ and back to $E_c + E_n$. If this signal is passed through an ideal peak detector, the detected output is the value of E_n, which varies at the rate f_{nc}.

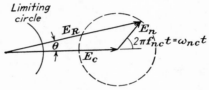

If the peak detector is followed by an audio amplifier which has a flat frequency response with a bandwidth f_2-f_1, then those noise components with frequencies near enough to the carrier frequency f_c, so that the detected noise frequency f_{nc} is within

FIG. 14-48. The combination of signal and noise in an f-m system.

the frequency range f_2-f_1, will produce an output noise signal. Noise components of equal amplitude within the amplifier frequency band will produce equal outputs.

If the carrier is amplitude-modulated 100 per cent, the peak signal output, which is again designated as E_c, appears in the peak detector output. Therefore, the signal/noise ratio for a single noise component is given by

$$\frac{S}{N} (100\% \text{ a-m}) = \frac{E_c}{E_n} \tag{14-100}$$

Now suppose that the same carrier and noise component are applied to an f-m system. The combination of potentials indicated in Fig. 14-47 and given by Eqs. (14-99) still applies. Now, however, Eqs. (14-99) are written as the single expression

$$e_R = E_c(1 + a \cos \omega_{nc}t) \cos (\omega_c t + a \sin \omega_{nc}t) \tag{14-101}$$

Note that now our interest is in the phase between E_c and E_n, rather than in the amplitude variations, which are removed by the limiter. The situation is now represented in Fig. 14-48 and by Eq. (14-101); the input to the receiver is an f-m wave with deviation ratio a. The phase displacement between E_c and E_R is $a \sin \omega_{nc}t$, as indicated in the figure. But the time rate of change of this displacement represents a departure in frequency of E_R due to noise. Hence, writing $\Delta\omega_n$ as this departure in frequency, then

$$\Delta\omega_n = \omega_{nc}a \cos \omega_{nc}t \qquad (14\text{-}102)$$

Because of the limiting, the only effect of the noise component which reaches the f-m detector is the frequency variation $\Delta\omega_n$. Consequently, the amplitude of the noise is directly proportional to f_{nc} and is zero when $f_{nc} = 0$.

The frequency deviation is f_d for 100 per cent modulation, and the signal/noise ratio for a single component of noise is

$$\frac{S}{N} (100\% \text{ f-m}) = \frac{\omega_d}{a\omega_{nc}} = \frac{f_d}{f_{nc}} \frac{E_c}{E_n} \qquad (14\text{-}103)$$

A comparison of this expression with Eq. (14-100) for the a-m case shows that this value is larger until f_{nc} becomes equal to f_d. But here, as for the a-m case, noise components producing frequency components greater than f_2 are eliminated by the audio system. Hence only those noise components which cause f_{nc} to be equal to f_2 are important.

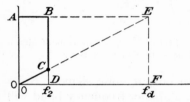

A comparison of the effect of noise in an a-m system with that in an f-m system is portrayed effectively in Fig. 14-49. Consider an a-m receiver which is provided with an ideal i-f system which has a bandwidth $2f_2$. Clearly, both the i-f and the a-f amplifiers will remove any noise outputs which have

FIG. 14-49. A graphical representation of the effect of noise in a-m and f-m systems.

been generated by components outside of f_2. Also from Eq. (14-100) the signal/noise ratio is independent of f_{nc}. Thus the rectangle $OABD$ represents the constant effect of noise for all frequencies for which $f_{nc} < f_2$.

In the case of an f-m receiver, according to Eq. (14-103), the relative effect of noise increases linearly and reaches E_n/E_c when $f_{nc} = f_d$. This is represented by the triangle OEF. In this case, the i-f bandwidth equals $2f_d$. But the a-f system again removes noise components above f_2. Hence the resultant is represented by triangle OCD. It is important to note that i-f components in the range from f_2 to f_d produce signals after detection which are within the a-f band. This situation arises from the fact that the original i-f components were produced by the audio signal within the bandwidth f_2.

To compare the two systems quantitatively, attention is first called to the fact that the noise is continuous over the audio band, whence an infinite number of noise components are contained in the band $\pm f_2$ centered about the carrier frequency f_c. If $E_n(f_{nc})\, df_{nc}$ denotes the peak amplitude of the noise potential in the frequency range df_{nc}, then the total noise in the a-m output is that contained in the frequency range $0 \leq f_{nc} \leq f_2$ and is

$$E_N(\text{a-m}) = \sqrt{\int_0^{f_2} E_n^2 \, df_{nc}} = E_n \sqrt{f_2} \qquad (14\text{-}104)$$

In the f-m case, it will be assumed that the detector recovery constant is K, which relates $\Delta\omega_n$ of Eq. (14-102) to the actual output potential. Then

$$E_n(f_{nc}) = K \frac{E_n}{E_c} f_{nc} \qquad (14\text{-}105)$$

It follows therefore that

$$E_N(\text{f-m}) = \sqrt{\int_0^{f_2} \left(\frac{E_n}{E_c}\right)^2 K^2 f_{nc}^2 \, df_{nc}} = K \frac{E_n}{E_c} f_2 \sqrt{\frac{f_2}{3}} \qquad (14\text{-}106)$$

Suppose that 100 per cent modulation is assumed in each case. Then the signal/noise ratio for the a-m system is

$$\frac{S}{N} (\text{a-m}) = \frac{E_c}{E_n \sqrt{f_2}} \qquad (14\text{-}107)$$

Also, the signal/noise ratio for the f-m case is given by

$$\frac{S}{N} (\text{f-m}) = \frac{K f_d}{K(E_n/E_c) f_2 \sqrt{f_2/3}} \qquad (14\text{-}108)$$

Consequently the ratio of these two quantities is

$$\frac{S/N(\text{f-m})}{S/N(\text{a-m})} = \sqrt{3} \frac{f_d}{f_2} \qquad (14\text{-}109)$$

This result shows that, for a deviation ratio $f_d/f_2 = 1$, the signal/noise improvement with an f-m system is $\sqrt{3}$ or 4.8 db. For a large deviation ratio, say, for example, $f_d = 75$ kc, $f_2 = 7.5$ kc, whence $\delta = 10$, the improvement is correspondingly higher and is 20 db.

14-21. Capture. A very interesting and important feature of an f-m system is known as *capture*. This is the tendency of the f-m system to ignore the weaker of two signals of nearly equal amplitude and equal or nearly equal frequencies. To examine this matter, consider the desired signal to have twice the amplitude of an unmodulated interfering one, the average frequency difference being f_i. The desired signal may be modulated, but if $f_i > f_m$, the conditions will be considered for a period which is short compared with f_m, so that the frequency of the desired modulated signal is essentially fixed. For added convenience, the situation will be examined at the time when the modulated signal is at the instantaneous frequency f_c, which occurs at a zero point in the cycle of the modulating frequency. The situation discussed may be depicted graphically, as in Fig. 14-50.   The similarity of this figure to Fig. 14-48 for the discussion of noise is evident.

Figure 14-50 is a representation of the desired signal plus the interfering signal.   Also shown is the limiting circle, which specifies the output after the limiter stage.   Note that, owing to the interference, the resultant signal may deviate $\pm\theta$ from the value of the signal E_s.   However, as long as $E_i < E_s$, the average angular position of E_R is just that of E_s, and the interfering signal does not change the average frequency of the desired signal.

The phase variation, or perturbation, occurs at the rate f_i.   But if f_i is outside of the audio range, the variations in frequency of E_R are not heard.   In the ideal case, the detector responds only to E_s, as long as

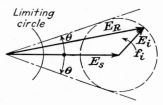

Fig. 14-50. The sinor representation of a desired signal plus an interfering signal.

$E_i < E_s$, and as long as f_i differs in frequency by more than f_2 of the audio system.

If the interfering-signal frequency f_i is in the audible range, the phase perturbation will produce a frequency deviation which may be heard. The equivalent frequency modulation that is produced is small, since $d\theta/dt$ is proportional to f_i [see Eq. (14-96)].   In any case, therefore, the interference is negligible, even if the signal and the interference are at exactly the same frequency.   In practice, most f-m detectors will ignore the interfering signal as long as the ratio of the desired- to interfering-signal amplitude is perhaps 3 or greater.

REFERENCES

1. Crosby, M. G., *RCA Rev.*, **5,** 89 (1940).
2. Morrison, J. F., *Proc. IRE*, **28,** 444 (1940).
3. Travis, C., *Proc. IRE*, **23,** 1125 (1935).
4. Foster, D. F., and S. W. Seeley, *Proc. IRE*, **25,** 289 (1937).
5. Arguimbau, L. B., "Vacuum Tube Circuits," pp. 486–494, John Wiley & Sons, Inc., New York, 1948.
   Sturley, K. R., *Wireless Eng.*, **21,** 72 (1944).
6. Seeley, S. W., and J. Avins, *RCA Rev.*, **8,** 201 (1947).
7. Bradley, W. E., *Electronics*, **19,** 88 (October, 1946).
   Television Project Engineers, "Introduction to Television Receiver Design," Philco Corporation, Philadelphia, 1951.

PROBLEMS

14-1. Determine and plot the instantaneous frequency corresponding to each of the phase functions in the figure.

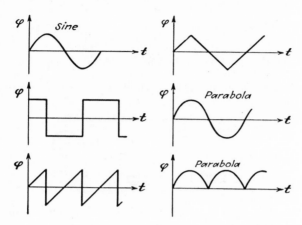

14-2. A 100-Mc f-m signal is modulated ±75 kc at a 400-cps rate. Write an expression for the instantaneous potential if the signal amplitude is 10 volts and if both the frequency and instantaneous magnitude are a maximum at $t = 0$ sec.

14-3. A wave is frequency-modulated at an audio rate of 5,000 cps. If the frequency deviation f_p is 75 kc, plot the spectrum of the wave, including all significant sideband components.

14-4. *a.* The amplitude of a 15-kc wave causes a 75-kc frequency deviation of an f-m wave. Plot the spectrum, and calculate the bandwidth required to pass all sidebands of appreciable magnitude.

b. Suppose that the amplitude is altered to give deviation ratios of 3 and 1. Repeat part *a* for these two cases.

c. From these results, estimate the value of the deviation ratio that may be used and still be within the FCC limitations of ±75 kc frequency band spread.

14-5. Consider the reactance-tube circuit shown in the diagram. Show that by choosing L properly Z is capacitive and is given by C/g_mR without approximation. Compare with Eq. (14-32).

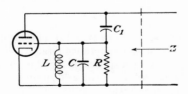

14-6. Given the reactance-tube circuit illustrated at the top of page 426. Show that if the reactance of C is negligible at the operating frequency, and if $\omega L \gg R$, the effective input impedance results from an inductance L/g_mR.

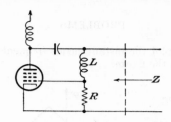

14-7. Consider the reactance tube and oscillator shown in the diagram for this problem. The oscillator is to operate at 5 Mc with a frequency deviation of ± 10 kc. What change in g_m is required to achieve the desired frequency modulation?

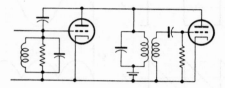

14-8. Assume that between the limits of -2 and -6 volts the (g_m, e_{c1}) characteristic of a 6SJ7 tube may be represented by the expression

$$g_m = 3,000 + 500e_c \qquad \mu\text{mhos}$$

This tube is connected as a reactance modulator, as illustrated in the accompanying figure. It is desired to have a center or carrier frequency of 5 Mc and a frequency deviation of 7.5 kc. Determine the correct setting of the oscillator tank capacitance and the required modulating potential.

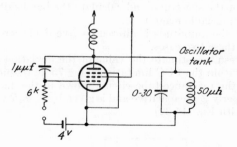

14-9. Carry out the analysis to show that Eq. (14-33) does give the equivalent output admittance of the inductive reactance circuit.

14-10. Obtain an approximate expression for the variation of the frequency of an f-m oscillator as the potential on the grid of an inductive reactance tube is varied. Proceed in a manner analogous to that employed in the text in obtaining the corresponding expression for a capacitive reactance tube.

14-11. The essential circuit of a balanced reactance tube is given in the accompanying figure (battery supplies have been omitted for convenience). Deduce an expression for the effective output impedance of this circuit. In this calculation, choose $X_1/R_1 = X_2/R_2 = \alpha$, $r_p = \infty$. Also, suppose that for a given audio signal the (g_m, e_c) relationship is the ideal curve shown on page 391.

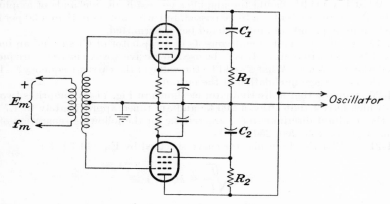

14-12. Calculate and plot the potential ratio for the preemphasis or accentuator circuit shown in the diagram as a function of frequency.   Plot the curve on semilogarithmic paper.

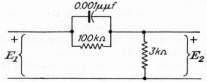

14-13. Calculate and plot the potential ratio for the deemphasis circuit shown in the accompanying figure as a function of frequency.   Plot the curve on semilogarithmic paper.

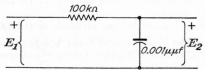

14-14. Determine the maximum frequency deviation possible with the Armstrong system of Fig. 14-22 if the distortion is to be less than 6 per cent.   The phase varies at a 60-cps rate.

14-15. What must be the ratio of sideband to carrier potentials in the Armstrong system to produce a frequency deviation of ±12.2 cps at the audio frequency of 400 cps?

14-16. Show by an analysis similar to that which leads to Eq. (13-6) for the a-m case that the output of a frequency doubler to which an f-m signal is applied is the f-m signal centered about the second harmonic of the carrier.

14-17. An f-m wave of the form given in Eq. (14-15) is combined with a large amplitude sine wave $E_0 \sin \omega_0 t$.   Show that if both waves are applied to a rectifier, the output will contain the f-m wave shifted in the frequency scale.

14-18. *a.* An incoming f-m wave is deviated ±75 kc at a 10-kc rate.   The local oscillator is so set that the i-f frequency is 13.7 Mc.   The signal is passed

through two stages of single tuned amplifiers.   Discuss the effect of the tuned
circuits on the important sidebands with respect to amplitude and phase.

b. What bandwidth should the amplifier possess if all sidebands of amplitude
greater than 0.01 per cent are to be passed, but with not more than a 30 per cent
reduction in amplitude of any sideband being permitted.

14-19. An antiresonant circuit consists of a capacitor of 65 $\mu\mu$f and an inductor of 0.4 mh and 16 ohms.   It is to be used to receive a wave having a frequency
modulation of 1.5 kc.   What should be the value of the carrier frequency?   Estimate the percentage modulation of the output.

14-20. Suppose that a discriminator as shown in Fig. 14-30 comprises two circuits which have bandwidths of 200 kc and are tuned approximately to 4.7 Mc.
Plot the resultant discriminator characteristic for the following separation of the
resonant peaks: 150, 200, 250, 300 kc.

14-21. *a.* Plot the discriminator curve specified by Eq. (14-70) for

$$\tfrac{1}{2} \sqrt{\frac{L_2}{L_1}} = kQ = 1$$

Write $2\delta Q = x$, and plot as a function of x.

b. Repeat for Eq. (14-81).

14-22. Use the curve of Prob. 14-21*b* to design a discriminator having a peak-
peak bandwidth of 400 kc at 15 Mc.

14-23. Show that, other things being equal, the output of the ratio detector
is down from that of the discriminator by a factor of 2.

14-24. Would it be more difficult to design a broad-band ratio detector than a
discriminator of the same bandwidth?   Explain.

14-25. Suppose that the dot on the secondary winding of the Bradley detector
of Fig. 14-38 were at the other terminal (i.e., that the mutual inductance is
reversed).   Discuss the mechanism of pull-in to synchronization.

14-26. Suppose that the i-f signal to grid 3 of the Bradley detector has a
1,000-cps 40 per cent amplitude modulation superposed.   The maximum phase
change is 25 deg.   Evaluate the a-f output as a fraction of that produced by a
400-cps f_d = 75 kc f-m signal.

14-27. Show that the ratio of the rms ordinate of $OABD$ in Fig. 14-49 to the
rms ordinate of OCD is the improvement ratio $\sqrt{3}\,f_d/f_2$.

14-28. Reconcile Eqs. (14-98) with the statements concerning variation of the
noise output with the bandwidth.

14-29. An a-m transmitter having an output power of 100 watts has a transmission-channel bandwidth of 10 kc and a signal/noise ratio of 15 db.   Suppose
that it is planned to replace this communication link by an f-m transmitter having
a transmission-channel bandwidth of 120 kc.   If it is desired that the signal/noise
ratio be 32 db, what is the required transmitter power?

14-30. A single-sideband suppressed carrier a-m signal is received on an f-m
receiver.   Discuss the character of the receiver output.

CHAPTER 15

INFORMATION THEORY

15-1. Introduction. This chapter will discuss several of the very important results of "information theory," or the synonymous "communication theory." The discussion is necessarily restricted in scope and will confine itself principally to certain topics that relate to transmission systems. Many of the finer points of the theory, as well as mathematical rigor, have been sacrificed in the interests of simplicity.

Of particular importance is the realization that it is possible to define and measure the quantity of information that is contained in a message. Moreover, it is possible to measure the capacity of a communication channel to transmit information. Since the definitions and measures are applicable to all modulation systems, it is therefore possible to compare the relative efficiencies of different modulation systems.

15-2. Discrete Systems. Before introducing numbers or formulas, certain fundamental considerations are important. Consider initially

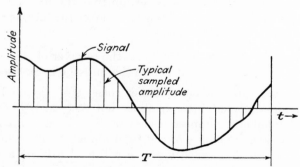

FIG. 15-1. A signal wave that is sampled at n points in the period T.

the term "message." In the discrete case, a message may be considered to be a sequence of choices of possible symbols. The possible symbols make up the *symbol alphabet*, a specified number of such letters of the alphabet making up a *message*. For example, in ordinary speech or writing, the alphabet may be the letters or the words. In telegraphy, the alphabet will be the dot and dash. In music, the alphabet will be the successive amplitudes of the signal wave.

429

Refer to Fig. 15-1, which shows a general signal of time duration T. It is supposed that the signal is sampled at n points which are uniformly spaced in time. A signal such as this may be sent from a transmitter to a receiver as the sequence of the sampled values. For the signal to carry information, there must be prior agreement between the transmitter and receiver as to what meaning should be attached to the sequence of values that have been received. When this has been done and when noise conditions are such that it is known from the received signal exactly what signal was transmitted, then all the information sent is received. In this case the number of different sampling levels L makes up the symbol alphabet, and a message may consist of the sequence of n sampling values. The maximum possible total number of different messages which are possible is L^n. If the different permutations of sampling values are not distinguishable in a transmission channel, then the maximum rate of transmission of information in the channel is greatly reduced. This problem will receive some attention below.

Consider now the term "information in a message." A definition of this expression is given in statistical terms. As stated by Goldman,[1] the amount of information received in a message is defined as

$$\text{Information received} = \log \frac{\text{probability at the receiver of the event after the message is received}}{\text{probability at the receiver of the event before the message is received}} \quad (15\text{-}1)$$

In the noiseless case the receiver is certain that the message received is correct, so that the probability of the event after the message is received is unity. Thus for the noiseless case

$$\begin{array}{l}\text{Information} \\ \text{received}\end{array} = -\log \left(\begin{array}{l}\text{probability at the receiver of the} \\ \text{event before the message is received}\end{array}\right) \quad (15\text{-}2)$$

Suppose now that the message alphabet consists of s symbols or letters and that the message contains n symbols (not necessarily different) from the message alphabet. Suppose also that there is associated the probability p_i with each symbol s_i of the total alphabet of s symbols. The average information H in each message will evidently be a function of these probabilities. Thus in functional notation

$$H = H(p_1, p_2, \ldots, p_n) \quad (15\text{-}3)$$

Shannon[2] chose the following general and reasonable properties that must be possessed by H:

1. H shall be continuous in the p_i.
2. If the probabilities p_i for each symbol of the set s are equal, then $p = 1/s$, and H shall increase monotonically with s.
3. If a selection of symbols is broken down into two successive selec-

tions, then H of the original selection of symbols should be equal to the weighted sum of the H's of the two successive selections.

Subject to these properties, he deduced the following expression for the average information in the message of n symbols:

$$H = -n \sum_{i=1}^{n} p_i \log p_i \qquad (15\text{-}4)$$

Since $\sum_i p_i = 1$, Eq. (15-4) may be written as

$$H = n \log n - n \log n \Sigma p_i - \Sigma n p_i \log p_i$$
$$= n \log n - \Sigma n p_i \log n - \Sigma n p_i \log p_i$$

or

$$H = n \log n - \Sigma n p_i \log n p_i \qquad (15\text{-}5)$$

Now for an *ergodic* system of symbols (one for which the occurrence of symbols is controlled by probability), the various messages become equally probable, for messages of sufficient length. In general, of course, messages of n symbols contain fewer than n different symbols, and these will generally occur with different frequencies. In fact, the number of occurrences of the ith symbol will be

$$n_i = n p_i \qquad (15\text{-}6)$$

Because of this repetition of symbols, the average information will be reduced. The reduction of information that is due to the repetition of the ith symbol may be written as

$$H_i = n_i \log n_i = p_i n \log p_i n \qquad (15\text{-}7)$$

[The basis for this expression follows as a consequence of Eq. (15-8) now being developed.] Thus, in the light of Eq. (15-7), Eq. (15-5) shows that the average information contained in a message of n different symbols is

$$H = n \log n \qquad (15\text{-}8)$$

since the reduction of information due to the repetition of symbols has been accounted for. But n^n gives the number of possible messages of n letters, all n letters being different. If M denotes this number of possible messages, then

$$M = n^n \qquad (15\text{-}9)$$

and the total information in the message is, from Eq. (15-8),

$$H = \log M \qquad (15\text{-}10)$$

Generally, in information theory, the base 2 of logarithms is chosen, and the unit of information is called the *binit*, which is a contraction of

the term binary unity of information.   Thus Eq. (15-4) may be written
as

$$H = -n \sum_i p_i \log_2 p_i \qquad \text{binits}$$

and similarly Eq. (15-10) is   (15-11)

$$H = \log_2 M \qquad \text{binits}$$

Consider now the expression for the average information per symbol,
which is

$$h = \frac{H}{n} = - \sum_i p_i \log_2 p_i \qquad \text{binits/symbol} \qquad (15\text{-}12)$$

This expression for information is similar to that for the entropy of a
system which is characterized by states of probabilities $p_1, \ldots, p_n$,
in the statistical sense of Boltzmann.   Accordingly, the terminology

$$h = - \sum_i p_i \log p_i = \text{entropy of the set of probabilities } p_i \qquad (15\text{-}13)$$

has become standard in information theory.   The relation to the entropy
concept of statistical mechanics is somewhat indefinite, but the use
of the entropy concept is a valid one.   That is, the order-disorder
notion of entropy is directly applicable to the process of communicating
information.

As an extreme example, consider the case when one symbol has a
probability of unity, the probability of all other symbols being zero.
According to Eq. (15-13), h is zero, as is expected, since there is no
uncertainty.   Consider now the case when all the possible symbols are
equally probable, and such that $\sum_i p_i = 1$.   In this case h attains its

maximum value.   This condition of maximum entropy is reasonable,
since the greatest uncertainty exists in the selection, since all possible
symbols are equally probable.

15-3. The Hartley Law.   The most significant early contribution to
the theory of information was that of Hartley,[3] who developed a quantitative measure of the amount of information in a message, and, based on
it, a measure of the capacity of a communication channel in terms of its
bandwidth.   Subsequent work has extended these results to include the
influence of noise.

Suppose that s, the number of letters in the symbol alphabet, is fixed
by the source or by other factors.   It is desirable to determine n, the
number of letters in the message, which can be sent in a period of time
T equal to the message duration.   That is, it is desired to find the rate
at which symbols can be transmitted through the channel.   It is antici-

pated, in the light of simple network considerations, that the transmission rate will depend on the bandwidth of the network. It is desired to obtain the relationship that exists.

Refer again to Fig. 15-1. If the signal is regarded as a single cycle of a repetitive wave, the graphical methods of Fourier analysis may be used to ascertain the amplitudes of the harmonic components which constitute the signal. A number of such graphical schedule methods of analysis exist (the Runge schedule would be particularly appropriate for a general signal wave.) For the case of n samples, n amplitudes may be determined. If the d-c component, if any, is omitted (since this can readily be determined with the aid of a planimeter or by one of several methods of numerical integration), the schedule analysis will yield the amplitude of $n/2$ sine terms and $n/2$ cosine terms. Thus the amplitudes of the fundamental and all harmonics up to the $(n/2)$th are known. The period of the highest harmonic is $2T/n$. The foregoing may be referred to as a sampling theorem in the time domain, and it permits the specification of continuous signals by discrete sets of values.

In the more general case, the waveform need not be periodic. Consider a signal, in the form of a continuous function, which has passed through a transmission system having a finite bandwidth. For signals of this type, Shannon[4] gives a sampling theorem which states:

If a function $f(t)$ contains no frequencies higher than B cycles per second, it is completely determined by giving its ordinates at a series of points spaced $1/2B$ seconds apart, the series extending throughout the time domain.

The proof of this theorem follows directly from considerations of the Fourier transform and is now given. If $F(\omega)$ denotes the frequency spectrum of $f(t)$, then

$$f(t) = \frac{1}{2\pi} \int_{-\infty}^{+\infty} F(\omega)e^{j\omega t}\, d\omega \qquad (15\text{-}14)$$

If $F(\omega)$ is assumed to be zero outside the band, the limits of the integral may be changed to the interval $-2\pi B$ to $+2\pi B$. Thus

$$f(t) = \frac{1}{2\pi} \int_{-2\pi B}^{+2\pi B} F(\omega)e^{j\omega t}\, d\omega \qquad (15\text{-}15)$$

Now let $t = n/2B$, where n is any positive or negative integer. Then

$$f\left(\frac{n}{2B}\right) = \frac{1}{2\pi} \int_{-2\pi B}^{+2\pi B} F(\omega)e^{j\omega n/2B}\, d\omega \qquad (15\text{-}16)$$

The left-hand side of this expression is the value of $f(t)$ at the nth sampling point. The integral on the right represents the nth coefficient of the complex Fourier-series coefficient obtained by expanding the function

$F(\omega)$ in a Fourier series in the range from $-2\pi B$ to $+2\pi B$. Thus the values of the sample $f(n/2B)$ determine the coefficients of a Fourier-series expansion of $F(\omega)$. Consequently they completely determine $F(\omega)$ itself in the specified range. Moreover, since $F(\omega)$ is the frequency spectrum of $f(t)$, the coefficients or samples therefore determine the function $f(t)$.

Suppose that it is desired to transmit a signal which contains no harmonic components higher than the $(n/2)$th. Since the period of the highest harmonic is $2T/n$, the bandwidth of the transmitting channel must be at least $n/2T$ to include all harmonics. Thus the bandwidth must be at least

$$B = \frac{n}{2T} \tag{15-17}$$

from which

$$n = 2BT \tag{15-18}$$

Consider now the problem of transmitting a message that consists of a series of n equally spaced binary (on or off) pulses contained in an interval of T sec. In so far as the transmitting channel is concerned, this problem is precisely the same as that considered above, and the bandwidth of the transmitting channel is given by Eq. (15-17). Moreover, since the number of possible messages with a symbol alphabet of 2 symbols, with n letters in the message, is $M = 2^n$, then, by Eq. (15-10), the total information in the message is

$$H = \log M = \log 2^n = n \log 2$$

When referred to the base 2 system of logarithms, this yields

$$H = n \qquad \text{binits} \tag{15-19}$$

Thus the amount of information that the transmitting channel of bandwidth B will carry in time T is

$$H = 2BT \qquad \text{binits} \tag{15-20}$$

This is the Hartley law.

The information capacity of the channel, C, is defined as the number of binits per second carried by the channel, so that

$$C = \frac{H}{T} = 2B \qquad \text{binits/sec} \tag{15-21}$$

15-4. Hartley's Law and Continuous Signals. Certain fundamental limitations exist in the Hartley law, which will now be discussed. In this connection, refer to Table 1-1, which gives the binary code for a 4-pulse code in pulse-code modulation. In this tabulation there is seen to be an alphabet of 2 symbols, and each message consists of 4 letters.   The total number of possible messages is $2^4 = 16$, as shown.   Note that each message specifies a sample point.   Clearly, the 4-pulse coded pulse-code modulation permits a total of 16 quantizing levels, the total information in each message being 4 binits.

Suppose now that the alphabet of 2 symbols be retained, but now consider that each message is to consist of 7 letters.   In this case the total number of possible messages is $2^7 = 128$, and each message contains an average information of 7 binits.   That the amount of information should increase with the number of letters per message is made evident by a simple example.   Suppose that a given wave is to be sampled.   If a 4-pulse code is used, 16 amplitudes may be represented.   If a 7-pulse code is used, 128 amplitudes may be represented.   Clearly, in the latter case, the available amplitude levels are specified within much narrower limits than in the former case, whence the uncertainty is less, or the information is greater.

In the limit for a signal that can be measured with an infinite degree of precision, an infinitely large amount of information is contained in each message.   The transmission could therefore take place at an infinite rate through a channel, if an infinite number of inputs can be correctly recognized at the output.   Observe that the output signal does not have to be identical with the input signal in this case, for if the channel alters the signal in some known fashion, a precise knowledge of this change will permit the recognition of the original signal.   Of course, if the signal is changed in some unknown or random fashion, the number of input signals which may be recognized becomes finite, when the channel capacity also becomes finite.   This means that random fluctuations or noise in a transmitting channel will limit a channel to finite capacity.

The foregoing discussion can be extended to the case of a continuous signal.   Refer again to Fig. 15-1, but consider the signal to be a finite length of continuous signal.   There is an infinite number of sample points, the value of each of which is its ordinate.   Moreover, there is an infinite number of possible values of the ordinate.   It would appear, therefore, that a continuous signal of finite length is represented by an alphabet containing an infinite number of symbols, there being an infinite number of symbols in each message.   This would lead to the conclusion that a continuous signal, even of finite length, contains an infinite amount of information.   Two reasons exist in the practical case why the foregoing is not true.   First, all actual signals possess spectra of finite bandwidth, and, according to the sampling theorem in the time domain, only the values of the signal at the sampling points can be chosen independently.   This reduces the continuous signal to the equivalent of a finite sequence of symbols.   Second, as noted above, random fluctuations or noise will limit a channel to finite capacity, since the number of distinguishable amplitude levels is reduced to a finite value.

Two important conclusions can be drawn at this point. First, it appears that continuous signals would be expected to have the same order of information as discrete signals. Second, information theory provides no significant information for continuous signals without noise.

15-5. The Modified Hartley Law. As noted in the foregoing section, a finite capacity of the transmitting channel is imposed by the presence of random fluctuations or noise. This finite capacity of the channel may be expressed in terms of the relative magnitudes of the signals and of the fluctuations that are imposed upon them during transmission.[5] If the fluctuations are of the character of random noise, then on the average a change in signal amplitude can be detected only if it is at least equal to the rms value E_N of the noise. In all practical types of detectors, the extraction of information from a mixture of signal and noise requires that some threshold level of S/N ratio be exceeded. Even above this threshold the reliability of information increases with S/N ratio. If E_S is the rms value of the signal, then for large S/N ratios (actually the ratio of peak signal to peak noise need only be greater than 2) the number of allowable letters in the symbol alphabet corresponding to the reliable recognition of the signal amplitude is $(E_S + E_N)/E_N$ or $1 + E_S/E_N$. Moreover, the sampling of the amplitudes may occur at the rate of $2B$ per second, since the signal is confined to the bandwidth B.

In the light of these considerations, the information H contained in a message containing n symbols chosen from an alphabet of s symbols is

$$H = \log M = \log s^n$$
$$= \log_2 \left(1 + \frac{E_S}{E_N} \right)^{2BT} \qquad \text{binits} \qquad (15\text{-}22)$$

which may be written

$$H = 2BT \log_2 \left(1 + \frac{E_S}{E_N} \right) \qquad \text{binits} \qquad (15\text{-}23)$$

This is the modified Hartley law. The corresponding channel capacity is

$$C = \frac{H}{T} = 2B \log_2 \left(1 + \frac{E_S}{E_N} \right) \qquad \text{binits/sec} \qquad (15\text{-}24)$$

This expression specifies the maximum channel capacity of a system for a specified S/N ratio and bandwidth B while at the same time obtaining a vanishingly small percentage of errors.

Equation (15-24) indicates that neither the bandwidth nor the signal/noise ratio inherently limits the channel capacity. That is, a given message can be transmitted through a given channel of fixed bandwidth in a certain time T with a specified signal/noise ratio. The same message can be transmitted through a different channel, if the factors are so chosen that the value of the right-hand side of Eq. (15-20) under the new conditions equals that under the original conditions. It must not be inferred, however, that the factors in the modified Hartley law may be varied at will. The type of modulation that is used will impose certain fundamental limitations on one or another of the parameters in the equation. In fact, only coded systems permit any flexibility in the magnitudes of the transmission factors.

Attention is called to the very important fact that the modified Hartley law expresses the optimum information capacity of a given transmitting channel. It says nothing about the actual capacity that may be realized by any particular type of modulation. Nor, in fact, does it say anything about the degree to which the parameters may be varied in any particular modulation system. The discussion in the next section will examine certain particular systems of modulation in the light of the foregoing.

A point of considerable practical importance that is contained in Eq. (15-24) is that bandwidth can be "traded" for signal/noise ratio in the ideal system. It is only with coded systems that one is able to achieve the full exchange of bandwidth for signal/noise ratio.

15-6. Evaluation of A-M, F-M, and Various Pulse Systems. It is desired to examine several important systems of modulation in the light of the modified Hartley Law. This evaluation may be accomplished relatively directly, if it is first noted that in a communication system one may refer to two transmission channels, the primary information channel and the transmission channel. The primary information channel refers to the information channel before modulation or after detection and in an a-m or f-m system for voice communication would denote the audio channel. The transmission channel refers to the carrier channel.

For the ideal case, we may write

$$2BT \log \left(1 + \frac{E_S}{E_N}\right) = 2B'T \log \left(1 + \frac{E_S'}{E_N'}\right)$$

where the unprimed quantities refer to the primary channel and the primed quantities refer to the transmission channel. This expression states that the information contained in the messages in a given time T is the same in both channels. It follows from this expression that

$$1 + \frac{E_S}{E_N} = \left(1 + \frac{E_S'}{E_N'}\right)^{B'/B} \tag{15-25}$$

Here B'/B is the bandwidth-expansion factor. This expression shows that the signal/noise ratio can be increased, at least ideally, by increasing the bandwidth.

a. A-M Systems. Consider that a 5-kc signal bandwidth is to be transmitted in a conventional double-sideband system. The transmission-channel bandwidth must be equal to twice the primary-information-channel bandwidth. In so far as fluctuation-noise interference is concerned, a greater transmission-channel bandwidth does not improve the transmission, nor does it permit the use of a lower signal/noise ratio. Conversely, a transmission-channel bandwidth narrower than twice the primary information channel will result in the loss of part of the information, and this loss cannot be compensated by increasing the signal/noise ratio. This means that bandwidth expansion cannot be employed in an a-m system to improve the signal/noise ratio.

In the case of single-sideband suppressed-carrier transmission an appreciable improvement over double-sideband transmission is possible. With single-sideband transmission, the transmission-channel bandwidth is equal to the primary-information-channel bandwidth. As a result of this factor of 2 in bandwidth, the improvement in signal/noise ratio over the double-sideband case is 3 db. Now also, since the power in the sidebands, for 100 per cent modulation, is one-half that contained in the carrier, then only one-third of the total transmitted power is intelligence. If the carrier is suppressed, there is a gain of 4.77 db. If the carrier and one sideband are suppressed, there is a gain of 6 db. Hence the single-sideband system possesses an inherent advantage of 9 db over the double-sideband system. The practical problem in comparing the actual advantage of single sideband over double sideband is complicated by the fact that single-sideband power amplification is accomplished in class B amplifiers, whereas double sideband is ordinarily produced in class C stages.

In so far as trading bandwidth for signal/noise ratio in single-sideband transmission is concerned, the same limitations exist as for the double-sideband system, and no effective exchange is possible.

b. F-M Systems. In the case of an f-m system, a certain amount of trading between bandwidth and signal/noise ratio is possible. The amount of signal/noise improvement that is possible was examined in some detail in Sec. 14-20. According to Eq. (14-103), which is valid provided that the peak noise amplitude is less than one-half the peak signal amplitude, the signal/noise ratio varies directly with the frequency deviation. Moreover, the total signal/noise ratio in the receiver output is dictated by the audio bandwidth, which would be set nearly equal to the bandwidth of the primary information channel. As illustrated in Fig. 14-49, the signal/noise ratio is proportional to the bandwidth expansion. The improvement can be made somewhat higher through the use of preemphasis circuits, since the preemphasis of the higher audio frequencies makes the noise relatively lower at these frequencies. However, the signal/noise improvement is not nearly as large as that permitted by the Hartley law.

c. *Pulse Systems.* The term pulse modulation as distinct from pulse-code modulation will be used to designate unquantized pulse modulation. The pulse-modulation systems to be considered are pulse-amplitude modulation (PAM), pulse-duration modulation (PDM), and pulse-position modulation (PPM).

The over-all bandwidth required for pulse-modulation systems depends on the pulse repetition rate, the pulse waveshape, and the pulse width. Under normal operation the r-f bandwidth required is given approximately by

$$B \doteq \frac{2}{\tau} \tag{15-26}$$

where τ is the pulse width in microseconds and B is in megacycles. Consequently pulse-modulation systems require relatively large bandwidths in their operation.

Pulse-amplitude modulation is the most efficient form of pulse modulation from the standpoint of bandwidth B. However, pulse-amplitude modulation is subject to the same transmission-link stabilities and signal/noise characteristics as any other a-m systems. That is, the bandwidth employed will govern the effect of the noise, broader bandwidth being accompanied by an increased noise without an improved signal. Hence pulse-amplitude modulation is not able to improve the signal/noise ratio in exchange for bandwidth.

Pulse-duration modulation and pulse-position modulation, both being of constant amplitude, permit the use of limiters. These do much to improve the signal/noise ratio of the system by reducing the effect of impulse noise, just as in frequency modulation. However, noise does remain, as discussed in Sec. 1-7, this noise appearing on the leading and trailing edges of the pulses. Impulse noise may cause a displacement of the pulse edge from the position corresponding to the modulating signal. Noise may also affect the pulse amplitude, shape, or slope of the pulse edges. In pulse-duration modulation the effect ultimately appears as a change in the effective duration. In pulse-position modulation the effect will appear as a change in position.

If the bandwidth in an uncoded pulse-modulation system is doubled, the transmission symbol can be located twice as accurately. In pulse-duration modulation and pulse-position modulation, since the uncertainty of the position of the pulse is a function of the rise time of the pulse, and also the decay time, both of which improve directly with the bandwidth, the signal/noise ratio is proportional to the bandwidth, and hence proportional to the bandwidth expansion. While this means that both pulse-duration modulation and pulse-position modulation trade bandwidth for an improvement in signal/noise ratio, it is not nearly so large an increase as is possible, according to the Hartley law.

In pulse-code modulation or other possible coded systems, full advantage can be made of added bandwidth. Suppose, for example, that the transmission-channel bandwidth is doubled. As a result, if the number of letters in the symbol alphabet is unchanged, a message containing twice as many symbols, or two messages of the original symbol content, can be transmitted in a given time. But if each message has $1 + E'_S/E'_N$ possible signal amplitudes, the combination of the two messages has $(1 + E'_S/E'_N)^2$ possible values. This states, in effect, that

$$1 + \frac{E_S}{E_N} = \left(1 + \frac{E'_S}{E'_N}\right)^2$$

where the exponent is the bandwidth-expansion factor. By comparison with Eq. (15-25), this is the form governing the signal/noise ratio improvement that is possible in the ideal system, as given by the Hartley law.

15-7. A Geometrical Approach to the Modified Hartley Law. A rather interesting geometrical approach to the modified Hartley law was developed by Shannon.[5] As discussed in Sec. 15-3, a signal of duration T and bandwidth B can be specified exactly by a set of $2BT$ numbers which are uniformly distributed in time, at the instants $1/2B$ sec apart. If one now considers a multidimensional space of $2BT$ dimensions, then the specification of $2BT$ coordinates defines a point in this $2BT$-dimensional space. Moreover, the "distance" from the origin to the point is the square root of the sum of the squares of the coordinates of the point. If the coordinates are potentials, the sum of the squares is a quantity that is proportional to the power in the signal. Hence all signals of total power less than P_S must lie inside a $2BT$-dimensional "sphere" having a radius that is proportional to $\sqrt{P_S}$.

Now consider the situation after the signal has been transmitted through a transmission channel, being thereby affected by noise. As a result, the signal point is displaced in signal space. But since the noise is random, the displacement of the signal point is equally probable in any direction, the amount of the displacement being proportional to $\sqrt{P_N}$. The situation is then somewhat like that illustrated graphically in Fig. 15-2 for the very simple case of a two-dimensional space. Since the total power of the perturbed signal is $P_S + P_N$, all such signals are confined to the sphere of radius $\sqrt{P_S + P_N}$. Also, the number of signals that can be reliably distinguished is the number of spheres of radius $\sqrt{P_N}$

that can be included in the sphere of radius $\sqrt{P_S + P_N}$. This number is given by the ratio of the volume of the large sphere to the volume of the

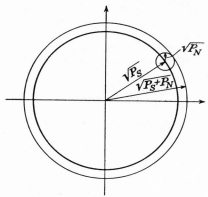

Fig. 15-2. Cross section of signal space showing the transmitted, random-noise, and received powers.

small sphere.   But since the volume of an n-dimensional sphere of radius r is[6]

$$V = \frac{\pi^{n/2}}{\Gamma\left(\dfrac{A}{2} + 1\right)} r^n$$

the ratio of the two volumes, and hence the ratio of distinguishable signals, is

$$M = \frac{(\sqrt{P_S + P_N})^{2BT}}{\sqrt{P_N}^{2BT}} = \left(\frac{P_S + P_N}{P_N}\right)^{BT} \tag{15-27}$$

Hence by Eq. (15-10) the total information in the message is

$$H = \log M = BT \log \frac{P_S + P_N}{P_N}$$

or

$$H = BT \log\left(1 + \frac{P_S}{P_N}\right) \tag{15-28}$$

This form of the modified Hartley law differs somewhat from that given in Eq. (15-23) and appears to be the more general form. Note, however, that since Eq. (15-23) is restricted to large S/N ratios, the two expressions are practically the same.

REFERENCES

1. Goldman, S., "Information Theory," Prentice-Hall, Inc., New York, 1953.
2. Shannon, C. E., "The Mathematical Theory of Communication," University of Illinois Press, Urbana, Ill., 1949.

3. Hartley, R. V. L., *Bell System Tech. J.*, **7**, 535 (1928).
4. Shannon, C. E., *Proc. IRE*, **37**, 10 (1949).
5. Tuller, W. G., *Proc. IRE*, **37**, 468 (1949).
6. Sommerville, D. M. Y., "An Introduction to the Geometry of N-dimensions," p. 135, E. P. Dutton, New York, 1929.
7. A good general discussion is given by:
   Leifer, M., and W. F. Schreiber, "Communication Theory," in L. Marton, ed., "Advances in Electronics," vol. III, Academic Press, Inc., New York, 1951.

PROBLEMS

15-1. How much information is contained in the message that a pair of dice' when rolled, resulted in a six?

15-2. A language is drawn from an alphabet of four symbols, A, B, C, D. It is encoded into a secondary channel having an alphabet of two symbols 1 and 0 according to the code

$$A \to 11 \qquad B \to 10 \qquad C \to 01 \qquad D \to 00$$

a. Assume that the symbol probabilities are each equal to 0.25. What is the language-transmission capacity of the secondary channel, for unit duration of the symbols 1 and 0?

b. The symbol probabilities are now, respectively, 0.3, 0.3, 0.2, 0.2. What is the language-transmission capacity of the secondary channel under these conditions?

15-3. The elements of a pulse-coding transmission system are illustrated in the accompanying figure. Specify the missing data called for on this figure, assuming a noiseless system.

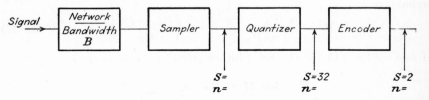

15-4. A 5 by 5 matrix of lights is available, any bulb of which can be lighted in 50 millisec. If a specification of the lighted bulb is transmitted by means of a sequence of on-off pulses:

a. What is the required bandwidth of the transmission channel?

b. What is the channel capacity in binits per second?

APPENDIX A

NOTES ON GENERAL NETWORK ANALYSIS*

A-1. Reference Conditions and Notation. Mention is made at several points in the text of the reference positive polarity and reference current direction. It is important to examine the significance of these terms and their relationship to general network analysis.

The solution of a network problem amounts to the finding of expressions for the potentials and currents at various points in the circuit. Sometimes charges and flux linkages are required also. For the a-c case the directions of the currents and the polarities of the potentials are continually reversing. Algebraic notation must always be employed.

All measurable electrical quantities (current, potential, etc.) are called *physical entities*. Their algebraic representations (e, i, etc.) are called *algebraic quantities*. Physical entities change their direction or polarity, while their algebraic representation changes their sense (algebraic sign).

The direction of current, when the symbol which represents it is positive, is called its *reference direction*. Similarly, the polarity of a potential, when the symbol which represents it is positive, is called its *reference polarity*. In this latter case, the $+$ and $-$ signs not only are used to designate the potential but also are used in algebraic interpretations. The two uses should not be confused. The general term reference *condition* is used to imply either a reference direction or a reference polarity. Thus, in general terms, the reference condition of a physical entity corresponds with the positive sense of the algebraic quantity which represents it.

A-2. Notation for Sinors. It is customary in the discussion of amplifier response to assume that the input signal is sinusoidal and of the general form

$$e_1 = \sqrt{2}\, E_1 \sin\,(\omega t + \theta)$$

Ordinarily the calculations are not carried out in terms of the trigonometric functions, but use is made of complex-number theory in a-c network analysis. The use of complex-number theory stems from the fact

---

* For more detail, refer to W. LePage and S. Seely, "General Network Analysis," McGraw-Hill Book Company, Inc., New York, 1952.

that the sinusoid may be expressed in exponential form by the relation

$$e_1 = \sqrt{2}\, E_1 \sin (\omega t + \theta_1) = \text{Im } \sqrt{2}\, E_1 e^{j(\omega t + \theta_1)} \qquad (A-1)$$

where Im denotes that the imaginary part of the Euler* expansion of this quantity is chosen. Now, it is found in subsequent analysis that the essential information relating to the sinusoid is contained in the quantity $E_1 e^{j\theta_1}$, which does not include the time. This permits the analysis to be carried out in terms of complex-number theory and the associated algebraic manipulations of this discipline, and, as a final step, the results may be correlated with, and written in trigonometric form involving the time.

Many of the results obtained by the use of complex numbers can be obtained through geometric means alone, by plotting the complex numbers as directed lines in a plane. The directed lines may be regarded as vectors in two dimensions. However, confusion with three-dimensional vectors can arise. Therefore, in electrical-engineering applications, quantities having two dimensions (complex quantities) are called *phasor* quantities. As discussed, therefore, phasor quantities can be used to represent symbolically sinusoidal functions of time. This is not the only use of them, however. For example, the impedance function $R + j\omega L$ of a simple series circuit is a complex number but represents quite a different quantity from the complex number which symbolically represents the sinusoid. Those complex quantities (phasor quantities) which symbolically represent sinusoidal functions are called *sinors*. Thus a sinor is a special type of phasor.

In setting up the correspondence between a sinor and a sinusoid, the sine form of writing the sinusoid is chosen arbitrarily. The correspondence between a sinor and sinusoid is written

$$E_1 e^{j\theta_1} \text{ symbolically represents } \sqrt{2}\, E_1 \sin (\omega t + \theta_1) \qquad (A-2)$$

The multiplier is introduced to make E_1 the effective value.

Emphasis is placed on the fact that either the sine or the cosine function could be used on the right-hand side of relation (A-2). However, in this text the foregoing symbolism *always* means the sine function. Without adherence to such a rule, the use of sinors and complex notation could lead to confusion.

Since a sinor is a complex quantity which symbolically represents a sinusoidally varying quantity, the previous definition of a reference condition would indicate that a sinor does not have a reference condition, since it is not a varying quantity. It is a directed line in a plane, but this direction is not an indication of a reference condition. It is related, however, to the reference condition in an indirect way, to be explained.

* The Euler expansion of an exponential has the form $E e^{j\alpha} = E(\cos \alpha + j \sin \alpha)$.

Figure A-1 illustrates how a potential or current is represented, first by a sinusoidal wave, and then in turn by a sinor. The meaning of the sinusoidal wave, in terms of the physical conditions shown on the circuit

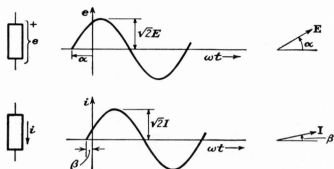

FIG. A-1. Interpretation of sinor notation in terms of a sinusoidal wave.

diagram, is discussed in Sec. A-1. The sinors **E** and **I** are interpreted by referring them to the sinusoidal waves; thus

$$\mathbf{E} \text{ symbolizes } e = \sqrt{2}\, E \sin (\omega t + \alpha)$$
$$\mathbf{I} \text{ symbolizes } i = \sqrt{2}\, I \sin (\omega t + \beta) \tag{A-3}$$

This gives meaning to the reference conditions, in terms of the instantaneous variables which are symbolized by the sinors.

A slightly different practice is shown in Fig. A-2. The sinor symbol is used on the circuit diagram, and the inter-mediate sinusoidal wave is omitted. This system is convenient, as it is more direct than that illustrated in Fig. A-1. In the event of any question of interpretation, the thought sequence indicated in Fig. A-1 is implied by Fig. A-2.

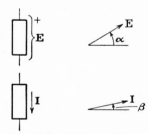

Double subscripts may be used on sinor symbols, to imply the reference condition for the variable which it symbolizes. In fact, it may be noted that identical systems of notation are applicable to instantaneous variables and sinors. The only difference is that, when applied to sinors, the connection with reference conditions

FIG. A-2. The use of sinor symbols on a circuit diagram to imply the reference conditions shown in Fig. A-1.

is indirect, through the intermediate variable quantity, as in Fig. A-1.

A-3. Loop Analysis. The general complete solution of a network by the loop method of analysis may be most easily presented in terms of a specific example. The circuit of Fig. A-3 serves this purpose. All sources are potential sources, and all have the same frequency. The impedances are drawn as boxes for simplicity. Each box is assumed to be no more complicated than a series combination of resistance, inductance, and capacitance.

By an application of the Kirchhoff potential law around each of the indicated loops, the equations that result are

$$(Z_a + Z_d)I_1 - Z_dI_2 + 0 = E_\alpha$$
$$-Z_dI_1 + (Z_b + Z_d + Z_e)I_2 - Z_eI_3 = E_\beta$$
$$0 - Z_eI_2 + (Z_c + Z_e)I_3 = -E_\beta$$

(A-4)

The solutions of Eqs. (A-4) are most easily written in terms of determinants, by the application of Cramer's rule. For writing these solutions,

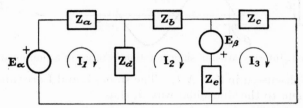

FIG. A-3. A typical network labeled for loop analysis.

it is convenient to define certain symbols to represent determinants. These are

$$\Delta = \begin{vmatrix} Z_a + Z_d & -Z_d & 0 \\ -Z_d & Z_b + Z_d + Z_e & -Z_e \\ 0 & -Z_e & Z_c + Z_e \end{vmatrix}$$

$$\Delta_1 = \begin{vmatrix} E_\alpha & -Z_d & 0 \\ E_\beta & Z_b + Z_d + Z_e & -Z_e \\ -E_\beta & -Z_e & Z_c + Z_e \end{vmatrix}$$

$$\Delta_2 = \begin{vmatrix} Z_a + Z_d & E_\alpha & 0 \\ -Z_d & E_\beta & -Z_e \\ 0 & -E_\beta & Z_c + Z_e \end{vmatrix}$$

$$\Delta_3 = \begin{vmatrix} Z_a + Z_d & -Z_d & E_\alpha \\ -Z_d & Z_d + Z_b + Z_e & E_\beta \\ 0 & -Z_e & -E_\beta \end{vmatrix}$$

(A-5)

In terms of these quantities, the three unknown currents are

$$I_1 = \frac{\Delta_1}{\Delta} \qquad I_2 = \frac{\Delta_2}{\Delta} \qquad I_3 = \frac{\Delta_3}{\Delta}$$

(A-6)

by the application of Cramer's rule.

It should be realized that, even though the example above is for three loops, the general form of the equations will be similar for a circuit of N loops. For the network with N loops, the general equations will be of the form

$$\varrho_{11}I_1 + \varrho_{12}I_2 + \cdots + \varrho_{1N}I_N = E_1$$
$$\varrho_{21}I_1 + \varrho_{22}I_2 + \cdots + \varrho_{2N}I_N = E_2$$
$$\cdots \cdots \cdots \cdots \cdots \cdots \cdots \cdots \cdots \cdots$$
$$\varrho_{N1}I_1 + \varrho_{N2}I_2 + \cdots + \varrho_{NN}I_N = E_N$$

(A-7)

In these equations, the quantities E_1, E_2, . . . denote the algebraic sums of all the sources on the various loop peripheries or contours, with a potential rise in the loop-current direction taken as positive.

The factors ϱ_{pq} have the dimensions of impedance.   When $p = q$, they are the sum of all impedances on a loop contour.   When $p \neq q$, ϱ_{pq} is $+$ or $-$ the impedance in the branch common to loops p and q, according as these loop currents are in the same or opposite directions in the common impedance.   The ϱ coefficients are given the name *copedance,* a contraction for the phrase, coefficient of impedance.

As an illustration, the analysis of Fig. A-3 may be written in the generalized notation of Eqs. (A-7).   In this case

$$\varrho_{11}I_1 + \varrho_{12}I_2 + \varrho_{13}I_3 = E_1$$
$$\varrho_{21}I_1 + \varrho_{22}I_2 + \varrho_{23}I_3 = E_2$$
$$\varrho_{31}I_1 + \varrho_{32}I_2 + \varrho_{33}I_3 = E_3$$

(A-8)

where

$$\varrho_{11} = Z_a + Z_c \qquad \varrho_{21} = \varrho_{12} = -Z_d \qquad E_1 = E_\alpha$$
$$\varrho_{22} = Z_b + Z_d + Z_e \qquad \varrho_{31} = \varrho_{13} = 0 \qquad E_2 = E_\beta \qquad \text{(A-9)}$$
$$\varrho_{33} = Z_c + Z_e \qquad \varrho_{23} = \varrho_{32} = -Z_e \qquad E_3 = -E_\beta$$

The resulting expressions are identical with those in Eq. (A-4), as they must be.

Special attention is required when magnetic coupling exists, as the formulas for the copedances of the elements off the diagonal of the determinants are affected.   In this connection, refer to Fig. A-4.   Without proof, it is noted that the sign to be associated with the term $j\omega M$ representing the effect of the mutual coupling is positive if the currents enter or leave the dotted terminals and is negative if one

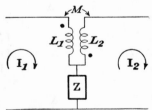

FIG. A-4. Example of magnetic coupling.

current enters and the second current leaves the dotted terminal.   For the case illustrated

$$\varrho_{21} = \varrho_{12} = -Z + j\omega M \qquad \text{(A-10)}$$

A-4. Junction Analysis.   The presentation of the junction analysis follows the same scheme as used for the loop analysis.   All sources have the same frequency, and all are current sources.   The admittances are drawn as boxes for simplicity. Each box is assumed to be no more complicated than a parallel combination of resistance, inductance, and capacitance.

The rules for writing the equilibrium equations, which are based on the Kirchhoff current law, are applied to the network of Fig. A-5. The equa-

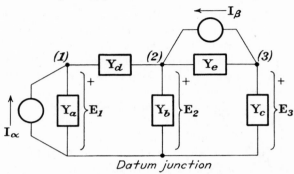

Fig. A-5. A typical network labeled for junction analysis.

tions are the following, when the current at each junction is equated to zero:

$$(\mathbf{Y}_a + \mathbf{Y}_d)\mathbf{E}_1 - \mathbf{Y}_d\mathbf{E}_2 + 0 = \mathbf{I}_\alpha$$
$$-\mathbf{Y}_d\mathbf{E}_1 + (\mathbf{Y}_b + \mathbf{Y}_d + \mathbf{Y}_e)\mathbf{E}_2 - \mathbf{Y}_e\mathbf{E}_3 = \mathbf{I}_\beta \qquad \text{(A-11)}$$
$$0 - \mathbf{Y}_e\mathbf{E}_2 + (\mathbf{Y}_c + \mathbf{Y}_e)\mathbf{E}_3 = -\mathbf{I}_\beta$$

The solution of this set of simultaneous equations is given by Cramer's rule. Write the determinants

$$\boldsymbol{\Delta} = \begin{vmatrix} \mathbf{Y}_a + \mathbf{Y}_d & -\mathbf{Y}_d & 0 \\ -\mathbf{Y}_d & \mathbf{Y}_b + \mathbf{Y}_d + \mathbf{Y}_e & -\mathbf{Y}_e \\ 0 & -\mathbf{Y}_e & \mathbf{Y}_c + \mathbf{Y}_e \end{vmatrix}$$

$$\boldsymbol{\Delta}_1 = \begin{vmatrix} \mathbf{I}_\alpha & -\mathbf{Y}_d & 0 \\ \mathbf{I}_\beta & \mathbf{Y}_b + \mathbf{Y}_d + \mathbf{Y}_e & -\mathbf{Y}_e \\ -\mathbf{I}_\beta & -\mathbf{Y}_e & \mathbf{Y}_c + \mathbf{Y}_e \end{vmatrix}$$

$$\boldsymbol{\Delta}_2 = \begin{vmatrix} \mathbf{Y}_a + \mathbf{Y}_d & \mathbf{I}_\alpha & 0 \\ -\mathbf{Y}_d & \mathbf{I}_\beta & -\mathbf{Y}_e \\ 0 & -\mathbf{I}_\beta & \mathbf{Y}_c + \mathbf{Y}_e \end{vmatrix} \qquad \text{(A-12)}$$

$$\boldsymbol{\Delta}_3 = \begin{vmatrix} \mathbf{Y}_a + \mathbf{Y}_d & -\mathbf{Y}_d & \mathbf{I}_\alpha \\ -\mathbf{Y}_d & \mathbf{Y}_b + \mathbf{Y}_d + \mathbf{Y}_e & \mathbf{I}_\beta \\ 0 & -\mathbf{Y}_e & -\mathbf{I}_\beta \end{vmatrix}$$

In terms of these determinants, the unknown potentials are given by the ratios

$$\mathbf{E}_1 = \frac{\boldsymbol{\Delta}_1}{\boldsymbol{\Delta}} \qquad \mathbf{E}_2 = \frac{\boldsymbol{\Delta}_2}{\boldsymbol{\Delta}} \qquad \mathbf{E}_3 = \frac{\boldsymbol{\Delta}_3}{\boldsymbol{\Delta}} \qquad \text{(A-13)}$$

by the application of Cramer's rule.

This type of solution can be written for a general network of N junctions plus the datum junction, by the set of equations

$$\begin{aligned}
\mathfrak{d}_{11}\mathbf{E}_1 + \mathfrak{d}_{12}\mathbf{E}_2 + \cdots + \mathfrak{d}_{12}\mathbf{E}_2 &= \mathbf{I}_1 \\
\mathfrak{d}_{21}\mathbf{E}_1 + \mathfrak{d}_{22}\mathbf{E}_2 + \cdots + \mathfrak{d}_{2N}\mathbf{E}_N &= \mathbf{I}_2 \\
\cdots\cdots\cdots\cdots\cdots\cdots\cdots\cdots \\
\mathfrak{d}_{N1}\mathbf{E}_1 + \mathfrak{d}_{N2}\mathbf{E}_2 + \cdots + \mathfrak{d}_{NN}\mathbf{E}_N &= \mathbf{I}_N
\end{aligned} \qquad \text{(A-14)}$$

The coefficients $\mathfrak{d}$ represent the various branch admittances in the following way: If $p = q$, $\mathfrak{d}_{pq}$ is the sum of all admittances connected to the path junction. If $p \neq q$, $\mathfrak{d}_{pq}$ is the negative of the admittance connecting junctions p and q directly. These coefficients are called *comittances*, as a contraction of the phrase, coefficients of admittance. The currents $\mathbf{I}_N$ appearing on the right are junction current sources. A junction current source is the algebraic sum of all current sources connected to the junction. A current having a reference direction toward the junction is taken as positive in forming the algebraic sum.

A-5. Network Theorems. A number of network theorems are ound to be of considerable assistance in solving the network problems involving vacuum tubes. Several such theorems will be given, although the proofs will not be given in all cases. The theorems which will here be given are the Helmholtz equivalent-source theorems (Thévenin and Norton theorems), the Millman theorem, and dual-circuit construction rules.

a. Helmholtz Equivalent-source Theorems. Let the rectangle of Fig. A-6 represent a general network with N independent loops, $M + 1$ junctions, N loop potential sources, and M junction current sources, all of the same frequency. One branch of this general network is shown isolated. Let the outside terminals be closed by a fictitious potential source, which may be the potential

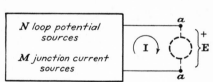

FIG. A-6. Circuit for illustrating the Helmholtz equivalent-source theorems (Thévenin and Norton theorems).

drop across a passive element between these two points. A general analysis of such an active network leads to the conclusion that any two-terminal linear network with any number of current and potential sources of the same frequency can be viewed as a source. This source can, in turn, be represented by either of the simple circuits of Fig. A-7. When the potential-source form is used, the network is said to be represented by a Helmholtz-Thévenin potential-source equivalent. The current-source form is called the Helmholtz-Norton current-source equivalent.

The series impedance $\mathbf{Z}_t$, or the shunt admittance $\mathbf{Y}_n$, appearing in Fig. A-7, are the inverse of each other, i.e., $\mathbf{Z}_t = 1/\mathbf{Y}_n$. Also, $\mathbf{Z}_t$ is the impedance of the network as measured at the terminals aa when all internal potential and current sources are reduced to zero.

The potential source E_t is the potential E which appears across the terminals aa when these terminals are an open circuit. Similarly, the current source I_n is the current in the short circuit which is placed across the terminals aa.

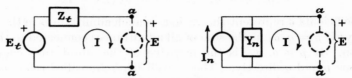

FIG. A-7. The Helmholtz equivalent-source representations.

The parameters E_t, I_n, Z_t, Y_n can be found by any method of circuit solution. They may also be found experimentally for physical systems.

b. *Millman Theorem.* Certain simple combinations of potential-source equivalents are of use because they offer simplification in the solutions of more extensive networks in which the combinations occur. Consider Fig. A-8a, which is typical of the situation to be considered first.

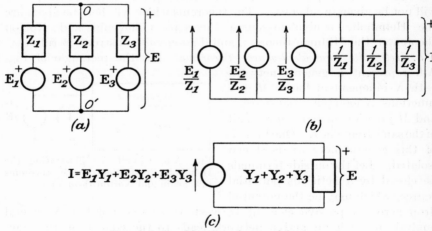

(a)

(b)

(c)

FIG. A-8. Combination of potential sources.

The solution of the network is accomplished by finding the potential E. To do this, let each potential source and its series impedance be replaced by a current-source equivalent, to yield the form shown in Fig. A-8b. In this diagram the sources have been separated from their individual admittances to give the grouped arrangement shown. This leads ultimately to the circuit of Fig. A-8c. The solution of this circuit for E is given directly by the relation

$$E = \frac{E_1 Y_1 + E_2 Y_2 + E_3 Y_3}{Y_1 + Y_2 + Y_3} \qquad (A\text{-}15)$$

c. *Duality and Dual-circuit Construction.* Throughout the development of network analysis a parallelism of statements is necessary, once for potentials and once for currents. There are potential sources and current sources; a Kirchhoff potential law pertaining to a loop, and a Kirchhoff current law pertaining to a junction, etc. These ideas are part of a larger pattern which exists in network analysis.

The simultaneous existence of two similar systems of analysis is given the name *duality* and is founded on the interchange of independent and dependent variables in the equations expressing the behavior of the circuit

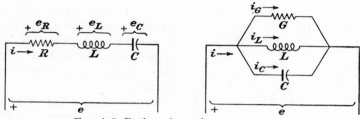

Fig. A-9. Basic series and parallel circuits.

elements. Duality does not imply equivalence; it means only that the mathematical representations of the circuits are similar in form.

Consider the basic series and parallel circuits illustrated in Fig. A-9. If the series combination is excited by a potential, and the parallel combination by a current, the appropriate relations for the respective circuits follow. For the series circuit,

$$e = e_R + e_L + e_C = Ri + L\frac{di}{dt} + \frac{1}{C}\int i\,dt \tag{A-16}$$

For the parallel circuit,

$$i = i_G + i_C + i_L = Ge + C\frac{de}{dt} + \frac{1}{L}\int e\,dt \tag{A-17}$$

Table A-1 contains the dually related quantities. Clearly, the two networks illustrated in Fig. A-9 are dually related.

TABLE A-1

DUAL RELATIONSHIPS

Loop concept	*Junction concept*
Loop interior	Junction other than datum junction
Circuit exterior	Datum junction
Potential source in an external branch	Current source with one terminal connected to the datum junction
Potential source in series in a common branch	Current source shunting a common branch
Loop current	Junction potential to the datum junction
Branch impedance	Branch admittance

It is of interest to compare Eqs. (A-4), which apply to Fig. A-3, with Eqs. (A-11), which apply to Fig. A-5. Since there is a systematic interchange of Z with Y and of I with E in these expressions, the two networks are dually related. Among the important dual relationships implied herein are those contained in Table A-1.

In the case of series or parallel circuits, the method of going from one circuit to its dual is illustrated in Fig. A-9. It is convenient to be able to construct a circuit which is the dual of another in the general case. A dual exists, and can be found, for any circuit, provided that it can be made flat and includes transformers in such a way that they can be replaced by equivalent circuits.

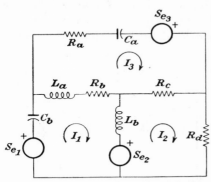

FIG. A-10. A typical circuit setup for loop analysis.

The essential problem to be solved is the following, and for convenience a typical three-loop network is to be considered. The network specified is represented by the equations

$$\varrho_{11}I_1 + \varrho_{12}I_2 + \varrho_{13}I_3 = S_{e1} - S_{e2}$$
$$\varrho_{21}I_1 + \varrho_{22}I_2 + \varrho_{23}I_3 = S_{e2} \qquad \text{(A-18)}$$
$$\varrho_{31}I_1 + \varrho_{32}I_2 + \varrho_{33}I_3 = S_{e3}$$

The symbols S_e are used to represent potential sources, and each I represents a loop current. It is now required to find the network which is represented by the equations

$$\mathfrak{d}_{11}E_1 + \mathfrak{d}_{12}E_2 + \mathfrak{d}_{13}E_3 = S_{i1} - S_{i2}$$
$$\mathfrak{d}_{21}E_1 + \mathfrak{d}_{22}E_2 + \mathfrak{d}_{23}E_3 = S_{i2} \qquad \text{(A-19)}$$
$$\mathfrak{d}_{31}E_1 + \mathfrak{d}_{32}E_2 + \mathfrak{d}_{33}E_3 = S_{i3}$$

in which each E is a junction response potential and each S_i is a current source. Each $\mathfrak{d}$ is to be the same as the corresponding ϱ.

The details of the construction follow: The new network must have three junctions, in addition to the datum junction. A dot is then placed in each loop, and the network is enclosed by a continuous line. Each internal dot becomes a nondatum junction, and the outside line is the datum junction. The junctions are numbered to correspond with the loops in which they appear. Junctions 1 and 2 are to be connected by a branch which is the dual of the branch common to loops 1 and 2. When this branch is drawn, it in essence crosses the branch to which it is dually related.   This procedure is carried out for each pair of junctions, including the datum junction.

In setting up the dual circuit, it is necessary to choose reference conditions in accordance with a consistent set of rules.   Two considerations are involved, (1) the reference direction of the current sources, and (2) the

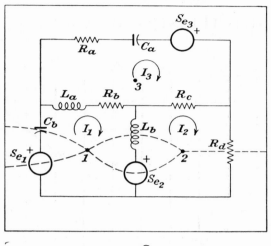

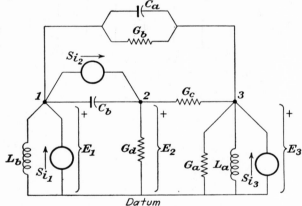

FIG. A-11. Two circuits which are duals of each other.

reference polarity at the junctions.   The rules for a consistent representation are:

1. If a potential source in a loop is a rise in the clockwise direction, its dual is a current source directed toward the dually related junction.

2. If a current has a clockwise direction in a loop, its dual is a positive potential at the dually related junction.

Based on the above, Fig. A-10, appropriately marked, and its dual are given in Fig. A-11.

APPENDIX B

PLATE CHARACTERISTICS OF VACUUM TUBES

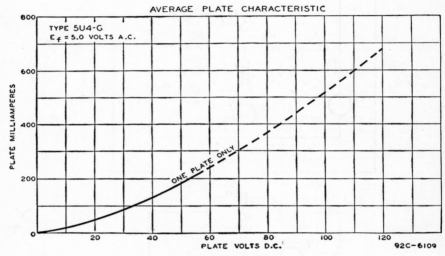

Fig. B-1. 5U4-G diode.

AVERAGE PLATE CHARACTERISTICS

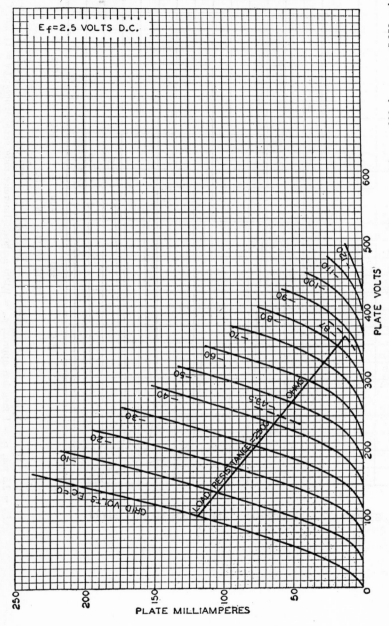

FIG. B-2. 2A3 triode. Class A amplifier: $E_b = 250$ volts, $E_c = -45$ volts, $I_b = 60$ ma, $\mu = 4.2$, $r_p = 800$ ohms, $g_m = 5,250$ μmhos. Interelectrode capacitances: $C_1 = 7$ μμf, $C_2 = 5$ μμf, $C_3 = 16$ μμf.

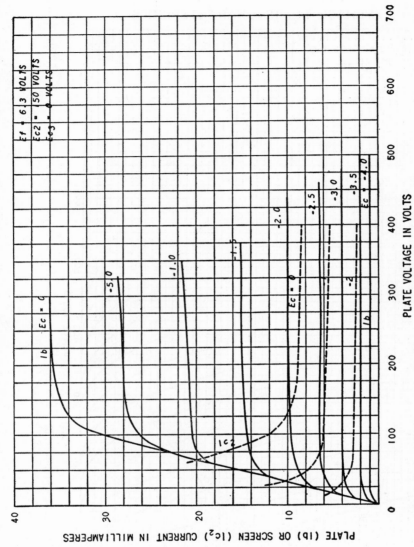

Fig. B-3. 6AC7 pentode. Class A amplifier: $E_b = 300$ volts, $E_{c2} = 150$ volts, $E_c = -2$ volts, $I_b = 10$ ma, $I_{c2} = 2.5$ ma, $r_p = 1$ megohm approx, $g_m = 9,000$ μmhos. Interelectrode capacitances: $C_1 = 11$ $\mu\mu$f, $C_2 = 5$ $\mu\mu$f, $C_3 = 0.015$ $\mu\mu$f.

456

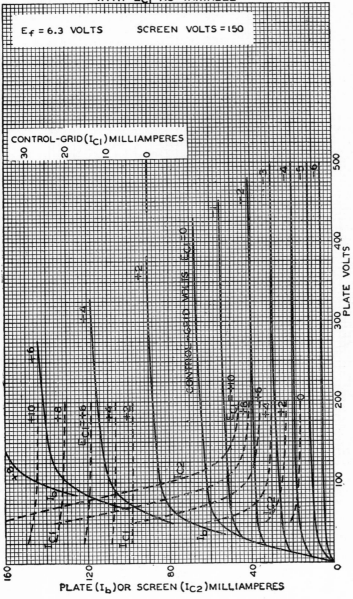

6AG7
AVERAGE PLATE CHARACTERISTICS
WITH E_{C1} AS VARIABLE

E_f = 6.3 VOLTS   SCREEN VOLTS = 150

CONTROL-GRID (I_{C1}) MILLIAMPERES

PLATE (I_b) OR SCREEN (I_{C2}) MILLIAMPERES

PLATE VOLTS

Fig. B-4. 6AG7 pentode.   Class A amplifier: E_b = 300 volts, E_{c2} = 150 volts, E_c = −3 volts, I_b = 30 ma, I_{c2} = 7 ma, r_p = 0.13 megohm approx, g_m = 11,000 μmhos.   Interelectrode capacitances: C_1 = 13 μμf, C_2 = 7.5 μμf, C_3 = 0.06 μμf.

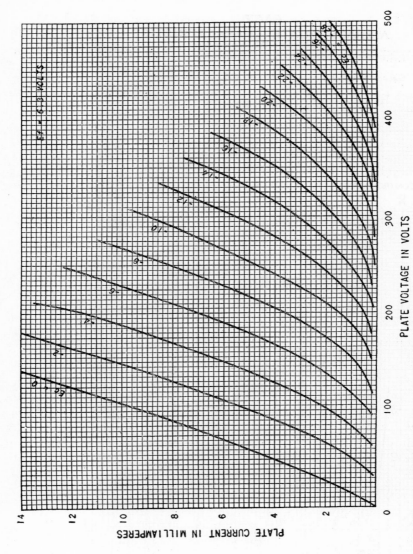

Fig. B-5. 6C5 triode. Class A amplifier: $E_b = 250$ volts, $E_c = -8$ volts, $I_b = 8$ ma, $\mu = 20$, $r_p = 10{,}000$ ohms, $g_m = 2{,}000$ μmhos. Interelectrode capacitances: $C_1 = 3$ $\mu\mu$f, $C_2 = 11$ $\mu\mu$f, $C_3 = 2.0$ $\mu\mu$f.

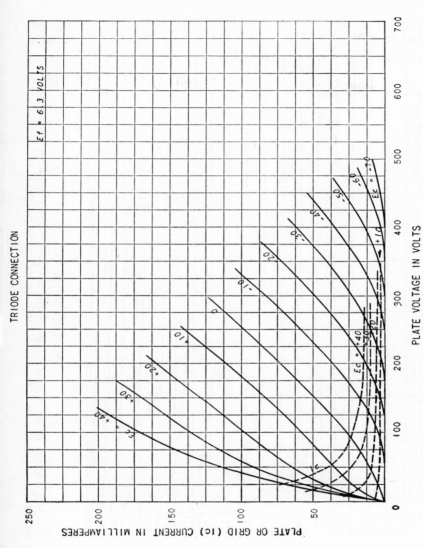

FIG. B-6. 6F6 triode (screen connected to plate). Class A amplifier: $E_b = 250$ volts, $E_c = -20$ volts, $I_b = 31$ ma, $\mu = 6.8$, $r_p = 2{,}600$ ohms, $g_m = 2{,}600$ μmhos.

459

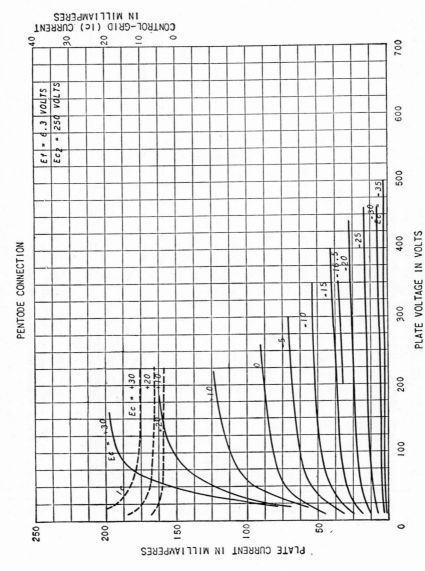

FIG. B-7. 6F6 pentode. Class A amplifier: $E_b = 250$ volts, $E_{c2} = 250$ volts, $E_c = -16.5$ volts, $I_b = 34$ ma, $r_p = 80,000$ ohms approx, $g_m = 2,500$ μmhos. Interelectrode capacitances: $C_1 = 6.5$ μμf, $C_2 = 13$ μμf, $C_3 = 0.2$ μμf.

460

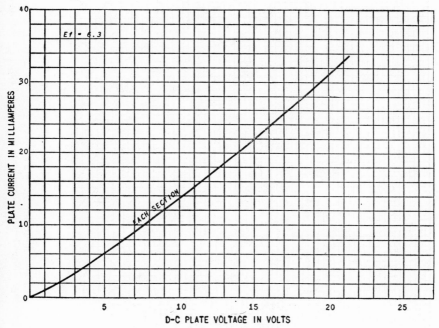

Fig. B-8. 6H6 diode.

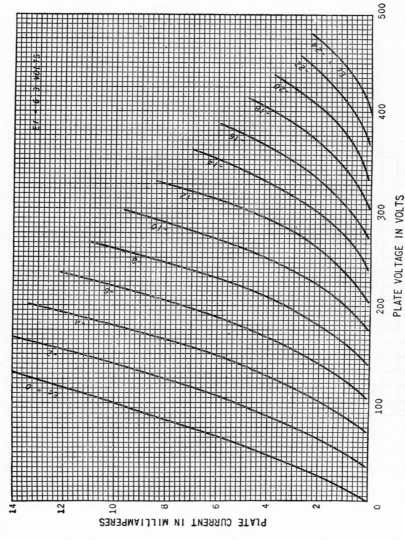

FIG. B-9. 6J5 triode. Class A amplifier: $E_b = 250$ volts, $E_c = -8$ volts, $I_b = 9$ ma, $\mu = 20$, $r_p = 7,700$ ohms, $g_m = 2,600$ μmhos. Interelectrode capacitances: $C_1 = 3.4$ μμf, $C_2 = 3.6$ μμf, $C_3 = 3.4$ μμf.

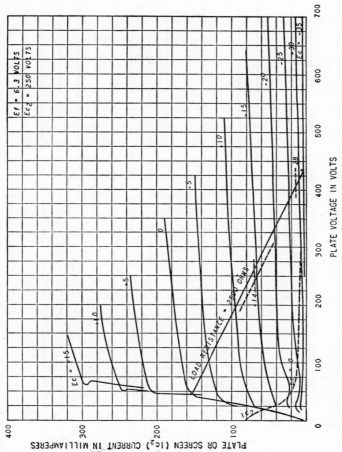

FIG. B-10. 6L6 beam tube. Class A amplifier: $E_b = 350$ volts, $E_{c2} = 250$ volts, $E_c = -18$ volts, $I_b = 54$ ma, $I_{c2} = 2.5$ ma, $r_p = 33,000$ ohms approx, $g_m = 5,200$ μmhos. Inter-electrode capacitances: $C_1 = 10$ μμf, $C_2 = 12$ μμf, $C_3 = 0.4$ μμf.

463

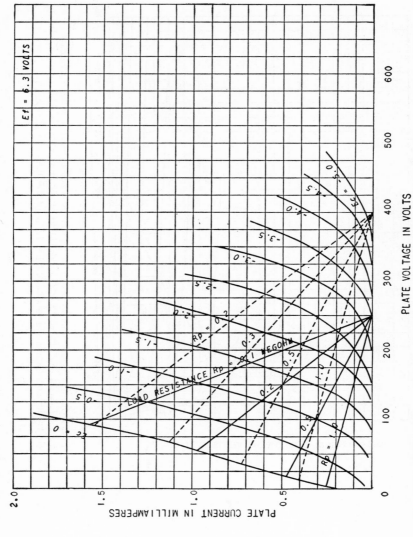

FIG. B-11. 6SF5 triode. Class A amplifier: $E_b = 250$ volts, $E_c = -2$ volts, $I_b = 0.9$ ma, $\mu = 100$, $r_p = 66,000$ ohms, $g_m = 1,500$ μmhos. Interelectrode capacitances: $C_1 = 4.0$ $\mu\mu$f, $C_2 = 3.6$ $\mu\mu$f, $C_3 = 2.4$ $\mu\mu$f.

AVERAGE PLATE CHARACTERISTICS

PENTODE CONNECTION

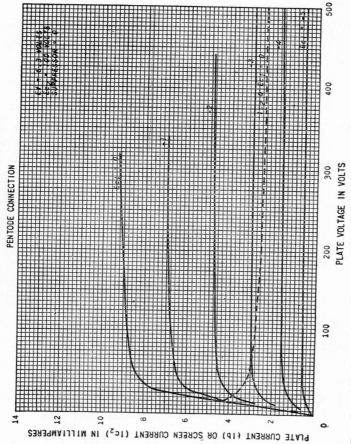

FIG. B-12. 6SJ7 pentode. Class A amplifier: $E_b = 250$ volts, $E_{c2} = 100$ volts, $E_c = -3$ volts, $I_b = 3$ ma, $I_{c2} = 0.8$ ma, $r_p = 1.0$ megohm approx, $g_m = 1,650$ μmhos. Interelectrode capacitances: $C_1 = 6.0$ μμf, $C_2 = 7.0$ μμf, $C_3 = 0.005$ μμf.

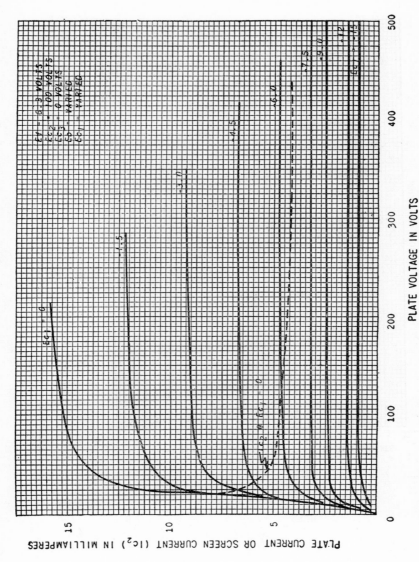

FIG. B-13. 6SK7 variable-mu pentode. Class A amplifier: $E_b = 250$ volts, $E_{c2} = 100$ volts, $E_c = -3$ volts, $I_b = 9.2$ ma, $I_{c2} = 2.6$ ma, $r_p = 0.8$ megohm approx, $g_m = 2,000$ μmhos. Interelectrode capacitances: $C_1 = 6.0$ $\mu\mu$f, $C_2 = 7.0$ $\mu\mu$f, $C_3 = .003$ μf.

EACH UNIT

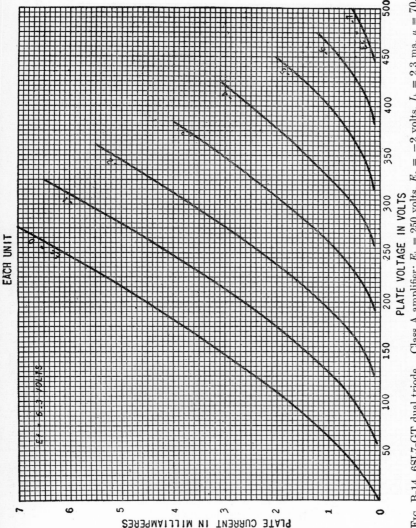

FIG. B-14. 6SL7-GT dual triode. Class A amplifier: $E_b = 250$ volts, $E_c = -2$ volts, $I_b = 2.3$ ma, $\mu = 70$, $r_p = 44{,}000$ ohms, $g_m = 1{,}600$ μmhos. Interelectrode capacitances: Unit 1: $C_1 = 3.0$ $\mu\mu$f, $C_2 = 3.8$ $\mu\mu$f, $C_3 = 2.8$ $\mu\mu$f. Unit 2: $C_1 = 3.4$ $\mu\mu$f, $C_2 = 3.2$ $\mu\mu$f, $C_3 = 2.8$ $\mu\mu$f.

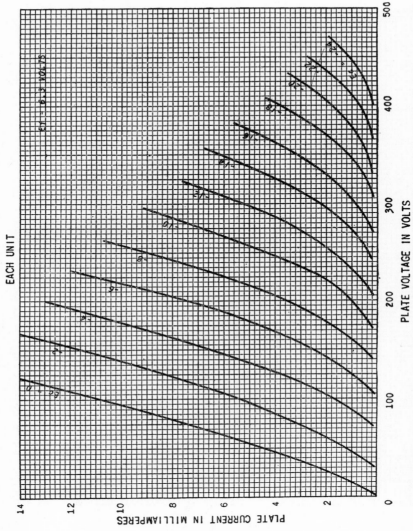

EACH UNIT

PLATE VOLTAGE IN VOLTS

FIG. B-15. 6SN7-GT dual-triode. Class A amplifier: $E_b = 250$ volts, $E_c = -8$ volts, $I_b = 9$ ma, $\mu = 20$, $r_p = 7{,}700$ ohms, $g_m = 2{,}600$ μmhos. Interelectrode capacitances: Unit 1: $C_1 = 3.2$ $\mu\mu f$, $C_2 = 3.4$ $\mu\mu f$, $C_3 = 4$ $\mu\mu f$. Unit 2: $C_1 = 3.8$ $\mu\mu f$, $C_2 = 2.6$ $\mu\mu f$, $C_3 = 4$ $\mu\mu f$.

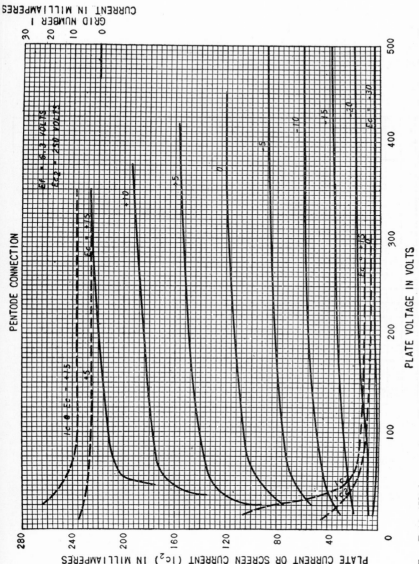

FIG. B-16. 6V6 beam tube. Class A amplifier: $E_b = 250$ volts, $E_{c2} = 250$ volts, $E_c = -12.5$ volts, $I_b = 45$ ma, $I_{c2} = 4.5$ ma, $r_p = 52{,}000$ ohms approx, $g_m = 4{,}100$ μmhos. Interelectrode capacitances: $C_1 = 10$ $\mu\mu$f, $C_2 = 11$ $\mu\mu$f, $C_3 = 0.3$ $\mu\mu$f.

469

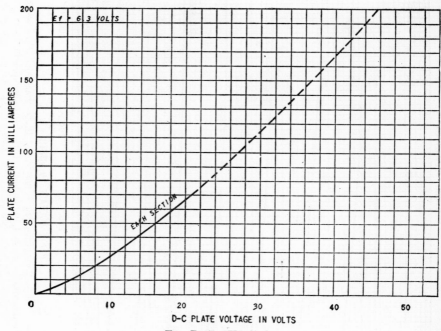

Fig. B-17. 6X5 diode.

APPENDIX C

CHARACTERISTICS OF TRANSMITTING TUBES

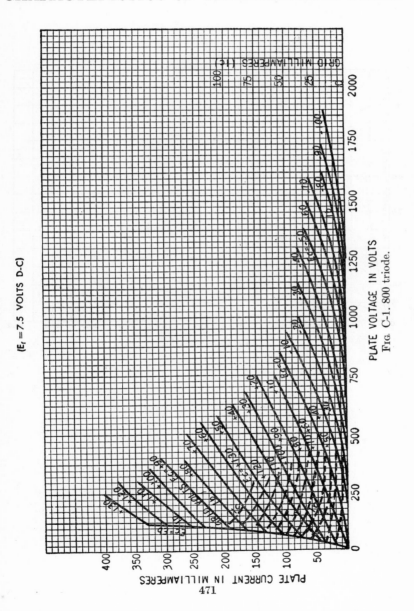

FIG. C-1. 800 triode.

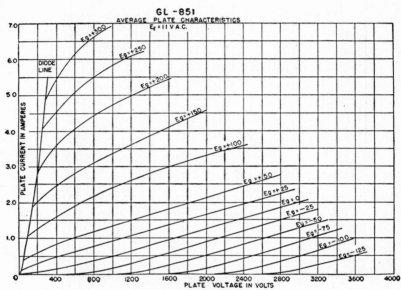

FIG. C-2. 851 triode.

APPENDIX D

TABLE OF BESSEL FUNCTIONS OF THE FIRST KIND

n	$J_n(1)$	$J_n(2)$	$J_n(3)$	$J_n(4)$	$J_n(5)$	$J_n(6)$	$J_n(7)$	$J_n(8)$	$J_n(9)$	$J_n(10)$	$J_n(11)$	$J_n(12)$	$J_n(13)$	$J_n(14)$	$J_n(15)$	$J_n(16)$	$J_n(17)$	$J_n(18)$	$J_n(19)$	$J_n(20)$
0	+0.7652	+0.2239	−0.2601	−0.3971	−0.1776	+0.1506	+0.3001	+0.1717	−0.0903	−0.2459	−0.1712	+0.0477	+0.2069	+0.1711	−0.0142	−0.1749	−0.1699	−0.0134	+0.1466	+0.1670
1	+0.4400	+0.5767	+0.3391	−0.0660	−0.3276	−0.2767	−0.0047	+0.2346	+0.2453	+0.0435	−0.1768	−0.2234	−0.0703	+0.1334	+0.2051	+0.0904	−0.0977	−0.1880	−0.1057	−0.0668
2	+0.1149	+0.3528	+0.4861	+0.3641	+0.0466	−0.2429	−0.3014	−0.1130	+0.1448	+0.2546	+0.1390	−0.0849	−0.2177	−0.1520	+0.0416	+0.1862	+0.1584	−0.0075	−0.1578	−0.1603
3	+0.0196	+0.1289	+0.3091	+0.4302	+0.3648	+0.1148	−0.1676	−0.2911	−0.1809	+0.0584	+0.2273	+0.1951	+0.0033	−0.1768	−0.1940	−0.0439	+0.1349	+0.1863	+0.0725	−0.0989
4	+0.0025	+0.0340	+0.1320	+0.2811	+0.3912	+0.3576	+0.1578	−0.1054	−0.2655	−0.2196	−0.0150	+0.1825	+0.2193	+0.0762	−0.1192	−0.2026	−0.1107	+0.0696	+0.1806	+0.1307
5		+0.0070	+0.0430	+0.1321	+0.2611	+0.3621	+0.3479	+0.1858	−0.0550	−0.2341	−0.2383	−0.0735	+0.1316	+0.2204	+0.1305	−0.0575	−0.1870	−0.1554	+0.0036	+0.1512
6		+0.0012	+0.0114	+0.0491	+0.1311	+0.2458	+0.3392	+0.3376	+0.2043	−0.0145	−0.2016	−0.2437	−0.1180	+0.0812	+0.2061	+0.1667	+0.0007	−0.1560	−0.1788	−0.0550
7		+0.0002	+0.0025	+0.0152	+0.0534	+0.1296	+0.2336	+0.3206	+0.3275	+0.2167	+0.0184	−0.1703	−0.2406	−0.1508	+0.0345	+0.1825	+0.1875	+0.0514	−0.1165	−0.1842
8			+0.0005	+0.0040	+0.0184	+0.0565	+0.1280	+0.2235	+0.3051	+0.3179	+0.2250	+0.0451	−0.1410	−0.2320	−0.1740	−0.0070	+0.1537	+0.1959	+0.0929	−0.0739
9			+0.0002	+0.0009	+0.0055	+0.0212	+0.0589	+0.1263	+0.2149	+0.2919	+0.3089	+0.2304	+0.0670	−0.1143	−0.2200	−0.1895	−0.0429	+0.1228	+0.1947	+0.1251
10				+0.0002	+0.0015	+0.0070	+0.0235	+0.0608	+0.1247	+0.2075	+0.2804	+0.3005	+0.2338	+0.0850	−0.0901	−0.2062	−0.1991	−0.0732	+0.0916	+0.1865
11					+0.0004	+0.0020	+0.0083	+0.0256	+0.0622	+0.1231	+0.2010	+0.2704	+0.2927	+0.2357	+0.0999	−0.0682	−0.1914	−0.2041	−0.1612	−0.0614
12					+0.0001	+0.0005	+0.0027	+0.0096	+0.0274	+0.0634	+0.1216	+0.1953	+0.2615	+0.2835	+0.2367	+0.1124	−0.0486	−0.1762	−0.2041	−0.1190
13						+0.0001	+0.0008	+0.0033	+0.0108	+0.0290	+0.0643	+0.1201	+0.1901	+0.2536	+0.2787	+0.2368	+0.1228	−0.0309	−0.1316	−0.2041
14							+0.0002	+0.0010	+0.0039	+0.0120	+0.0304	+0.0650	+0.1188	+0.1855	+0.2464	+0.2724	+0.2368	+0.1316	−0.0151	−0.1464
15								+0.0003	+0.0013	+0.0045	+0.0130	+0.0316	+0.0656	+0.1174	+0.1813	+0.2399	+0.2666	+0.2356	+0.1316	−0.0008
16									+0.0004	+0.0016	+0.0051	+0.0140	+0.0327	+0.0661	+0.1162	+0.1775	+0.2340	+0.2611	+0.2356	+0.1452
17									+0.0001	+0.0005	+0.0019	+0.0057	+0.0149	+0.0337	+0.0665	+0.1150	+0.1739	+0.2286	+0.2559	+0.2331
18										+0.0002	+0.0006	+0.0021	+0.0063	+0.0158	+0.0346	+0.0669	+0.1138	+0.1706	+0.2235	+0.2511
19											+0.0002	+0.0008	+0.0025	+0.0068	+0.0166	+0.0354	+0.0671	+0.1127	+0.1676	+0.2189
20												+0.0003	+0.0009	+0.0028	+0.0074	+0.0173	+0.0362	+0.0673	+0.1116	+0.1647
21													+0.0003	+0.0010	+0.0030	+0.0079	+0.0180	+0.0369	+0.0674	+0.1106
22													+0.0001	+0.0004	+0.0012	+0.0034	+0.0084	+0.0187	+0.0375	+0.0676
23														+0.0001	+0.0004	+0.0013	+0.0036	+0.0089	+0.0193	+0.0381
24															+0.0001	+0.0005	+0.0015	+0.0039	+0.0094	+0.0199

INDEX